WITHDRAWN

CONCORDIA UNIVERSITY

3 4211 00136 2220

Y0-BCS-252

TECHNIQUES OF CHEMISTRY

ARNOLD WEISSBERGER, *Editor*

VOLUME I

PHYSICAL METHODS OF CHEMISTRY

PART IIB
Electrochemical Methods

TECHNIQUES OF CHEMISTRY

ARNOLD WEISSBERGER, *Editor*

VOLUME I

PHYSICAL METHODS OF CHEMISTRY, in Five Parts
Incorporating Fourth Completely Revised and Augmented Edition
of Physical Methods of Organic Chemistry.
Edited by Arnold Weissberger and Bryant W. Rossiter

VOLUME II

ORGANIC SOLVENTS, Third Edition
John A. Riddick and William S. Bunger

TECHNIQUES OF CHEMISTRY

VOLUME I

PHYSICAL METHODS OF CHEMISTRY

INCORPORATING FOURTH COMPLETELY REVISED AND AUGMENTED
EDITION OF TECHNIQUE OF ORGANIC CHEMISTRY,
VOLUME I, PHYSICAL METHODS OF ORGANIC CHEMISTRY

Edited by

ARNOLD WEISSBERGER

AND

BRYANT W. ROSSITER

Research Laboratories
Eastman Kodak Company
Rochester, New York

PART IIB

Electrochemical Methods

KLINCK MEMORIAL LIBRARY
Concordia Teachers College
River Forest. Illinois 60305

WILEY-INTERSCIENCE

A DIVISION OF JOHN WILEY & SONS, INC.
New York · London · Sydney · Toronto

Copyright © 1971, by John Wiley & Sons, Inc.

All rights reserved. Published simultaneously in Canada.

No part of this book may be reproduced by any means, nor transmitted, nor translated into a machine language without the written permission of the publisher.

Library of Congress Catalogue Card Number: 77-114920

ISBN 0 471 92728 7

Printed in the United States of America

10 9 8 7 6 5 4 3 2 1

107598

PLAN FOR
PHYSICAL METHODS OF CHEMISTRY

PART I
Components of Scientific Instruments, Automatic Recording and Control, Computers in Chemical Research

PART II
Electrochemical Methods

PART III
Optical, Spectroscopic, and Radioactivity Methods

PART IV
Determination of Mass, Transport, and Electrical-Magnetic Properties

PART V
Determination of Thermodynamic and Surface Properties

AUTHORS OF PART II

RALPH N. ADAMS,
    Department of Chemistry, University of Kansas, Lawrence, Kansas

BERNARD D. BLAUSTEIN,
    Pittsburgh Coal Research Center, Bureau of Mines, U.S. Department of the Interior, Pittsburgh, Pennsylvania

ERIC R. BROWN,
    Research Laboratories, Eastman Kodak Company, Rochester, New York

RICHARD P. BUCK,
    University of North Carolina, Chapel Hill, North Carolina

JACK CHANG,
    Research Laboratories, Eastman Kodak Company, Rochester, New York

JOHN L. EISENMANN,
    Ionics, Inc., Watertown, Massachusetts

YUAN C. FU,
    Pittsburgh Coal Research Center, Bureau of Mines, U.S. Department of the Interior, Pittsburgh, Pennsylvania

DAVID M. HERCULES,
    Department of Chemistry, University of Georgia, Athens, Georgia

SEYMOUR L. KIRSCHNER,
    Food and Drug Research Laboratories, Inc., New York, New York

ROBERT F. LARGE,
    Research Laboratories, Eastman Kodak Company, Rochester, New York

FRANK B. LEITZ,
   Ionics, Inc., Watertown, Massachusetts
LOUIS MEITES,
   Department of Chemistry, Clarkson College of Technology, Potsdam, New York
OTTO H. MÜLLER,
   State University of New York, Upstate Medical Center, Syracuse, New York
ROYCE W. MURRAY,
   University of North Carolina, Chapel Hill, North Carolina
RICHARD C. NELSON,
   Department of Physics, The Ohio State University, Columbus, Ohio
STANLEY PIEKARSKI,
   Plastics Department, E. I. du Pont de Nemours & Company, Wilmington, Delaware
GERHARD POPP,
   Research Laboratory, Eastman Kodak Company, Rochester, New York
LEO SHEDLOVSKY,
   Consulting Chemist, New York, New York
THEODORE SHEDLOVSKY,
   The Rockefeller University, New York, New York
MICHAEL SPIRO,
   Imperial College of Science and Technology, London, England
STANLEY WAWZONEK,
   University of Iowa, Iowa City, Iowa

NEW BOOKS AND NEW EDITIONS OF BOOKS OF THE TECHNIQUES OF ORGANIC CHEMISTRY WILL NOW APPEAR IN TECHNIQUES OF CHEMISTRY. A LIST OF PRESENTLY PUBLISHED VOLUMES IS GIVEN BELOW.

TECHNIQUE OF ORGANIC CHEMISTRY
ARNOLD WEISSBERGER, *Editor*

INTRODUCTION TO THE SERIES

Techniques of Chemistry is the successor to the Technique of Organic Chemistry Series and its companion—Technique of Inorganic Chemistry. Because many of the methods are employed in all branches of chemical science, the division into techniques for organic and inorganic chemistry has become increasingly artificial. Accordingly, the new series reflects the wider application of techniques, and the component volumes for the most part provide complete treatments of the methods covered. Volumes in which limited areas of application are discussed can be easily recognized by their titles.

Like its predecessors, the series is devoted to a comprehensive presentation of the respective techniques. The authors give the theoretical background for an understanding of the various methods and operations and describe the techniques and tools, their modifications, their merits and limitations, and their handling. It is hoped that the series will contribute to a better understanding and a more rational and effective application of the respective techniques.

Authors and editors hope that readers will find the volumes in this series useful and will communicate to them any criticisms and suggestions for improvements.

Research Laboratories
Eastman Kodak Company
Rochester, New York

ARNOLD WEISSBERGER

PREFACE

Physical Methods of Chemistry succeeds, and incorporates the material of, three editions of *Physical Methods of Organic Chemistry* (1945, 1949, and 1959). It has been broadened in scope to include physical methods important in the study of all varieties of chemical compounds. Accordingly, it is published as Volume I of the new Techniques of Chemistry series.

Some of the methods described in *Physical Methods of Chemistry* are relatively simple laboratory procedures, such as weighing and the measurement of temperature or refractive index, and determination of melting and boiling points. Other techniques require very sophisticated apparatus and specialists to make the measurements and to interpret the data; x-ray diffraction, mass spectrometry, and nuclear magnetic resonance are examples of this class. Authors of chapters describing the first class of methods aim to provide all information that is necessary for the successful handling of the respective techniques. Alternatively, the aim of authors treating the more sophisticated methods is to provide the reader with a clear understanding of the basic theory and apparatus involved, together with an appreciation for the value, potential, and limitations of the respective techniques. Representative applications are included to illustrate these points, and liberal references to monographs and other scientific literature providing greater detail are given for readers who want to apply the techniques. Still other methods that are successfully used to solve chemical problems range between these examples in complexity and sophistication and are treated accordingly. All chapters are written by specialists. In many cases authors have acquired a profound knowledge of the respective methods by their own pioneering work in the use of these techniques.

In the earlier editions of *Physical Methods* an attempt was made to arrange the chapters in a logical sequence. In order to make the organization of the treatise lucid and helpful to the reader, a further step has been taken in the new edition—the treatise has been subdivided into technical families:

Part I   Components of Scientific Instruments, Automatic Recording and Control, Computers in Chemical Research

Part II   Electrochemical Methods

Part III   Optical, Spectroscopic, and Radioactivity Methods

Part IV   Determination of Mass, Transport, and Electrical-Magnetic Properties

Part V   Determination of Thermodynamic and Surface Properties

This organization into technical families provides more consistent volumes and should make it easier for the reader to obtain from a library or purchase at minimum cost those parts of the treatise in which he is most interested.

The more systematic organization has caused additional labor for the editors and the publisher. We hope that it is worth the effort. We thank the many authors who made it possible by adhering closely to the agreed dates of delivery of their manuscripts and who promptly returned their proofs. To those authors who were meticulous in meeting deadlines we offer our apologies for delays caused by late arrival of other manuscripts, in some cases necessitating rewriting and additions.

The changes in subject matter from the Third Edition are too numerous to list in detail. We thank previous authors for their continuing cooperation and welcome the new authors to the series. New authors of Part II are Ralph N. Adams, Bernard D. Blaustein, Eric R. Brown, Richard P. Buck, Jack Chang, John L. Eisenmann, Yuan C. Fu, David M. Hercules, Seymour L. Kirschner, Robert F. Large, Frank B. Leitz, Royce W. Murray, Richard C. Nelson, Stanley Piekarski, and Gerhard Popp.

We are also grateful to the many colleagues who advised us in the selection of authors and helped in the evaluation of manuscripts. They are for Part II: Dr. Roger C. Baetzold, Dr. Charles J. Battaglia, Dr. Eric R. Brown, Dr. Jack Chang, Dr. Donald L. Fields, Dr. Robert L. Griffith, Dr. Arthur H. Herz, Mrs. Ardelle Kocher, Dr. Robert F. Large, Dr. Louis Meites, Dr. Louis D. Moore, Jr., Dr. Charles W. Reilley, Mrs. Donna S. Roets, Dr. Willard R. Ruby, Mr. Calvin D. Salzberg, Miss Dianne C. Smith, Dr. Donald E. Smith, Dr. Benjamin B. Snavely, Dr. R. Eliot Stauffer, and Dr. John R. Wilt.

The senior editor expresses his gratitude to Bryant W. Rossiter for joining him in the work and taking on the very heavy burden with exceptional devotion and ability.

ARNOLD WEISSBERGER
BRYANT W. ROSSITER

April 1970
Research Laboratories
Eastman Kodak Company
Rochester, New York

CONTENTS

Chapter **X**

ELECTROCHEMICAL SYNTHESIS

Jack Chang, Robert F. Large, and Gerhard Popp

I INTRODUCTION

Synthesis of compounds by passing an electrolytic current through a solution is a phenomenon that has been known for a long time but unfortunately is still not widely used. Recent advances in large-scale application of electrochemical reactions are evidence of some progress, but an awakening of broad interest in electrochemical synthesis has not yet occurred. Many factors have been cited as contributing to the lack of full application of electrochemistry in a broader sense [1] and electrochemical syntheses in particular [2]. Among such factors the lack of an adequate basis for rationalizing the products of electrolysis, or even the proper tools to provide that basis, seems to the authors to have been most significant.

Within the last decade important advances in scientists' ability to probe electrochemical reactions in detail have been made. It follows that this capability will afford a more detailed understanding of electrochemical reactions of synthetic value and subsequently more extensive application of these reactions.

Electrochemical synthesis is a logical area for the application of many of the techniques described in the preceding chapters of this volume. Conversely, a thorough understanding of reaction kinetics and mechanisms requires a knowledge of the products of the reaction. Thus the somewhat mechanistic approach to electrochemical synthesis of this chapter arises from the belief that both synthetic and mechanistic electrochemistry have a common ground in their mutual need for further understanding of complex reactions.

The objective of this chapter is to provide an introduction to electrochemical synthesis for the chemist having little or no background in the subject, with particular attention given to recently developed techniques. Thus a review of the important variables of the method together with a discussion of physical factors that are of synthetic importance constitute the initial section. This is followed by an illustration of the scope of the synthetic method through discussions of selected areas of current research. This section also provides the opportunity to note that many of the other techniques discussed in this volume can be employed to advantage, or in some cases should be employed, in studies aimed toward syntheses. Examples in which electrochemical syntheses serve as an important tool in other areas of research are also provided. A discussion of some of the experimental aspects of electrochemical syntheses concludes the chapter, with particular attention paid to the problems that arise with the use of nonaqueous solvent systems.

2 FACTORS INFLUENCING REACTION MECHANISMS

Electrochemical synthesis requires the application of a unique combination of physical and chemical properties. Reactions that occur at an electrode surface are governed by phenomena which the chemist interested only in synthesis may choose to ignore. Conversely, electrochemists having a sharp focus on the electrode surface sometimes may not give full consideration to some important chemical concepts.

This section reviews the primary physical and chemical phenomena that govern the course of an electrochemical reaction used for chemical synthesis. The treatment is limited in depth since many of the necessary concepts in electrochemistry are covered elsewhere in this volume.

The Interdependency of Current, Potential, Concentration, and Time

Electrochemistry is governed by the four interdependent variables: current, potential, concentration, and time. In an electrochemical synthesis, one is concerned with passing a sufficient number of coulombs, the product of current and time, to convert a reactant into a product. The current flow through the electrochemical cell is a function of the applied potential, time, and concentration. Other experimental variables, of course, determine the quantity of current flow attainable under a given set of conditions and are discussed in more detail later, but an understanding of the interrelations between these four variables is most essential.

An electrolysis is effected under defined conditions by controlling either the current or the potential. Under either of these constraints, control of the concentration may be used advantageously. The voltage applied to the cell, which is related to the potential, may also be controlled. The difference between voltage and potential becomes obvious in the subsequent discussion.

For the following discussion, a reaction sequence comprised of a reduction of a substance R^+ to a desired product Z is assumed by the reaction scheme

$$R^+ + e^- \rightleftharpoons R\cdot$$
$$2R\cdot \rightarrow Z$$
$$R\cdot + e^- \rightleftharpoons R^-$$
$$R^- + H^+ \rightarrow RH$$

where $R\cdot$ represents an intermediate radical. Further reduction of $R\cdot$ to the anion R^- is possible at more cathodic potentials and the final product of this reaction is RH. A current-potential curve for this model system is illustrated in Fig. 10.1. An electrolysis is to be carried out in a solution containing a large excess of a salt having an oxidizable anion X^- and a cation

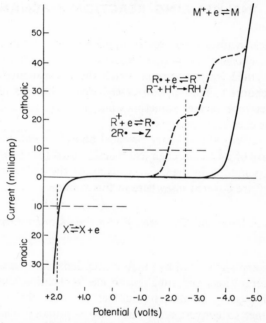

Fig. 10.1. Current-potential curve for a model reaction system. Current-potential curve of the solvent-supporting electrolyte system, ————; current-potential curve of the model system, – – – – – –; constant-current line, – – – – – – –; constant-voltage line, ------------.

M^+, which is reducible, but less readily than substance R^+. The reaction conditions are such that the supply of R^+ to the electrode is controlled by mass transfer processes in the solution. Two identical inert electrodes serving as a working electrode (the electrode at which the reaction of prime interest occurs) and an auxiliary electrode are assumed. In the absence of substance R^+, the relations between current and potential for the working and auxiliary electrodes are shown in Fig. 10.1, each drawn from an arbitrarily selected reference potential of zero. The potential values at which a significant current is observed from electrolysis of the supporting electrolyte are termed the limiting anodic and cathodic potentials of the solvent-supporting electrolyte system used, E_ℓ^a and E_ℓ^c, respectively. At potentials anodic of E_ℓ^a or cathodic of E_ℓ^c, the discharge of either the supporting electrolyte ions or the solvent molecule itself consumes a significant amount of the current through the cell. The following discussion assumes the presence of R^+ at a concentration such that the maximum current that can be obtained by the reduction of R^+ is 20 mA.

Many electrochemical syntheses described in the literature have been carried out with a constant applied current. When a constant current is applied, an equivalent quantity of electrochemical reaction must take place at both electrodes. If a constant current of 10 mA is applied to the model system as defined, the potentials of the working and auxiliary electrode are approximated by the intersections of the constant-current lines with the current-potential curve for the system. The reaction at the working electrode (since reduction is taking place at the working electrode, it is the cathode of the cell) is the desired reduction of R^+ to $R\cdot$ radical followed by a chemical reaction of $R\cdot$ to form Z. Subsequent reduction of $R\cdot$ to R^- does not occur since the potential of the working electrode is not sufficiently cathodic to allow this reaction to proceed to an appreciable extent. At the auxiliary electrode, oxidation of X^- to $X\cdot$ radical occurs to an extent to support the 10-mA current flow.

As the electrolysis proceeds, the concentration of R^+ diminishes and a point is eventually reached at which the mass transfer of R^+ to the working electrode is not sufficient to allow a 10-mA current flow since the current is directly proportional to the bulk concentration of R^+. Under such conditions the potential of the working electrode increases to a point at which the current flow can be maintained and the second reduction, $R\cdot$ to R^-, commences. Different reactive intermediates do not often follow the same chemical reaction path. In this case protonation of R^- is assumed to be the preferred reaction. Thus as the potential of the electrode shifts cathodically, RH is formed instead of the desired product Z.

The remedy to this problem, under constant-current conditions, is to assure that the concentration of R^+ is sufficient to maintain the desired current flow at all times. This has the disadvantage of the electrolysis being incomplete. However, under continuous operating conditions in which the product can be removed and the reactant replenished, electrolysis at constant current can be effectively employed. This technique is best employed when the reaction is fully characterized rather than in those stages of a study in which the reaction pathway is uncertain.

Indiscriminate variation of reactant concentration may lead to other problems. In the reaction system chosen for illustration, an increase in reactant concentration might prove favorable since the rate of the reaction R· to Z is increased. Side reactions of R· that are first order in R· would be less affected. Other reaction systems may have the opposite concentration dependency.

The problem of a potential shift can also be minimized by using a smaller value of current so that the potential is not shifted appreciably until the reactant is 80 to 90% electrolyzed. The consequence of this approach is that a longer electrolysis time is required to convert an equivalent amount of reactant to product. In some cases an increase in the time of electrolysis is undesirable; for example, a side reaction of slow rate may become more important.

Another problem associated with the constant-current technique is that the constant potential achieved is usually at the foot or on the rising portion of the current-potential curve. This is of little consequence if the electron-transfer step associated with the particular current-potential curve is simply a one-electron process. However, there are cases in which two one-electron processes are associated with one limiting-current step. If the working electrode is at potentials on the rising portion of the step, a one-electron intermediate may be favored. This effect is illustrated in the reduction of benzaldehyde. With the potential of the working electrode held at the limiting current region of the current-potential curve, a quantitative yield of benzyl alcohol was obtained. However, if electrolysis is conducted with the potential held at the foot of the step, hydrobenzoin is also obtained as a product through the dimerization of the intermediate radical [3].

Application of a constant voltage across the cell has also been used extensively in electrochemical syntheses, primarily owing to the simplicity of the instrumentation. Sufficient voltage must be applied for reactions to occur at both electrodes. For the model system an applied voltage of approximately 4 V is required to approach a current of 10 mA. With a constant applied voltage, the maximum possible current tends to flow and the potentials at the respective electrodes are the values satisfying that condition. If more than approximately 5 V were applied to the cell, reduction of R· to R⁻ would also occur. Constant-voltage electrolysis with an applied voltage of approximately 4.5 V would be chosen for the conditions defined to selectively reduce R⁺ to Z.

The preceding discussion has neglected the important effect of the cell resistance, R_{cell}, across which the current flows. An emf opposed to the applied voltage is generated by the iR_{cell} drop such that the effective potential difference between the electrodes is

$$E_{eff} = V_{app} - iR_{cell}.$$

Assuming a current flow of 20 mA and a cell resistance of 10 Ω, the actual applied voltage is reduced by 0.2 V, and approximately 4.7 V are required to establish a 4.5-V potential difference between the working and auxiliary electrodes. As the electrolysis proceeds, the current decreases as does the iR_{cell} drop. In maintaining the constant applied voltage, the potentials of the working and auxiliary electrodes must shift accordingly and the second electron transfer may commence. Moreover, cell resistance values are commonly much greater than 10 Ω, often reaching several hundred ohms if nonaqueous solvents are employed. Thus variation of the effective potential difference between the electrodes may be large during the electrolysis, which constitutes a real disadvantage.

Many adverse effects of controlled-current and/or controlled-voltage electrolysis can be avoided through controlled-potential (potentiostatic) methods. In these techniques the potential between the working electrode and a third electrode of constant potential (a reference electrode) is continuously controlled at a selected value. If the reference electrode potential is arbitrarily set at 0 V, the potential of the working electrode could be selectively maintained at −2.5 V in the example to discriminate against the interfering reactions. The potential of the auxiliary electrode shifts to the value required to support a current level equivalent to that attainable for the working electrode at the chosen potential. With a highly resistive solution, the output voltage of an instrument necessary to effect electrolysis may be very high. This creates experimental problems which are discussed in Section 4.

The importance of a controlled potential with respect to product formation and distribution is best illustrated by examples. If controlled-potential electrolysis of 9,10-dimethylanthracene (**I**) is carried out at +1.1 V versus the saturated calomel electrode (SCE) in an acetic acid medium, a dimeric acetate (**IV**) is obtained [4]. However, if the potential is changed to +1.8 V, 9,10-diacetoxy-9,10-dimethylanthracene (**VI**) is obtained as the major product. The difference in products obtained at these two different potentials can be understood by considering the competition between deprotonation of the radical cation (**II**) and the second electron–transfer reaction. With a controlled potential of +1.1 V, the deprotonation is predominant and leads to the benzyl radical (**III**). Subsequent reaction of the benzyl radical with the radical cation yields the dimeric intermediate, eventually yielding (**IV**). As the potential becomes more anodic, the second electron–transfer reaction commences, forming the dication (**V**). Subsequent reaction with acetate ion yields (**VI**).

A similar potential dependency is illustrated by the preferential formation of carbonium ion intermediates in the Kolbe electrolysis when a large voltage is applied to the electrochemical cell [5]. Several other examples of potential dependency are noted in Section 3.

Other, less clear, dependencies of the product distribution on potential have been reported. For example, the reduction of 4-cyanopyridine in a phosphate buffer (pH = 6.4) proceeds via an overall four-electron process yielding the corresponding 4-picolylamine [6]. However, as the potential shifts cathodically, an unusual carbon-carbon bond scission occurs, generating pyridine and cyanide ion, and the overall reaction changes to a two-electron process. The yield of the carbon–carbon bond cleavage products reaches a maximum at a certain potential. This unusual potential dependence has been rationalized as resulting from changes in the orientation of the 4-cyanopyridine molecule at the electrode surface as the potential of the working electrode changes [6].

In some cases it has been noted that the potential exerts a specific influence on the stereochemistry of the product. The ratio of *cis*- to *trans*-stilbenediol in the reduction of benzil increases over the potential range from −0.70 to −0.95 V and then decreases as the potential of the working electrode becomes more cathodic [7].

Obviously, there is much yet to be learned of the detailed effects of the potential of the electrode on the course of electrochemical reactions. However, experimentation with carefully defined conditions, especially with respect to the electrode potential, can do much to increase the overall level of understanding.

Other Important Factors

A number of other factors have a significant effect on the course of an electrochemical reaction. The preceding discussion assumed that the electrode is inert, an assumption that is not always valid. At least a part of the expected usefulness of electrochemical synthesis arises through specific interactions with the electrode other than that for the simple transfer of an electron. The medium in which an electrochemical reaction is carried out may influence the processes that occur at the electrode. Once a species is formed at the electrode, it must come to chemical equilibrium with the medium. New species may result as equilibrium is reached and the chemical properties of the solvent-supporting electrolyte system may be the governing factor in determining the structure of the final products.

The Electrode Material

An electrode is often presumed to serve only as an inert source or acceptor of electrons in an electrochemical reaction. In fact, the detailed nature of the electrode material can exert a strong influence on the pathway of an electrochemical synthesis. These influences vary from a change in the overall rate of the reaction to a complete change in the product formed. The following discussion points out some effects resulting from the choice of the electrode material, or the mere presence of the electrode, which have been noted and in some cases characterized. Unfortunately, detailed knowledge of this most vital factor is sparse, especially as applied to electrochemical synthesis.

The extent and rate of electrochemical reductions in aqueous or partially aqueous media are often a function of the electrode material. In general, more complete and rapid reductions are obtained at electrodes of high hydrogen overvoltage.* In the electrolytic reduction of streptomycin to dihydrostreptomycin [8, 9], the rate of electrolysis was found to be dependent on the atomic number of the metal electrode in the same periodic group. The hydrogen overvoltage of these metals increases accordingly. The yield of tetrahydroquinoline in the electrolysis of quinoline in acidic medium has also been noted to parallel the hydrogen overvoltage of the metal electrode. Thus high yields of tetrahydroquinoline were obtained by using lead, tantalum, indium, and cadmium electrodes, whereas niobium, nickel, and cobalt electrodes were practically inactive [10–12]. A similar dependence on

---

* Overvoltage (or overpotential) is the difference between the reversible potential of a couple and the actual applied potential required to cause the reaction to proceed to an appreciable rate.

electrode material has been demonstrated in the electrolytic reduction of acetone in alkaline solution [13].

However, in many cases the hydrogen overvoltage is not the deciding factor. Swann [14] has studied many examples in which the highest yield of product was not necessarily obtained at electrodes of high hydrogen overvoltage. For example, the reduction of methyl n-propyl ketone to pentane proceeds readily on cadmium, zinc, lead, and mercury, but tin and aluminum, both electrodes of high hydrogen overvoltage, are practically inactive [15]. The exact nature of the influence of the electrode material in these cases is not clear.

The reduction of some compounds may also proceed via different mechanistic pathways at different electrodes. For example, dicyandiamide undergoes a four-electron reduction at mercury and lead electrodes to yield aminomethylene guanidine. At a palladium black electrode, the same compound is reduced to the dihydro compound. It has been suggested that this difference in product formation is the result of a direct electron transfer reaction occurring at the mercury cathode, while reduction by chemisorbed hydrogen occurs at the palladium black electrode [16].

The physical structure and properties of the metal electrode may also affect the yield and course of the electrochemical process. Swann [14] has pointed out many examples in which casting temperature, surface treatment, and cold-working change the effectiveness of some metal electrodes.

The effect of the crystallographic properties of a metal electrode on the reduction of pyruvic acid has been studied. It was found that the rate of reduction is slowest at the [100]-plane and highest at the [111]-plane of silver single-crystal electrodes. On copper the reduction rate is higher than it is on silver but the relative activities of the crystal planes are the same [17]. Similar dependencies on crystal structure were found in the electrochemical reduction of o- and p-nitrophenols in alkaline buffer solutions [18]. The electrolysis of a Ziegler electrolyte at a germanium electrode presumed to be polycrystalline yields germanium alkyls as products. However, n- and p-type germanium single-crystal electrodes were found to be inactive for the synthesis of germanium alkyls [19].

The influence of the composition of a cadmium amalgam electrode on the electrolytic reduction of methyl n-propyl ketone is interesting. The yield of pentane correlates with the melting point of the cadmium-mercury alloy system. In some cases the yield of pentane can be altered significantly by a slight change in the composition of the alloy [20].

Electrochemical syntheses yielding stereospecific products not normally obtained in chemical redox reactions would be of significance. That the electrode in some cases exerts a very specific influence on the stereochemical course of the electrochemical reaction has been noted. The anodic side chain acetoxylation of 2-*tert*-butylindan, for example, yields the thermodynamically less stable *cis* isomer as a major product. It is argued that this stereospecific acetoxylation results from an association of the 2-*tert*-butylindan with the electrode such that the configuration of the product is dictated by the ease of approach of the acetate ion to the adsorbed molecule [21]. Similar considerations have been used to rationalize the *cis* addition of methoxide ion in electrolyses of *cis*- and *trans*-stilbenes [22].

The stereospecificity of the 2-butene-1,4-diol obtained from the electrochemical reduction of 2-butyne-1,4-diol is dependent on the electrode material. The *cis* form is obtained with silver, copper, nickel, cobalt, iron and platinum or palladium black electrodes, and the *trans* form is obtained when zinc, lead, tin, cadmium, or copper amalgam electrodes are used [23].

The geometric configuration of the molecule with respect to the electrode also plays an important role in stereospecific product formation. The reductive elimination of halide from geminal dihalocyclopropanes yields the *cis* isomer predominantly [24]. It is suggested that steric constraints predetermine the reductive elimination of the "outside" halogen and the resulting carbanion retains the configuration in the subsequent protonation. The reductive elimination of chloride from 2-phenyl-2-chloropropionic acid is accompanied by an inversion of configuration. The symmetry of the lowest antibonding orbital, together with the effects of electronic repulsion in the radical anion, was cited as leading to the inversion of configuration [7].

In some cases the intermediate species generated at an electrode may vary with different electrode materials. Koehl [25] has shown that the electrolyses of aliphatic acids with carbon anodes under the normal Kolbe reaction conditions produce high yields of products resulting from carbonium ion intermediates. However, if carried out at platinum electrodes, similar reactions produce products that are the result of a free-radical intermediate. Preferential generation of carbonium ion intermediates at a carbon electrode has also been reported for the anodic oxidations of other alkane carboxylates [26, 27], alkane boronates, and alkyl halides [26], and for the anodic acetoxylation and methylation of aromatic hydrocarbons [28]. The mechanism of the formation of carbonium ion intermediates is not known. However, Ross and Finkelstein [29] have recently suggested that the free radicals formed in the initial one-electron transfer step tend to be adsorbed at the paramagnetic centers of the carbon electrode and thereby promote a second electron transfer. In any event the implication is clear that the products of such electrochemical syntheses may be significantly altered by the nature of the electrode material.

Direct participation of the electrode in the electrochemical reaction is important in the synthesis of organometallic compounds. Some examples of reactions of this type are discussed in Section 3.

The Solvent-Supporting Electrolyte System

The influence of the solvent and supporting electrolyte on the course of an electrochemical reaction is frequently of major consequence. Most electrochemical reactions proceed through reactive intermediates whose subsequent chemical reactions occur predominantly in solution. In view of this, it is not surprising that a relatively inert nonaqueous medium at times leads to products that differ greatly from those obtained in, for example, an aqueous medium. Several examples illustrating this point are found in Section 3.

A number of specific interactions that may be put to synthetic use occur between an electrochemically produced intermediate and the ions of the supporting electrolyte. Anodic substitution reactions (see Section 3) are based on such an interaction.

Although the supporting electrolyte is, in general, added for the purpose of maintaining a current flow through the cell, the supporting electrolyte is sometimes discharged and reacts with a substrate before it undergoes a direct electron transfer reaction. In Section 3 it is shown that the selective reductive cleavage of benzoates, tosylates, and sulfones is only possible if tetramethylammonium ions are a component of the supporting electrolyte. Investigators [30] propose that this cation is discharged and forms a layer on the mercury surface which subsequently reacts with the substrate molecules.

The anodic oxidation of mesitylene and toluene in an acetic acid medium containing tetramethylammonium nitrate yields mainly products that arise from a substitution in the side chain, benzyl acetates and benzyl nitrates, for example. However, if potassium acetate is used as the supporting electrolyte instead of tetramethylammonium nitrate, the main reaction path is a ring substitution [31]. Since the nitrate ion has a relatively low discharge potential [32] and the existence of the nitrate radical is well-established [33, 34], it is assumed that the formation of a nitrate radical is responsible for the generation of the side-chain derivatives. By the same effect the yield of bibenzyl in the anodic oxidation of toluene is dramatically decreased if sodium or lithium perchlorate is used as the supporting electrolyte instead of lithium nitrate [35].

More subtle influences of the supporting electrolyte are observed if specific solvation or adsorption of its ions occurs. A pertinent example is the specificity afforded by tetraethylammonium-p-toluenesulfonate in the hydrodimerization of activated olefins. The use of sodium instead of tetraethylammonium salts increases considerably the formation of the hydrogenated monomer over the hydrodimer. This effect has been attributed to specific adsorption of tetraalkylammonium ions on the electrode [36, 37], but it appears that the details of this phenomenon are still not completely understood.

Nyberg has reported [38] that the oxidation of hexamethylbenzene in wet acetonitrile–acetic acid in the presence of sodium perchlorate yields mainly benzylacetamide and only little benzylacetate. However, this product ratio can be inverted if tetrabutylammonium fluoroborate is used as the supporting electrolyte instead of sodium perchlorate. Nyberg relates this phenomenon to a preferred solvation of the tetrafluoroborate ion by acetic acid, which increases the concentration of acetic acid at the electrode surface.

Compared with the explosion of literature on the general subject of organic electrochemical syntheses during recent years, study of the stereochemical aspects of electrochemical reactions has been neglected. From the few systematic investigations of this subject, it appears that the stereochemical course of electrochemical reactions is mainly governed by the solution conditions. This may be illustrated by the cathodic pinacolizations of acetophenone [39] and propiophenone [40], which yield slightly more *d,l-* than *meso* product in acidic media. A dramatic increase in the formation of the *d,l-*form is observed (3:1) when the reactions are carried out in basic media. Cathodic reduction of 2-acetylpyridine in acidic media yields the *meso*-pinacol as the major product and the preference for this form increases with increasing pH of the solution [41]. Reduction of benzaldehyde in acidic aqueous solutions affords slightly more *meso*-hydrobenzoin than *d,l-*compound and this preference for the *meso* form becomes more pronounced when tetraethylammonium or iodide ions are present in solution [42].

The pH of the medium exerts a strong influence on the overall course of electrochemical reactions. The ease of bond fission in reductive eliminations depends in many cases upon the pH of the medium. The yields of hydrodimer in electrolytic hydrodimerization reactions are also susceptible to changes in pH. Well-investigated examples of the dependence of the product distribution on pH are provided by the numerous electrolytic reductions of organic nitro compounds, which have been reviewed recently [43]. In general, if acids or bases are subjected to electrolysis, the pH of the solution has to be considered as one of the prime reaction variables.

Temperature

The influence of temperature on the formation and distribution of products in electrochemical syntheses is most important for cases in which the overall reaction includes a chemical reaction coupled to the electron transfer. Frequently, an electrochemically generated intermediate can undergo several chemical reaction paths resulting in the formation of two or more reaction products. These reactions may have different activation energies through which a temperature effect on the product distribution may result.

The cathodic reduction of nitrobenzene in sulfuric acid yielding aniline and aminophenol is illustrative [44]. The common intermediate of both end products is phenylhydroxylamine, which can either be reduced further to aniline or rearrange to form p-aminophenol. A higher temperature facilitates the rearrangement and thus favors the formation of p-aminophenol. The yield of p-aminophenol increases from 43 to 58% when the temperature is raised from 50 to 90°C.

If the electroactive species is generated through a preceding chemical reaction, the rate of which is a positive function of temperature, the overall rate of the electrochemical reaction will be accelerated by a rise in temperature. Reductions of aldoses and hexoses are examples of reactions subject to such an effect. Wiesner [45] has shown that the rate-controlling reaction in this case is the conversion of the nonreducible cyclic hemiacetal to the reducible free aldehyde. To the authors' knowledge, no examples of this type have been reported in actual syntheses.

Mass transport in electrolyses for synthetic purposes is governed by both diffusion and convection. The diffusion coefficient, D, of a reactant increases as the temperature is increased. The efficiency of convective mass transfer is a function of the viscosity of the medium. An increase in temperature leads to an increase in convective mass transfer as a result of a decrease in the viscosity of the medium. The net consequence of the increases in diffusion coefficient and convective mass transfer is that the rate of electrolysis is increased.

The hydrogen overvoltage of a metal electrode is also dependent on the temperature. The cathodic overvoltage usually decreases as the temperature increases. This decrease in overvoltage with temperature may affect the electrochemical hydrogenation of organic substrates.

Solution Convection

Electrochemical syntheses are carried out under conditions of convective mass transfer since the rate of electrolysis can thereby be significantly increased. Convective mass transfer can also affect the product distribution of a reaction. With a rotated electrode, for example, the tangential motion around the electrode tends to sweep a reactive intermediate into the bulk of the solution. The conditions in solution may differ sufficiently from those at the electrode surface that a different reaction occurs. The rate of rearrangement of phenylhydroxylamine has been noted earlier to be increased by elevating the temperature of the solution. The same result can be realized if the intermediate phenylhydroxylamine is swept rapidly into the bulk of the solution rather than being allowed to remain at the electrode surface to accept another electron. Wilson and Udupa [44] found that the yield of aminophenol at an electrode rotated at 250 rpm was about 20% and that the yield increased to almost 75% at rotation rates of 2500 rpm.

Many different means of establishing high rates of convective mass transfer are available. The book by Adams [46] provides a summary of these and a discussion of the pertinent theory.

3 THE SCOPE OF ELECTROCHEMICAL SYNTHESIS

A synergistic relationship frequently exists between the physical factors governing electrochemical reactions and the chemical properties of a class of compounds. An illustration of these relationships requires discussion of specific examples of electrochemical syntheses.

The material that follows is not a comprehensive review of electrochemical synthesis but rather an illustration of the scope of the method through discussions of a number of selected areas. Within these areas an effort has been made to summarize the available mechanistic information, and examples of most of the generalized reaction pathways are presented. References to reviews of particular areas are given for those who desire a more complete summary of the compounds that have been synthesized. Emphasis is placed on the recent literature since in several instances current work provides an understanding of mechanisms that was not available from the earlier work. Unfortunately, it becomes evident that in many cases knowledge of the mechanism is far from complete.

This discussion provides an introduction to a number of important electrochemical syntheses from the dual perspective of how the reaction occurs as well as how it can be used.

Anodic Substitution Reactions

The electrochemical oxidation of carboxylate ions, known as the Kolbe synthesis, has been a subject of continuing interest and investigation. The general course of the reaction can be expressed by a sequence such as the following.

$$RCOO^- \rightarrow RCOO\cdot + e^-$$
$$RCOO\cdot \rightarrow R\cdot + CO_2$$
$$RCOO\cdot + R\cdot \rightarrow RCO_2R$$
$$R\cdot + R\cdot \rightarrow R\text{---}R$$

Although many studies have shown that some substitution products are formed that cannot be accounted for by this mechanism, for many years this reaction sequence was not seriously questioned. It is not surprising to find then that, until recently, the subject of anodic substitution was considered under the general topic of the Kolbe synthesis. In the past 5 years, important advances have been made in the general area of anodic substitution reactions and they now comprise an important area of preparative organic electrochemistry.

The overall scheme of anodic substitution reactions is the replacement of a hydrogen atom by another atom or functional group. Thus the following scheme describes the substitution reactions most generally.

$$R — H + A^- \rightarrow R — A + H^+ + 2e^-$$

The substituent group A^- can be a variety of anions. Thus the general area of anodic substitution reactions includes hydroxylation, alkoxylation, alkylation, cyanation, halogenation, pyridination, acetoxylation, thiocyanation, and acetamidation.

Although anodic substitution reactions have been studied by many investigators and are also a subject included in several recent reviews [46–52], the mechanism of these reactions is still a subject of much debate and investigation. The lack of a general agreement upon a unified mechanism(s) is probably attributable to the experimental difficulties in obtaining quantitative electrochemical data. Though powerful, modern electroanalytical techniques do not always provide decisive information on substitution reactions since these reactions do not always have sufficiently high coulombic yields to make good use of the techniques. Thus the mechanism(s) of these reactions often must be formulated from the standpoint of product analysis alone. Unfortunately, it is not often possible to perform a complete product analysis. A proposed mechanism based on partial product analysis may not represent the reaction scheme as a whole, but rather a simplified version of it to account for the identified and analyzed products.

Acetoxylation and Alkylation

Anodic acetoxylation of an aromatic substrate is usually accomplished by electrolysis of glacial acetic acid solutions in the presence of acetate ion. For some time the mechanism of this reaction was presumed to be related to that of the Kolbe synthesis. Thus electrolyses of naphthalene [53], anisole, or toluene [54] in the above medium, giving acetoxy compounds as final products, were taken as evidence for a mechanism involving discharge of the acetate ion to form the acetoxy radical as the primary electrode process.

Recent anodic voltammetric measurements [55], determination of the acetoxy radical lifetime [56], and anode potential studies [57–58] in combination with product analysis [59–60] have provided evidence that the initial electrode process is not the discharge of the acetate ion, but rather the discharge of the aromatic hydrocarbon. Thus the substitution of a ring hydrogen by an acetoxy group (nuclear acetoxylation) is viewed by Eberson [61] as involving a stepwise two-electron transfer, which is assisted by acetate ion, followed by a proton ejection. This mechanism requires that the oxidation potential of the aromatic substrate is more cathodic than that for the discharge of acetate ion and that acetate ion be present. Both of these requirements have been verified by Eberson and Nyberg [55].

However, it has been proposed that the substitution of an α-hydrogen on the side chain of an alkyl aromatic compound (side-chain acetoxylation) involves the formation of a benzyl-type carbonium ion by a stepwise two-electron oxidation of the aromatic substrate followed by the loss of a proton from an α-carbon. The resulting carbonium ion can then react either with the solvent or acetate ion to yield the side-chain acetoxylated product. In this mechanism the initial anodic oxidation of the aromatic hydrocarbon is still required, although acetate ion need not be present. Eberson [61] has shown that side-chain acetoxylation can be accomplished in acetic acid containing perchlorate, sulfate, or toluenesulfonate as the supporting anion.

The above mechanisms suggest that preferential nuclear or side-chain acetoxylation can be achieved by appropriate choice of the anion of the electrolyte. Thus ethylbenzene gives exclusively the α-acetoxy derivative when electrolyzed in acetic acid containing sodium perchlorate, whereas both side-chain and nuclear-substituted ethyl phenylacetates are obtained from a similar electrolysis if sodium acetate is present [55].

Similar nuclear and side-chain acetoxylations have been reported for substituted phenols [62], furan [63–65], indan [21], cyclooctatetraene [66], and dimethylformamide [67, 68] in a glacial acetic acid–acetate ion medium. The electrolysis of triphenylacetic acid in dimethylformamide afforded N-methyl-N-(triphenylacetoxy methyl)formamide [69].

The formyloxylation of dimethylformamide is less clear-cut since the discharge of a formic acid–formate ion medium occurs at a more cathodic potential than that of the acetic acid–acetate ion medium. Furthermore, the addition of dimethylformamide to a solution of a formate in formic acid does not alter the current potential curve observed in its absence. Both of these results suggest that the formation of formate radical might also be involved in the initial anodic process [32, 67, 68].

With anions that are oxidized easily, the initial electron transfer step has been shown to involve the formation of the corresponding radical [31]; for example, the nitrate ion is oxidized to the nitrate radical. The radical can then abstract a hydrogen atom from the α-position of the alkyl aromatic hydrocarbon. The resulting benzyl radical is oxidized to the benzyl cation with a subsequent solvolysis reaction leading to the product. Thus electrolysis of toluene in the presence of nitrate ion gives exclusively the side-chain acetoxylated product [31]. The formation of benzyl radical as an intermediate is further substantiated by the formation of bibenzyl through a radical dimerization reaction.

Anodic addition of acetate ion to a conjugated double bond, such as found in 4,4′-dimethoxystilbene, can also be accomplished by electrolysis of an acetic acid–sodium acetate solution of the hydrocarbon. It has been suggested that the mechanism of addition involves an initial oxidation of the hydrocarbon substrate to a dication intermediate [70].

As the potential of the working electrode is shifted anodically, the discharge of acetate ion becomes more important. Thus at large applied voltages or high current densities, the mechanism of the electrode reaction may be altered accordingly. The acetoxy radical formed from the discharge of acetate ion can decompose to methyl radical and carbon dioxide. The resulting methyl radical can then undergo homolytic methylation of the aromatic hydrocarbon. To demonstrate this competing reaction, Eberson and Nyberg [55] have carried out the oxidation of naphthalene in acetic acid–sodium acetate solutions at +1.0 V versus SCE and +1.7 V. The yield of methylated naphthalene increased from 0.4 to 4% at the more anodic potential and the yield of the acetoxylated product decreased from 24 to 16%. Thus it is apparent that at less anodic potentials acetoxylation is preferred over methylation, while at more anodic potentials the discharge of acetate ion becomes more important and methylation competes successfully.

Similar methylations of cyclooctatetraene [66], pyridine [71], and benzaldehyde [72], and phenylations of aromatic hydrocarbons [73] and pyridine [74] have been reported.

Alkoxylation

Depending on the starting material, there appear to be two electrochemical methods of preparing alkoxylated aromatic hydrocarbons. In the first a Kolbe electrolysis of an aromatic acid in alcohol, under appropriate conditions, provides alkoxylated derivatives in good yield (60%) [75]. The second method involves electrolysis of alcohol solutions of aromatic hydrocarbons.

The voltammetric behavior of methanol in the presence of sodium perchlorate indicates that appreciable electrolysis of methanol occurs at +1.5 V versus SCE [76]. Thus carboxylic acids and hydrocarbons that are more difficult to oxidize than methanol, when oxidized, also discharge methanol. Inoue et al. [77] found that the relative reactivity (based on the percent yield of methoxy derivatives) of hydrocarbons was quite in accord with their reactivity in many types of free-radical reactions. The first step of the reaction is assumed to be the formation of a methoxy radical, although there is no direct evidence for its existence in the electrolysis.

The methoxy radical resulting from the initial oxidation of methoxide ion can abstract a hydrogen atom from the aromatic hydrocarbon. The hydrocarbon radical thus formed can either combine with another methoxy radical at the electrode surface [76] or be further oxidized to a carbonium ion [77–79] which subsequently reacts with methanol. The existence of a carbonium ion as an intermediate has also been demonstrated by the electrolysis of norbornene in methanol [22]. The main product is *exo-syn*-2,7-dimethoxybicyclo-[2.2.1]heptane, which is the rearrangement product of the norbornyl cation.

$$CH_3O^- \longrightarrow CH_3O\cdot + e^-$$

The methoxylation of alkyl-substituted aromatic hydrocarbons usually occurs at the α-hydrogen of the side chain [77, 78], but nuclear methoxylation has been reported [79].

Alkoxylation of furan [80, 81] and substituted furans [82–86] can also be achieved electrochemically in the presence of alcohol and ammonium bromide. The electrolytic method is considered to be superior to the chemical method with respect to the yield (70 to 80%) and the purity of the products obtained. The mechanism of the methoxylation of furan was originally thought to be analogous to that of the chemical method, which uses large quantities of bromine as a reagent. Thus the electrochemical process was viewed as merely a means of continuous generation of bromine. However, this mechanism cannot be the only one involved in the production of methoxylated furan since the same products are obtained with anions other than bromide [63, 64, 87]. Alternative mechanisms involving an initial oxidation of methoxide ion to methoxy radical [63], nitrate ion to nitrate radical, or furan to its cation radical [88] have been proposed.

In contrast to methoxylations of furans and hydrocarbons, methoxylations of tertiary and aromatic amines have been viewed as occurring via the initial discharge of the adsorbed amines [89–92]. The electrolysis of N,N-dimethyl-benzylamine in either methanolic potassium hydroxide or a methanol–methoxide ion medium afforded α-methoxy-N,N-dimethylbenzylamine and N-methoxymethyl-N-methylbenzylamine in a ratio of 1:4, respectively. The preferential methoxylation of the methyl rather than the benzyl group is assumed to be associated with the steric constraints of the adsorbed amine molecule.

The presence of a base is necessary for the methoxylation of amines since changing the electrolyte anion from methoxide to nitrate in the electrolysis of N,N-dimethylaniline yielded N,N,N',N'-tetramethylbenzidine as the mono-nitrate salt [89, 90]. The absence of a base near the electrode surface excludes the base-assisted deprotonation, and the radical cation formed in the electrode reaction tends to undergo a coupling reaction instead of methoxylation.

Since the potentials employed in the electrolysis of some of these amines are fairly anodic, the initial electrode reaction may also include the discharge of methoxide ion [92, 93].

Methoxylation of vinyl ether [94], cyclohexyl isocyanide [95], several aliphatic ethers [96], and dimethylformamide [32] has been reported.

The stereospecific *cis* addition of the methoxy group in the electrolysis of *cis*- and *trans*-stilbenes should be mentioned. The electrolysis of *trans*-stilbene in methanol gave *d,l*-hydrobenzoin dimethyl ether in a yield about two times that of the *meso* isomer; however, the *meso* isomer was obtained from *cis*-stilbene in a yield about 1.5 times that of the *d,l*-isomer. This stereospecific *cis* addition to stilbene has been rationalized by consideration of the geometry of the adsorbed stilbene on the electrode [22, 97].

Anodic addition of methoxide ion to styrene [98] and aliphatic olefins [99] has been reported.

Cyanation

In contrast to the other anodic substitution reactions, anodic cyanation is a relatively new area of investigation. Koyama and co-workers [100] were the first to describe the direct electrolytic cyanation of organic compounds. The constant-current electrolysis was carried out in a mixture of hydrogen cyanide, aromatic hydrocarbon, and methanol containing sodium cyanide. The mechanism proposed originally was a homolytic substitution by anodically generated cyanide radical. It was later shown that the cyanation reaction of anisole is highly potential dependent. Thus no cyanation occurred when the potential of the electrode was just sufficient to oxidize cyanide ion but not anodic enough to oxidize the aromatic substrate. When the potential of the electrode was shifted to that required for the oxidation of the aromatic hydrocarbon, the yield of the cyanation reaction increased rapidly [101–103].

It appears then that the radical mechanism is not adequate to describe these reactions. Furthermore, the predominant *ortho* and *para* nuclear substitution of toluene in anodic cyanation also suggests a polar mechanism involving an initial oxidation of the aromatic substrate to form an electrophilic intermediate, which then reacts with cyanide ion to yield the aromatic nitrile [78, 101–105]. The overall mechanism of cyanation is then essentially the same as that of anodic nuclear acetoxylation. In the case of cyanation, the nuclear reaction is predominant [101].

With di- or trimethoxybenzene, direct replacement of a methoxy group by cyanide occurs when the methoxy groups are situated in positions *ortho* and *para* to each other. With anisole or *meta*-substituted dimethoxybenzene, replacement of hydrogen on the aromatic nucleus predominates [102]. Similar anodic cyanations have also been reported for tertiary amines [102] and 2,5-dimethylfurans [106].

Acetamidation and Hydroxylation

Eberson and Nyberg [107] reported that carbonium ions generated in the anodic oxidation of carboxylates could be trapped by acetonitrile in a Ritter-type reaction. Thus the transformation of an acid into the corresponding acetamide can be accomplished by carrying out the usual Kolbe electrolysis in acetonitrile. The same authors also demonstrated that anodic oxidation of durene and hexamethylbenzene in acetonitrile leads to the formation of substituted N-benzylacetamides (40% yield) [108].

Since these latter products are formed at potentials considerably more cathodic than required for the discharge of the solvent, it was proposed that the primary electrode reaction is the formation of an aromatic dication. Coleman et al. [109] verified this two-electron oxidation mechanism by rapid cyclic voltammetry. Unfortunately, as pointed out later by Parker [110], this affirmation is not necessarily valid since the experimental current function can also be interpreted as the result of a one-electron oxidation followed by a very rapid deprotonation and a subsequent second electron transfer (an ECE mechanism). The formation of bibenzyl in the electrolysis of toluene in wet acetonitrile also suggests that the benzyl radical must be formed as an intermediate [35]. Further support of an initial one-electron transfer came from studies with the structurally similar hexaethylbenzene [110].

Parker and Burgert [35] found that it was necessary to invoke an unknown radical X· as the hydrogen abstractor in the electrolysis of toluene in wet acetonitrile. The half-wave oxidation potential of toluene is $+2.3$ V versus SCE, however, N-benzylacetamide was obtained at anode potentials as low as $+1.6$ V versus SCE. The ionization potential of the benzyl radical has been estimated to be 7.76 eV [111], which is much less than that of toluene (8.82 eV). Therefore, if the benzyl radical were formed near the surface of the electrode, the potential of which is anodic enough to oxidize toluene, the benzyl radical would be immediately oxidized to the benzyl carbonium ion and no bibenzyl would be observed. If the benzyl radical is formed by a reaction in the bulk of the solution, then it is reasonable to expect bibenzyl as the coupling product. The exact nature of X· is not known; however, one could speculate that the presence of water (5.5 M) might be responsible for its formation. When the concentration of water is decreased to 0.1 M, the predominant product (99%) is N-benzylacetamide.

The mechanism of acetamidation in acetonitrile must then involve the initial one-electron oxidation of the aromatic substrate followed by a rapid deprotonation to form a radical intermediate, which can be further oxidized to a carbonium ion. The addition of acetonitrile to this carbonium ion yields a nitrilium salt and, finally, on treatment with water, an N-benzylacetamide results. The carbonium ion can also react with water, if any is present, to form the hydroxylated product, benzyl alcohol [35, 112].

Pyridination

The controlled-potential electrolysis of anthracene in acetonitrile in the presence of pyridine results in the formation of 9,10-dihydroanthryldipyridinium ion.

It was postulated by Lund [113] that the first step of the oxidation is a loss of two electrons from the aromatic system followed by a nucleophilic attack by pyridine to yield the observed product. Subsequent work by Peover and White [114] has provided evidence favoring an initial one-electron process in acetonitrile for the oxidation of polycyclic aromatic hydrocarbons. Recently, Adams et al. [115], using rotating disk electrode measurements, obtained unequivocal evidence that the reaction sequence consists of an initial one-electron oxidation of the aromatic hydrocarbon followed by a nucleophilic reaction with pyridine. The pyridinated intermediate can lose one more electron and addition of one more pyridine to this dication gives a stable dipyridinium salt.

Similar reactions were also demonstrated for 3,4-dimethoxypropenylbenzene [116] and several substituted anthracenes [117–119]. The anodic pyridination of tris-p-anisylethylene [120], by analogy with tetraanisylethylene [121], could have a two-electron oxidation product as an intermediate.

Halogenation and Thiocyanation

Electrochemical halogenation of aromatic compounds can be accomplished by electrolyses in the presence of different halide salts [122]. Since halide ions, except fluoride, are easily oxidized, the electrochemical oxidation merely serves as a means to generate reactive atomic or molecular halogen so that chemical substitution can be accomplished. The products obtained in anodic halogenation reactions are usually *ortho*- and *para*-substituted halogen derivatives.

Inoue et al. [22] found that stilbene and styrene can be brominated by electrolysis of a methanol solution containing a bromide salt as the supporting electrolyte. The by-products of this reaction are methoxylated derivatives. In the case of ethylbenzene, both *ortho*- and *para*-brominated products have been identified [76].

The electrochemical oxidation of iodide ion in the presence of an aromatic hydrocarbon may not yield the iodinated aromatic compound as a product. This result suggests that neither atomic nor molecular iodine are active iodination agents [123]. It is also well known that positive halogen species can be anodically generated in acetonitrile and other nonaqueous solvents. Under these conditions iodination may be feasible since positively charged iodine can be an active iodination agent. Miller [123] has carried out the controlled-potential oxidation of iodine in an acetonitrile–lithium perchlorate solution in the presence of several aromatic molecules. Except for anthracene and nitrobenzene, aromatic iodination was indeed successful. The utility of positively charged halogen species generated electrochemically in aprotic solvents has not been explored extensively.

Anodic fluorination is of considerable interest in the production of fluorinated hydrocarbons. The mechanistic pathway for the production of these fluorinated hydrocarbons is not clear. Since no elemental fluorine is evolved during the reaction, it has been assumed that the fluorination reaction occurs via the adsorbed fluorine atom [52]. However, it has been proposed that the electrochemical addition of fluoride to 1,1-diphenylethylene proceeds via the oxidation of the aromatic substrate [124].

The pseudohalide, thiocyanate, can also be substituted onto the aromatic ring via anodic oxidation in the presence of a thiocyanate salt. In this manner thiocyanate derivatives of phenol and of primary, secondary, and tertiary aromatic amines have been obtained [125]. Recent studies by Cauquis and Pierré [126] show that the oxidation of thiocyanate ion in acetonitrile is a one-electron process and gives the thiocyanate radical as an intermediate. Thus the mechanism of thiocyanation may be analogous to that of the bromination reactions.

Anodic Dimerization

A great number of anodic oxidations proceed with the formation of radical intermediates. The importance of hydrogen abstractions by radical intermediates has been shown in the previous section. One of the alternative stabilization reactions of radicals, a dimerization, is especially favored under high radical concentrations.

Mechanistic Considerations

It is difficult to formulate one general pathway for anodic dimerizations since the reactions are dependent on the nature of the starting material. If the starting material is a neutral molecule, dimerization may either occur via the radical cation initially generated by a one-electron transfer or the radical cation may deprotonate first and then dimerize as a free radical. Occasionally, the radical cation can react with a nucleophile in solution to yield a secondary free radical which dimerizes.

$$RH \rightleftharpoons RH^{.+} + e^-$$
$$RH^{.+} + RH^{.+} \rightarrow R\!-\!R + 2H^+$$
$$RH^{.+} \rightarrow R^. + H^+$$
$$R^. + R^. \rightarrow R\!-\!R$$
$$RH^{.+} + A^- \rightarrow RHA^.$$
$$RHA^. + RHA^. \rightarrow AHR\!-\!RHA$$

If the starting material is an anion, then the initial oxidation should yield an uncharged radical, which can either dimerize directly or attack a species such as an olefin in solution to generate a secondary radical. Dimerization of this secondary radical can also occur.

$$R^- \rightleftharpoons R\cdot + 1e^-$$

$$R + R\cdot \longrightarrow R\text{—}R$$

Dimerization reactions are available for a variety of compounds, as the following examples should demonstrate.

Examples of Oxidative Dimerization

The mechanism of the Kolbe synthesis is generally assumed to include the intermediacy of free radicals. The hydrocarbon radicals thus generated often yield dimeric products. The general scope of the Kolbe synthesis and its utility in organic electrochemical syntheses have recently been reviewed [127, 128].

A recent example of the Kolbe reaction is the electrolysis of methyl hydrogen *cis*-cyclopropane-1,2-dicarboxylate in methanol solution containing sodium methoxide giving dimethylbicyclopropyl-2,2'-dicarboxylate in 25% yield [129]. A similar coupling product is obtained in the electrolysis of

1-hydroxycyclohexylacetic acid in dimethylformamide (40% yield) [130].

When dicarboxylates are electrolyzed under the usual Kolbe conditions, olefins or bicyclic products are formed. The mechanism may involve an intramolecular coupling of biradical species. Thus electrolysis of *trans, trans, trans*-1,3-dicarboxy-2,4-dicarbomethoxycyclobutane yields *cis*-2,4-dicarbomethoxybicyclobutane as the major product [131, 132]. Olefins are formed when the two carboxylic acid groups are located vicinal to each other [133]. The yield of olefin is around 30 to 50% and the electrochemical process is generally superior to the use of lead tetraacetate. Thus electrolysis of

3-carboethoxy-tricyclo[3.2.2.0]non-8-ene-6,7-dicarboxylic acid in pyridine yields 3-carboethoxytricyclo[3.2.2.0]nona-6,8-diene.

The exact mechanism of these reactions is not known. The isolation of lactones under the reaction conditions may indicate that carbonium ions are also formed as intermediates [134].

The anodic oxidation of esters of malonic acid often produces radical intermediates. The electroactive species is the carbanion of the ester. Thus electrolysis of sodium diethylmalonate in the presence of potassium iodide in acetonitrile [135] or in N,N-dimethylacetamide [136] yields tetraethyl ethanetetracarboxylate. Similar coupled products are obtained with ethyl

acetoacetate and ethyl phenylacetate in acetonitrile. Ethanol was found to be a poor medium for ester coupling since it participates in the reaction scheme to produce acetaldehyde as a by-product [137].

The dialkyl malonyl radical formed at the electrode can also attack the double bond of an olefin, forming a secondary radical that can either abstract a hydrogen atom or dimerize. The controlled-potential electrolysis of sodium

dimethylmalonate in the presence of styrene yields tetramethyl 3,4-diphenyl-1,1,6,6-hexanetetracarboxylate [138].

An olefin can also be oxidized to a radical cation which deprotonates and

subsequently dimerizes [139]. In the presence of a nucleophile such as methoxide ion, the radical cation may undergo a nucleophilic reaction to yield a secondary radical which then dimerizes. Thus electrolysis of styrene in

methanol–sodium methoxide solution yields 1,4-diphenyl-1,4-dimethoxy-butane (60% yield) [140].

The electrochemical oxidation of tetraphenylborate anion serves as an interesting example of an intramolecular dimerization [141, 142]. The formation of biphenyl via intramolecular coupling has been established by the electrolysis of mixtures of perdeuterated and ordinary tetraphenylborate. Since no mixed biphenyl was found in the product an intermolecular dimerization was ruled out.

In contrast to alkyl iodides, aryl iodides do not undergo carbon–iodide bond scission when oxidized, but couple [143]. Thus electrolysis of iodobenzene in acetonitrile in the presence of lithium perchlorate at $+1.65$ V versus the Ag/Ag$^+$(0.01 M) electrode yields 4-iododiphenyliodonium perchlorate (45% yield). The reactivity of the iodobenzene radical cation toward

other aromatic hydrocarbons was demonstrated by the formation of diphenyliodonium perchlorate when benzene was added to the solution.

The electrolysis of substituted phenols in basic solution favors the formation of dimers. The phenolate anion probably is the electroactive species and is oxidized to an intermediate phenoxy radical. Symmetrical dimerization of this radical yields dehydrogenodimers. Johnston [144] studied the oxidation of several *ortho*-hydroxybenzophenones in methanolic aqueous sodium hydroxide solution and obtained the corresponding dehydrogenodimer in 20 to 50% yield. Similar dimerizations also occur with 2,6-dihydroxyaceto-phenone [144], corypalline [145], and vanillin [146].

The anodic oxidation of 2,4,6-triphenylphenol in basic medium yields a dimer coupled through oxygen [62]. However, the structurally similar tri-*tert*-butylphenol does not yield any dimeric product [147]. The absence of a

dimeric product was interpreted as the result of the lack of a methylene quinone intermediate. However, steric crowding may have also prevented the dimerization reaction.

Anodic oxidation of aromatic amines is probably one of the most quantitatively studied areas of organic electrochemistry. Quite a variety of radical couplings have been observed from such reactions. An overall view of this area has been presented by Adams [46]. The initial oxidation of an aromatic amine is a one-electron transfer process to form a reactive radical cation intermediate. The existence of this radical cation has only been verified for the cases in which coupling reactions have been sterically blocked [148].

In aqueous acidic solutions, the polymeric and/or dimeric products formed in the oxidation of aniline and *N*-substituted anilines indicate the presence of rapid, following chemical reactions [149]. Recently, Bacon and Adams [150] have demonstrated by cyclic voltammetry that *p*-aminodiphenylamine is the predominant product of the oxidation of aniline in the pH range 0 to 6.5, although benzidines are also found in the more acidic range. By assuming an initial one-electron oxidation, *p*-aminodiphenylamine can be formed by a coupling reaction such as that outlined. The coupling reaction seems to be

107598

preferentially directed to the *para* position since no *ortho* coupling products are detected. Because both benzidine and *p*-aminodiphenylamine are more easily oxidized than aniline, the products formed can be oxidized further.

A similar mechanistic pathway has been suggested for the oxidation of 9-amino-10-phenylanthracene in acetonitrile [151].

In the presence of a base, such as pyridine, the anodic oxidation of aniline in acetonitrile proceeds through a different route [152, 153]. The initial oxidation is still probably the formation of a radical cation; however, the presence of a base tends to promote a deprotonation reaction which leads to a neutral radical. Coupling of the neutral radicals at the nitrogen atom yields hydrazobenzene as an initial product. Since hydrazobenzene is much easier to oxidize than the starting aniline, a further two-electron oxidation occurs.

$$\langle\!\!\bigcirc\!\!\rangle\!\!-\!\!\underset{\underset{\text{H}}{|}}{\text{N}}\!\!-\!\!\underset{\underset{\text{H}}{|}}{\text{N}}\!\!-\!\!\langle\!\!\bigcirc\!\!\rangle + 2B \rightarrow \langle\!\!\bigcirc\!\!\rangle\!\!-\!\!N\!\!=\!\!N\!\!-\!\!\langle\!\!\bigcirc\!\!\rangle + 2BH^+ + 2e^-$$

In a mixture of anilines, good yields of mixed azobenzenes can be obtained under constant-voltage electrolysis conditions. Controlled-potential electrolysis can selectively afford only the azobenzene of the most easily oxidized aniline. Recently, Cauquis et al. [154] have demonstrated that the presence of base is necessary for the formation of azo products.

In contrast to the primary aromatic anilines, secondary and tertiary aromatic amines form N-substituted benzidines. In aqueous solution, the oxidation of N-methylaniline yields N,N'-dimethylbenzidine [155] and the oxidation of N,N-dimethylaniline yields N,N,N',N'-tetramethylbenzidine [148, 156–159]. The same products are obtained from electrolysis in acetonitrile [160, 161].

Heterocyclic compounds such as carbazole are also oxidized to dimeric products in acetonitrile [162].

Hydrodimerization

One of the early attempts to dimerize acrylonitrile electrochemically resulted in a polymeric product [163]. However, because of its potential importance for the production of polyamides, chemists continued to investigate this challenging problem. Knunyants reinvestigated this dimerization reaction and obtained the hydrodimer adiponitrile by reduction of acrylonitrile with alkali-metal amalgams [164] which could be generated electrochemically [165]. By then, "hydrodimerization" (Knunyants) was still far from being a high-yield process and it was not until this decade, when the electrochemical version was investigated thoroughly by Baizer and co-workers, that it was put into commercial practice. In the meantime hydrodimerization has become a basic reaction principle of organic electrochemical synthesis with a wide spectrum of applications.

Scope and Mechanism

Hydrodimerization or, more generally, electrolytic reductive coupling, can be performed with olefins that contain activating or electron-withdrawing groups. These activating groups, E, may not be reduced themselves under the conditions of the electrolysis.

The reaction can proceed intermolecularly between two similar or two dissimilar olefin molecules and the overall reaction is described by the scheme

where E and E' can be $-COOR$, $-CONR_2$, $-CONH_2$, $-CN$, $-C_6H_5$, $-COR$, and so on. If E and E' are identical, only one dimeric product is obtained. In cases in which E and E' differ, three different products may be isolated from the reaction mixture.

A reductive coupling can also be achieved between one olefin and unsaturated compounds containing other than carbon-carbon multiple bonds, for example, benzalaniline or azobenzene. This reaction gives rise to heterocyclic compounds [166].

A second variation of the above principle results if the electrochemically active species is not an activated olefin but a ketone [167, 168] or a compound of the general formula $L(CH_2)_nE$, where L is a leaving group [169, 170]. It has been postulated that in the former case a carbanion [168] or a radical [171] is produced, which subsequently attacks an olefin molecule. The mechanism of the latter reaction supposedly involves the formation of the anion $(CH_2)_nE^-$ by way of the reductive elimination of L from $L(CH_2)_nE$. This anion is believed to be the active agent [169, 170].

In cases in which molecules with two activated double bonds are subjected to a cathodic reduction, the coupling can proceed intramolecularly and give rise to a variety of cyclic compounds. The overall reaction is

where E and E' are activating groups of the same kind as noted above and Z can be $\left[\!-\!C\!-\!\right]_n$ or a variation including a heteroatom.

Several correlations exist between the structure of the activated olefin and the readiness with which it undergoes dimerization. The yield of hydrodimer increases with increasing Michael acceptor ability of the starting monomeric olefin [169, 172]. For example, $C_6H_5CH=CHCOOC_2H_5$ is much less reactive than $CH_2=CHCOOC_2H_5$, which in turn is less reactive than $CH_2=CHCN$. Two activating groups instead of one increase the coupling activity of the monomer [172].

The hydrodimerization process is more difficult for ring olefins containing endocyclic double bonds and is inhibited by the presence of three alkyl groups in the position beta to the double bond [172].

In some cases in which activated bis-olefins are reduced, the resulting cyclic compounds have a preferred configuration [173]. For example, 87% *trans*- and 13% *cis*-diethyl-1,2-cyclohexane diacetate were obtained from diethyl-2,8-decadiene-1,10-dioate [173].

From the results of a great number of investigations, several experimental variables have been identified as significant. The yield of hydrodimers can be increased if metals of high hydrogen overvoltage such as cadmium, tin, lead, and mercury are used as the electrode material [174]. The use of so-called McKees "hydrotropic solvents" [175, 176] (saturated aqueous solutions of alkali metal sulfonates) as supporting electrolytes is advantageous since these solvents are capable of dissolving considerable amounts of acrylonitrile or other organic compounds. Tetraalkylammonium salts of *p*-toluenesulfonate are preferred as supporting electrolytes to alkali metal salts. The yield of the hydrodimer increases with different cations in the order [177]:

$$Li^+ < Na^+ < N(C_2H_5)_3H^+ < N(CH_3)_4^+ < N(C_4H_9)_4^+ < N(C_2H_5)_4^+$$

In order to obtain a high yield of hydrodimer, the concentration of the monomer has to be kept at a certain value [174]. High water content of the medium favors the formation of the hydrogenated monomer, thus the water content of the solution is kept at a minimum. The pH of the solution should be kept between 7 and 9.5 [174].

Two electrons are consumed for the formation of one molecule of hydrodimer [178, 179] and the current is diffusion-controlled [180]. However, differentiation between radical, radical anion, or dianion mechanisms has been a subject of controversy since this reaction was first studied. Baizer in his early papers [174], Tomilov [181], and Asahara [182] favor an initial transfer of two electrons with a following attack of this dianion on a molecule of starting material. The resulting dimeric dianion is subsequently protonated by water to yield the hydrodimer. In the hydrodimerization of acrylonitrile, a cyanoethyl radical has been proposed to be the reactive intermediate [183]. This species may arise from an initial one-electron transfer, with a following protonation. The radical subsequently may react with a molecule of the starting olefin and the product of this reaction is reduced further and protonated to yield the hydrodimer.

However, molecular orbital calculations indicate that the formation of a dianion of the monomer is energetically highly improbable [184]. Moreover, if a radical were operative as an intermediate, cyanoethyl mercury derivatives resulting from the attack of the cyanoethyl radical on the mercury electrode should be detected at least as by-products of the reaction. Recent electrochemical mechanistic studies indicate that electron transfer and coupling occur simultaneously in the reduction of activated bis-olefins [180].

On the basis of coulometry, macroelectrolyses, and kinetic studies by means of voltammetry, Baizer et al. [179] proposed the following mechanism.

Step 1 $ECH{=}CHE' + e^- \rightarrow E\dot{C}H{-}\bar{C}HE'$

Step 2 $E\dot{C}H{-}\bar{C}HE' + ECH{=}CHE' \rightarrow E\bar{C}H{-}CHE'{-}CHE{-}\dot{C}HE'$

Step 3 $E\bar{C}H{-}CHE'{-}CHE{-}\dot{C}HE' + e^- \rightarrow E\bar{C}H{-}CHE'{-}CHE{-}\bar{C}HE'$

Step 4 $E\bar{C}H{-}CHE'{-}CHE{-}\bar{C}HE' + 2H_2O \rightarrow ECH_2{-}CHE'{-}CHE{-}CH_2E' + 2OH^-$

Olefin molecules are adsorbed between tetraalkylammonium ions at the surface of the electrode. In addition to being difficult to reduce, the bulky tetraalkylammonium ions seem to prevent a protonation or coupling of the adsorbed olefin radical anion (step 1) in an, as yet, unclear manner. In a second layer other olefin molecules are oriented and polarized under the influence of the electric field. Thus a coupling with the radical anion at the electrode surface can occur easily (step 2). After the transfer of a second electron (step 3), the resulting dimeric dianion is expelled from the surface of the electrode and is protonated in the solution by water.

Obviously, this intriguing reaction will be the subject of continuing mechanistic studies.

Preparative Applications

As mentioned earlier, the spectrum of preparative applications of electrolytic reductive coupling is wide and encompasses a great number of different compounds. Among the hydrodimerization reactions that have been performed with pairs of similar olefins, the coupling of acrylonitrile [164, 171], various acrylates [172], vinylpyridines [185], unsaturated acids [178, 186] and benzal derivatives of ketones may be mentioned [187, 188].

Electrolytic reductive coupling between two dissimilar olefins can lead to the formation of three different hydrodimers. However, if reaction conditions are chosen properly [166, 174], any one of the three possible dimers can be obtained preferentially. For example, good yields of the cross hydrodimer are obtained if the reduction potentials of the monomers differ at least by 0.2 V and the more difficultly reduced monomer is present in excess.

Acrylonitrile [187–189] and various acrylates [187, 189] have been coupled with a number of olefins and other unsaturated compounds that contain

heteroatoms [166, 190]. Coupling reactions of olefins with reactive intermediates of the type (R—E)⁻ have been performed using sulfonium [169]
and phosphonium [170] compounds for the formation of these intermediates.
Many intramolecular coupling reactions have been reported [191, 192] in
which Z and E encompass a number of different molecular groups as defined
earlier.

Reductive Elimination

The first systematic electrochemical studies on the nature of the carbon–
halogen bond date back more than 30 years. In those early days polarographic
investigations of the reduction of alkyl and aryl halides were conducted by
Brdička [193], Pasternak and von Halban [194], and von Stackelberg and
Stracke [195]. The results of these studies can be summarized in the equation

$$R—X + 2e^- + H^+ \rightarrow R—H + X^-$$

where X is halogen. This work gave an impetus to a great number of further
studies aimed either at elucidation of the mechanism of these reductions or at
exploration of the preparative use of the reaction.

In a broader sense electrochemical reductive eliminations can be performed
with a variety of compounds that incorporate functional groups capable of
leaving the molecule as so-called "leaving groups" (L). Leaving groups for
electrochemical elimination reactions are essentially the same as those of
common organic elimination reactions:

$$L = F, Cl, Br, I, CN, SCN, SH, TOS, OR, N_2^+, NH_2, NRR'.$$

In some special cases phenyl, substituted phenyl, and alkyl groups can be
considered as the leaving moiety [196, 197]. The principle of some elimination
reactions in organic chemistry is the formation of a moiety which is capable
of donating electrons into the C—L bond. Bases, for example, can abstract
protons from alkyl halides thus forming an anionic moiety which exerts an
"electron pressure" on the C—L bond and causes the group L to leave the
molecule.

In electrochemical reductive eliminations this "electron pressure" is exerted
by reactions at the electrode. Since potentials can be adjusted very precisely,
the use of an electrode for elimination reactions seems both logical and
promising. It has been demonstrated by Horner and Singer [198] that acyl
groups can be eliminated from amides very selectively at a mercury electrode.

Since the same selectivity of bond cleavage was observed in the reduction of tosylates and benzoates and, moreover, the reduction proceeds with retention of the configuration, benzoyl and tosyl groups have lately gained increased consideration as protective groups in peptide synthesis [30].

Halogens

Efforts toward an elucidation of the mechanism of reductive eliminations have been concentrated on alkyl and aryl halides. However, it appears that the same mechanism, in a gross sense, applies to reactions with other leaving groups. From a great number of investigations, several facts concerning the scission of the carbon–halogen bond can be summarized.

The bond rupture is eased with decreasing electronegativity of the halogen, von Stackelberg [195], Elving [199], Hush [200], and Lund [201] all reporting that the order of more facile bond fission is

$$F < Cl < Br < I.$$

An increase of the number of halogen atoms attached to the same carbon atom also leads to more ready bond scission. Lund [201] and, recently, Stocker and Jenevein [202] have observed surprisingly anodic reduction potentials for the reductive elimination of fluorine from the trifluoromethyl group. A double or triple bond in the 2,3-position to the halogen-bearing carbon atom facilitates the elimination reaction, whereas a double or triple bond in the 1,2-position makes it harder [195]. The bond rupture is more difficult with an increase in the chain length of the reducible compound [195, 203]. However, this effect seems to level off if the number of carbon atoms in the chain is about four to five [195]. If steric hindrance prevents the leaving group from approaching the electrode closely [204–206], elimination is more difficult.

The pH of the solution also influences the bond scission for species subject to acid-base reactions. For example, α-halogen acids are more easily reduced than their corresponding anions [207–211]. A similar effect is observed for nitrogen bases such as halogenated pyridines and quinolines in which the protonation of the basic nitrogen causes remarkable anodic shifts in reduction potentials [212, 213]. In some cases protons seem to facilitate the carbon–fluorine bond scission in a kind of "push-pull" action. It has been noted by Elving and Leone [214] that the ease of the carbon–fluorine bond rupture in phenacyl fluoride depends on variations of the pH in the range 1 to 7.

The influence of steric hindrance on the ease of bond rupture has already been mentioned. A remarkable correlation between torsion angles and reduction potentials of vicinal dihalides has been reported by Závada et al. [204]. A plot of the torsion angles, φ, of a great number of vicinal dihalogen compounds versus the corresponding half-wave potentials reveals that at

$\varphi = 180°$ (*anti*-periplanar arrangement) and at $\varphi = 0°$ (*syn*-periplanar arrangement) the reduction potentials are at a minimum cathodic value (bond scission is easier) and at $\varphi = 90°$ are at a maximum (bond scission is more difficult).

Polarographic, cyclic-voltammetric, and coulometric studies provide the experimental facts that two electrons are transferred for the rupture of one carbon–halogen bond, the overall reaction is irreversible, and the process is diffusion controlled [199]. If the transfer of two electrons occurs in two discrete steps through an electron transfer, a chemical reaction, and a second electron transfer (an ECE mechanism), a radical should result as an intermediate species. Some investigators [199, 215–218] indeed argue for this mechanism on the basis of isolated products such as dimers or mercury compounds which can arise only through an intermediate radical species. Others [219–223] present equally strong arguments for an anionic mechanism wherein either the transfer of the second electron occurs very shortly after the ejection of the halide ion or even before the ejection [223] (the latter being an EC mechanism).

Nearly all of the cases wherein a radical species has been proposed as an intermediate concern the electrolysis of benzyl halides. Therefore whether the radical or the anionic mechanism is operative seems to be a matter determined by the structure of the compound to be reduced. The most likely general mechanism can be depicted as follows:

Step 1 $\qquad\qquad$ R—X $+ e^- \rightarrow$ [R $\cdots\cdots$ X]$^- \rightarrow$ R· $+$ X$^-$

$\qquad\qquad\qquad\qquad\qquad\qquad$ transition state

Step 2 $\qquad\qquad$ R· $+ e^- \rightarrow$ R$^-$

Step 3 $\qquad\qquad$ R$^-$ $+$ H$^+ \rightarrow$ R—H

In summary, it can be noted that step 1 seems to be quite discrete from step 2 in cases in which benzyl halides and 6-bromo-1-hexene [218] are reduced and the intermediate radical has the opportunity to undergo typical radical reactions. The overall mechanism thus can be described as being an ECEC mechanism. In all the other cases, step 2 either follows so shortly after step 1 that a radical intermediate cannot be detected or two electrons are transferred before the halide ion is ejected.

A number of reductive eliminations have been performed in macroscale electrolyses at mercury electrodes. Elimination of fluorine from the tri-fluoromethyl group of α,α,α-trifluoroacetophenone was reported by Stocker and Jenevein [202]. Depending on the reduction potential, the main product

$\qquad\qquad$ —C—CF$_3$ $\xrightarrow[\substack{-0\cdot 90\text{ V} \\ (\text{Ag/AgCl})}]{\substack{+6e^-,\ +3\text{H}^+}}$ —C—CH$_3$ $\qquad$ (87%)

$\qquad\qquad\quad\ \|$ $\qquad\qquad\qquad\qquad\qquad\qquad\quad\ \|$
$\qquad\qquad\quad\ $O $\qquad\qquad\qquad\qquad\qquad\qquad\quad\ $O

was either acetophenone or acetophenone pinacol. A great number of fluorinated 1,3- and 1,4-cyclohexadienes were converted by Pedler et al. [224] into the corresponding fluorobenzenes.

$$\xrightarrow[\substack{-1\cdot45\ \text{V (SCE)},\\ pH = 7\cdot1}]{+2e^-,\ -2F^-}$$

(47·5%)

$$\xrightarrow[\substack{-1\cdot75\ \text{V (SCE)},\\ pH = 8\cdot4}]{+2e^-,\ -2F^-}$$

(62·7%)

Chlorine and bromine are the leaving groups in electrochemical reductions of a series of haloketones performed by McDowell [225]. If these reductions are carried out under anhydrous conditions in the presence of alkylating agents, ketones of an increased chain length are obtained.

The preparation of various small ring compounds by reductive elimination of bromine or chlorine has been described (see Section 3 pp. 45–46). The formation of polymers by reductive elimination of halide ions from o- and p-haloxylenes was reported by Covitz [223] and by Gilch [226]. The proposed intermediates are xylylenes which can either dimerize to form [2,2]p-cyclophanes or polymerize to polyxylenes. Covitz proposes an anionic mechanism

$$\xrightarrow[-0\cdot80\ \text{V (SCE)}]{}$$

(90%)

(5–10%)

including a simultaneous ejection of two halide ions in this reductive elimination.

Tomilov et al. [227, 228] have observed that reductions of 3-halopropionitriles at lead, tin, thallium, and mercury working electrodes afford a variety of 2-cyanoethyl-metal derivatives. Further discussion of similar reactions

$$2I-CH_2-CH_2-CN \xrightarrow[-1.03\ \text{V SCE}]{+2e^-} 2I^- + 2NC-CH_2-CH_2\cdot$$

$$2NC-CH_2-CH_2\cdot \xrightarrow{Hg} (NC-CH_2-CH_2)_2Hg$$

leading to organometallic compounds can be found in Section 3, pages 55–57.

The cyano group is considered by Arapagos and Scott [229] as the leaving group in the electrolytic reduction of 1,1'-dicyanobicyclohexyl to bicyclohexylidene (20%) and bicyclohexane (80%). Since the reaction was carried out in anhydrous amine solutions, solvated electrons are thought to be the reducing agent (see Section 3, pp. 59–63).

Other Leaving Groups

As mentioned, a number of chemical species may serve as leaving groups. Baillie and Tafel [230], Kindler [231], and Gawrilow [232] have shown that the reduction of amides of carboxylic acids at a lead electrode in sulfuric acid proceeds completely from the carbonyl to the methylene group. However, if this reduction is performed at a mercury electrode with tetraalkylammonium salts present as the supporting electrolyte, a scission of the carbon–nitrogen or carbon–oxygen bond is observed [30]. Horner and co-workers have studied this cathodic cleavage of amides and esters of carboxylic and sulfonic acids extensively [30, 198, 233]. They believe that tetraalkylammonium ions are discharged and form a product layer on the surface of the mercury [30], which serves as a medium for electron transfer. The overall reaction can be formulated as follows:

$$RSO_2R' \xrightarrow{+2e^-, +H^+} RSO_2^- + R'H$$

$$RCONR'R'' \xrightarrow{+4e^-, +4H^+} RCH_2OH + HNR'R''$$

$$RCOOR' \xrightarrow{+4e^-, +4H^+} RCH_2OH + HOR'$$

The reduction potentials are distinctly dependent on the substituents R, R', and R''. Therefore, very selective reductive cleavage reactions can be performed within a group of compounds [198]. If benzoylated or tosylated amino acids or peptides are subjected to this reductive cleavage, the reaction proceeds with retention of the configuration of the amino acid [30].

$$TOS\text{-}L(-)\text{-}Tyr \xrightarrow{+2e^-, +H^+} TOS^- + L(-)\text{-}Tyr$$

$$Benzoyl\text{-}D,L\text{-}Meth \xrightarrow{+4e^-, +4H^+} Benzyl\ alcohol + D,L\text{-}Meth$$

Rambacher and Mäke [234] have observed that the electrolytic reduction of isocystine at a copper electrode proceeds to the corresponding amino acid with the evolution of hydrogen sulfide. The reaction can also be performed with 2-mercaptoacetic and 2-mercaptopropionic acids.

$$HS-CH_2-CH_2-C\overset{O}{\underset{OH}{\big\backslash}} \xrightarrow{+2e^-, +H^+} CH_3-CH_2-C\overset{O}{\underset{OH}{\big\backslash}} + H_2S$$

Polarographic studies and preparative electrolyses of quarternary ammonium [235], phosphonium [196], arsonium, and sulfonium salts [197, 236] revealed that these compounds can be degraded electrochemically to the corresponding tertiary amines, phosphines, and thio ethers. From the results of a great number of electrolyses, Horner and co-workers concluded that the ease of bond fission increases in the following order in a series of phosphonium salts

$$CH_3 < C_6H_5 < C_2H_5 < n\text{-}C_4H_9 < i\text{-}C_3H_7 < tert\text{-}C_4H_9 < CH_2C_6H_5$$

and arsonium salts [197]:

$$CH_3 < C_2H_5 < p\text{-}CH_3\text{—}C_6H_4 < n\text{-}C_4H_9 < C_6H_5 < CH_2C_6H_5 \sim CH_2COC_6H_5$$

Thus, for example, the reduction of (trimethyl)benzylphosphonium ion can be formulated:

$$(CH_3)_3\overset{+}{P}\text{-}CH_2C_6H_5 \xrightarrow{+2e,-+H^+} (CH_3)_3P + C_6H_5\text{—}CH_3$$

Uncertainties as to the mechanism of these reductions have not yet been resolved. While some workers argue for two discrete electron transfer steps [237, 238], others report a one-step, two-electron transfer for the same compounds [239, 240].

Detailed possible mechanisms would include a one-step, two-electron transfer with the subsequent ejection of an anion (EC mechanism) and the

$$R_4P^+ \xrightarrow{+e^-} R_4P\cdot \xrightarrow{+e^-} R_4P^- \to R_3P + R^- \xrightarrow{+H^+} R_3P + RH$$

transfer of one electron, ejection of a radical, and a subsequent transfer of a second electron (ECE mechanism). Horner and Haufe have some evidence

$$R_4P^+ \xrightarrow{+e^-} R_4P\cdot \to R_3P + R\cdot \xrightarrow{+e^-} R_3P + R^- \xrightarrow{+H^+} R_3P + RH$$

for the existence of an anion, R_4P^-, in support of the former mechanism [241]. Apart from these mechanistic considerations, the selective reductive cleavage of phosphorus–carbon, nitrogen–carbon, and arsenic–carbon bonds has become a powerful tool in syntheses of optically active "onium salts" and tertiary phosphines and arsines [197, 198].

The amino group has been proposed as a leaving group by Janik and Elving [242] on the basis of polarographic studies on 6-aminopurine.

Kochi [243] reported that the electrolytic reduction of diazonium salts affords nitrogen and the corresponding aryl radicals. The reaction products are the corresponding mercury compounds and unidentified tarry materials.

Ring Closure Reactions

A great number of syntheses of ring compounds in organic chemistry are accomplished through intramolecular or intermolecular reactions in which a nucleophilic group, such as an amino group, attacks an electrophilic carbon atom with the subsequent elimination of either water or ammonia. A typical example of such an intramolecular reaction is the formation of piperidine from

pentamethylenediamine hydrochloride. The preparation of quinoxaline from o-phenylenediamine and glyoxal is a typical example of an intermolecular cyclization reaction.

Electrochemically effected ring closure reactions may follow the above general reaction paths through the electrochemical formation of suitable functional groups. For example, selective reduction of the nitro group to the amino group and its subsequent attack on a neighboring group of the opposite electronic character is described herein. However, electrochemical reactions proceed with the formation of reactive intermediates such as carbonium ions, carbanions, carbenes, or radicals in the first step of the overall reaction. Subsequent reactions of these intermediates can lead to cyclic end products.

Thus the scope of electrochemical reactions that lead to ring compounds is very broad, encompassing a wide spectrum of chemical principles and reaction mechanisms. This discussion of electrochemically effected ring closure reactions is not an exhaustive summary of all the examples described in the literature but is rather a demonstration of several of the different approaches that have been used to achieve a ring closure.

With the exception of Lund's, Baizer's, and Rifi's work (*vide infra*), no systematic studies on the scope and limitations of electrochemical cyclizations are available. It seems that in many of the documented examples the generation of a cyclic product or by-product was more an incidental than planned reaction.

Intramolecular Cyclization

Intramolecular cyclization reactions accomplished through electrochemical reactions are widely documented. Examples of a variety of reaction mechanisms are available which cover a large span of years of investigation.

Reductive formation of reactive functional groups was described in 1902 by Wohlfarth with the electrolytic formation of benzo[c]cinnoline from 2,2′-dinitrobiphenyl [244]. The reaction was carried out to 95% yield in a cell in which the nickel cathode and the lead anode were separated by a diaphragm and the supporting electrolyte was sodium acetate. The mechanism of this reaction was explored later by Lund [245] and shown to involve the formation of an azoxy compound which can be isolated and reduced further to benzo[c]-cinnoline. The intermediate (VII) could not be isolated but reacted instan-

taneously to give (VIII). The mechanism of this reaction is supported by polarography, coulometry, and controlled-potential electrolysis.

Ring closure reactions of this type have been studied extensively by Lund. The main reaction step is in most cases the reduction of a nitro group and the reductive formation of a suitable leaving group. Since the reduction of a nitro group is very sensitive to pH changes, these reactions have to be carried out at controlled pH. The following examples have been reported by Lund [246]. The reduction of 2-nitro-1-(2-nitrophenyl) ethanol leads in two steps to the intermediate 2-hydroxylamino-1-(2-hydroxylaminophenyl) ethanol (IX). In alkaline medium the intermediate (IX) forms cinnoline. The initiating step of this condensation seems to be the elimination of water from the —CH—CH— group.

$$\begin{array}{cc} \text{—CH—CH—} \\ \quad | \quad | \\ \text{OH} \quad \text{H} \end{array}$$

Other examples of this type include the formation of anthranil from *o*-

nitroacetophenone, the formation of hydroxamic acids, and the formation

of benzotriazenes from *o*-nitrophenylhydrazine derivatives [247].

Cathodic reduction of 1,3 dioximes such as acetylacetone dioxime in acidic media (lead electrode, 30% sulfuric acid) results in the formation of pyrazolidine derivatives [248].

Although a mechanistic study on this reaction has not yet been performed, it seems likely that the first step is the formation of an amino group and its following nucleophilic attack on the neighboring protonated hydroxylamino group.

Depending on the reaction conditions, the electrochemical oxidation of alcohols, amines, and carboxylates can afford carbonium ions as reactive intermediates [26, 249–252]. Among the factors that determine whether an electrolysis of carboxylates follows a normal Kolbe path (radical mechanism) or an abnormal Hofer-Moest (carbonium ion) path are the choice of solvent and working electrode material. Graphite electrodes seem to promote the carbonium ion reaction path [27]. The first step in these reactions is the

$$CH_3-CH_2-CH_2-CO_2^- \xrightarrow{-e^-,-CO_2} CH_3-CH_2-CH_2 \cdot \xrightarrow{-e^-} CH_3-CH_2-CH_2^+$$

abstraction of one electron with a following elimination of either carbon dioxide, hydroxyl radical, or boric acid, if alkane boronic acids are oxidized. The resulting alkyl radical is then oxidized further to the corresponding carbonium ion, which undergoes the well-known stabilization reactions (reported yields for the cyclic products are around 5 to 10%).

Anodic oxidation of substituted carboxylic acids does not always result in the Kolbe reaction. If p-hydroxyphenylpropanoic acids are oxidized anodically, the end products are spirolactodienones which can be rearranged to

hydroxycoumarin in an acid-catalyzed reaction [253, 254]. A similar formation of a lactone was observed by Kenner and co-workers in the anodic oxidation of diphenyl-2-carboxylic acids [255]. Unfortunately, in both cases the mechanisms are only based on reasonable assumptions and not on the determination of electrochemical parameters such as oxidation potentials, number of electrons transferred, reversibility of the considered process, and so on.

If tyrosyl peptides are subjected to this oxidative treatment in a flow cell, the peptide bonds are cleaved selectively in a nonenzymic way [254, 256].

Diketones can be subject to both anodic oxidation or cathodic reduction to produce cyclic compounds. Anodic oxidation of suitable diketones (e.g., 1,5-diketones) yields pyrylium salts [257]. The reaction seems to proceed through an ene-diketone intermediate which can cyclize. Thus Dilthey's original oxidative procedure employing ferric chloride can also be accomplished electrochemically [258].

Radicals have also served as intermediates in intramolecular cyclization reactions as exemplified by the electrolytic reduction of ketones to pinacols [39, 259]. The reduction of the keto function in the presence of proton donors results first in the formation of a radical which subsequently can dimerize. If 1,3- 1,5-, or 1,6-diketones are used as substrates in these reductions, the dimerization of the intermediately formed radicals can proceed intramolecularly to give cyclic diols [260, 261].

This procedure was used by McCartney and co-workers to demonstrate that Clemmensen reductions proceed via cyclopropanediol intermediates. However, these species are subject to fragmentation reactions in acidic media and thus yield rearranged products [262, 263].

The key intermediate (**XI**), which is not stable under Clemmensen conditions, was prepared electrochemically by reduction of (**X**) in acetonitrile at a mercury pool. The treatment of (**XI**) with the Clemmensen reduction mixture [Zn(Hg) + HCl] gave (**XII**) and (**XIII**), similar to the genuine Clemmensen reduction of (**X**).

Electrochemical reductive elimination reactions can lead to the production of carbanions as reactive intermediates (see Section 3, pp. 34–39). Using these cathodic eliminations, Rifi developed a method for the synthesis of small-ring compounds from suitable alkyl halides [221, 222], for example,

1,3-dimethylbicyclobutane from 1,3-dibromo-1,3-dimethylcyclobutane, spiro-

$$\text{H}_3\text{C} \diagdown \overset{\text{Br}}{\underset{\text{CH}_3}{\bowtie}} \diagup \text{Br} \xrightarrow[-2\text{Br}^-]{+2e^-} \text{H}_3\text{C}\!-\!\langle\rangle\!-\!\text{CH}_3$$

pentane from 1,3-dibromo-2,2-bis(bromomethyl)propane, and cyclopropane

$$\underset{\text{BrH}_2\text{C}}{\overset{\text{BrH}_2\text{C}}{\diagup}}\!\!\times\!\!\underset{\text{CH}_2\text{Br}}{\overset{\text{CH}_2\text{Br}}{\diagdown}} \xrightarrow[-4\text{Br}^-]{+4e^-} \bowtie$$

from 3-bromopropyltriethylammonium bromide. In all cases the assumption

$$\text{BrCH}_2\!-\!\text{CH}_2\!-\!\text{CH}_2\overset{+}{\text{N}}(\text{C}_2\text{H}_5)_3\,\text{Br}^- \xrightarrow[-\text{Br}^-]{+2e^-} \bar{\text{C}}\text{H}_2 \overset{\text{CH}_2}{\diagdown} \text{CH}_2\!-\!\overset{+}{\text{N}}(\text{C}_2\text{H}_5)_3\,\text{Br}^-$$

$$\downarrow$$

$$\triangle\ +\ (\text{C}_2\text{H}_5)_3\text{N}\ +\ \text{Br}^-$$

of a carbanion as the reactive intermediate seems valid and is supported by polarographic and cyclic voltammetric investigations. Thus the mechanism of these reactions can be generally outlined by the following scheme, where X is halogen.

$$\text{X}\!-\!\langle\rangle\!-\!\text{X} \xrightarrow{+e^-} \left[\text{X}\!-\!\langle\rangle\!-\!\text{X}\right]^{\cdot-} \longrightarrow \text{X}\!-\!\langle\rangle\!\cdot\ +\ \text{X}^-$$

$$\text{fast}\Big\downarrow +e^-$$

$$\langle\rangle\ +\ \text{X}^- \longrightarrow \text{X}\!-\!\langle\rangle$$

Electrolytic reductive coupling (see Section 3, pp. 30–34) can proceed intra- as well as intermolecularly and the mechanism for such an intramolecular reaction can be described as follows [191, 264],

$$\underset{\text{CH}=\text{CHE}}{\overset{\text{CH}=\text{CHE}}{(\text{CH}_2)_n}} \xrightarrow{+e^-} \underset{\text{CH}-\dot{\text{C}}\text{HE}}{\overset{\text{CH}-\bar{\text{C}}\text{HE}}{(\text{CH}_2)_n}} \xrightarrow[\text{fast}]{+e^-,\ +2\text{H}_2\text{O}} \underset{\text{CH}-\text{CH}_2\text{E}}{\overset{\text{CH}-\text{CH}_2\text{E}}{(\text{CH}_2)_n}}$$

$$+2\text{OH}^-$$

where E is an activating group such as —COOR, —CN, —RCO, and so on.

Starting with diolefins of the general type,

$$Z \Big\langle \begin{matrix} CH\!=\!CHE \\ \\ CH\!=\!CHE \end{matrix}$$

where Z can be varied among a number of chemical groups, Baizer and co-workers prepared a wide variety of cyclic compounds. In some cases ring closure was achieved by reduction of an activated double bond, with simultaneous displacement of a suitable leaving group.

Intermolecular Cyclization

Intermolecular ring closure reactions are not as common in electrochemistry as intramolecular reactions. In most cases a reactive intermediate (e.g., carbene, radical, or radical cation) is formed electrochemically. These reactive species can either dimerize, react with the starting material, or react with another suitable compound.

The anodic oxidation of 3,4-dimethoxy-1-propenylbenzene leads to the formation of 1,2-dihydro-2,3-dimethyl-6,7-dimethoxy-1-p-veratrylnaphthalene [116].

The first step in this cyclization is the reversible one-electron oxidation of (XIV) to the radical cation (XV) at $+0.98$ V. The radical cation dimerizes and forms the dication (XVI). The positive carbon atom of the dication attacks the benzene nucleus with a following ejection of a proton. The authors claimed to have isolated (XVII) as a purple perchlorate, but one would expect such a species to be very unstable. Treatment of this perchlorate salt with base leads to the final product (XVIII).

By-products of this anodic oxidation are small quantities of 2,3,6,7-tetramethoxyanthraquinone and 2,3,6,7-tetramethoxy-9,10-diethyl-9,10-dihydroanthracene (XIX). The formation of these anthracene derivatives can be rationalized on the basis of an acid-catalyzed dimerization of 3,4-dimethoxypropenylbenzene. Two possible products of this reaction are the 2,3,6,

7-tetramethoxy-9,10-diethyl-9,10-dihydroanthracene (**XIX**) and the indan derivative (**XX**). The indan derivative is indeed observed as a major product

of the electrolysis. In some cases, it has been observed that electrochemically generated products react with starting material and complicate the reaction mechanism. In this particular case electrochemically generated protons catalyze a dimerization reaction. (In another reported example, $NI_3 \cdot NH_3$, an oxidizing agent, is generated anodically and causes the formation of a heterocyclic ring compound [265].) In a recent communication [70] the mechanism depicted above was substantiated for the anodic oxidation

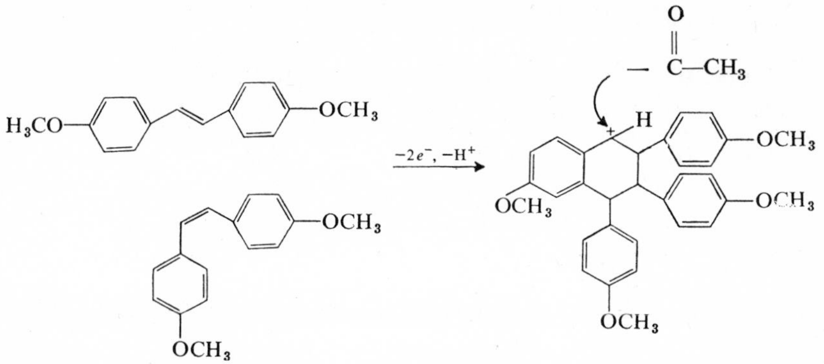

of 4,4'-dimethoxystilbene in acetate-containing solutions. As might be expected, the authors isolated an acetoxyl derivative which arose from a nucleophilic attack of the acetate ion on the 1,2,3,4-tetrahydro-7-methoxy-1,2,3-trimethoxyphenylnaphthalenium ion.

The formation of a cation, a nucleophilic attack of the solvent (acetonitrile), and a subsequent elimination of a tertiary butyl group are the main reaction steps in the anodic formation of 3-methyl-5,7-di-*tert*-butyl-1,2-benzisoxazole from 2,4,6-tri-*tert*-butylphenol [147].

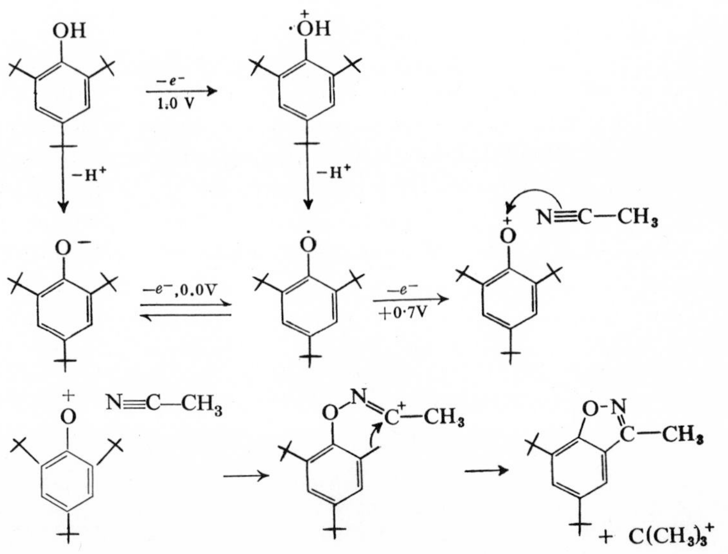

Anodic oxidations of sodium malonates yield radicals that can dimerize [138]. If this oxidation is performed in the presence of suitable olefins, the malonyl radicals add to the olefins and the resulting radical is either subject to various stabilization reactions (such as hydrogen atom abstraction or dimerization) or is oxidized further to the corresponding cation. This cation is stabilized by reaction with a suitable nucleophile, either intramolecularly or intermolecularly [138].

Octafluorophenazine is formed in a low yield (6%) during the anodic oxidation of pentafluoroaniline at a platinum anode in acetone–aqueous sodium acetate [266]. The key step of this reaction seems to be a radical displacement of fluorine after the initial attack of the imino radical on the aromatic nucleus. The oxidation was carried out at a controlled potential of +1.5 to +1.6 V versus SCE. An observation of fluorine formation was not mentioned.

Reductive elimination of halogen from alkyl halides can ultimately lead to the formation of carbenes. According to Wawzonek and Duty [267], the electrolysis of carbon tetrachloride in acetonitrile in the presence of tetramethylethylene yields 1,1-dichloro-2,2,3,3-tetramethylcyclopropane. It is thought that dichlorocarbene is formed by reduction and adds to the double bond of tetramethylethylene.

$$CCl_4 \xrightarrow[-2Cl^-]{+2e^-} :CCl_2$$

Reactions of Organometallic Compounds

The previous discussions have presented several of the applications of electrochemical syntheses to organic chemistry. A similar discussion of electrochemical reactions of inorganic compounds could be presented. In fact, commercial application of electrochemical reactions is much more advanced in inorganic systems than in organic systems. Organometallic electrochemistry has received far less study than either organic or inorganic electrochemistry. However, efforts within the past decade have brought organometallic electrochemistry to a point such that many reactions of synthetic value are now characterized and others are likely to appear in the near future. The following discussion treats a few selected areas in organometallic electrochemistry which illustrate important concepts or unique reactions. A more comprehensive summary of organometallic electrochemistry is currently in preparation [268].

Reduction or Oxidation to a Stable Radical

Certainly one of the most important advances in modern electrochemistry is the development of the capability to prepare stable or semistable radical species. No doubt this capability has largely evolved from the trend toward the use of more inert solvent systems. Or conversely, the interest in more detailed knowledge of radical and other highly reactive species has encouraged the development of techniques by which inert but often highly resistive solvent systems can be employed adequately in studies of electrochemical reactions. In either case a number of systems are now known that yield stable radical species upon electrochemical reduction or oxidation. Coordination compounds in particular, but not exclusively, yield such species. The following examples illustrate the variety of compounds that have been shown to yield stable radicals and point out the areas of further research in which these electrochemical reaction products have been useful.

To label all one-electron reduction products of coordination compounds which are of unique interest as radical species is an oversimplification of an important issue. When a compound accepts an electron, in the extremes, the added electron may be totally localized on the metal, leading in essence to a separate oxidation state of the metal, or it may be predominantly localized on the ligand yielding species that have been denoted as "metal-stabilized radical-ligand" chelates [269]. In many cases, of course, the actual situation is something between these two limits with unpaired spin density present at both the metal-atom center and on the ligands. Reactions in which the free electron is apparently localized on the metal atom with a new oxidation state resulting are included under the general heading of stable radical species for convenience in the present discussion.

One of the largest areas of research in electrochemically produced radical species has evolved around compounds that can be represented by the general formulae

$$\ce{R-\overset{X}{\underset{Y}{C}}}\,M/2 \quad \text{or} \quad \ce{\overset{X}{\underset{Y}{C}}}\,M/2$$

in which X and Y have now been varied through a wide series of permutations [270–281]. For example, within this general series of compounds, cases with X = Y = O, or X = Y = NH, X = O, Y = S, X = S, Y = NH, have all received study. The metal centers of the compounds examined have included nickel, cobalt, zinc, cadmium, copper, and palladium (all possible permutations not implied).

Radicals of these compounds have been prepared and isolated in sufficient quantities for physical examination in several cases. For example, the 0, −1, and −2 formal oxidation states of the bis(toluene-3,4-dithiolene)nickel chelates have been prepared and isolated [273].

An interesting example of the differences between chemical and electrochemical reductions arises through examinations of glyoxal bis(2-mercaptoanil)nickel [282]. Electrochemical reduction yields the anion of (XXI), while

(XXI)

borohydride reduction yields a compound resulting from addition of hydrogen across the conjugated bridge.

The work of Dessy and co-workers [283–286] on the electrochemical reactions of a number of transition metal organometallic compounds has presented a number of examples of stable radical species. The following two examples illustrate the wide variety of compounds that show this behavior.

Bis(cyclopentadienylnickel)diphenylacetylene (XXII) undergoes reduction to the stable radical anion at −2.2 V versus Ag/0.001 M AgClO$_4$ in glyme (0.1 M in tetrabutylammonium perchlorate). Reduction of pentaphenyl-

(XXII)   (XXIII)

phosphocyclopentadiene (XXIII) and other similar compounds with group--III, -IV, and -V metals to stable radical anions occurs at approximately −2.6 V in glyme. The mechanism of the reduction is complex, proceeding through the dianion with the radical anion generated by a disproportionation reaction.

Further application of stable radical species in synthetic studies, electrophilic substitution, for example, has not been explored to date. It seems probable that the unusual properties of these compounds will open new synthetic routes.

An interesting example of the use of unusual species prepared through electrochemical reactions is provided by the work of Dessy and Wieczorek [287] concerning the transmission of charge in the bonding of organometallic carbonyl compounds. Species of the general type $LM(CO)_5$, $L_2M(CO)_4$, and $[LM(CO)_4]_2$, where L is a ligand (typically, pyridine for $LM(CO)_5$, bipyridyl for $L_2M(CO)_4$, and $P(CH_3)_3$ for $[LM(CO)_4]_2$) and M is chromium, tungsten, or molybdenum, respectively, were subjected to electrolysis to produce the corresponding radical anions or dianions. Measurements of the carbonyl stretching frequencies of the reduction products and the parent compounds formed the basis for examination of the bonding in the compounds. Since the added electron is essentially ligand localized, there is a large difference in the nature of the ligand. Thus a technique for examining ligand bonding without significantly altering the molecular geometry is made available.

An illustration of electrochemical reactions that lead to stable products with the unpaired spin density localized on the metal is provided by the recent work of Olson and Vasilevskis [288]. Oxidation and reduction of some square planar complexes of nickel(II) and some tetradentate macrocyclic amine ligands led to stable species isolated as the perchlorate or tetrafluoroborate salts. One-electron reductions to nickel(I) species, and one-electron oxidations to nickel(III) species, all accomplished in acetonitrile, were confirmed by polarographic, cyclic voltammetric, and coulometric studies. The nature of the ligands (no π-orbitals in some cases) and the magnetic susceptibilities of the salts confirm the assignment of the compounds as complexes of nickel(I) and nickel(III).

The Preparation of Bimetallic Compounds

Reduction of suitable compounds to radical species with a subsequent dimerization of the radicals has become an important synthetic use of electrochemical reactions in organic systems. Conceptually, similar reactions are of value for the synthesis of organometallic compounds.

The reduction of group-IV and -V organometallic compounds of the type ϕ_3MX or ϕ_2MX, where X is typically a halogen, has been examined in some detail by Dessy and co-workers [289, 290]. The overall pathway of reduction encompasses the reactions

$$\phi_3MX + e^- \rightarrow \phi_3M\cdot + X^-$$
$$2\phi_3M\cdot \rightarrow \phi_3MM\phi_3$$
$$\phi_3M\cdot + \text{Solvent(H)} \rightarrow \phi_3MH + \text{Solvent}\cdot$$
$$\phi_3MM\phi_3 + 2e^- \rightarrow 2\phi_3M^-$$

for the group-IV compounds. Corresponding reactions are noted for the group-V compounds. The reactivity of the di- or triphenyl metal radical appears to be the primary factor in determining the course of the reactions. For the silicon, germanium, and phosphorus compounds, abstraction of a hydrogen atom from the solvent is predominant. The tin, arsenic, antimony and, most likely, bismuth compounds lead to the dimeric metal–metal-bonded compounds. These latter compounds can be further reduced to yield anionic species of the ϕ_3M^- or ϕ_2M^- types which range, under an inert atmosphere, from highly stable (ϕ_2Sb^- or ϕ_3Sn^-) to very unstable (ϕ_2Bi^-).

The work by Dessy et al. [289] on the ϕ_3PbX compound was carried out at a mercury electrode and the reaction

$$2\phi_3Pb\cdot + 3Hg \rightarrow 3\phi_2Hg + 2Pb$$

occurs more rapidly than the other reactions shown. Reduction of hexaphenyldilead yields the triphenyllead anion; thus the lead compound would probably follow the pathway of the tin compound at an inert electrode.

Reaction of the electrochemically produced anions with an appropriate ϕ_3MX salt leads to the formation of heterobimetallic compounds [291] for systems in which the triphenyl metal radicals are not highly reactive.

Dessy and co-workers [291, 292] have also examined the electrochemical reduction of some transition metal compounds, some of which yield bimetallic products.

From their work on both the main group and transition metal compounds, a general basis for the preparation of bimetallic compounds has evolved [293]. The general reaction sequence is to prepare the anion and allow it to react with a suitable R_xMX compound. Thus, for example, reduction of $[(\pi\text{-}C_5H_5)\,Fe(CO)_2]_2$ leads to the anion, $[(\pi\text{-}C_5H_5)\,Fe(CO)_2]^-$, which is then allowed to react with ϕ_3SnCl to form a heterodimetallic compound with an iron–tin bond. A characterization of the nucleophilicities of the anions [294] and studies of redistribution reactions [295] among the

$$R_3M^- + R_3M'M''R_3 \rightleftharpoons R_3MM''R_3 + R_3M'^-$$

various species studied has provided a framework of knowledge for a systematic approach to such reactions.

Reactions at Active Electrodes

Electrochemical reaction of an organic species at a metal electrode in a process that consumes the electrode can be used in the preparation of organometallic compounds. This subject has been discussed in some detail in a review by Marlett [296]. Since these reactions can yield commercially important compounds such as tetraalkylleads, the significantly greater effort in this area of organometallic electrochemistry is understandable.

Several anodic processes have been described for the production of metal alkyls. The present interests do not extend to the relative merits of these processes and since little detailed information on the nature of the reactions is available, only an outline of the processes is given.

The electrolysis of complex salts such as $NaF \cdot 2Al(C_2H_5)_3$ with an attackable anode forms metal alkyls [296]. The complex salt serves as the electrolyte with the system held at elevated temperatures. The net cell reaction results in the deposition of aluminum at the cathode and the production of ethyl radicals at the anode, the latter eventually forming the metal alkyl. Compounds of lead, zinc, antimony, indium, tin, gallium, thallium, silicon, germanium, aluminum, magnesium, cadmium, bismuth, and gold have been reported from systems of this general type [296]. Extensions of this basic concept, with modifications and practical improvements, have afforded a number of related processes [296]. Many of these developments are the result of the work of Ziegler and Lehmkuhl [297] whose names this process bears.

The electrolysis of Grignard reagents in ether solutions also provides metal alkyls from an attackable electrode. The review by Marlett [296] includes a discussion and references on this subject from the view of commercial application. Mechanistic information of these reactions which would offer a basis for their extension is sparse. Evans and co-workers [298, 299] have suggested anodic alkyl radical production from which metal alkyls eventually result. The anode reactions are described as

$$R_2MgX^- \rightarrow R\cdot + RMgX + e^-$$
$$R_3Mg^- \rightarrow R\cdot + R_2Mg + e^-$$
$$RMgX_2^- \rightarrow R\cdot + MgX_2 + e^-$$

on the basis of the species shown to be present in Grignard solutions. Other descriptions of the anodic process as simply

$$4R^- + Pb \rightarrow R_4Pb + 4e^-$$

have appeared [2, 300] without further mechanistic justification. Cathodic reactions of Grignard solutions have been examined in detail recently by Psarras and Dessy [301]. The complex nature of the Grignard reagent precludes simplicity in its electrochemistry.

Reactions that consume the electrode material have also been noted for cathodic processes. A guide to the early work is given by Marlett [296]. The reduction of alkyl halides at a lead electrode has received attention in recent years. Again, the production of an alkyl radical,

$$RX + e^- \rightarrow R\cdot + X^-$$

followed by attack of the electrode by the radical, can formally describe the reaction. Galli [302] has studied the reduction of ethyl bromide at a lead electrode in propylene carbonate on the basis of this mechanism. At overpotentials of 1.4 V, essentially all dissolved lead is found as tetramethyllead.

At lesser values of the potential, lower lead alkyls are held to be formed with subsequent dismutation reactions such as

$$2Pb(C_2H_5)_2 \rightarrow Pb + Pb(C_2H_5)_4$$

resulting in a partial yield of the desired tetraethyllead.

The reduction of alkyl halides at a lead electrode in acetonitrile has been examined by Ulery [303]. The reaction is viewed mechanistically as proceeding through surface alkylation reactions, the first species appearing in solution being triethyllead in the reduction of ethyl bromide. Steric factors are believed

$$(Pb)_xPb + RX + e^- \rightarrow (Pb)_xPbR + X^-$$

$$(Pb)_xPbR + RX + e^- \rightarrow (Pb)_xPbR_2 + X^-$$

$$(Pb)_xPbR_2 + RX + e^- \rightarrow (Pb)_xPbR_3 + X^-$$

$$(Pb)_xPbR_3 + RX + e^- \rightarrow (Pb)_x + PbR_4 + X^-$$

$$2(Pb)_xPbR_3 \rightleftharpoons 2(Pb)_x + 2PbR_3 \cdot$$

$$2PbR_3 \cdot \rightleftharpoons Pb_2R_6$$

to be the determining factor in the extent to which the surface reactions proceed prior to species being expelled from the electrode (surface species denoted by subscript x). If R is methyl, the reaction proceeds at the surface to PbR_4. Larger alkyl groups lead to lower alkylated species appearing in solution.

Considerable work on the nature of the reductive elimination reaction has appeared (see Section 3, 34–39), but more study of the nature of such reactions at an active electrode surface is required before a thorough understanding of the complete mechanism is at hand.

The participation of the electrode material in a reaction in a secondary manner is also possible. For example, the conversion of tetramethyltin to trimethyltin carboxylates has been described [304]. The reaction is described by the sequence

$$2Hg \rightarrow Hg_2^{+2} + 2e^-$$

$$Hg_2^{+2} + 2(CH_3)_4Sn \rightarrow 2(CH_3)_3Sn^+ + Hg + (CH_3)_2Hg$$

$$2(CH_3)_3Sn^+ + 2RCOO^- \rightarrow 2(CH_3)_3SnOOCR$$

for electrolyses carried out in methanol with a sodium carboxylate supporting electrolyte.

Other Recent Developments

The electrochemical generation of sulfonium and phosphonium ylides from the corresponding "onium" salts has been the subject of some recent studies. Shono and Mitani demonstrated the formation of the phosphonium [305] and sulfonium ylides [306] through electrolysis followed by reaction with an appropriate acceptor, that is, benzaldehyde. The reactions were carried out at a carbon electrode (no further definition) with high applied voltages (15 to 50 V) in aqueous solutions, in mixed solutions of the acceptor and dimethyl sulfoxide, or in a solution of the acceptor. Without detailed information, these authors view the mechanism as possibly occurring through a radical intermediate

$$\phi_3\overset{+}{P}CH_2R \xrightarrow{+e^-} (\phi_3\overset{\cdot}{P}CH_2R)$$
$$\downarrow$$
$$\phi_3P{=}CHR + H\cdot$$

because the ylide can be detected in the absence of an acceptor and electrolysis of carboethoxymethyldimethylsulfonium bromide in dimethylformamide in the presence of a small amount of cyclohexene yields ethyl acetate.

Iverson and Lund [307] point out that the formation of an ylide is an acid-base reaction rather than a redox reaction. A solution of azobenzene, benzaldehyde, and benzyltriphenylphosphonium bromide in dimethylformamide with a lithium chloride supporting electrolyte was electrolyzed at a potential (-0.9 V versus Ag/AgCl) where only the azobenzene is reduced. The hydrazobenzene abstracts a proton from the phosphonium salt in the course of rearrangement to benzidine and diphenylene, forming the ylide which subsequently reacts with the benzaldehyde.

$$C_6H_5N{=}NC_6H_5 \xrightarrow{+2e^-+2H^+} C_6H_5NHNHC_6H_5$$

$$C_6H_5NHNHC_6H_5 \xrightarrow{+H^+} \text{benzidine} + \text{diphenylene}$$

$$(C_6H_5)_3\overset{+}{P}CH_2C_6H_5 \xrightarrow{-H^+} (C_6H_5)_3P{=}CHC_6H_5$$

$$(C_6H_5)_3P{=}CHC_6H_5 \xrightarrow{C_6H_5CHO} (C_6H_5)_3PO + \text{stilbene}$$

Thus the mechanism of the formation of the ylide is an open question and may involve no direct electrochemical reaction of the phosphonium salt. Nonetheless, in both of these papers it is pointed out that the electrolytic technique provides a less stringent set of reaction conditions for the formation of the ylide than the highly basic conditions commonly employed.

The reduction of the triphenylsulfonium ion and related compounds at a mercury electrode differs significantly from the results of Shono and Mitani. The final products of reduction at a mercury electrode have been demonstrated to be diphenylsulfide and benzene by McKinney and Rosenthal [308]. However, the reaction appears to proceed through a complex mechanism involving the participation of the electrode, mercury in this case, adsorption of the electroreactive species, and a chemical reaction of the intermediate radical, $(C_6H_5)_3S \cdots Hg\cdot$. Thus the reaction sequence is

$$(C_6H_5)_3S^+ + Hg + e^- \rightarrow [(C_6H_5)_3S \cdots Hg\cdot]$$
$$2[(C_6H_5)_3S \cdots Hg\cdot] \rightarrow 2(C_6H_5)_2S + (C_6H_5)_2Hg + Hg$$

if electrolysis is carried out at the first of the two observed polarographic waves. If electrolysis is carried out at the more cathodic second response, the reaction

$$(C_6H_5)_3S \cdots Hg\cdot + e^- + H^+ \rightarrow (C_6H_5)_2S + C_6H_6 + Hg$$

occurs and the overall reaction is as follows.

$$(C_6H_5)_3S^+ + 2e^- + H^+ \rightarrow (C_6H_5)_2S + C_6H_6$$

Thus an example of the importance of the electrode potential in determining the course of a reaction is at hand.

Electrochemical reactions of boron compounds have received attention in recent years, two separate studies of the reduction of decarborane [14], $B_{16}H_{14}$, being reported. Smith et al. [309] studied the reaction in glyme solutions and Chambers et al. [310] employed acetonitrile solutions. Both groups agree that the overall reaction formally is

$$2B_{10}H_{14} + 2e^- \rightleftharpoons B_{10}H_{15}^- + B_{10}H_{13}^-$$

although the mechanistic data obtained in the two solvents do not agree.

Smith et al. propose an initial one-electron reduction leading, through an uncharacterized $B_{10}H_{14}^-$ intermediate, to the $B_{10}H_{14}\cdot^-$ radical ion. Subsequent

$$2B_{10}H_{14}\cdot^- \rightleftharpoons B_{10}H_{13}^- + B_{10}H_{15}^-$$

disproportionation provides the final products. Chambers et al. propose an initial two-electron reduction to $B_{10}H_{14}^{-2}$. The subsequent reaction, through

$$B_{10}H_{14} + B_{10}H_{14}^{-2} \rightleftharpoons B_{10}H_{13}^- + B_{10}H_{15}^-$$

an uncharacterized $B_{10}H_{15}^-$ intermediate species, gives the final products. The presence of a specific solvent effect seems likely. In spite of the mechanistic questions remaining, these studies have already shown the pathway of the overall reduction much more distinctly than had the previous chemical reductions.

The electrochemical oxidation of $B_{12}H_{12}^{-2}$ to $B_{24}H_{23}^{-3}$ by a one-electron-per-molecule reaction has been reported by Wiersma and Middaugh [311, 312], again illustrating the utility of electrochemical reactions in a synthesis difficult to achieve by chemical means. Other boron systems have received attention [141, 142, 313, 314] outside the use of boron compounds in metal alkyl synthesis [296]. Thus considerable application of electrochemical reactions in the chemistry of boron compounds seems possible.

Reduction through Electrochemically Generated Solvated Electrons

After the early work of Birch [315], electrochemical generation of solvated electrons did not attract much attention until the recent studies of Sternberg et al. [316, 317] with ethylenediamine solutions and Benkeser and Kaiser [318] with methylamine solutions. The recent interest in electrochemically generated solvated electrons has been stimulated by the reduction of benzene and unconjugated dienes or monoenes which are usually very difficult to reduce electrochemically. Although alkali metal–amine solutions can also furnish solvated electrons, these reagents are usually not selective. The monoolefins produced in these reductions are often isomeric mixtures of closely related structures, which makes separation of individual components a rather difficult task [319]. Furthermore, the cost and handling difficulties of lithium metal makes lithium metal–amine reagents rather unsuitable for large-scale production [319]. Thus the use of solvated electrons electrochemically generated from alkali metal salts is a logical alternative.

The direct electrochemical reduction of benzene and alkylbenzenes has not been reported; however, the more easily reduced naphthalene can be reduced directly via electron transfer in an acetonitrile–water solvent. The product obtained is predominantly 1,4-dihydronaphthalene. The current efficiency reaches a maximum of 75% with a 3:1 acetonitrile–water mixture. Only a small amount ($< 5\%$) of tetralin was found [320].

The work to date on electrochemically generated solvated electrons has involved reactions of organic compounds. The selectivity of this technique suggests applications to synthetic usage on a broader chemical basis.

Mechanisms

The primary electrode reaction in reductions through solvated electrons is the reduction of the alkali metal ion in solution to its corresponding metal followed by a dissolution step to form solvated electrons. The existence of the solvated electron under electrolytic conditions has been established either by its characteristic blue coloration or by electron spin resonance (ESR) measurements [321, 322]. Following the generation, the solvated electron can interact with the unsaturated hydrocarbon. Since simple electron transfer between the solvated electrons and the hydrocarbon is not a thermodynamically favored process [317], the reduction step is assisted to some extent by the subsequent protonation of the anion radical. Thus the overall mechanism of reduction can be summarized by the following sequence of reactions

$$M_s^+ + e^- \rightleftharpoons [M^+ \cdots e^-]_s$$
$$[M^+ \cdots e^-]_s + R \rightarrow R \cdot^- + M_s^+$$
$$R \cdot^- + H^+ \rightarrow RH \cdot$$
$$[M^+ \cdots e^-]_s + RH \cdot \rightarrow RH^- + M_s^+$$
$$RH \cdot + e^- \rightarrow RH^-$$
$$RH^- + H^+ \rightarrow RH_2$$

where M^+ represents an alkali metal ion and R represents the hydrocarbon.

The RH· formed can undergo a second electron transfer by the solvated electrons. Since RH· is known to be reduced easier than the corresponding R· [323], a direct electron transfer from the electrode is also possible. In either case the carbanion formed from the second electron transfer can be protonated to yield the dihydro product. Further reduction may occur if unsaturation remains.

The source of protons for these reactions can be either the solvent itself, such as methylamine [324], or an additive such as alcohol in hexamethylphosphoramide [321, 325] or alcohol–water in diglyme [322].

The current efficiency, yield, and degree of reduction are rather sensitive to the conditions of electrolysis as is discussed in the following examples.

Examples

Electrochemical reduction of benzene by solvated electrons in methylamine [318, 319, 324] is particularly interesting since the products obtained can be selectively either 1,4-cyclohexadiene in a single-compartment cell or cyclohexene in a cell divided into auxiliary and working electrode compartments. In a divided cell the lithium methylamide that results from the

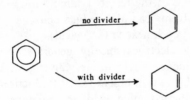

protonation reaction causes a rapid isomerization of the unconjugated 1,4-dihydrobenzene to the conjugated 1,2-dihydrobenzene. Further reduction by the solvated electron to cyclohexene then occurs. In an undivided cell the lithium methylamide formed is neutralized by the acidic species generated at the anode and the electrolysis stops at the 1,4-dihydrobenzene stage. The similar reduction using chemically generated solvated electrons gave cyclohexene as the only product. The yield of the electrochemically initiated reduction is usually 50 to 80% [318].

The electrochemically initiated reaction can also be terminated at the dihydro stage by the addition of an acid stronger than ethylenediamine as a proton donor. Thus in the presence of ethanol, 1,4-dihydrobenzene can be isolated as the final product even in a divided cell [324].

Electrolytic reduction of benzene in ethylenediamine and in hexamethylphosphoramide–ethanol (1:2) is not as selective as the reaction in methylamine with the formation of mixtures of cyclohexadiene, cyclohexene, and cyclohexane [326, 327]. With ethylenediamine as the solvent, the major product is cyclohexene, while the hexamethylphosphoramide–ethanol solvent system leads to cyclohexane as the major product. The yield of more highly hydrogenated product in the latter solvent system is also a function of the proton donor concentration. Thus the higher the alcohol concentration, the higher is the yield of completely saturated product until the alcohol concentration is sufficiently high that hydrogen evolution becomes the predominant electrode reaction.

It should also be pointed out that the addition of hexamethylphosphoramide to the alcohol medium tends to decrease the side reaction of hydrogen evolution. This remarkable suppression of hydrogen evolution has been rationalized on the basis of preferential adsorption of hexamethylphosphoramide on the working electrode [326]. Two other factors could also contribute to this effect. First, hexamethylphosphoramide is a rather viscous solvent and the addition of a large quantity is likely to decrease the rate of diffusion of hydrogen ion (or $C_2H_5OH_2^+$) considerably. Being a highly polar molecule, hexamethylphosphoramide also tends strongly to form hydrogen bonds with the alcohol and thus decreases its autoprotolysis.

Recent investigations by Osa et al. [322] indicate that solvated electrons can also be generated electrochemically at a mercury electrode in ether solvents in the presence of the tetrabutylammonium ion. Solvated electrons generated in these solvents can also reduce benzene to the dihydro product (50 to 70% yield) and cyclohexene (5% yield).

Reduction through electrochemically generated solvated electrons has been achieved for toluene, ethylbenzene, cumene, and *tert*-butylbenzene in methylamine [316, 317] and in ethers [320]. Reduction of dialkylacetylenes, such as 5-octyne, in methylamine yields *trans*-olefins stereospecifically. The internal *trans*-olefins cannot be reduced further to alkanes under these conditions [324, 326] but can be reduced in the hexamethylphosphoramide–ethanol solvent system [326]. Conjugated aromatic acetylenes can also be reduced to the corresponding alkylbenzenes in methylamine. However, nonconjugated acetylenes such as 4-phenyl-1-butyne can be reduced selectively to aromatic olefins. Further reduction of these aromatic olefins occurs on the aromatic ring instead of at the nonconjugated olefinic bond [324]. As noted by Benkeser [324], this selective reduction of a benzene ring in the presence of an isolated double bond is the reverse of the results obtained by catalytic reduction with Raney nickel.

Primary, secondary, and tertiary aliphatic amides can be reduced to the corresponding alcohols in 65 to 84% yield [324].

$$R-\overset{\displaystyle O}{\overset{\|}{C}}-NR_2{}' \xrightarrow[+e^-]{MeNH_2, Li^+} RCH_2OH$$

Reduction of quaternary ammonium salts in liquid ammonia has also been studied [329, 330]. For example, the reduction of β-naphthyltrimethyl-ammonium ion gave naphthalene. Further reduction of naphthalene can be achieved at -2.83 V versus the silver wire electrode. The final product is 1,4-dihydronaphthalene.

An interesting use of electrochemically generated solvated electrons is the reductive elimination of a cyano group [229] from dihydroabietonitrile:

and from 1,1'-dicyanobicyclohexyl:

In the case of dehydroabietene, the aromatic ring is not reduced by the solvated electrons. The same products are obtained using solvated electrons generated by sodium in liquid ammonia [331].

4 EXPERIMENTAL CONSIDERATIONS

Much experimentation in electrochemistry is common to all techniques. However, if a synthesis is the objective, several experimental factors are of particular importance and others are viewed from a perspective differing from that of an electroanalytical study. This discussion, coupled with its counterpart in other chapters of this volume, provides the information necessary for adequate design and control of laboratory experimentation in electrochemical synthesis.

An electrochemical synthesis of large quantities (kilograms) of material presents experimental difficulties that are significantly different from those of a laboratory-scale synthesis. Design and construction of electrodes, control of the electrode potential, and dissipation of heat are examples of experimental factors requiring thorough consideration in planning a large-scale synthesis. Solution to a problem in any of these areas probably requires as much expertise in engineering as in electrochemistry. Moreover, such a solution can only be sought within the context of a particular synthesis. Proper laboratory-scale experimentation, to which this discussion is limited, and the resulting more complete understanding of a reaction may simplify the scale-up of a synthesis.

More use of nonaqueous solvents is noted in recent work. Although the discussion is, in general, applicable to experimentation with either aqueous or nonaqueous media, some emphasis is placed on solution of the particular problems associated with the use of nonaqueous solvent systems.

Instrumentation

Depending upon the parameter of control, there are three principal methods used to carry out an electrochemical synthesis: constant voltage, constant current, or constant potential. Since the instrumentation for the first two techniques is simple and is easily set up in the laboratory, most of the electrochemical syntheses to date have been performed by these methods.

The controlled-potential technique is more difficult to set up and the instrumentation required is more complicated and certainly more expensive. However, the selectivity offered by the controlled-potential technique tends to offset these disadvantages. Recent literature shows a trend toward increased use of this method.

The controlled-voltage method involves applying a constant voltage between a working electrode and an auxiliary electrode. This constant voltage is maintained by a power supply as shown in Fig. 10.2. The applied voltage V_{app} can be divided into two parts:

$$V_{app} = E_{eff} + iR_{cell},$$

where E_{eff} is the potential difference between the working and auxiliary electrodes referred to a reference electrode and iR_{cell} is the voltage drop resulting from the presence of solution resistance in the cell across which the current flows. At the beginning of electrolysis, the cell current is at its maximum value, thus the resistive drop is also at its maximum. As the electrolysis proceeds, the current decreases with respect to time as does the voltage drop resulting from the cell resistance. If the applied voltage across the cell is held constant, the potential difference between the working and auxiliary electrodes must change accordingly. As a result of this change, the potential of the working electrode must shift accordingly and the mechanistic pathway of the electrochemical reaction may also be altered, as discussed in Section 2.

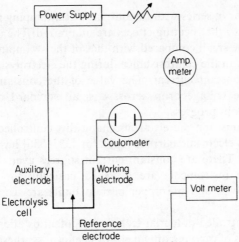

Fig. 10.2. Block diagram for constant-voltage electrolysis.

The power supply in Fig. 10.2 is either a bank of storage batteries or an electronic power supply. The current passing through the cell at any time may be measured by an ammeter and/or integrated by an electronic or chemical coulometer. The potential of the working electrode against a reference electrode is measured by a high-impedance voltmeter, such as a vacuum-tube voltmeter. The voltage imposed on the cell can be easily changed by a small slide-wire resistance in series with the cell if batteries are used, or simply adjusted as desired if a variable electronic power supply is used.

Figure 10.3 shows the block diagram for a constant-current electrolysis system. The coulometer in the controlled-voltage circuit of Fig. 10.2 has been replaced by a timer since the product of the current flow and the time required for electrolysis yields the total coulombs directly. The potential of the working electrode is measured by means of a high-impedance voltmeter. The constant-current source can be constructed from a power supply by connecting a large

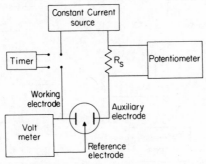

Fig. 10.3. Block diagram for constant-current electrolysis.

swamping resistor in series with the output. The swamping resistor should be of high wattage so that heating effects are minimized. The total resistance of the cell should be small compared with that of the swamping resistor so that minor variations in the cell resistance during the electrolysis will not cause a change in the constant current. The value of the constant current can be measured by the voltage drop across a small standard resistor R_S while the electrolysis is in progress.

Circuit diagrams for an electromechanically controlled current source [332] and for an electronic current regulator [333–336] have been described in the literature. There are constant-current sources available commercially [337], but these instruments are designed basically for constant-current coulometric analysis and the upper current limits are usually in the range of 50 to 100 mA.

Use of the controlled-potential technique (potentiostatic technique) is by far a better means of carrying out an electrochemical synthesis. This technique involves automatic control of a constant potential between the working electrode and a reference electrode. Thus in contrast to the above two methods, the potentiostatic technique requires three electrodes. A schematic diagram of a potentiostatic circuit is given in Fig. 10.4.

The general principle of potentiostatic control involves continuous comparison of the potential difference between the working electrode and a reference electrode with a preset voltage. The error voltage between these two signals is detected and amplified electronically and an appropriate amount of current is then passed between the working and the auxiliary electrode in such a way that the error voltage is minimized.

The input impedance of the reference electrode part of the circuit should

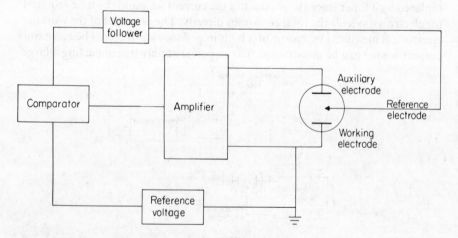

Fig. 10.4. Block diagram for potentiostatic electrolysis.

be high so that only a negligible amount of current is drawn between the working and reference electrodes. This condition is usually met through a very high input impedance follower circuit.

The prime advantage of using potential control instead of voltage or current control is that a specific electrode reaction can be maintained. Thus electrochemically generated intermediates can be more selectively formed at the electrode. Furthermore, the current-time relationship obtained under controlled-potential conditions may be used to gain additional information concerning the pathway of the overall reaction and some of its kinetic parameters [3].

There are two general types of potentiostats, electromechanical and electronic. The electromechanical devices are slower in response (rise time) than the electronic devices. The rise time of a potentiostat used for synthetic purposes is not as important as that for an instrument used for transient electroanalytical techniques. However, if the same instrument is to be used for short-time-scale experiments, a short rise time is required and the electronic devices are preferred.

The most important criteria for selection of an instrument for use in electrochemical syntheses are the voltage and current outputs of the instrument. Since the potentiostat is an electronic device, it has a maximum wattage limit beyond which the instrument does not maintain the necessary potential control. The current output of a potentiostat used for synthetic purposes should be in the range of 1 to 10 A. Assuming that the solution has a resistance of between 50 and 100 Ω between the working and auxiliary electrodes, the voltage output for an ideal potentiostat should be between 50 and 1000 V.

The electronic potentiostats available at present cannot deliver this voltage output at the required current level. Thus some compromise between high current output and high voltage output of a potentiostat must be made. A smaller current demand can be achieved by using a lower concentration of the electroactive species, a lower rate of convective mass transfer, or a smaller electrode area. Alternatively, the electrolysis may be performed at a potential that is on the rising portion of the current-potential curve. All these changes tend to increase the time required to complete an electrolysis. Furthermore, variations in the potential used in the electrolysis may alter the final products obtained [3]. The best method of accommodating the voltage limit is to decrease the overall cell resistance. Considerable effort has been spent by many investigators in decreasing the cell resistance. This problem is even more serious when nonaqueous solvents are used.

The controlled-potential range of a potentiostat should be wide enough that many different types of electrochemical syntheses can be carried out. A range of ± 3.5 V is usually sufficient.

The ac noise superimposed on the dc potential and the dc stability of the instrument are important factors which determine the accuracy of the potential control. Normally, 1 to 2 mV of noise and a stability of the same magnitude are acceptable in electrochemical syntheses.

There are several high-output potentiostat circuits described in the literature [338–341]. High-capacity potentiostats are also commercially available [342].

The major disadvantage of controlled-potential electrolysis is instrumental complexity. However, in studies of reaction pathways, the use of controlled potential offers such advantages that there is little reason to employ the other methods. However, when large amounts of products are desired, the constant-current method may offer the advantage of being easy to set up as well as to control in a practical sense. The constant-current method is especially useful when the controlled-potential condition can be translated into the constant-current condition by proper choice of experimental conditions of concentration, time, and current.

Electronic and chemical coulometers for the integration of current have been discussed by Meites in a chapter of this volume. The copper coulometer, although not often used in analytical coulometry, has been used in electrochemical syntheses and detailed procedures for its preparation are available [14].

Cell Design

The shape, size, and many individual details of an electrolysis cell are largely a matter of personal taste and, of course, vary with the nature of the problem. A large-scale electrolytic cell requires features differing significantly from those of a cell for preparations in gram quantities. The following discussion is mainly concerned with problems of cell design for gram-level syntheses and some consideration is given to a scale-up of electrolysis cells.

There are two basic types of electrolysis cells, those in which the working and auxiliary electrodes are not separated and those in which these two electrodes are separated by a diaphragm. Very often species electrochemically generated at the working electrode can react at the auxiliary electrode and give undesired by-products. In these cases the use of a divided electrolytic cell is a necessity.

The use of divided cells has become more common since potentiostats have been commercially available. By definition, a potentiostat controls the potential of the working electrode. In order to drive the necessary amount of current through the solution, the potential of the counter electrode frequently reaches very anodic or cathodic values and thus leads to the formation of unwanted by-products if a one-compartment cell is used.

In some cases a single-compartment cell is useful. An example is the electrolysis of benzene solutions, discussed in Section 3, wherein 1,4-cyclohexadiene is obtained selectively as the reduction product with an undivided cell, whereas the use of a divided cell yields cyclohexene under the same experimental conditions otherwise.

Naturally, the use of a diaphragm or membrane as a cell divider causes a higher overall cell resistance and thus places demands on the voltage output of the instrument. The use of nonaqueous solvents leads to problems as well. To maintain a high current flow at a low voltage between the working and auxiliary electrodes, the two electrodes have to be placed as close together as possible. Limits on the electrode separation are dictated by the presence of a membrane and by the capacity of the potentiostat. It would be convenient to have a cell design wherein the distance between both electrodes can be changed easily. This should be possible without interrupting the electrolysis since the resistance of a diaphragm may increase during electrolysis by accumulation of products.

The ratio of the surface area of the electrodes to the volume of the cell should be made as large as possible, limited only by the capacity of the potentiostat. The development of porous electrodes [343], gauzes and wool from metals and, recently, fluidized bed electrodes, has contributed considerably to the higher efficiency of electrochemical processes.

The question of whether one is concerned with an oxidation or a reduction dictates not only the choice of the electrode material but also the proper placing of the working electrode. If a divided cell is used, the volume of the compartment that contains the auxiliary electrode can be made as small as possible without loss in electrode surface area. The working electrode should be placed such that a salt bridge for the connection with the reference electrode can be placed close to the electrode surface.

When the salt bridge of the reference electrode cannot be placed close to the working electrode, a parallel placing of both electrodes becomes important. Highly inhomogeneous electrical fields caused by nonparallel electrodes or electrodes of different shapes and sizes may result in incorrect indications of the electrode potential.

Since many electrochemical reactions are controlled by the rate of mass transfer, effective agitation of the electrolyte may be part of a successful electrochemical preparation. Mechanical or electromagnetic stirring is often used. Agitation by ultrasonic means or by vibration has been reported and some investigators have used rotating electrodes to increase the mass transfer [344]. Other solutions to this problem are circulation of the electrolyte by pumps and the use of flow cells.

Membranes for the division of electrolytic cells into two compartments should offer little resistance to the passing current and high resistance to the diffusion of the organic substrate molecules. In addition, they should be resistant to clogging during electrolysis and to corrosion by electrolytes and solvents, even at elevated temperatures. A number of materials fulfill these requirements well.

Alundum is highly resistant toward corrosion by solvents and supporting electrolytes. It offers a low resistance not only to a current flow, but also to organic molecules, and might clog during electrolysis. It can be cleaned by soaking in 50% nitric acid for 12 hr. After it is heated to 100°C, it is washed with water and dried [121]. Fritted glass disks of various pore sizes are available. They are resistant toward almost any combination of solvent and supporting electrolyte. However, they too might occasionally clog. Swann [14] has described a method to decrease the pore size of fritted glass disks. Cellophane can serve as a membrane in aqueous acidic or alkaline solutions and is resistant to alcohol–water mixtures with up to 50% alcohol content. It has a low resistance with respect to current flow and blocks the diffusion of large organic molecules. Ion-exchange resins [345] have a high specific conductivity and offer a large resistance to the diffusion of organic molecules. They are useful in cases in which the auxiliary compartment contains an aqueous electrolyte. However, they deteriorate at temperatures above 70°C. Porous Vycor is a special glass that has been used successfully as a diaphragm in work with nonaqueous solvents [346, 347].

Nonaqueous solvents and diaphragms both cause a higher cell resistance which results in the formation of heat. A condenser may be used for heat dissipation if the electrolysis is performed at the boiling temperature of a particular solvent. In other cases the electrolysis cell can be equipped with a water jacket which can be thermostated. Internal cooling by cooling coils has been reported, as well as the circulation of the electrolyte through cooling

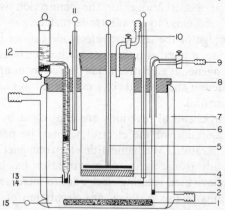

Fig. 10.5. Two-compartment cell for general use. 1, Stirring bar; 2, gas dispersion tube; 3, working electrode; 4, fritted glass disk; 5, auxiliary electrode; 6, compartment for auxiliary electrode; 7, water jacket; 8, gas-tight Teflon top; 9, two-way stopcock for gas collection or gas passage; 10, stopcock for gas collection or gas passage; 11, micro working electrode for cyclic voltammetry; 12, saturated calomel reference electrode; 13, Teflon sleeve on salt bridge; 14, plug of porous Vycor; 15, contact for mercury electrode, if used.

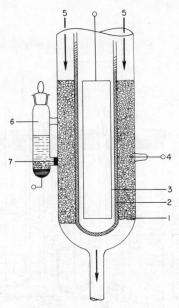

Fig. 10.6. Center portion of a flow cell. 1, Working electrode (metal beads, metal wool, metal gauze, and so on); 2, diaphragm; 3, cylindrical auxiliary electrode; 4, contact for working electrode; 5, flow of electrolyte; 6, saturated calomel reference electrode; 7, plug of porous Vycor.

devices. In some cases the use of internally cooled electrodes has proven to be useful.

Some electrochemical reactions may proceed with the evolution of gases, in which case the electrolysis cell can be equipped with a device for the collection of gases, the volume of which can be determined with a gas buret.

Electrochemical reactions in which air- or moisture-sensitive intermediates are generated have to be carried out under an inert atmosphere. This becomes almost a necessity if metal organic compounds are the reactants or products. Therefore devices for maintaining a controlled, inert atmosphere have to be included in the cell construction. Prepurified nitrogen or helium can be used.

The following illustrations of three different types of electrolysis cells are provided as examples.

Figure 10.5 shows a two-compartment cell [348] that can be used for either oxidations or reductions and incorporates many of the features discussed. If reductions are performed, the working electrode may be replaced by a mercury pool which is contacted by a platinum lead.

Figure 10.6 is a schematic drawing of the center part of a flow cell, and Fig. 10.7 shows the principal construction details of a continuously working electrolytic cell for hydrodimerization reactions [174].

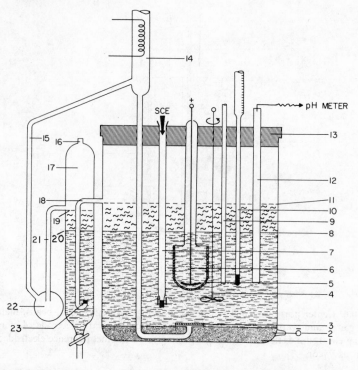

Fig. 10.7. Continuously working cell for hydrodimerization. 1, Mercury pool electrode; 2, contact for mercury electrode; 3, fritted glass disk for gas dispersion; 4, stirrer; 5, diaphragm; 6, auxiliary electrode; 7, salt bridge for SCE reference electrode; 8, catholyte level; 9, tube for the addition of acid; 10, thermometer; 11, level of supernatant monomer; 12, pH-indicating electrode; 13, gas-tight cell top, 14, condenser; 15, riser of a liquid–liquid extractor; 16, water inlet; 17, washer; 18, overflow tube; 19, supernatant level; 20, water level; 21, overflow tube; 22, boiler; 23, disperser. After Baizer [174].

A variety of conventional cells for general purposes have been described elsewhere [121, 221, 349–353], and construction details of cells for special purposes can be found in the literature [165, 174, 181, 182]. Flow cells for chemical [347, 354–360] and biochemical [361] problems have been described for preparative work on a laboratory scale. A two-stage flow cell [362] has been used in the preparation of organic radicals and their immediate characterization by ESR measurements.

The scale-up of electrolysis cells from the gram level to the kilogram level is not a simple matter of increasing the cell elements proportionally. It often creates problems with respect to rapid heat dissipation, removal of products, mass transfer, current distribution, and a proper ratio of the electrode area to the cell volume [363, 364].

Electrodes

The choice of electrode material for a given electrochemical synthesis is not an easy task and often requires experience and/or knowledge of results for related systems. However, some general guidelines can be helpful in the selection of a working electrode.

It is generally preferable to have a working electrode that is relatively inert in the medium of interest so that the course of the electrochemical and chemical reactions is not altered by the presence of the electrode. Reactions that proceed to a specific product as a result of the nature of the electrode are exceptions (see Section 2). In other cases, such as electrochemical synthesis of organometallic compounds, the electrode material is chosen as a reagent.

In aqueous and partially aqueous media, the hydrogen overvoltage of the electrode material appears to be important, electrodes having greater overvoltages yielding products that are more completely reduced. The physical state of the electrode may often play an important role. A spongy cathode may perform more effectively than a smooth electrode although hydrogen overvoltage on these rough electrodes is usually low. Apparently, the larger effective surface area and more active sites for reaction tend to compensate for the differences in overvoltage. In nonaqueous aprotic solvents, the overvoltage requirement is not important.

The material used for the electrode should also have high electrical conductance so that the electrical power loss in the electrode itself is minimized.

In some cases the corrosive nature of the solvent system, as with a strongly acidic or basic solution, also limits the materials that can be used as electrodes.

Many different forms of electrodes have been used in electrochemical synthesis. Electrodes in the form of bars, sheets, liquid amalgams, gauzes, rods, and sticks have been used in many cases. The recent advances in the use of fluidized bed electrodes have revolutionized the concept of the electrode [354].

In addition to pure metal electrodes, electroplated metals, metal amalgams, and alloys such as monel metal and phosphor bronze have also been used, as have certain metal oxides, such as lead oxide. In some cases the lead oxide anode has been shown to give better yields than the lead anode [365].

Platinum, mercury, tin, nickel, cadmium, copper, and zinc are useful cathodes for preparative work [14]. The number of materials useful as anodes is limited by the corrosion of many metals. Platinum, graphite, and lead oxide are used as anodes. Tungsten carbide has also been demonstrated to be useful in the electrochemical oxidation of aldehydes and formic acid [366]. The presence of surface platinum oxide may retard the oxidation of some organic species [367, 368]. The choice of an auxiliary electrode is simple since this electrode serves only as a current-passing terminal. Especially in a divided cell, the products formed at the auxiliary electrode should not in any way influence the products in the working electrode compartment. Platinum or graphite generally serves the purpose.

Almost all the established reference electrodes [369] can be used in electrochemical syntheses. The most common reference electrodes are the saturated calomel electrode in aqueous solution and Ag/Ag^+ (0.01 M) in acetonitrile solution. The aqueous reference electrodes are also suitable in nonaqueous solution if proper precautions are taken to ensure no leakage of water to the cell. In this laboratory a double porous Vycor bridge has been found to minimize the water leakage acceptably.

Solvents and Supporting Electrolytes

In electrochemical synthesis it is necessary to use a suitable electrolyte to increase the conductivity of the solution. Mineral acids and alkali hydroxides are often used in acidic and basic solutions. Neutral salts, such as alkali metal halides, sulfates, nitrates, and certain perchlorates are also employed as supporting electrolytes. The criteria for selecting a particular salt as a supporting electrolyte is discussed in more detail later.

The electrochemistry of organic compounds often involves reactions in which protons are either formed or consumed, and therefore the pH of the solution must be kept under proper control. The importance of this point has already been noted with respect to the product distribution and pathway of the product formation in Section 2. The buffers used in synthetic organic electrochemistry are essentially the same as those employed for mechanistic studies, and their preparation can be found in many books [370, 371] or in the literature [207, 209, 214]. The concentration and buffer capacity of the selected buffer should be high so that a certain hydrogen ion concentration in the electrolyte is maintained throughout the electrolysis. The overall capacities of the buffers are often limited by the solubility of the salts selected. This problem is more serious when partially nonaqueous solvents are used. It is necessary then to incorporate into the cell design some means of adding buffer solution continuously during the electrolysis (see Fig. 10.7). Highly volatile buffer components, such as ammonia, should be avoided unless extra precautions are taken to ensure that little or no escape of these components is taking place during the time of the electrolysis.

Very often electrochemical reactions that do not have a counterpart in aqueous systems can be achieved in nonaqueous solvents. Furthermore, many organic solvents are more difficult to oxidize or reduce than water. In connection with proper supporting electrolytes, these solvents offer a greater "electrochemical domain" than aqueous systems. For these reasons many of the advances in organic electrochemistry in recent years are attributable to the use of nonaqueous solvents.

Since most organic solvents are toxic in one way or another, electro-chemical experiments that employ nonaqueous systems should be performed in well-ventilated areas and handbooks should be consulted with respect to the toxicity of a particular solvent before using it [372, 373].

The choice of a proper solvent and a supporting electrolyte depends largely upon experience and knowledge of solvent properties. Specific suggestions cannot therefore be made here; however, a number of books [374–376] and review articles [347–388] treat this topic in detail. The follow-ing constitutes a general outline of the considerations that govern the choice of a particular solvent and supporting electrolyte.

A prime requirement for an electrolyte is a high ionic conductance. Since most organic solvents have lower dielectric constants than water, not too many inorganic salts are soluble in them. However, a number of tetraalkyl-ammonium, sodium, and lithium perchlorates, as well as some iodide, bromide, hexafluorophosphate, and tetrafluoroborate salts are sufficiently soluble in nonaqueous solvents for electrochemical purposes.

Table 10.1 Voltammetric Potential Ranges of Common Organic Solvents*

Solvent	Dielectric Constant	E_ℓ^c	E_ℓ^a
Tetrahydrofuran	7.6	−2.10	+1.10
Methyl formate	8.5	−1.60	+1.20
Methylene chloride	9.08	−1.70	+1.35
Pyridine	12.0	−2.10	+1.20
Acetone	21.0	−1.60	+1.00
Ethanol	24.3	−1.20	+0.65
Benzonitrile	25.5	−1.96	+1.70
Methanol	32.6	−1.00	+0.70
Nitromethane	35.7	−1.15	+1.15
Dimethylformamide	36.7	−2.60	+1.30
Acetonitrile	37.5	−2.30	+2.10
N,N-Dimethylacetamide	37.8	−2.30	+1.10
Dimethyl sulfoxide	46.6	−2.70	+1.20
Propylene carbonate	64.4	−1.50	+1.20
1-Methyl-2-pyrolidone	—	−1.10	+1.10

* The data were obtained with 0.1 M tetrabutylammonium perchlorate at a platinum electrode with an aqueous satur-ated (KCl) calomel reference electrode.

In general, it is not desirable for the solvent or supporting electrolyte to react with starting material, reactive intermediates, or end products. This requirement cannot always be fulfilled, especially with respect to reactions with reactive intermediates.

The useful potential range of the solvent-supporting electrolyte system is a most important consideration. Table 10.1 summarizes the useful potential ranges of 15 commonly used solvents [348]. The data were obtained on a platinum working electrode of 0.008-cm² surface area at a scan rate of 10 V/min. The E_ℓ^c and E_ℓ^a values, the limiting cathodic and anodic potentials, respectively, were evaluated at the point in potential where the current reached a value of 1 μA.

The E_ℓ^c and E_ℓ^a values are a function of the electrode and the solvent-tetrabutylammonium perchlorate system and reflect the purity of the solvents as well as their electrochemical inertness. The limiting cathodic potential for all solvents on a mercury electrode is usually more cathodic than on platinum. The presence of water in organic solvents tends to decrease the cathodic potential limit on a platinum surface. The wider available potential range for electrochemical study is certainly one of the major reasons for acetonitrile being the most popular aprotic solvent used in electrochemistry.

The dielectric constant, ϵ, of the solvent is important with respect to the

Table 10.2 Discharge Potentials of Some Cations and Anions in Acetonitrile

Ion	Discharge Potential (V)	Working Electrode	Reference Electrode	Ref.
CNS⁻	+0.55	Pt	SCE	[348]
Cl⁻	+1.1	Pt	SCE	[389]
Br⁻	+0.70	Pt	SCE	[389]
I⁻	+0.30	Pt	SCE	[389]
ClO_4^-	+0.60	Hg	SCE	[390]
ClO_4^-	+2.10	Pt	SCE	[348]
BF_4^-	+2.91	Pt	$Ag/10^{-2}M Ag^+$	[388]
PF_6^-	+3.02	Pt	$Ag/10^{-2}M Ag^+$	[388]
Li⁺	−1.95	Hg	SCE	[391]
Na⁺	−1.85	Hg	SCE	[391]
K⁺	−1.96	Hg	SCE	[391]
Rb⁺	−1.98	Hg	SCE	[391]
Cs⁺	−1.97	Hg	SCE	[391]
NH_4^+	−1.83	Hg	SCE	[390]
$(n\text{-}C_4H_9)_4N^+$	−2.30	Pt	SCE	[348]

electrolytic conductivity of a solution. The solubility and dissociation of inorganic and organic salts become limiting factors for current passage as the dielectric constant of the solvent drops below 3.

Table 10.2 summarizes discharge potentials of some cations and anions with acetonitrile as the solvent. Though relative rather than absolute, these data should provide a basis for selection of the solvent-supporting electrolyte system that best meets the requirements of a particular experiment.

Auxiliary Techniques

A basic understanding of the mechanistic pathways of a reaction of synthetic interest, although not required, offers greater possibilities in improving the process itself and in finding routes to other syntheses. In many of the cases discussed in this chapter, product analysis was the primary means of studying the reaction. This approach yields useful information concerning the possible mechanistic pathways of the synthesis but it does not often yield conclusive evidence to exclude other mechanisms. Thus an electrochemical synthesis, as well as other synthetic procedures, must rely on other physico-chemical techniques for a complete elucidation of the mechanistic pathway of a reaction.

In general, electroanalytical techniques are preferred since they offer the advantage of allowing the reaction mechanism to be studied under the same conditions used for the synthesis. Furthermore, the wide variety of experimental time scales available through electroanalytical techniques gives one the ability to characterize a spectrum of reactive intermediates which may exist in the solution at different times. Techniques such as cyclic voltammetry, ac and dc polarography, chronoamperometry, and chronopotentiometry and its various modifications detect and identify intermediates ranging in lifetime from a few milliseconds to several seconds. Controlled-potential coulometry serves to fill the time gap between the mechanistic information obtained by the above techniques and the large-scale electrochemical synthesis. The electroanalytical techniques mentioned above have been described in detail in other chapters of this volume. Recent advances in rotating disk and ring disk electrode techniques should also lead to their increased use in the detection and identification of reactive intermediates.

Optical spectroscopic methods can also provide useful information aiding identification of intermediates as well as of final products of electrode reactions. Kuwana et al. [392–394] have shown that tin oxide-coated glass surfaces can be used as electrodes with intermediates monitored directly by carrying out electrolysis in a cell positioned in the light beam of a spectrophotometer. Similar studies can also be carried out with platinum or gold deposited on glass serving as an electrode [395]. Recent studies of Heineman et al. [396] and Tallant and Evans [397] have extended this approach to the infrared region of the spectrum. Spectrofluorometric techniques could also be used *in situ*; however, the utility of this approach has been examined only briefly [391]. By and large, fluorescence analysis has been used only in the identification of final products.

Rapid scanning spectrophotometers are now available commercially and moderately short-lived intermediates should be amenable to *in situ* study with this technique.

Radical intermediates are quite often encountered in electrochemical synthesis. Application of ESR spectrometry has proven to be a most powerful means for achieving a positive identification of a radical species. Several different designs of *in situ* ESR electrochemical cells are available [398–400].

References

1. J. O'M. Bockris, *J. Electroanal. Chem.*, **9**, 408 (1965).
2. S. Wawzonek, *Science*, **155**, 39 (1967).
3. L. Meites, "Controlled Potential Electrolysis," in *Physical Methods of Chemistry*, Part II, A. Weissberger and B. W. Rossiter, Eds., Interscience, New York, 1971.
4. V. D. Parker, *Chem. Commun.*, **1969**, 848.
5. E. J. Corey, N. L. Bauld, R. T. La Londe, J. Casanova, Jr., and E. T. Kaiser, *J. Am. Chem. Soc.*, **82**, 2645 (1960).
6. J. Volke and A. M. Kardos, *Collection Czech. Chem. Commun.*, **33**, 2560 (1968).
7. Z. R. Grabowski, B. Czochralska, A. Vincenz-Chodkowska, and M. S. Balasiewicz, *Discussions Faraday Soc.*, **1968**, 145.
8. N. E. Khomutov, V. V. Skornyakov, and V. V. Belik, *Russ. J. Phys. Chem. (English Transl.)*, **39**, 119 (1965).
9. A. T. Petrenko, *Soviet Electrochem. (English Transl.)*, **3**, 219 (1967).
10. N. E. Khomutov and V. V. Tsodikov, *Soviet Electrochem. (English Transl.)*, **3**, 1280 (1967).
11. N. E. Khomutov and V. V. Tsodikov, *Soviet Electrochem. (English Transl.)*, **2**, 669 (1966).
12. N. E. Khomutov and V. V. Tsodikov, *Soviet Electrochem. (English Transl.)*, **1**, 417 (1965).
13. M. G. Smirnova, V. A. Smirnov, and L. I. Antropov, *Tr. Novocherk. Politekh. Inst.*, **79**, 43 (1959); *Chem. Abstr.*, **54**, 24011 (1960).
14. S. Swann, Jr., "Electrolytic Reactions," in *Technique of Organic Chemistry*, A. Weissberger, Ed., Interscience, New York, 1956.
15. S. Swann, Jr., and J. Feldman, *Trans. Electrochem. Soc.*, **67**, 195 (1935).
16. K. Sugino, K. Odo, and E. Ichikawa, *J. Electrochem. Soc.*, **110**, 918 (1963).
17. V. N. Nikulin and P. V. Zamuragin, *Russ. J. Phys. Chem. (English Transl.)*, **35**, 287 (1961).

18. V. N. Nikulin and P. V. Zamuragin, *Tr. Kazansk. Khim. Tekhnol. Inst.*, **1960**, 232; *Chem. Abstr.*, **56**, 13955 (1962).

19. R. J. Flannery, J. E. Thomas, Jr., and D. Trivich, *J. Electrochem. Soc.*, **110**, 1054 (1963).

20. S. Swann, Jr., H. J. Read, and F. C. Howard, *Trans. Electrochem. Soc.*, **69**, 345 (1936).

21. E. Bernhardsson, L. Eberson, and H. Sternerup, Spring Meeting, Electrochemical Society, New York, May 4, 1969, Extended Abstracts, p. 311.

22. T. Inoue, K. Koyama, T. Matsuoka, and S. Tsutsumi, *Bull. Chem. Soc. Japan*, **40**, 162 (1967).

23. M. Sakuma, *Denki Kagaku*, **28**, 164 (1960); *Chem. Abstr.*, **61**, 14188 (1964).

24. A. J. Fry and R. H. Moore, *J. Org. Chem.*, **33**, 1283 (1968).

25. W. J. Koehl, *J. Am. Chem. Soc.*, **86**, 4686 (1964).

26. J. T. Keating and P. S. Skell, *J. Org. Chem.*, **34**, 1479 (1969).

27. D. L. Muck and E. R. Wilson, Spring Meeting, Electrochemical Society, New York, May 4, 1969, Extended Abstracts, p. 308.

28. V. D. Parker, *Chem. Commun.*, **1968**, 1164.

29. S. D. Ross and M. Finkelstein, *J. Org. Chem.*, **34**, 2923 (1969).

30. L. Horner and H. Neumann, *Chem. Ber.*, **98**, 1715 (1965); **98**, 3462 (1965).

31. S. D. Ross, M. Finkelstein, and R. C. Petersen, *J. Am. Chem. Soc.*, **89**, 4088 (1967).

32. S. D. Ross, M. Finkelstein, and R. C. Petersen, *J. Am. Chem. Soc.*, **88**, 4657 (1966).

33. H. S. Johnston, *J. Am. Chem. Soc.*, **75**, 1567 (1953).

34. J. Schott and N. Davidson, *J. Am. Chem. Soc.*, **80**, 1841 (1958).

35. V. D. Parker and B. E. Burgert, *Tetrahedron Letters*, **1968**, 2411.

36. J. P. Petrovich, M. M. Baizer, and M. R. Ort, *J. Electrochem. Soc.*, **116**, 743 (1969).

37. I. Gillet, *Bull. Soc. Chim. France*, **1968**, 2919.

38. K. Nyberg, *Chem. Commun.*, **1969**, 774.

39. J. H. Stocker and R. M. Jenevein, *J. Org. Chem.*, **33**, 294 (1968).

40. J. H. Stocker and R. M. Jenevein, *J. Org. Chem.*, **33**, 2145 (1968).

41. J. H. Stocker and R. M. Jenevein, *J. Org. Chem.*, **34**, 2807 (1969).

42. V. J. Puglisi, G. L. Clapper, and D. H. Evans, *Anal. Chem.*, **41**, 279 (1969).

43. A. Tallec, *Ann. Chim. (Paris)*, **4**, 67 (1969).

44. C. L. Wilson and H. V. Udupa, *J. Electrochem. Soc.*, **99**, 289 (1952).

45. K. Wiesner, *Collection Czech. Chem. Commun.*, **12**, 67 (1947).

46. R. N. Adams, *Electrochemistry at Solid Electrodes*, Marcel Dekker, New York, 1969.

47. S. D. Ross, *Trans. N.Y. Acad. Sci.*, **30**, 901 (1968).

48. K. Sasaki and J. Newby, *J. Electroanal. Chem.*, **20**, 137 (1969).

49. N. L. Weinberg and H. B. Weinberg, *Chem. Rev.*, **68**, 449 (1968).

50. A. P. Tomilov, *Russ. Chem. Rev.*, **30**, 640 (1960).

51. M. Fleischmann and D. Pletcher, *RIC Rev.*, **1969**, 87.

52. K. M. Johnston, *Educ. Chem.*, **5**, 15 (1968).

53. D. R. Harvey and R. O. C. Norman, *J. Chem. Soc.*, **1964**, 4860.

54. L. Eberson and K. Nyberg, *Acta Chem. Scand.*, **18**, 1568 (1964).
55. L. Eberson and K. Nyberg, *J. Am. Chem. Soc.*, **88**, 1686 (1966).
56. W. Braun, L. Rajbenbach, and F. R. Eirich, *J. Phys. Chem.*, **66**, 1591 (1962).
57. H. W. Salzberg and M. Leung, *J. Org. Chem.*, **30**, 2875 (1965).
58. H. W. Salzberg, M. Leung, and J. Herz, *J. Org. Chem.*, **30**, 310 (1965).
59. S. Ross, M. Finkelstein, and R. C. Petersen, *J. Am. Chem. Soc.*, **86**, 4139 (1964).
60. F. D. Mango and W. A. Bonner, *J. Org. Chem.*, **29**, 430, 1367 (1964).
61. L. Eberson, *J. Am. Chem. Soc.*, **89**, 4669 (1967).
62. F. W. Streuber and K. Dimroth, *Chem. Ber.*, **99**, 258 (1966).
63. C. L. Wilson and K. E. Kolb, *Chem. Commun.*, **1966**, 271.
64. A. J. Baggaley and R. Brettle, *J. Chem. Soc. C*, **1968**, 969.
65. A. J. Baggaley and R. Brettle, *Chem. Commun.*, **1968**, 108.
66. L. Eberson, K. Nyberg, M. Finkelstein, R. C. Petersen, and S. D. Ross, *J. Org. Chem.*, **32**, 16 (1967).
67. S. D. Ross, M. Finkelstein, and R. C. Petersen, *J. Org. Chem.*, **31**, 128 (1966).
68. S. D. Ross, M. Finkelstein, and R. C. Petersen, *J. Am. Chem. Soc.*, **86**, 2745 (1964).
69. L. Rand and A. F. Mohar, *J. Org. Chem.*, **30**, 3156 (1965).
70. V. D. Parker and L. Eberson, *Chem. Commun.*, **1969**, 340.
71. S. Goldschmidt and M. Minsinger, *Chem. Ber.*, **87**, 956 (1954).
72. A. Takeda, S. Torii, and H. Oda, *Tetrahedron Letters*, **1968**, 1781.
73. K. Koyama, T. Ebara, and S. Tsutsumi, *Bull. Chem. Soc. Japan*, **41**, 2668 (1968).
74. D. H. Hey and P. J. Bunyan, *J. Chem. Soc.*, **1960**, 3787.
75. R. P. Linstead, B. R. Shephard, and B. C. L. Weedon, *J. Chem. Soc.*, **1951**, 2854.
76. K. Sasaki, K. Uneyama, H. Vrata, and S. Nagaura, *Electrochim. Acta*, **12**, 137 (1967).
77. T. Inoue, K. Koyama, and S. Tsutsumi, *Bull. Chem. Soc. Japan*, **37**, 1597 (1964).
78. S. Tsutsumi and K. Koyama, *Discussions Faraday Soc.*, **1968**, 247.
79. T. Inoue, K. Koyama, T. Matsuoka, K. Matsuoka, and S. Tsutsumi, *Kogyo Kagaku Zasshi*, **66**, 1659 (1963).
80. N. Clauson-Kaas, F. Limborg, and K. Gleus, *Acta Chem. Scand.*, **6**, 531 (1952).
81. N. Clauson-Kaas, *Acta Chem. Scand.*, **6**, 556 (1952).
82. N. Clauson-Kaas, F. Limborg, *Acta Chem. Scand.*, **6**, 551 (1962).
83. N. Clauson-Kaas, F. Limborg, and P. Dietrich, *Acta Chem. Scand.*, **6**, 545 (1952).
84. N. Clauson-Kaas, *Acta Chem. Scand.*, **6**, 556 (1952).
85. N. Elming, *Acta Chem. Scand.*, **6**, 572 (1952).
86. N. Clauson-Kaas and Z. Tyle, *Acta Chem. Scand.*, **6**, 667 (1952).
87. N. Clauson-Kaas and Z. Tyle, *Acta Chem. Scand.*, **6**, 962 (1952).
88. S. D. Ross, M. Finkelstein, and J. J. Uebel, *J. Org. Chem.*, **34**, 1018 (1969).
89. N. L. Weinberg and T. B. Reddy, *J. Am. Chem. Soc.*, **90**, 91 (1968).

90. N. L. Weinberg and E. A. Brown, *J. Org. Chem.*, **31**, 4058 (1966).
91. N. L. Weinberg, *J. Org. Chem.*, **33**, 4326 (1968).
92. N. L. Weinberg, Symposium on Synthetic and Mechanistic Aspects of Electro Organic Chemistry, U. S. Army Research Office, Durham, North Carolina, October 14–16, 1968, p. 263.
93. P. J. Smith and C. K. Mann, *J. Org. Chem.*, **33**, 316 (1968).
94. B. Belleau and Y. K. Au-Young, *J. Can. Chem.*, **47**, 2117 (1969).
95. T. Shono and Y. Matsumura, *J. Am. Chem. Soc.*, **90**, 5937 (1968).
96. T. Shono and Y. Matsumura, *J. Am. Chem. Soc.*, **91**, 2803 (1969).
97. T. Inoue, K. Koyama, and T. Matsuoka, *Tetrahedron Letters*, **1963**, 1409.
98. T. Inoue and S. Tsutsumi, *Bull. Chem. Soc. Japan*, **38**, 661 (1965).
99. T. Shono and T. Kosaka, *Tetrahedron Letters*, **1968**, 6207.
100. K. Koyama, T. Susuki, and S. Tsutsumi, *Tetrahedron Letters*, **1965**, 627.
101. L. Eberson and S. Nilsson, *Discussions Faraday Soc.*, **1968**, 243.
102. S. Andreades and E. W. Zahnow, *J. Am. Chem. Soc.*, **91**, 4181 (1969).
103. V. D. Parker and B. E. Burgert, *Tetrahedron Letters*, **1965**, 4065.
104. V. D. Parker and B. E. Burgert, *Tetrahedron Letters*, **1968**, 2415.
105. K. Koyama, T. Susuki, A. Omori, and S. Tsutsumi, *Bull. Chem. Soc. Japan*, **41**, 2663 (1968).
106. K. Yoshida and T. Fueno, *Bull. Chem. Soc. Japan*, **42**, 2411 (1969).
107. L. Eberson and K. Nyberg, *Acta Chem. Scand.*, **18**, 1567 (1964).
108. L. Eberson and K. Nyberg, *Tetrahedron Letters*, **1966**, 2389.
109. A. B. Coleman, H. H. Richtol, and D. A. Aiken, *J. Electroanal. Chem.*, **18**, 165 (1968).
110. V. D. Parker, *J. Electroanal. Chem.*, **21**, App. 1 (1969).
111. L. Eberson, *Acta Chem. Scand.*, **17**, 2004 (1963).
112. V. D. Parker and R. N. Adams, *Tetrahedron Letters*, **1969**, 1721.
113. H. Lund, *Acta Chem. Scand.*, **11**, 1323 (1957).
114. M. E. Peover and B. S. White, *J. Electroanal. Chem.*, **13**, 93 (1967).
115. G. Manning, V. D. Parker, and R. N. Adams, *J. Am. Chem. Soc.*, **91**, 4584 (1969).
116. J. J. O'Connor and I. A. Pearl, *J. Electrochem. Soc.*, **111**, 335 (1964).
117. V. D. Parker and L. Eberson, *Tetrahedron Letters*, **1969**, 2839.
118. V. D. Parker and L. Eberson, *Tetrahedron Letters*, **1969**, 2843.
119. V. D. Parker and L. Eberson, *Chem. Commun.*, **1969**, 973.
120. V. D. Parker and L. Eberson, *Chem. Commun.*, **1969**, 451.
121. V. D. Parker, K. Nyberg, and L. Eberson, *J. Electroanal. Chem.*, **22**, 150 (1969).
122. M. J. Allen, *Organic Electrode Processes*, Chapman and Hall, London, 1958.
123. L. L. Miller, *Tetrahedron Letters*, **1968**, 1831.
124. H. Schmidt and H. Meinert, *Angew. Chem.*, **72**, 109 (1960).
125. F. Fichter and P. Schönmann, *Helv. Chim. Acta*, **19**, 1411 (1936).
126. G. Cauquis and G. Pierré, *Compt. Rend.*, **266**, 883 (1968).
127. G. E. Svadkovskaya and S. A. Voitkevich, *Russ. Chem. Rev.*, **29**, 161 (1960).
128. B. C. L. Weedon, *Advan. Org. Chem.*, **1**, 1 (1960).
129. T. D. Binns, R. Brettle, and G. B. Cox, *J. Chem. Soc. C.*, **1968**, 584.

130. L. Rand and C. S. Rao, *J. Org. Chem.*, **33**, 2704 (1968).
131. T. Campbell, A. Vellturo, and G. W. Griffin, *Chem. Ind. (London)*, **1969**, 1235.
132. A. F. Vellturo and G. W. Griffin, *J. Am. Chem. Soc.*, **87**, 3021 (1965).
133. P. Radlick, R. Klem, S. Spurlock, J. J. Sims, E. E. VanTamelen, and T. Whitesides, *Tetrahedron Letters*, **1968**, 5117.
134. H. H. Westberg and H. J. Dauben, Jr., *Tetrahedron Letters*, **1968**, 5123.
135. T. Okubo and S. Tsutsumi, *Bull. Chem. Soc. Japan*, **37**, 1794 (1964).
136. R. Brettle and J. G. Parkin, *J. Chem. Soc. C*, **1967**, 1352.
137. T. D. Binns and R. Brettle, *J. Chem. Soc. C*, **1966**, 336.
138. H. Schäfer and A. Alazrak, *Angew. Chem. Intern. Ed. Engl.*, **7**, 474 (1968).
139. J. M. Fritsch and H. Weingarten, *J. Am. Chem. Soc.*, **90**, 793 (1968).
140. H. Schäfer and E. Steckhan, *Angew. Chem.*, **81**, 532 (1969).
141. D. H. Geske, *J. Phys. Chem.*, **63**, 1062 (1959).
142. D. H. Geske, *J. Phys. Chem.*, **66**, 1743 (1962).
143. L. L. Miller and A. K. Hoffman, *J. Am. Chem. Soc.*, **89**, 593 (1967).
144. K. M. Johnston, *Tetrahedron Letters*, **1967**, 837.
145. G. F. Kirkbright, J. T. Stock, R. D. Pugliese, and J. M. Bobbitt, *J. Electrochem. Soc.*, **116**, 219 (1969).
146. F. J. Vermillion, Jr., and I. A. Pearl, *J. Electrochem. Soc.*, **111**, 1392 (1964).
147. A. B. Suttie, *Tetrahedron Letters*, **1969**, 953.
148. E. T. Seo, R. F. Nelson, J. M. Fritsch, L. S. Marcoux, D. W. Leedy, and R. N. Adams, *J. Am. Chem. Soc.*, **88**, 3498 (1966).
149. D. M. Mohilner, R. N. Adams, and W. J. Argersinger, Jr., *J. Am. Chem. Soc.*, **84**, 3618 (1962).
150. J. Bacon and R. N. Adams, *J. Am. Chem. Soc.*, **90**, 24 (1968).
151. G. Cauquis, J. Badoz-Lambling, and J. P. Billon, *Bull. Soc. Chim. France*, **1965**, 1433.
152. S. Wawzonek and T. W. McIntyre, *J. Electrochem. Soc.*, **114**, 1025 (1967).
153. S. Wawzonek, T. H. Plaisance, L. M. Smith, Jr., and E. B. Buchanan, Jr., *Symposium on Synthetic and Mechanistic Aspects of Electro Organic Chemistry*, U. S. Army Research Office, Durham, North Carolina, October 14–16, 1968, p. 247.
154. G. Cauquis, J. P. Coquand, and J. Rigaudy, *Compt. Rend.*, **268**, 2265 (1969).
155. Z. Galus and R. N. Adams, *J. Phys. Chem.*, **67**, 862 (1963).
156. Z. Galus, R. M. White, F. S. Rowland, and R. N. Adams, *J. Am. Chem. Soc.*, **82**, 2065 (1962).
157. Z. Galus and R. N. Adams, *J. Am. Chem. Soc.*, **84**, 2061 (1962).
158. T. Mizoguchi and R. N. Adams, *J. Am. Chem. Soc.*, **84**, 2058 (1962).
159. J. E. Dubois, P. C. Lacaze, and A. Aranda, *Compt. Rend.*, **260**, 3383 (1965).
160. R. F. Nelson and R. N. Adams, *J. Am. Chem. Soc.*, **90**, 3925 (1968).
161. V. Dvořák, I. Němec, and J. Zyka, *J. Microchem.*, **12**, 99, 325 (1967).
162. J. F. Ambrose and R. F. Nelson, *J. Electrochem. Soc.*, **115**, 1159 (1968).
163. W. Kern and H. Quast, *Makromol. Chem.*, **10**, 202 (1953).
164. I. L. Knunyants and N. P. Gambaryan, *Usp. Khim.*, **23**, 781 (1954).
165. I. L. Knunyants and N. S. Vyazankin, *Izv. Akad. Nauk SSSR, Otd. Khim. Nauk.*, **2**, 238 (1957).

166. M. M. Baizer, J. D. Anderson, J. H. Wagenknecht, M. R. Ort, and J. P. Petrovich, *Electrochim. Acta*, **12**, 1377 (1967).

167. K. Sugino and T. Nonaka, *J. Electrochem. Soc.*, **112**, 1241 (1965).

168. K. Sugino and T. Nonaka, *Electrochim. Acta*, **13**, 613 (1968).

169. M. M. Baizer, *J. Org. Chem.*, **31**, 3847 (1966).

170. J. H. Wagenknecht and M. M. Baizer, *J. Org. Chem.*, **31**, 3855 (1966).

171. O. R. Brown and K. Lister, *Discussions Faraday Soc.*, **1968**, 106.

172. M. M. Baizer and J. D. Anderson, *J. Electrochem. Soc.*, **111**, 223 (1964).

173. M. M. Baizer, *Tetrahedron Letters*, **1966**, 973.

174. M. M. Baizer, *J. Electrochem. Soc.*, **111**, 215 (1964).

175. R. H. McKee, *Ind. Eng. Chem.*, **38**, 382 (1946).

176. H. S. Both, *Ind. Eng. Chem.*, **40**, 1491 (1948).

177. F. Beck, *Ber. Bunsenges. Phys. Chem.*, **72**, 379 (1968).

178. I. G. Sevast Yanova and A. P. Tomilov, *Zh. Obshch. Khim.*, **33**, 2815 (1963).

179. J. P. Petrovich, M. M. Baizer, and M. R. Ort, *J. Electrochem. Soc.*, **116**, 743 (1969).

180. J. P. Petrovich, J. D. Anderson, and M. M. Baizer, *J. Org. Chem.*, **31**, 3897 (1966).

181. A. P. Tomilov and A. K. Klimov, *Elektrokhimiya*, **3**, 232 (1967).

182. T. Asahara, M. Seno, and T. Arai, *Bull. Chem. Soc. Japan*, **42**, 1316 (1969).

183. F. Beck, *Chem. Ing. Tech.*, **37**, 607 (1965).

184. S. Lazarov, A. Trifonov, and T. Vitanov, *Z. Physik. Chem. (Leipzig)*, **226**, 221 (1964).

185. J. D. Anderson, M. M. Baizer, and E. J. Prill, *J. Org. Chem.*, **30**, 1645 (1965).

186. J. P. Petrovich, M. M. Baizer, and M. R. Ort, *J. Electrochem. Soc.*, **116**, 749 (1969).

187. M. M. Baizer and J. D. Anderson, *J. Org. Chem.*, **30**, 1348 (1965).

188. M. M. Baizer and J. D. Anderson, *J. Org. Chem.*, **30**, 3138 (1965).

189. M. M. Baizer, *J. Org. Chem.*, **29**, 1670 (1964).

190. J. J. Eisch, D. D. Koska, and C. J. Peterson, *J. Org. Chem.*, **31**, 453 (1966).

191. J. D. Anderson and M. M. Baizer, *Tetrahedron Letters*, **1966**, 511.

192. J. D. Anderson, M. M. Baizer, and J. D. Petrovich, *J. Org. Chem.*, **31**, 3890 (1966).

193. R. Brdička, *J. Gen. Physiol.*, **19**, 899 (1936).

194. R. Pasternak and H. von Halban, *Helv. Chim. Acta*, **29**, 190, 761 (1946).

195. M. von Stackelberg and W. Stracke, *Z. Elektrochem.*, **53**, 118 (1948).

196. L. Horner and A. Menthrup, *Ann. Chem.*, **646**, 65 (1961).

197. L. Horner and J. Haufe, *Chem. Ber.*, **101**, 2903 (1968).

198. L. Horner and R. J. Singer, *Ann. Chem.*, **723**, 1 (1968).

199. P. J. Elving, *Record Chem. Progr. (Kresge-Hooker Sci. Lib)*, **14**, 99 (1953).

200. N. S. Hush, *Z. Elektrochem.*, **61**, 734 (1957).

201. H. Lund, *Acta Chem. Scand.*, **13**, 192 (1959).

202. J. H. Stocker and R. M. Jenevein, *Chem. Commun.*, **1968**, 934.

203. F. L. Lambert and K. Kobayashi, *J. Am. Chem. Soc.*, **82**, 5324 (1960).

204. J. Závada, J. Krupička, and J. Sicher, *Collection Czech. Chem. Commun.*, **28**, 1664 (1963).

205. F. L. Lambert, A. H. Albert, and J. P. Hardy, *J. Am. Chem. Soc.*, **86**, 3156 (1964).

206. J. W. Sease, P. Chang, and J. L. Groth, *J. Am. Chem. Soc.*, **86**, 3154 (1964).

207. I. Rosenthal, C. H. Albright, and P. J. Elving, *J. Electrochem. Soc.*, **99**, 227 (1952).

208. P. J. Elving, I. Rosenthal, and A. J. Martin, *J. Am. Chem. Soc.*, **77**, 5218 (1955).

209. P. J. Elving, I. Rosenthal, and M. Koll-Kramer, *J. Am. Chem. Soc.*, **73**, 1717 (1951).

210. E. Gergely and T. Iredale, *J. Chem. Soc.*, **1951**, 13.

211. E. Gergely and T. Iredale, *J. Chem. Soc.*, **1951**, 3502.

212. R. F. Evilia and A. J. Diefenderfer, *J. Electroanal. Chem.*, **22**, 407 (1969).

213. T. Fujinaga and K. Takaoka, *J. Electroanal. Chem.*, **16**, 99 (1968).

214. P. J. Elving and J. T. Leone, *J. Am. Chem. Soc.*, **79**, 1546 (1957).

215. A. Streitwieser and C. Perrin, *J. Am. Chem. Soc.*, **86**, 4938 (1964).

216. J. Grimshaw and J. S. Ramsey, *J. Chem. Soc.*, B **1968**, 60.

217. G. Klopman, *Helv. Chim. Acta*, **44**, 1908 (1961).

218. J. W. Sease and R. C. Read, Spring Meeting, Electrochemical Society, May 4, 1969, New York, Extended Abstracts, p. 328.

219. L. W. Marple, E. I. Hummelstedt, and L. B. Rogers, *J. Electrochem. Soc.*, **107**, 437 (1960).

220. S. Wawzonek, R. C. Duty, and J. H. Wagenknecht, *J. Electrochem. Soc.*, **107**, 74 (1964).

221. M. R. Rifi, *J. Am. Chem. Soc.*, **89**, 4442 (1967).

222. M. R. Rifi, Spring Meeting, Electrochemical Society, May 4, 1969, New York, Extended Abstracts, p. 320.

223. F. H. Covitz, *J. Am. Chem. Soc.*, **89**, 5403 (1967).

224. A. M. Doyle, A. E. Pedler, and J. C. Tatlow, *J. Chem. Soc.*, C **1968**, 2740.

225. C. S. McDowell, *Dissertation Abstr.* B **28**(6), **1967**, 2348.

226. H. G. Gilch, *J. Polymer. Sci.*, *Part A*-1, **4**, 1351 (1966).

227. A. P. Tomilov, Y. D. Smirnov, and S. L. Varshavskii, *Zh. Obshch. Khim.*, **35**, 391 (1965).

228. A. P. Tomilov, *Zh. Obshch. Khim.*, **38**, 214 (1968).

229. P. G. Arapagos and M. K. Scott, *Tetrahedron Letters*, **1968**, 1975.

230. B. Baillie and J. Tafel, *Ber. Deut. Chem. Ges.*, **32**, 68 (1899).

231. K. Kindler, *Ber. Deut. Chem. Ges.*, **57**, 773 (1924).

232. N. J. Gawrilow, *J. Gen. Chem. USSR* (*Engl. Transl.*), **9**, 1934 (1939).

233. L. Horner and R. J. Singer, *Tetrahedron Letters*, **1969**, 1545.

234. P. Rambacher and S. Mäke, *Angew. Chem.*, **80**, 666 (1968).

235. L. Horner and A. Mentrup, *Ann. Chem.*, **646**, 49 (1961).

236. L. Horner, F. Röttger, and H. Fuchs, *Chem. Ber.*, **96**, 3141 (1963).

237. S. Wawzonek and J. H. Wagenknecht, in *Polarography 1964*, G. J. Hills, Ed., Macmillan, London, 1966.

238. E. L. Colichman, *Anal. Chem.*, **26**, 1204 (1954).

239. H. Matsuo, *J. Sci. Hiroshima Univ. Ser. A*, **22**, 51 (1958).

240. H. Matschiner and K. Issleib, *Z. Anorg. Allgem. Chem.*, **354**, 60 (1967).

241. L. Horner and J. Haufe, *J. Electroanal. Chem.*, **20**, 245 (1969).

242. B. Janik and P. J. Elving, *J. Electrochem. Soc.*, **116**, 1087 (1969).

243. J. K. Kochi, *J. Am. Chem. Soc.*, **77**, 3208 (1955).

244. T. H. Wohlfarth, *J. Prakt. Chem. Ser. 2*, **65**, 295 (1902).

245. H. Lund, *Acta Chem. Scand.*, **21**, 2525 (1967).

246. H. Lund, Symposium on Synthetic and Mechanistic Aspects of Electro Organic Chemistry. U. S. Army Research Office. Durham, North Carolina, October 14–16, 1968, Extended Abstracts p. 197.

247. H. Lund, Spring Meeting, Electrochemical Society, May 4, 1969, New York, Extended Abstracts, p. 349.

248. J. Tafel and E. Pfeffermann, *Chem. Ber.*, **36**, 219 (1903).

249. M. Silver, *J. Am. Chem. Soc.*, **82**, 2971 (1960).

250. P. S. Skell and I. Starer, *J. Am. Chem. Soc.*, **81**, 4117 (1959).

251. P. S. Skell and I. Starer, *J. Am. Chem. Soc.*, **82**, 2971 (1960).

252. K. K. Barnes and C. K. Mann, *J. Org. Chem.*, **32**, 1474 (1967).

253. A. I. Scott, P. A. Dodson, F. McCapra, and M. B. Meyers, *J. Am. Chem. Soc.*, **85**, 3702 (1963).

254. H. Iwasaki, L. A. Cohen, and B. Witkop, *J. Am. Chem. Soc.*, **85**, 3701 (1963).

255. G. W. Kenner, M. A. Murray, and C. M. B. Taylor, *Tetrahedron*, **1**, 259 (1957).

256. H. Iwasaki and B. Witkop, *J. Am. Chem. Soc.*, **86**, 4698 (1964).

257. C. Bratu and A. T. Balaban, *Rev. Roumaine Chim.*, **10**, 1001 (1965).

258. W. Dilthey, *J. Prakt. Chem. Ser. 2*, **94**, 53 (1916); **95**, 107 (1917); **101**, 177 (1921).

259. F. D. Popp and H. P. Schultz, *Chem. Rev.*, **62**, 19 (1962).

260. W. D. Hoffman, W. E. McEwen, and J. Kleinberg, *Tetrahedron*, **5**, 293 (1959).

261. R. N. Gourley and J. Grimshaw, *J. Chem. Soc. C*, **1969**, 2388.

262. T. J. Curphey and R. L. McCartney, *J. Org. Chem.*, **34**, 1964 (1969).

263. T. J. Curphey, C. W. Amelotti, T. P. Layloff, R. L. McCartney, and J. H. Williams, *J. Am. Chem. Soc.*, **91**, 2817 (1969).

264. J. P. Petrovich, J. D. Anderson, and M. M. Baizer, *J. Org. Chem.*, **31**, 3890 (1966).

265. S. H. Wilen and A. W. Levine, *Chem. Ind. (London)*, **1969**, 237.

266. A. G. Hudson, A. E. Pedler, and J. C. Tatlow, *Tetrahedron Letters*, **1968**, 2143.

267. S. Wawzonek and R. C. Duty, *J. Electrochem. Soc.*, **108**, 1135 (1961).

268. R. E. Dessy, private communcation.

269. E. I. Stiefel, J. H. Waters, E. Billig, and H. B. Gray, *J. Am. Chem. Soc.*, **87**, 3016 (1965).

270. A. Davison, N. Edelstein, R. H. Holm, and A. H. Maki, *J. Am. Chem. Soc.*, **85**, 2029 (1963).

271. A. Davison, N. Edelstein, R. H. Holm, and A. H. Maki, *Inorg. Chem.*, **2**, 1227 (1963).

272. A. L. Balch, F. Rohrscheid, and R. H. Holm, *J. Am. Chem. Soc.*, **87**, 2301 (1965).

273. R. Williams, E. Billig, J. H. Waters, and H. B. Gray, *J. Am. Chem. Soc.*, **88**, 43 (1966).

274. M. J. Baker-Hawkes, E. Billig, and H. B. Gray, *J. Am. Chem. Soc.*, **88**, 4870 (1966).

275. D. C. Olson, V. P. Mayweg, and G. N. Schrauzer, *J. Am. Chem. Soc.*, **88**, 4876 (1966).

276. A. L. Balch and R. H. Holm, *J. Am. Chem. Soc.*, **88**, 5201 (1966).

277. F. Rohrscheid, A. L. Balch, and R. H. Holm, *Inorg. Chem.*, **5**, 1542 (1966).

278. A. Davison and E. T. Shawl, *Chem. Commun.*, **1967**, 670.

279. R. H. Holm, A. L. Balch, A. Davison, A. H. Maki, and T. E. Berry, *J. Am. Chem. Soc.*, **89**, 2866 (1967).

280. J. A. McCleverty, J. Locke, E. J. Wharton, and M. Gerlock, *J. Chem. Soc. A*, **1968**, 816.

281. A. L. Balch, *J. Am. Chem. Soc.*, **91**, 1948 (1969).

282. F. Lalor, M. F. Hawthorne, A. H. Maki, K. Darlington, A. Davison, H. B. Gray, Z. Dori, and E. I. Stiefel, *J. Am. Chem. Soc.*, **89**, 2278 (1967).

283. R. E. Dessy, F. E. Stary, R. B. King, and M. Waldrop, *J. Am. Chem. Soc.*, **88**, 471 (1966).

284. R. E. Dessy, R. B. King, and M. Waldrop, *J. Am. Chem. Soc.*, **88**, 5112 (1966).

285. R. E. Dessy and R. L. Pohl, *J. Am. Chem. Soc.*, **90**, 1995 (1968).

286. R. E. Dessy, R. Kornmann, C. Smith, and R. Haytor, *J. Am. Chem. Soc.*, **90**, 2001 (1968).

287. R. E. Dessy and L. Wieczorek, *J. Am. Chem. Soc.*, **91**, 4963 (1969).

288. D. C. Olson and J. Vasilevskis, *Inorg. Chem.*, **8**, 1611 (1969).

289. R. E. Dessy, W. Kitching, and T. Chivers, *J. Am. Chem. Soc.*, **88**, 453 (1966).

290. R. E. Dessy, W. Kitching, and T. Chivers, *J. Am. Chem. Soc.*, **88**, 467 (1966).

291. R. E. Dessy, F. E. Stary, R. B. King, and M. Waldrop, *J. Am. Chem. Soc.*, **88**, 471 (1966).

292. R. E. Dessy, R. B. King, and M. Waldrop, *J. Am. Chem. Soc.*, **88**, 5112 (1966).

293. R. E. Dessy and P. M. Weissman, *J. Am. Chem. Soc.*, **88**, 5124 (1966).

294. R. E. Dessy, R. L. Pohl, and R. B. King, *J. Am. Chem. Soc.*, **88**, 5121 (1966).

295. R. E. Dessy and P. M. Weissman, *J. Am. Chem. Soc.*, **88**, 5129 (1966).

296. E. M. Marlett, *Ann. N. Y. Acad. Sci.*, **125**, 12 (1965).

297. See Ref. 296 for further references and patent listings.

298. W. Evans and R. Pearson, *J. Am. Chem. Soc.*, **64**, 2865 (1942).

299. W. Evans, R. Pearson, and D. Braithwaite, *J. Am. Chem. Soc.*, **63**, 2574 (1941).

300. *Chem. Eng. News*, **42** (49), 52 (1964).

301. T. Psarras and R. E. Dessy, *J. Am. Chem. Soc.*, **88**, 5132 (1966).

302. R. Galli, *J. Electroanal. Chem.*, **22**, 75 (1969).

303. H. E. Ulery, *J. Electrochem. Soc.*, **116**, 1201 (1969).

304. V. Peruzzo, G. Plazzogna, and G. Tagliavini, *J. Electroanal. Chem.*, **18**, 89 (1969).

305. T. Shono and M. Mitani, *J. Am. Chem. Soc.*, **90**, 2728 (1968).

306. T. Shono and M. Mitani, *Tetrahedron Letters*, **1969**, 687.
307. P. E. Iverson and H. Lund, *Tetrahedron Letters*, **1969**, 3523.
308. P. S. McKinney and S. Rosenthal, *J. Electroanal. Chem.*, **16**, 261 (1968) and references therein.
309. D. E. Smith, E. B. Rupp, and D. F. Shriver, *J. Am. Chem. Soc.*, **89**, 5562 (1967).
310. J. Q. Chambers, A. D. Norman, M. R. Bickell, and S. H. Cadle, *J. Am. Chem. Soc.*, **90**, 6056 (1968).
311. R. J. Wiersma and R. L. Middaugh, *J. Am. Chem. Soc.*, **89**, 5078 (1967).
312. R. J. Wiersma and R. L. Middaugh, *Inorg. Chem.*, **8**, 2074 (1969).
313. W. R. Turner and P. Elving, *Anal. Chem.*, **37**, 207 (1965).
314. L. I. Zakharkin, U. N. Kalinin, and A. P. Snyakin, *Izv. Akad. Nauk. SSSR Ser. Khim.*, 194 (1968).
315. A. J. Birch, *Nature*, **158**, 60 (1946).
316. H. W. Sternberg, R. E. Markby, and I. Wender, *J. Electrochem. Soc.*, **110**, 425 (1963).
317. H. W. Sternberg, R. E. Markby, I. Wender, and D. M. Mohilner, *J. Electrochem. Soc.*, **113**, 1060 (1966).
318. R. A. Benkeser and E. M. Kaiser, *J. Am. Chem. Soc.*, **85**, 2858 (1963).
319. R. A. Benkeser, E. M. Kaiser, and R. F. Lambert, *J. Am. Chem. Soc.*, **86**, 5272 (1964).
320. A. Misono, T. Osa, and T. Yamagishi, *Bull. Chem. Soc. Japan*, **40**, 427 (1967).
321. H. W. Sternberg, R. E. Markby, I. Wender, and D. M. Mohilner, *J. Am. Chem. Soc.*, **89**, 186 (1967).
322. T. Osa, T. Yamagishi, T. Kodama, and A. Misono, Symposium on Synthetic and Mechanistic Aspects of Electro Organic Chemistry, U. S. Army Research Office, Durham, North Carolina, October 14–16, 1968, p. 157.
323. R. Dietz and M. E. Peover, *Trans. Faraday Soc.*, **62**, 3535 (1966).
324. R. A. Benkeser, Symposium on Synthetic and Mechanistic Aspects of Electro Organic Chemistry, U. S. Army Research Office, Durham, North Carolina, October 14–16, 1968, p. 189.
325. T. Asahara, M. Seno, and H. Kaneko, *Bull. Chem. Soc. Japan*, **41**, 2985 (1968).
326. H. W. Sternberg, R. E. Markby, I. Wender, and D. M. Mohilner, *J. Am. Chem. Soc.*, **91**, 4191 (1969).
327. H. W. Sternberg, Symposium on Synthetic and Mechanistic Aspects of Electro Organic Chemistry, U. S. Army Research Office, Durham, North Carolina, Octover 14–16, 1968, p. 179.
328. R. A. Benkeser and C. A. Tincher, *J. Org. Chem.*, **33**, 2727 (1968).
329. J. T. Wrobel and A. R. Krawczyk, *Chem. Ind. (London)*, **1969**, 656.
330. J. T. Wrobel, K. M. Pazdro, and A. S. Bien, *Chem. Ind. (London)*, **1969**, 1759.
331. P. G. Arapakos, *J. Am. Chem. Soc.*, **89**, 6794 (1967).
332. J. J. Lingane, *Anal. Chem.*, **26**, 1021 (1954).
333. C. A. Vicent and J. G. Ward, *J. Chem. Educ.*, **46**, 613 (1969).
334. Philbrick Applications Manual, Philbrick Research, Inc., June 1966.
335. D. D. DeFord, C. J. Johns, and J. W. Pitts, *Anal. Chem.*, **23**, 941 (1951).

336. H. B. Thomson, M. J. Boehm, and M. T. Rogers, *J. Chem. Educ.*, **32**, 463 (1955).
337. P. F. Lott, *J. Chem. Educ.*, **42**, A261, A361 (1965).
338. J. Tacussel, *Electrochim. Acta*, **11**, 381 (1966).
339. A. Hickling, *Electrochim. Acta*, **5**, 161 (1961).
340. F. G. Will, *Electrochim. Acta*, **14**, 749 (1969).
341. A. Bewick and O. R. Brown, *J. Electroanal. Chem.*, **15**, 129 (1967).
342. Descriptive literature from Brinkman Instrument, Inc., Princeton Applied Research, Inc., Ryaby Associates, and National Instrument Laboratory, Inc.
343. See, for example, literature on fuel cells.
344. R. Kanakam, M. S. V. Pathy, and H. V. K. Udupa, *Electrochim. Acta*, **12**, 329 (1967).
345. Descriptive literature about Amberplex, Rohm and Haas Co., Philadelphia, Pennsylvania.
346. Descriptive literature about porous Vycor, Corning Glass Works, Corning, New York.
347. D. K. Roe, *Anal. Chem.*, **36**, 2371 (1964).
348. J. Chang, unpublished results.
349. P. K. Das, H. A. O. Hill, J. M. Pratt, and J. P. Williams, *J. Chem. Soc. A*, **1968**, 1261.
350. R. Pasternak, *Helv. Chim. Acta*, **31**, 753 (1948).
351. S. Karp and L. Meites, *J. Electroanal. Chem.*, **17**, 253 (1968).
352. D. Peltier, M. LeGuyader, and J. Tacussel, *Bull. Soc. Chim. France*, **1963**, 2609.
353. C. Barry and G. Cauquis, *Bull. Soc. Chim. France*, **1966**, 1032.
354. J. R. Backhust, J. M. Coulson, F. Goodridge, R. E. Plimley, and M. Fleischmann, *J. Electrochem. Soc.*, **116**, 1600 (1969).
355. J. Molnar, *Magy. Kem. Folyoirat*, **68**, 504 (1962).
356. W. J. Blaedel and J. H. Strohl, *Anal. Chem.*, **36**, 1245 (1964).
357. R. E. Sioda, *Electrochim. Acta*, **13**, 375 (1968).
358. T. Fujinaga, T. Nagai, S. Okazaki, and Ch. Takagi, *J. Chem. Soc. Japan*, **84**, 941 (1963).
359. N. E. Khomutov and T. N. Shornyakova, *J. Appl. Chem. USSR*, **36**, 1772 (1963).
360. M. J. Allen, *J. Electrochem. Soc.*, **109**, 731 (1962).
361. S. Isoe and L. A. Cohen, *Arch. Biochem. Biophys.*, **127**, 522 (1968).
362. A. E. J. Forno, *Chem. Ind. (London)*, **1968**, 1728.
363. S. Nojima, *Kagaku Kogyo*, **19**, 724 (1968).
364. J. Newman, *Ind. Eng. Chem.*, **60**, 12 (1968).
365. V. G. Khomyakov, N. G. Bakhchrisaraits'yan, M. Ya Fioshin, S. S. Kruglikov, and L. I. Kazakova, *Tr. Mosk. Khim.-Tekhnol. Inst.*, **1961**, 249.
366. H. Binder, A. Köhling, W. Kuhn, and G. Sandstede, *Angew. Chem. Intern. Ed. Engl.*, **8**, 757 (1969).
367. M. Fleischmann, J. R. Mansfield, and L. Wayne-Jones, *J. Electroanal. Chem.*, **10**, 511 (1965).
368. B. E. Conway, *Rev. Pure Appl. Chem.*, **18**, 105 (1968).

369. D. J. G. Ives and G. J. Janz, *Reference Electrodes, Theory and Practice*, Academic, New York, 1961.

370. R. G. Bates, *Determination of pH, Theory and Practice*, Wiley, New York, 1964.

371. H. T. S. Britton, *Hydrogen Ions*, Van Nostrand Reinhold, New York, 1929.

372. *The Merck Index*, 7th ed., 1960, Merck and Co., Rahway, New Jersey.

373. N. I. Sax, *Dangerous Properties of Industrial Materials*, Van Nostrand Reinhold, New York, 1968.

374. C. K. Mann, in *Electroanalytical Chemistry*, A. J. Bard, Ed., Vol. 3, Marcel Dekker, New York, 1969.

375. G. Cauquis, *Introd. Method Electrochim., Rec. Trav. S. 1964–1965*, Vol. 1, Masson, Paris. 1967.

376. A. Charlot, J. Badoz-Lambling, and B. Tremillon, *Electrochemical Reactions*, Elsevier, Amsterdam, 1962, Chapter XIII.

377. T. Fujinaga and T. Arai, *Denki Kagaku Oyobi Kogyo Butsuri Kagaku*, **37**, 238 (1969).

378. H. Normant, *Angew. Chem. Intern. Ed. Engl.*, **6**, 1046 (1967).

379. J. Courtot-Coupex and M. Le Demezet, *Bull. Soc. Chim. France*, **1967**, 4744.

380. J. Perichon and R. Buvet, *Bull. Soc. Chim. France*, **1968**, 1279.

381. J. Martinmaa, *Suomen Kemistilehti, B*, **42**, 33 (1969).

382. G. Cauquis and D. Serve, *Bull. Soc. Chim. France*, **1966**, 302.

383. S. Wawzonek, R. Berkey, and D. Thomson, *J. Electrochem. Soc.*, **103**, 513 (1956).

384. M. Breant, M. Bazouin, C. Buisson, M. Dupin, and J. M. Rebattu, *Bull. Soc. Chim. France*, **1968**, 5065.

385. J. P. Billon, *J. Electroanal. Chem.*, **1**, 486 (1959).

386. J. E. Dubois, *Rev. Gen. Elec.*, **77**, 269 (1968).

387. N. S. Moe, *Acta Chem. Scand.*, **19**, 1023 (1965).

388. M. Fleischmann and D. Pletcher, *Tetrahedron Letters*, **1968**, 6255.

389. I. M. Kolthoff and J. F. Coetzee, *J. Am. Chem. Soc.*, **79**, 1852 (1956).

390. I. M. Kolthoff and J. F. Coetzee, *J. Am. Chem. Soc.*, **79**, 870 (1956).

391. J. F. Coetzee and J. J. Campion, *J. Am. Chem. Soc.*, **89**, 2513 (1967).

392. J. W. Strojek and T. Kuwana, *J. Electroanal. Chem.*, **16**, 471 (1968).

393. T. Osa and T. Kuwana, *J. Electroanal. Chem.*, **22**, 389 (1969).

394. J. W. Strojek, T. Kuwana, and S. W. Feldberg, *J. Am. Chem. Soc.*, **90**, 1353 (1968).

395. A. Yildiz, P. T. Kissinger, and C. N. Reilley, *Anal. Chem.*, **40**, 1018 (1968).

396. W. R. Heineman, J. N. Burnett, and R. W. Murray, *Anal. Chem.*, **40**, 1974 (1968).

397. D. R. Tallant and D. H. Evans, *Anal. Chem.*, **41**, 835 (1969).

398. L. H. Piette, P. Ludwig, and R. N. Adams, *Anal. Chem.*, **34**, 916 (1962).

399. G. Cauquis, *Bull. Soc. Chim. France*, **1968**, 1618.

400. Literature bulletin from Varian Associates, Palo Alto, California.

Chapter **XI**

ORGANIC REACTIONS IN ELECTRICAL DISCHARGES

Bernard D. Blaustein and Yuan C. Fu

91

I INTRODUCTION

At pressures and temperatures near ambient, gases are poor conductors of electricity. However, at high temperatures or at reduced pressures, gases conduct electricity if subjected to a strong electrical field; the gas becomes partially ionized and the free electrons and ions carry current through the gas. Early workers in the field spoke of the "discharge" of electricity through the gas, and the term "gaseous electrical discharge" was used to describe the phenomenon. Gas discharge tubes are quite common; two everyday examples are neon signs and fluorescent lights.

A partially ionized, electrically conducting, luminous gas is called a "plasma." Thus the term "plasma chemistry" is often used to describe the reactions that can be carried out in these gas discharges. In a discharge the free electrons pick up energy from the electrical field, collide with gas molecules, and transfer energy to them. The electron-molecule collisions cause the molecules to become excited and they may dissociate and/or ionize to form excited, chemically reactive species—atoms, free radicals, positive and negative ions, and various types of excited molecules; ultraviolet, visible, and infrared radiation is also emitted. These reactive species then cause chemical reactions in the discharge.

Some examples of reactions that can be carried out in discharges are the formation of acetylene, ethylene, and ethane from methane [1]; formaldehyde and methanol from methane and water [2, 3]; methane, ethane, acetylene, and higher hydrocarbons from $H_2 + CO$ [4]; glycine from acetic acid and nitrogen [5]; benzene from cyclohexadiene [6]; benzene from pyridine [7]; biphenyl from benzene [8, 9]; naphthalene from phenylbutadiene [10]; C_6D_5Cl from C_6D_5Br and Cl_2 [11]; methyldisilane from silane and dimethyl ether [12]; and carboranes from diborane and acetylene [13, 14]. This chapter also discusses reactions of atomic H, atomic O, and active nitrogen with hydrocarbons, other organic compounds, and carbonaceous materials using electrical discharge techniques. Studies of simple atom-molecule reactions provide important clues to the understanding of the mechanisms of discharge reactions of more complicated systems.

One of the difficulties in dealing with discharge reactions is the complexity of the reaction products. Yields of specific products are often very low; many organic reactions can be carried out in discharges, but major problems remain in learning how to control experimental conditions to achieve specific reactions in high yields. This review is meant to be an introduction to the techniques developed for carrying out chemical reactions in electrical discharges. It is not all-inclusive, although for some topics and some reactions detailed discussions are given.

Books and Reviews

Several books and monographs covering all or part of the subject of chemical reactions in electrical discharges have recently appeared; these are by McTaggart [15], Baddour and Timmins [16], Venugopalan and Jones [17], Wright and Winkler [18], and Venugopalan [19]. The proceedings of several recent symposia have also been published: two held in Moscow, one emphasizing the production of acetylene from hydrocarbons [20], a second devoted to low-temperature plasmas [21]; and one held in Miami Beach in 1967, covering the whole field of chemical reactions in electrical discharges [22].

Many review articles have also appeared recently. These include general reviews by Kondrat'ev [23], Jolly [24], Kana'an and Margrave [25], von Engel [26], Coffman and Browne [27], Hollahan [28], and Spedding [29], and reviews on the chemical physics of discharges [30], the production of atoms and simple radicals in discharges [31], inorganic syntheses in discharges [32, 33], chemistry of dissociated water vapor [34], chemical processing by microwave radiation [35a], a comparison of radiation chemistry and electric discharge chemistry [35b], the production of organic surface films [36], reactions of active nitrogen with organic molecules [37], synthesis of organic compounds under primordial conditions [38, 39], the preparation of tritium-labeled compounds in discharges [40], electrocracking of hydrocarbons [41], formation of acetylene from methane and other hydrocarbons [42], the reactions of silicon compounds under radiation and in discharges [43], a comparison of various discharge devices used as chemical reactors [44], the chemical engineering aspects of discharges [45, 46], plasmas for high-temperature chemistry including a brief discussion of cold plasmas [47a], and plasma chemical and process engineering [47b,c].

Use of Electrical Discharges for Organic Syntheses

In a series of classic experiments, Miller [48–53] passed a continuous electric spark from a high-voltage high-frequency Tesla coil through a mixture of CH_4, NH_3, H_2, and H_2O vapor and produced a mixture of organic compounds containing carboxylic (formic, glycolic, lactic and so on) and amino acids (glycine, alanine, and so on). Figure 11.1 shows one apparatus used, made of Pyrex with tungsten electrodes. The water in flask A was boiled to promote circulation of the gas mixture. The products from the discharge were condensed, flowed through the U-tube (which prevented circulation in the wrong direction), and the nonvolatiles were accumulated in flask A. Gases at the end of a run contained CO, CO_2, and N_2, in addition to the remaining reactants. The compounds formed were separated by ion-exchange and chromatography and then identified by R_f values and preparation of derivatives. When the discharge ran for a week, the total conversion of CH_4 to other organic compounds was about 50%.

To determine the direct products of the discharge, samples were withdrawn from the U-tube. The concentrations of NH_3, HCN, aldehydes, and amino acids, as a function of time, are shown in Fig. 11.2. Miller showed that an aqueous solution containing NH_3, HCN, HCHO, CH_3CHO, and CH_3CH_2CHO when boiled in the apparatus for a week with no discharge

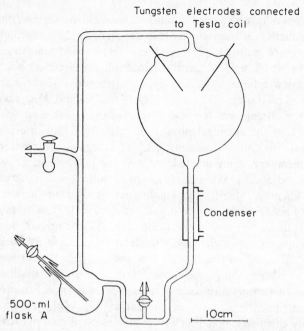

Tungsten electrodes connected
to Tesla coil

Condenser

500-ml
flask A

10cm

Fig. 11.1 Spark discharge apparatus used by Miller in his experiments on the abiotic synthesis of amino acids [52].

produced carboxylic and amino acids. Presumably, amino- and hydroxy-nitriles formed in solution from HCN, aldehydes, and NH_3 and then hydrolyzed to acids. In the discharge HCN would have formed from the reaction of active nitrogen species with CH_4 (or CH_x produced from CH_4), HCHO from the reaction of CH_4 or CH_x with H_2O or active oxygen species produced from H_2O, and CH_3CHO could have been formed from an insertion reaction between CH_2 and HCHO. Thus the simple species or molecules produced in the discharge react downstream in the solution to produce the more complex molecules found.

To synthesize those compounds containing one or more carbons, CH_4 does not have to be present initially. Abelson [54, 55] produced the same spectrum of products, starting with CO or CO_2, as long as the conditions in the gas were reducing, that is, H_2 was also present in excess.

Before considering the nature of discharges in detail, let us look at another example. Figure 11.3 shows a reactor in which gas is contained in the annular space between two cylindrical glass (or quartz) tubes. Electrodes are on the inside of the inner tube and the outside of the outer tube. This is a so-called ozonizer or concentric-tube reactor. Lunt [56] and Epple and Apt [57] showed that $H_2 + CO$ and $H_2 + CO_2$ react in this apparatus to give CH_4 in high

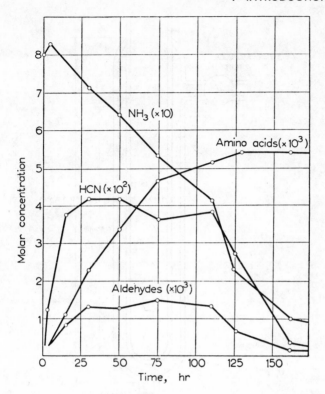

Fig. 11.2 Concentrations of ammonia, hydrogen cyanide, and aldehydes in the U-tube, and amino acids in the 500-ml flask, while sparking a mixture of methane, ammonia, water, and hydrogen in the apparatus of Fig. 11.1.

yield, when using high-voltage radiofrequency alternating current (2 to 110 MHz) to produce the discharge. Water is also a product, but acetylene, polymers, and oxygenated compounds are not formed in a batch reactor at pressures as high as 300 torr. It is most unusual that methane is formed in the discharge but acetylene and other hydrocarbons are not, even when the discharge is maintained for several minutes. As we shall see later, for other conditions, it is impossible to have CH_4 in a discharge without converting it to mixtures of C_2H_2, C_2H_4, and C_2H_6.

To summarize, organic syntheses can be carried out in discharges, but in many cases the reactions are not specific, mixtures of products are formed, the yield of a particular compound may be low, and polymers and tars are often produced. However, as we have seen from the $H_2 + CO \rightarrow CH_4 + H_2O$ reaction, a specific organic compound can be produced in good yield under the appropriate conditions. In the following discussion our attention is

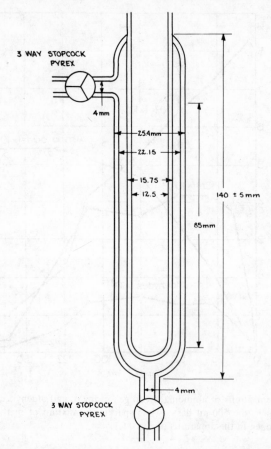

Fig. 11.3 Concentric-tube reactor used by Epple and Apt [57]. Electrodes are positioned along the inside wall of the inner tube and the outside wall of the outer tube.

focused on certain crucial problems including (1) the difficulty of characterizing discharge conditions, (2) the determination of the important variables controlling the reactions, (3) the mechanisms of the formation of the products, and (4) the methods for producing the desired specific compounds selectively in high yields.

2 DISCHARGE EQUIPMENT

Types of Discharges

Before describing further organic reactions in discharges, we must consider the processes responsible for initiating and maintaining discharges. For many years physicists and engineers have studied gas discharges in great detail and there are many recent books and reviews on the subject [58–72].

Glow, Corona, and Arc Discharges

Figure 11.4 shows a simple type of discharge tube with two metal electrodes

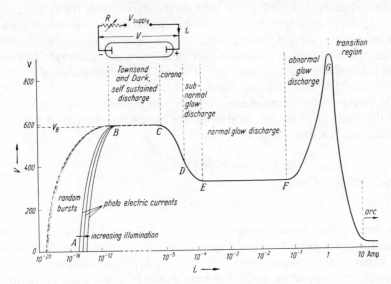

Fig. 11.4   The dependence of potential upon current for various kinds of discharges [58] The numerical values apply approximately to discharges in neon at $p = 1$ mm in a tube 50 cm long, with flat copper electrodes of area 10 cm². In some gases the curve shows a slight maximum in the region BCD.

sealed into a glass tube a few centimeters in diameter [58]. If a small dc voltage V is applied to the electrodes, and the gas in the tube is at a pressure of a few torr, a very low current I ($\sim 10^{-15}$ A) flows, owing to the presence of very low concentrations of electrons and ions. These arise from the action of ultraviolet and cosmic radiation and background radioactivity on both the gas and the electrodes. If V is increased, I increases very rapidly to a value of the order of 10^{-10} to 10^{-6} A (region BC, Fig. 11.4), determined by the resistance R in the external electrical circuit and is independent of any external source of ionization. There is now a self-sustained discharge in the gas. The voltage at which this occurs is called the minimum sparking or breakdown voltage V_B. For a particular gas V_B is a function of $p \times d$ (spark parameter), where p is the gas pressure and d the interelectrode distance.

In a self-sustained discharge, each electron that leaves the cathode is accelerated toward the anode by the electrical field and acquires kinetic energy from the field. As a result of the passage of electrons through the gas, electron-molecule collisions produce excited molecules and ions. Some excited molecules radiate photons which strike the cathode and release additional electrons. Positively charged ions formed in the gas are accelerated toward the cathode, strike it, and release electrons. If at least one new electron is formed at the cathode for each electron transferred from the cathode to the anode, the process repeats itself and the discharge becomes self-sustaining. As long as the current flowing is very small, little light is emitted from the discharge; therefore, it is called a dark or a Townsend discharge; Townsend was the first to propose a quantitative theory for the ionization of gas molecules caused by collision with electrons [62, 66].

If, in the discharge, an electron creates α new electrons in a path of 1 cm (in the direction of the electrical field), the increase in electrons produced by n electrons in a distance dx is

$$dn = \alpha n dx,$$

which integrates to

$$n = n_0 \exp (\alpha x),$$

where n_0 is the electron concentration at $x = 0$ and n is the electron concentration at a distance x from the cathode. The quantity α is called the first Townsend ionization coefficient. For any gas α is proportional to the pressure at constant temperature, and it has been shown [62] that α/p is a function of E/p, where E is the electric field strength (in volts per centimeter). α/p has been measured experimentally as a function of E/p for many gases [61, 65, 70]. Actually, as Phelps [72] has discussed, it would be better to characterize gas discharges by use of the parameter E/N, where N is the total gas density. He cites several references in which the E/N parameter has been used to compare measurements of the rate coefficients for the ionization of gaseous atoms and molecules by electron impact. It is very probable that E/p or E/N is one of the more important variables controlling the rates of chemical reactions in discharges, but there is no general agreement on this. It is unfortunate that in most cases this important variable has not been measured by chemists.

Referring to Fig. 11.4, if the current is allowed to increase to about 10^{-4} A or higher, two effects are observed: (1) the discharge becomes faintly visible with light and dark spaces arranged along the tube in a characteristic manner (this is discussed in more detail later) and (2) the voltage across the electrodes drops considerably to point E. The region EF between 10^{-4} and 10^{-1} A, is called the normal glow discharge region.

In practice it is not necessary to go through the above process to obtain a glow discharge. If a voltage $V > V_B$ is applied across the electrodes, the first random electron produced near the cathode will start a self-sustained discharge. (Often, the action of a Tesla coil is used to "start" the discharge.) The process described by the curve *ABCDE* takes place in a fraction of a second, until the current rises to a value satisfying the equation

$$V_{\text{discharge}} + IR = V_{\text{supply}}.$$

The voltage needed to start the glow discharge is higher than that needed to maintain it (the maintenance or glow discharge potential V_g); once the discharge has been started, the voltage may be decreased.

Current values intermediate between those in a dark discharge and a glow discharge produce the so-called corona discharge shown in portion *CD* of the curve in Fig. 11.4. This term is usually limited to a discharge in which at least one of the electrodes is a thin wire or point. Because of the high voltage gradient near a wire or any metal surface with a small radius of curvature, the discharge becomes intense enough to glow, at least over that portion of the interelectrode distance near the wire or point surface. The term corona is derived from the French word *couronne*, literally *crown*, which typifies one of the forms observed [64].

If the current is allowed to increase above about 10^{-4}A the voltage remains constant, even when the current increases by two to three orders of magnitude. In a normal glow discharge, the cathode remains near the temperature of the surroundings; therefore the discharge is called a cold-cathode discharge. As the current is increased, the discharge covers more of the cathode. When the discharge covers the whole cathode and the current is further increased, the potential drop across the discharge rises considerably, as shown in the abnormal (or anomalous) glow discharge region (*FG*). A still further increase in current causes the voltage to rise to a maximum and then to fall to a very low value, the arc discharge region. Here, processes such as heating of the gas and the electrodes (which now emit electrons thermionically) become important. Cobine presents a good discussion of the glow-to-arc transition [59].

In an arc discharge gas temperatures can reach several thousand degrees Kelvin, particularly at gas pressures near atmospheric. At these temperatures thermal dissociation of the gas molecules has an important influence on reactions occurring in the arc. Therefore an arc discharge is sometimes referred to as a "disruptive" discharge, compared to the low-temperature discharges such as corona and glow, which are called "nondisruptive" discharges. The latter are sometimes also called "silent" discharges to distinguish them from the "noisy" types of discharges such as the passage of a spark through air at atmospheric pressure. A spark discharge is also an unstable and discontinuous, on-off, form of discharge.

AC Discharges

With low-frequency alternating current, for example, 60 Hz, the processes in a glow discharge generated between electrodes are essentially the same as for the dc discharge, except that breakdown must take place again at the beginning of each half-cycle of current. Since the ionization in the discharge path has time to reach a low level before the voltage has time to build up in the reverse direction, the discharge is in effect extinguished at zero current and restarted as the current builds up again. At these low frequencies the discharge conditions adjust themselves at times much less than one half-period. However, as the frequency is increased, the state of the discharge changes little during a half-cycle, and the degree of ionization of the gas remains nearly constant. Thus a discharge between electrodes can be initiated by either a dc or an ac voltage.

It is also possible to have a discharge confined between two dielectric (insulating) surfaces, for instance, glass, as long as high-voltage alternating current is used to generate the discharge. This type of discharge, in which the gas is not in contact with the metal electrodes, is commonly referred to as an "electrodeless" discharge.

In any self-sustained discharge the rate of electron production from ionizations induced by electron-molecule collision must be equal to the rate of electron loss. Electron loss processes other than at the electrodes include diffusion of electrons and ions to the walls where they recombine, electron-ion recombination in the gas phase, or attachment of electrons to neutral molecules to produce molecule-anions. A high-frequency electrodeless discharge is thus often referred to as a "diffusion-controlled" discharge.

Discharge Reactors

Many types of reactors have been used to carry out chemical reactions in gas discharges. It seems that there are almost as many different reactor designs as there are workers in the field. Here, we classify reactors into six basic types and are concerned only with low-temperature reactors. The question of temperature in a discharge is covered more fully later; for the moment, by "low-temperature" we mean a discharge in which the bulk gas temperature is from a few hundred degrees above ambient to not more than 1000°C. By comparison, in an arc discharge or plasma jet, temperatures are usually several thousand degrees Celsius and the reactions that occur are essentially thermal. Low-temperature discharge reactors are usually constructed of glass, 96% silica glass (Vycor), or quartz. Complete descriptions of reactors and ancillary equipment can be found in Refs. 15–17, 22–25, 28, 29, 33, 44–47a, and 73.

Various reactors may be distinguished as follows: (1) whether or not electrodes are in contact with the discharge and, if they are, the geometrical arrangement of these electrodes; (2) the frequency of electrical power used to generate the discharge, that is, direct current, low-frequency alternating current (50 Hz to approximately 10 kHz), radiofrequency (200 kHz to approximately 150 MHz), or microwave (approximately 150 MHz to approximately 3000 MHz). Unfortunately, little attention has been devoted to the effect of reactor design or different frequencies upon reactions or compound formation. However, the frequency of the electrical power generator used often determines other characteristics of the reactor and is therefore a criterion for differentiating between reactor systems. Much work needs to be done to compare reactors and frequencies to determine in detail how they affect a given reaction. Spedding [29], Flinn and Goldberger [44], Thornton [45, 46], and Hesp and Rigby [74] have discussed this matter.

There is an additional problem in comparing reactors. Very little work has been done on the effect that various fundamental physical and chemical parameters have on the discharge reaction. Phelps [72] states in his review: "Combinations of the experimental parameters of electric field strength, frequency, gas density, container dimension, fractional ionization, and duration of applied voltage can be used to relate experimental data for electrical breakdown and for steady state discharges in simple gases over a wide range of these parameters. It is important that studies of the chemical effects of electrical discharges make use of these combinations of parameters and discover the additional parameters appropriate to the chemical aspects of the discharges." In almost all cases reported, this has not been done.

Reactor with Plane Parallel Electrodes. Glow Discharge Reactor

Figure 11.4 shows a schematic diagram of this type of reactor with a dc power supply. Jolly [24] discusses dc and ac discharge circuits. The reactor is simply a glass tube, often cylindrical, with metal electrodes sealed through the glass walls, and containing gas at subatmospheric pressure. (Gas discharge reactors are often operated at low pressures, ~1 to 100 torr, but they can operate at pressures up to atmospheric.) Radiofrequency (rf) power can also be used to generate a discharge between electrodes [75].

Usually, a reactor with electrodes is operated in the glow discharge region of the current-voltage curve (Fig. 11.4) and because of this is referred to as a glow discharge reactor. However, the same reactor can be operated at higher current densities as an arc discharge.

Figure 11.5 shows a low-frequency power supply and glow discharge tube used by Shaw [73]. This particular design is also known as a Wood's tube because he used it as a source of H-atoms by dissociation of H_2 [76]. Discharge reactors are used very frequently in gas flow systems as a source of atoms and

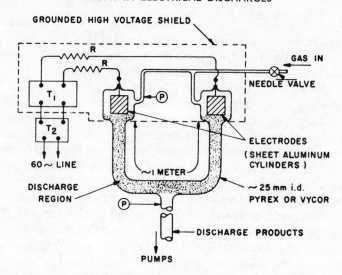

Fig. 11.5 Low-frequency discharge tube and power supply [73]. *P*, pressure gauge; *R*, current-limiting resistors; T_1, high-voltage transformer; T_2, adjustable autotransformer.

free radicals [31, 73, 77], whose subsequent reactions with various compounds are studied downstream from the discharge.

A dc (cold-cathode) glow discharge is not uniform; that is, the space between the cathode and the anode consists of several luminous and dark regions shown schematically in Fig. 11.6 [62]. (See also Refs. 58, 59, and 66.) The large change in voltage near the cathode, called the cathode fall, is responsible for the acceleration of the positively charged ions as they approach the cathode. These energetic ions, on striking the cathode, release the electrons needed to sustain the discharge. The positive column region of the discharge, where the field strength is constant, is the most uniform part of the discharge and the most amenable to physical characterization.

Mass spectrometric analysis of ions in several glow discharge systems shows that the concentrations of various positive ions varies from region to region in the discharge. This is interesting because there is evidence that the rate of a chemical reaction is different in the different regions of the dc glow discharge [78–81]. An ac-operated glow discharge reactor has been described [82a] in which the positive column of the glow discharge between aluminum electrodes is confined primarily to the reaction chamber, and thus presumably the discharge is kept uniform.

In his study of the reaction of methane, Tickner [81] describes a glass reactor (Fig. 11.7) containing stainless steel electrodes, one of which is movable. This reactor is cooled in a liquid N_2 bath, a procedure often used to isolate the primary products of a discharge reaction and to avoid secondary

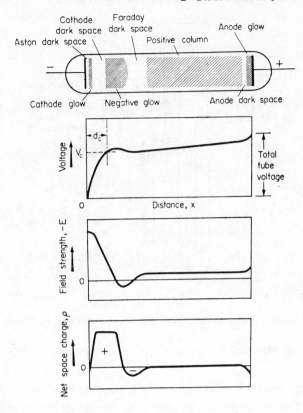

Fig. 11.6 Various characteristics of a glow discharge at low pressure as shown by Howatson [62].

reactions. Also, in some cases the product yield is increased by cooling the reactor. Streng et al. [82b] also describe a cooled reactor with copper electrodes.

Kraaijveld and Waterman [83] describe an apparatus used for studying the reactions of methane, benzene, and alkylbenzenes in a high-voltage ac discharge in which an inert gas (in this case, N_2) flows over the aluminum electrodes. They believed that this would eliminate any effects attributable to the metallic nature of the electrode surfaces. The possible catalytic nature of the electrode surfaces is always difficult to assess in a reactor and is one of the reasons for the preference shown by many workers for electrodeless reactors in which there are no metal electrodes in contact with the discharge. Shaw [73] suggests that in the absence of metal electrodes, which effect the recombination of radicals, the yield of radicals from a discharge is increased. Sputtering [66, 84], in which ionic bombardment of the electrodes causes

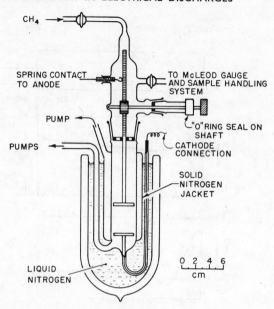

Fig. 11.7   Liquid nitrogen-cooled glow discharge reactor used by Tickner [81].

evaporation of the metal, also leads to contamination of the discharge products.

Reactor with Point or Thin-Wire Electrodes. Corona Reactor

Figure 11.1 shows an apparatus employing "point" electrodes in which the electrical field (in volts per centimeter) is very high in the vicinity of a point or a thin wire. Because of the high voltage gradient near a surface with a small radius of curvature, breakdown occurs more readily from a point or wire than from a planar electrode. A discharge from a point or wire is called a corona discharge [64] and, in general, exists at current densities lower than for a glow discharge (see Fig. 11.4).

Figure 11.8 shows a system used by Ranney and O'Connor [85] to study the reaction of benzene. The electrode in contact with the gas is a threaded steel rod running down the center of the apparatus. A second electrode of coiled copper tubing is on the outside of the reactor and is separated from the gas by a glass dielectric (insulating) layer. The discharge tends to occur as a corona from the sharp edges of the threaded rod. Since there is a dielectric between the outer electrode and the gas, an apparatus of this type is called a semicorona reactor. Usually, in a semicorona reactor the inner electrode is a thin wire. McTaggart [15] describes examples of this type of reactor. Corona and semicorona reactors can be run with dc [64], low-frequency ac [85], or radiofrequency [49] power.

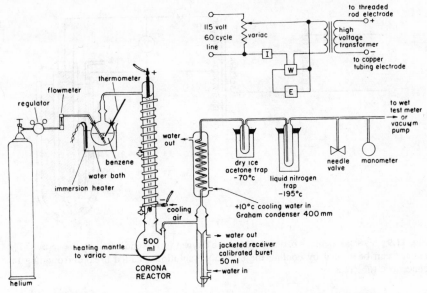

Fig. 11.8   Reactor flow system used by Ranney and O'Connor [85].

High-Voltage, Electrodeless, Concentric-Tube Reactor. Ozonizer Reactor

A reactor in which the gas is confined to the annular space between two concentric glass (dielectric) cylinders is usually referred to as an ozonizer, regardless of the reaction being carried out in it. Figure 11.9 shows a Siemens ozonizer used for the continuous production of ozone in a flowing stream of oxygen at atmospheric pressure. Quite often, the discharge in an ozonizer is referred to as a silent electric discharge, a barrier discharge, or a glow discharge. In this type of reactor, the gas does not contact electrodes but is between electrically insulating surfaces. A voltage of at least several kilovolts ac is used to maintain the discharge. It would be more appropriate and in this chapter we shall call this a high-voltage, electrodeless, concentric-tube reactor rather than an ozonizer. In addition, ozone can be produced in other types of reactors, including some in which metal electrodes contact the gas. McTaggart [15] describes several examples. In concentric-tube reactors the electrodes act as a capacitor in the electrical circuit. Such capacitively coupled discharges are also called polarization discharges, since the electrical field in the discharge is caused by oscillating electrostatic charges at the dielectric barrier covering each electrode.

Figure 11.3 shows a concentric-tube reactor designed for batch operation, in which rf (2- to 110-MHz) power is supplied to metal electrodes located inside of the inner tube and outside of the outer tube. Golesworthy and Shaw

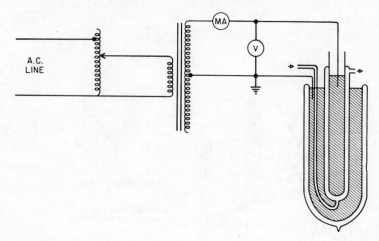

Fig. 11.9 Typical Siemens ozonizer [24]. The oxygen flow is indicated by the arrows. The reactor can be cooled by cooling the electrolyte solution (shaded area) surrounding the concentric-tube reactor.

[43, 86] describe a related apparatus having eight concentric-tube reactors in parallel capable of handling 500 gm of starting material in a continuous operation lasting days.

Although many chemical reactions have been carried out in concentric-tube reactors using low-frequency ac power, the nature of the discharge under these conditions is still open to question. In a recent summary of his work, concerned primarily with the production of ozone, Suzuki discusses the nature of the discharge in concentric-tube reactors [87]. Although the discharge zone between the deilectric barriers appears uniform and faintly luminous, the actual discharge phenomenon is not uniform. The discharge actually consists of an ensemble of small discharges occurring from small points on one surface to small points on the opposite surface. The site of reaction is inside these "columns of discharge," each of which is approximately 1 mm in diameter. Some of the chemical species, which are products of electron-molecule collisions or secondary reactions, may diffuse outside of the columns to an electron-free zone where they undergo further reaction(s). Normally, there are three kinds of oscillatory current within the discharge: (1) the basic 50-Hz alternating current which maintains the discharge; (2) a high-frequency current of the order of a few kilohertz which is equal to the number of pulses mentioned above; and (3) an oscillation current of hundreds of kilohertz. According to Suzuki, the latter is the one mainly responsible for reactions in the discharge.

A recent paper by Aiba and Freeman [88a] discusses in detail the chemical, energetic, and electrical characteristics of a concentric-tube reactor used for both 60 Hz and rf (1 to 20 MHz) operation in oxygen. In the high-frequency operation in which behavior of the discharge is dominated by a steady-state accumulation of excess positive ions in the gap, the best energy efficiency is several orders of magnitude lower than at low frequencies. A simple model, assuming minimization of the rate of production of entropy, relating the electrical parameters and the observed contraction of the discharge accounts for this difference in chemical efficiency. McInally [88b] also discusses the mechanism of ozone formation in a concentric-tube reactor.

Electrodeless Reactors Using High-Frequency Power. Radiofrequency Reactor

As pointed out in the previous sections, rf power can be used to generate discharges between plane parallel or point electrodes, that is, in glow discharge or corona reactors. It can also be used in capacitively coupled, electrodeless, concentric-tube reactors [56]. Shaw [73] states that at radiofrequencies both the power required for breakdown and that required to sustain the discharge are lower than that required for dc or low-frequency ac operation because at high frequencies losses of electrons and ions to electrodes are reduced to a negligible amount relative to the losses that occur at low frequencies.

Figure 11.10 shows the two most common types of reactors employing rf

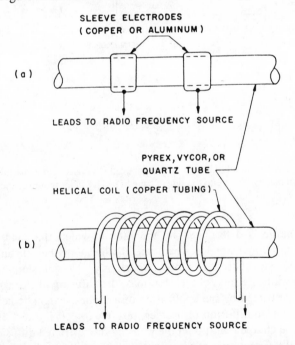

Fig. 11.10 Typical coupling arrangements for use with rf discharge reactors [73].

power. The top of the diagram shows an example of capacitive coupling and the bottom is an example of inductive coupling (also referred to as a ring discharge [61]). The simple design of electrodeless reactors is one of their major advantages. Rf reactors are being used more and more for chemical studies and good discussions of rf reactors and power supplies can be found in McTaggart [15], Hollahan [28], and Reed [47a].

F. Swift [89] describes an rf power generator and vacuum system for studying the reaction of CCl_4. This article contains striking color photographs of the discharge and various discharge products condensed in cold traps. A water-cooled rf reactor is described by Prodell and Kusch [90].

One interesting modification of the rf reactor is the magnetically focused rf discharge glow system [91] shown in Fig. 11.11. The power necessary to

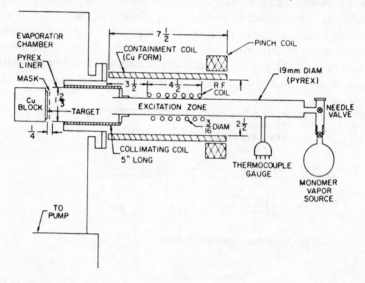

Fig. 11.11 Schematic cross-sectional diagram of magnetically focused glow discharge system. Apparatus shown incorporated into the side of a metal bell jar of a vacuum evaporation system [91].

maintain an rf discharge is determined by the rate at which the charged particles (electrons and ions) are lost from the discharge, either through recombination in the gas phase or, more importantly, by diffusion and recombination at the walls. Because of their low mass the diffusion of electrons to the walls is easily restricted by the application of a modest magnetic field. However, the constraint on diffusion of heavier, positive ions is indirect and arises from the positive charge built up on the walls by the restricted diffusion of electrons to the walls. The nature of the discharge is thus altered drastically by the magnetic field and the discharge may be maintained at pressures and rf field intensities below those that are otherwise possible. In addition, Connell and Gregor [91] believe that at low power levels, the low-lying excited states and particularly the lowest-energy process leading to ionization or excitation should be preferred. This amounts to the exclusion of high-energy processes which tend to give rise to a greater variety of reaction products.

Connell and Gregor used the magnetic focusing technique to deposit thin polymer insulating films on solid surfaces downstream from the discharge. Advantages of magnetic focusing are shown by the following results. When operating at pressures of 20 to 100 μ of divinylbenzene vapor, a pale blue discharge was obtained with the magnetic field on, and a tough, coherent, colorless, transparent polymer film formed on the substrate. At lower values of the magnetic field and higher rf power (needed to sustain the discharge), a bright white arclike discharge was obtained, which was characterized by the generation of a great deal of heat, consumption of comparatively large quantities of monomer vapor, and formation of a thick brownish deposit on all adjacent surfaces; little or no film was formed at the cooled substrate surface downstream from the discharge.

This technique has also been used by Davidse and Maissel [92–94] to deposit various inorganic insulator films on substrates. Rony [95] used a magnetic field to increase the efficiency of production of H-atoms and O-atoms in a microwave-generated discharge. Discussions of the effect of a magnetic field on a discharge appear in several textbooks [62, 63, 68].

Electrodeless Reactors Using Microwave Power. Microwave Reactor

Electrical energy in the microwave frequency range can be transferred to electrons in a partially ionized gas contained within a glass or quartz tube. These energetic electrons in turn excite, dissociate, and ionize the gas molecules. Thus microwave energy provides another (but no fundamentally different) means of generating and maintaining an electrodeless discharge. Microwaves, however, instead of being carried by wires, must be transmitted via coaxial cables or metallic waveguides. McTaggart presents a good discussion of microwave power sources and apparatus [15].

A simple way to generate a discharge with microwave energy, though not the most efficient from the standpoint of power utilization, is to place the reactor tube inside a waveguide, as shown in Fig. 11.12 [73]. The waveguide, which carries the microwave energy from the generator to the point where it will be used, propagates the energy in the form of an electromagnetic wave "filling" the waveguide. In order to carry this radiation efficiently, the dimension of the waveguide should be $\sim 0.7\ \lambda$, where λ is the wavelength of the radiation. For the commonly used frequency of 2450 MHz, the long dimension of the waveguide is approximately 10 cm. The glass or quartz walls of the

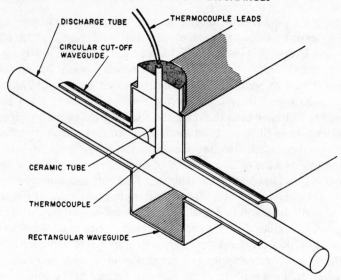

Fig. 11.12   Cut-away sketch showing arrangement of discharge tube in microwave waveguide [73]. The reactor tube can be cooled by forcing cool air into the circular waveguides.

reactor tube are essentially transparent to microwave energy; therefore the reactor is electrodeless since no metal electrodes are in the gas.

Figure 11.13 shows a complete microwave reactor system [96] using a tapered waveguide resonator [97] which contains a slotted opening into which the reactor tube is positioned. A waveguide resonator focuses microwave

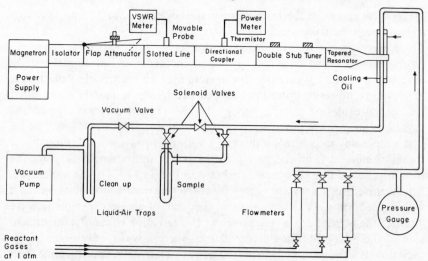

Fig. 11.13   Microwave reactor system used by Baddour and Dundas [96].

energy more efficiently than would a straight waveguide; thus power is more efficiently coupled to the gas in the reactor. Bennett et al. [98] describe a microwave waveguide reactor system employing silica or alumina reactor tubes.

Figure 11.14 shows a cavity resonator which handles up to 2.5 kW of microwave energy at 2450 MHz [99]. This resonator has one feature not common to other cavity resonators, namely, the strength of the E-field can be

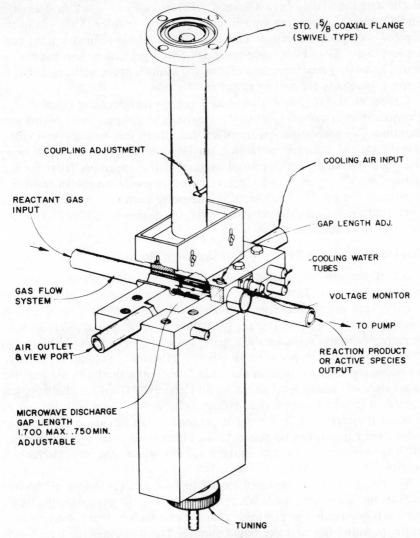

Fig. 11.14 Microwave cavity resonator designed by Varian [99].

measured inside the resonator. Other types of cavity resonators [100] use coaxial cables to transfer power from the microwave generator to the reactor. Another means of transferring microwave energy to gases is described by Zacha et al. [101] and consists of an antenna and reflector combination connected to a coaxial cable inside of which is located the reactor tube. Cylindrical metal cavities, of the order of 3 in. in diameter, through which the reactor tube passes are also used to focus microwave energy (see Ref. [15]). Bache and Lisk [102] discuss several different types of microwave cavities and a means of improving the efficiency of energy transfer to the gas in the tapered waveguide resonator. This is useful since this resonator is so convenient to use. Since microwave-generated discharges tend to heat the reactor walls, because of recombination of ions and radicals at the walls, most cavity resonators require air cooling of the reactor tube.

Callear et al. [103] have described a microwave generator coupled to a cavity capable of delivering into a gas a pulse of 80 kW peak power of 10 μsec duration. The absorption spectra of excited atoms, free radicals, and vibrationally excited diatomic molecules can be observed during and following the pulse discharge. An improved version of the apparatus [104] gives a pulse of 400 kW power for 3.5 μsec. A similar apparatus, capable of delivering a pulse of 300 kW for 5 μsec used a microwave horn to focus the radiation onto a tube containing the gas [105]; here, the discharge was confined to the gas near the walls of the tube.

Gas-Liquid Discharge Reactor (Glow Discharge Electrolysis)

All of the reactors discussed above have been used primarily for the reactions of gases. Liquids and solutions can also react with the active species from a gas discharge through a technique called glow discharge electrolysis. Hickling and Ingram [106] have reviewed this field extensively. A more descriptive term for the apparatus (see Fig. 11.15) would be to call it a gas-liquid discharge reactor. In this apparatus a dc discharge is passed to a conducting solution from an electrode (usually the anode) in the gas; the other electrode (cathode) is in the liquid electrolyte. Once the discharge has started, it can be maintained at voltages above 500 V and with the gas at reduced pressure, usually the vapor pressure of the liquid. In this manner substantial currents can be passed to the liquid surface. Hough and Denaro [107] have designed a current regulator for use in glow discharge electrolysis studies.

The chemical effects produced appear to be a result primarily of the free radicals formed in the liquid. When the anode is in the gas space, the liquid surface is bombarded by positively charged gaseous ions that are accelerated in the potential fall near the liquid surface. The ions enter the liquid with energies of the order of 100 eV. These energetic ions excite and dissociate

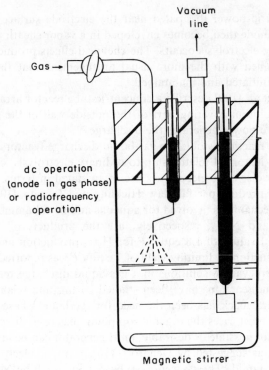

Fig. 11.15 Glow discharge electrolysis or gas-liquid discharge reactor, as shown by Hickling and Ingram [106].

the solvent molecules and produce large concentrations of free radicals, H and OH, for example, in water. Hickling and Ingram compare the chemical effects of glow discharge electrolysis with those occurring in the radiolysis of solutions. Although the energies of the bombarding ions in glow discharge electrolysis are extremely low per particle compared with any type of ionizing radiation, the dose rate is much greater.

If the electrode in the gas space is the cathode, most of the voltage drop occurs near the cathode with only a relatively small potential drop occurring near the liquid surface. Chemical effects produced in the solution with this arrangement are small. In the process the cathode becomes hot and may melt.

Alternating current can also be used for glow discharge electrolysis, but most of the reaction probably occurs only during the half-cycles in which the electrode above the surface is positive.

Glow discharge electrolysis can be carried out at atmospheric pressure by a technique termed "contact glow discharge electrolysis" [108]. Here, the anode, a thin wire, is immersed in the electrolyte. On passing a small current, conventional electrolysis occurs. If the current is increased, a point is reached at which electric power dissipated near the electrode surface vaporizes the solvent. The anode then becomes enveloped in a vapor sheath through which glow discharge electrolysis occurs. The chemical effects produced are similar to those obtained with the more usual arrangement, but the discharge is more readily initiated and maintained.

Yokohata et al. [109] describe a concentric-tube reactor arranged horizontally with a solution covering part of the outside wall of the reactor. Here, high-voltage ac power generates the discharge.

Most of the reactions studied in gas-liquid discharge reactors are inorganic. Because of its historical relationship to ordinary electrolysis, efficiencies and yields of glow discharge electrolysis are often stated in terms of equivalents (or moles) of product per faraday. Hickling and Ingram [106] discuss the free-radical mechanisms involved for aqueous and liquid ammonia solutions, where H_2O_2 and N_2H_4, respectively, are the products of interest. They obtained initial values of 1.8 equiv/F for H_2O_2 production and 2.5 moles/F for N_2H_4 production. A limiting yield of 7 equiv/F was reported for oxidation of alkaline ferrocyanide solutions in a gas-liquid discharge reactor [110].

Some organic reactions have been studied by this and related techniques, but a major drawback has been the need for the liquid phase to contain an electrolyte. In most cases the organic compound has been dissolved in water. When this is not possible or desirable, an rf generator can be used to generate the discharge, as suggested by Denaro [111a]. Here, no electrolyte would be needed in the liquid. The concentric-tube reactor used by Yokohata [109] could probably be used as an rf-powered gas-liquid discharge reactor.

Power Measurements in a Discharge

The electrical power used to maintain a discharge is one of the important variables controlling the reactions in the discharge. The equipment and experiment should be designed from the beginning with power measurement in mind. Spedding [29] and Reynolds [111b] discuss power measurement in some detail.

For a dc discharge the power is equal to voltage × current, $P = VI$. For an ac discharge the instantaneous power varies periodically, since both the current and voltage vary periodically. Thus some sort of average power is what is measured. If the voltage and current both vary sinusoidally, power is usually taken as $P = V_{rms}I_{rms} \cos \varphi$, where the root-mean-square voltage, $V_{rms} = V_{max}/\sqrt{2}$, $I_{rms} = I_{max}/\sqrt{2}$, and $\cos \varphi$ is the power factor, where φ is the angle by which the current lags in phase behind the voltage. For instance, in a concentric-tube reactor in which the discharge is generated by a source of high-voltage alternating current, φ would have to be measured using an oscilloscope because of the capacitive nature of the reactor.

Sometimes, because of the nature of the discharge and/or the associated electrical circuit, the voltage and current wave forms are not sinusoidal. Here, one can measure power with a wattmeter, an instrument designed to measure the average power in the circuit, whatever the wave forms of voltage and current [112].

In their work on the reactions of CH_4 in an ac-generated anomalous glow discharge between graphite electrodes, Hesp et al. [113] showed by oscillographic measurements that while there was no phase shift between current and voltage both were distorted compared with the normal sine curve—indeed, the current wave form was triangular. Accordingly, since they measured current and voltage with separate instruments, they estimate that the true power was about 14% less than the product of voltage × current.

Fraser [114] gives a detailed discussion of the generation and measurement of audiofrequency power for chemical-electrical discharge processes involving ac discharges at higher frequencies.

For rf-generated discharges commercially available rf generators usually include an rf wattmeter to measure both the input power to the reactor and the power "reflected" back from the reactor resulting from any mismatch in impedance between the discharge reactor and the generator [28]. Thus the net power into the discharge is the difference between the input (forward) and the reflected power.

Another method of measuring power input to an rf discharge is to surround the reactor with a cooling jacket through which oil is circulated. From measurements of the temperature change of the oil and its flow rate, and knowledge of its specific heat, the power into the discharge can be approximated [115]. A discussion of the measurement of power for rf-generated arcs is given by Reed [47a], Beguin et al. [116], and Waller [117].

McTaggart [15] discusses the measurement of power in microwave-generated discharges. Here also, there are commercially available power meters that connect into either the waveguide or coaxial cable used to carry the microwave power from the generator to the resonator. Again, because of the impedance mismatch between the generator and the resonator the net power input to the discharge is the difference between the forward and the reflected power.

Safety and Discharge Reactors

In addition to the usual precautions needed in working with any electrical equipment, particularly high-voltage and high-amperage apparatus, there are other safety factors that must be considered with discharge reactors and power generators. Gas discharges are good sources of ultraviolet light and are used for this purpose in many applications [97, 118, 119a, 119b]. Thus if the reactor is made of Vycor or quartz, which is transparent to ultraviolet, some type of safety goggles should be worn when observing the discharge for any length of time.

The eye is also particularly sensitive to microwave radiation [120, 121] and great caution is needed when working with it since the harmful effects are irreversible. Table 11.1 briefly summarizes the biological effects of non-ionizing high-frequency radiation [120]. Hoffart [122] also discusses the biological effects:

"In general, the effects of electromagnetic radiation on living tissue have been thought to be primarily thermal. Although the eyes and testes are the

Table 11.1 Biological Effects of Nonionizing High-Frequency Radiation*

Frequency (MHz)	Wavelength (cm)	Type of Radiation	Site of Major Tissue Effects	Major Biological Effects
More than 10,000	Less than 3	Microwave	Skin	Skin surface acts as reflector or absorber with heating effects
10,000	3	Microwave	Skin	Skin heating with sensation of warmth
10,000 to 3,300	3 to 10	Microwave	Top layers of skin, lens of eye	Lens of eye particularly susceptible
10,000 to 1,000	3 to 30	Microwave	Lens of eye	Critical wavelength band for eye cataracts
1,200 to 150	25 to 200	Radiofrequency	Internal body organs	Damage to internal organs from overheating
Less than 150	Above 200			Body is transparent to waves above 200 cm †

* Adapted from *Microwave Radiation Hazards*, Bureau of Occupational Health, Technical Information Service, California State Department of Public Health, Berkeley, 1964.

† There is also the "pearl-chain" effect as described by Hoffart [122]; see the text.

most vulnerable parts of the human body, other parts which can be affected include the brain, nerves, skin, and muscles. The effects will vary, depending on the frequency and the intensity of the incident energy. The effects of electromagnetic radiation can be in the form of a mild heating of the skin or an internal organ to the other extreme of damage to the central nervous system . . . . However, on biological substances, such as those in man, radio-frequency radiation can cause other effects.

"One of the athermal effects is the 'Pearl-Chain' formation which occurs at approximately 21 MHz. Since this is a unique effect, it requires some explanation. The human body is composed of various tissues which may be considered as a transmission medium exhibiting the characteristics of a complex dielectric material. The cross section of the body mass can be considered to consist of two distinct layers and an interior central mass, all of which have different dielectric and conductance characteristics. Particles, suspended in a fluid whose dielectric constant is different from that of the particle, become electrically polarized when they are subjected to a high frequency alternating field. The result is that electrical charges appear on the particle boundaries. In effect, an electrical dipole is formed which is then influenced by the electric field so as to align with the field . . . . When the distance between particles is small and field strength is of sufficient magnitude, characteristic chains will form. These are called 'pearl-chain' formations, and can occur in the blood stream of man and mammals. An analogy is the pearl-chain formation of oil droplets on water when a dc magnetic field is applied."

For some time a safety limit of 10 mW/cm² has been proposed as the allowable exposure to microwave radiation [121]. However, there are other, lower, limits in effect [122]. Several electromagnetic radiation safety meters are commercially available [120, 123] to monitor the output of high-frequency equipment and the connectors and cavities where "leaks" may occur.

A recent symposium [124a] on "Radio and Microwave Radiations—Applications and Potential Hazards," included several papers on the biological effects of nonionizing radiation and developments in radiation hazard monitors. The problem has also been discussed by Gross [124b] and by Cade [125].

Additional precautions must be observed with rf or microwave equipment in the choice of frequencies. For industrial, scientific, and medical equipment, the U.S. Federal Communications Commission has allocated the following frequencies (in megahertz): 13.56, 27.12, 40.68, 915, 2450, 5800, and 22,125. Power generators that tend to "broadcast," particularly at high power levels, or the use of other frequencies may violate the regulations [126].

3 ELEMENTARY CHEMICAL PROCESSES IN GAS DISCHARGES

Electron-Molecule Collisions. Temperature in a Discharge

In a self-sustained electrical discharge, the free electrons produced by ionization of a small fraction of the gas molecules acquire energy from the applied electrical field and transfer it to the gas by electron-molecule collisions. The kinetic energy of the molecules is increased by elastic collisions, but excitation and ionization of the molecules also takes place owing to inelastic collisions. In an inelastic electron-molecule collision, a significant fraction of the energy of the electron is transferred to the molecule and results in an increase in the rotational, vibrational, or electronic energy of the molecule. The excited molecules may undergo dissociation, emit radiation, and drop back to a lower energy level, or they may transfer their excitation energy to other molecules via collision processes. Electron-atom, electron-molecule, and other types of collision processes have been studied for many years and reviewed extensively [30, 31, 67, 127–132a].

As a result of the elastic collision of an electron with a molecule, there is a very slight loss of energy by the electron and a small amount of momentum is transferred to the molecule. If there were no other types of collisions taking place (and this is not the case for any system of chemical interest), eventually a steady-state condition would exist in which the energy that the free electrons pick up from the electric field between collisions would be equal to the energy transferred from the electron to the much heavier particles through collision.

Fite [30] shows that under these conditions the mean energy of the electrons in the steady state is

$$\tfrac{1}{2}m(\bar{c})^2 \simeq \tfrac{1}{2}\sqrt{\frac{M}{m}}\, qE\lambda, \tag{11.1}$$

where m is the electron mass, $\bar{c}$ the mean speed of the electrons, M the mass of the gas molecule (or atom), q the electron charge, E the electric field strength, and λ the mean free path. (The mean free path is the average distance a particle travels in a gas between collisions; λ is inversely proportional to gas pressure.) Thus for electrons moving through a gas where $M = 30$ amu, $p = 0.25$ torr, and values of E are a few tenths of a volt per centimeter, electron energies are several electron volts. Translated into temperature, this comes to about $30,000°K$; the electrons are at a very high temperature. However, at low gas pressures up to a few torr, the temperature of the molecules in the gas does not increase more than several hundred degrees Celsius at most, and the discharge is described as a "low-temperature" discharge. The situation is not one of thermal equilibrium since the electrons are at a high temperature while the molecules are at a low temperature.

As the pressure in a discharge increases, the electron temperature decreases and the gas temperature increases, owing to more frequent electron-molecule collisions. Eventually, in an arc discharge at atmospheric pressure, the electrons and molecules (or excited species) are more or less in thermal equilibrium with each other at several thousand degrees Kelvin. Reed [47a] compares these "high" and "low" temperature discharges. (See also Section 10.)

Dissociation of Diatomic Molecules

The production of atoms from their diatomic molecules in electrical discharges can occur via the following processes:

1. Direct electron impact dissociation via initial formation of an electronically excited state with energy greater than the dissociation energy of the molecule, for example,

$$e^- + H_2 \rightarrow H_2{}^* + e^- \tag{11.2}$$

$$H_2{}^* \rightarrow H + H \tag{11.3}$$

2. Electron-ion recombination at the wall or in the gas phase, for example,

$$e^- + H_2{}^+ \rightarrow H + H \tag{11.4}$$

$$e^- + H_3{}^+ \rightarrow H_2 + H \tag{11.5}$$

3. Ion-molecule reactions, for example,

$$H_2{}^+ + H_2 \rightarrow H_3{}^+ + H \tag{11.6}$$

4. Neutral-neutral dissociation reactions between energetic metastable and neutral molecules.

The use of electrical discharges for the production of H-, N-, and O-atoms followed the discovery by Wood [76] that hydrogen at 0.2 to 1.0 torr could be largely dissociated into atoms in a low-frequency ac glow discharge. Recent workers have preferred electrodeless rf or microwave-generated discharges which can be operated at higher pressures [100, 132b, 182]. Also, in the absence of metal electrodes, which are effective for the recombination of radicals, the yield of atoms from a discharge is increased. No systematic studies have been made of the factors affecting the yield of atoms or radicals produced in an rf discharge, though a few studies have been made of the production in microwave discharges [73, 95].

Hydrogen and Deuterium

It has been reported that 60% dissociation of H_2 occurs in an rf-generated (9.7 MHz) discharge [133]. Complete dissociation is not to be expected as

10% or more of H_3^+ is found by mass spectrometry in the beam from such sources; these ions are produced by the ion-molecule reaction $H_2^+ + H_2 \rightarrow H_3^+ + H$ and require the presence of undissociated H_2. In a microwave-generated discharge, 90% dissociation of H_2 was obtained at a pressure of 0.5 torr with 100 W of power (3000 MHz) dissipated in the discharge and a flow rate of 10^{-5} mole per second [73]. Bak and Rastrup-Andersen [134] also discuss the dissociation of H_2 and D_2 in a microwave discharge. In contrast to the production of atomic O and active N_2, there is no evidence for the existence of H and H_2 in other reactive or metastable states downstream from a low-pressure H_2 discharge.

For H_2 in a microwave discharge, the yield of atoms is influenced by pressure, flow rate, and power [73, 132b]. A discharge can be maintained in H_2 at pressures as high as 450 torr [100]. (See also ref. 182.) Rony [95] reports an improvement in atom production in a very low pressure microwave discharge by the use of an external magnetic field. Lunt [135] discusses in detail several papers dealing with the production of H-atoms and shows that the efficiency with which energy is used to dissociate H_2 in a discharge has a limit of about 0.045 molecule H_2 dissociated per electronvolt, or 3.4 gram-atoms H per kilowatt-hour. Bergh [136] reviews the production of atomic hydrogen and its use as a reducing agent, particularly for inorganic systems.

Many investigators have obtained an increase in the production of H-atoms by the addition of small quantities of impurities, such as H_2O or O_2, or by coating the walls downstream from the discharge with substances such as syrupy H_3PO_4 or Dri-Film, a mixture of dimethylchlorosilane and methyl-dichlorosilane [31, 73, 136–138]. The H-atom yield downstream from a discharge can be increased by factors of 10 or so when "dry" H_2 (passed through a liquid N_2 trap) is changed to H_2 containing 0.1 to 0.3% H_2O. Kaufman [31] has concluded, on the basis of calculating the rate of dissociation of H_2 in a discharge as compared with the mechanisms by which H-atoms are "lost" in the discharge, for example, recombination, that the net dissociation of H_2 is mainly controlled by surface recombination of H-atoms and that the effect of small quantities of added H_2O or O_2 must be through their influence on the surface in the discharge, that is, poisoning of the wall, which lowers the efficiency of the surface recombination, hence greatly increases the yield of atoms.

Oxygen

As with the production of H-atoms, the production of O-atoms has been found to be greatly influenced by small amounts of added impurities such as N_2, NO, N_2O, or H_2 [139, 140]. Very pure O_2 gave only 0.6% atoms, but when 0.01 to 0.05% of N_2, NO, or N_2O was added, O-atom production rose by about 40 atoms of O for each atom of N added. Addition of H_2 produced

160 to 200 O-atoms for each added H_2 molecule. Kaufman [31] concluded that the O-atom yield downstream from the discharge is also principally controlled by surface recombination in the discharge and that the large "catalytic" effect of adding H_2 is probably attributable to the effects of H_2 on the wall. But the similar effects of nitrogen compounds are not easily understandable, as such compounds should not be strongly adsorbed on the surface.

Unlike the dissociation of H_2, oxygen gives rise to various excited species when passed through a discharge. Calorimetric [141], spectroscopic [142], and mass spectrometric studies [143, 144] of electrically discharged oxygen have shown that the gas stream contains about 10 to 20% of $O_2(^1\Delta_g)$, the first excited electronic state of O_2, one form of so-called "singlet" oxygen, and about 0.1% of $O_2(^1\Sigma_g^+)$, the next higher excited electronic state of O_2. Ogryzlo and co-workers [145–147] have studied the reactions and emission spectra of these excited species. $O_2(^1\Delta_g)$ is an unusual electronically excited molecule because of its very long radiative lifetime [147, 148] and its relative immunity to collisional deactivation. $O_2(^1\Sigma_g^+)$, however, is rapidly quenched (by H_2O, for example) back to the ground state $O_2(^3\Sigma_g^-)$. Kaplan and Kelleher [149a] describe an apparatus in which $O_2(^1\Delta_g)$ is the only active species downstream from a microwave discharge.

Small amounts of ozone are also present in electrically discharged oxygen, formed mainly via the reactions

$$O + O_2 + O_2 \rightarrow O_3 + O_2 \tag{11.7}$$

$$O + O_3 \rightarrow O_2 + O_2 \tag{11.8}$$

and the O_3 concentration downstream from a discharge in oxygen reaches a maximum at a certain residence time [149b]. The occurrence of a maximum rather than a steady-state O_3 concentration was attributed to the presence of excited O_2^* molecules capable of dissociating O_3 [150],

$$O_3 + O_2^* \rightarrow O_2 + O_2 + O \tag{11.9}$$

Johnston [151] has recently reviewed the subject in detail, in particular the gas phase reaction kinetics of the neutral oxygen species.

Nitrogen

When molecular nitrogen is subjected to an electrical discharge, a characteristic yellow "nitrogen afterglow" is produced. This is attributed to the formation of "active nitrogen," which contains ground state atoms, excited atoms, and vibrationally and electronically excited molecules. Theories of active nitrogen and its chemical reactivity have been summarized by Mannella [152] and discussed in great detail by Wright and Winkler [18]. N_2 is dissociated less efficiently than H_2 or O_2 in glow discharges (McCarthy [132b] gives a figure of 0.58 gram-atom N/kW-hr), but the N-atom yield is also greatly increased by addition of small amounts of impurities. There is evidence that the presence of H_2O [153, 154], or O_2, NO, or SF_6 [155], may facilitate the dissociation process of N_2 in a discharge, although for the moment this observation can be understood only in terms of surface poisoning in the discharge.

The species that may be present in active nitrogen in significant concentrations are ground state $N(^4S)$ atoms, vibrationally excited ground state N_2^* molecules, plus a small quantity of $N_2(A\ ^3\Sigma_u^+)$ excited molecules. Kaufman and Kelso [156] have presented strong physical evidence for the presence of N_2^* in the products of a microwave discharge, with a lifetime of about 0.05 sec. Evidence for the presence of N_2^* has also been obtained by vacuum ultraviolet absorption measurements [157, 158] and mass spectrometry [159]. Young [160] has suggested that in long-lived afterglows N_2^* may be present in excited energy levels capable of causing chemical reactions and that $N_2(A\ ^3\Sigma_u^+)$ molecules, which are continuously produced during first positive emission $(B\ ^3\Pi_g \rightarrow A\ ^3\Sigma_u^+)$, may be quickly converted to highly excited N_2^* by reaction with $N(^4S)$.

The triplet-state, metastable $N_2(A\ ^3\Sigma_u^+)$ molecule has 6.17 eV of energy (above the ground state) in its zero vibrational level. Its presence in active nitrogen has long been postulated, but positive identification has been made only recently by mass spectrometry [161] at a pressure of 0.45 torr and by measurements [162] on emission of the Vegard-Kaplan bands $(A\ ^3\Sigma_u^+ \rightarrow X\ ^1\Sigma_g^+)$ at pressures from 20 to 760 torr. Different values for the radiative lifetime of $N_2(A\ ^3\Sigma_u^+)$ have been given by various authors: 2.6×10^{-2} sec from the intensity of the absorption of the Vegard-Kaplan bands [163], 0.9 sec from decay of its emission from a pulsed discharge [164], about 1 sec from its behavior in active nitrogen [157], 2 sec from the emission of the Vegard-Kaplan bands [165], and 12 sec from the first positive emission in the afterglow [166]. It appears that $N_2(A\ ^3\Sigma_u^+)$ molecules have relatively long radiative lifetimes and are reasonably stable toward deactivation by collisions with ground state molecular N_2 or the wall [161].

Excited states of atomic N are also present in active nitrogen [161, 162]; the reported abundance ratios [161] are $^4S:^2D:^2P = 1:0.007:0.003$.

Production of Other Atomic Species

Other atomic species such as F, Cl, Br, I, P, and S can be produced in discharges; McTaggart [15] and Shaw [73] discuss the relevant work. In a recent paper Shirk and Bass [167a] produced atomic Cu, Ag, Cd, and Fe by bombarding metals with positive ions generated by passing Xe through a microwave discharge. The metal atoms were immediately trapped in an inert gas matrix on a cold window and their ultraviolet spectra observed. It may be possible to modify this procedure so as to study the reactions of metal atoms with various compounds condensed on the cold surface, or to mix the gas stream containing the metal atoms with a second gas stream. Sputtering of metals [66, 84] also produces metal atoms, but this technique is used mainly to deposit metal films on surfaces.

Production of Free Radicals

When a polyatomic molecule is subjected to an electrical discharge, free radicals are formed by dissociation of the parent molecule. Discharges are simple and efficient ways of producing radicals, but basic information is lacking about the dissociation processes, which may be very complex with many possible modes of dissociation [167b]. Many varieties of radicals have been found by optical spectroscopic, mass spectroscopic, chemical, and other methods. Since the electrons in a discharge have a distribution of energies, the high-energy electrons often disrupt polyatomic molecules extensively to form mainly atomic and diatomic fragments. Among the diatomic radicals that were first identified by their emission band spectra were CH, C_2, OH, NH, CN, and CS. Radicals may be formed in discharges by the removal of one or more atoms, such as formation of CH_3, CH_2, and CH from methane, or by the rupture of the molecule. In addition to the reference text edited by Bass and Broida [168], several other reviews have appeared on the preparation, trapping, and characterization of free radicals [31, 169–172].

Aside from the dissociation of molecules, radicals are also formed in discharge reactions of gas mixtures or in atom-molecule reactions. For example, O_2H radicals are found to be produced by electrical discharge through H_2O_2, by the reactions of H with O_2, of H with O_3, of H with H_2O_2, of O with H_2O_2, and of OH with H_2O_2 [17].

The spectra of polyatomic radicals such as NH_2, CF_2, C_2H_x, (where $x = 1$, 2, or 3), C_6H_5, $C_6H_5CH_2$, and HCOO have been reviewed by Ramsay [173]. In general, the production of specific radicals by discharge methods is difficult because discharges tend to dissociate molecules into many fragments. In a few instances under mild conditions, however, these methods have been used successfully to measure the emission spectra of various radicals. For example, o-, m-, and p-$CH_3C_6H_4CH_2$ and related species were obtained from dialkylbenzenes [174], o-, m-, and p-$FC_6H_4CH_2$ from the corresponding fluorotoluenes [175], o-, m-, and p-$ClC_6H_4CH_2$ from the corresponding chlorotoluenes [176], and $CH_3C_{10}H_6CH_2$ from various dimethylnaphthalenes [177] by flowing the vapor of the parent compound at very low pressures through an rf-generated (6-MHz) discharge operated at the minimum power level needed to maintain the discharge.

Another method for producing free radicals, sometimes a specific one, is by H-atom bombardment of solid compounds or compounds dissolved in aqueous solutions. The incoming H-atoms may abstract a H-atom from a C—H bond in saturated compounds, add to an unsaturated carbon in an olefinic or aromatic type of molecule, or replace a hydrogen, carboxyl or amino group from a C—X bond. The literature contains many descriptions of the use of this technique. Some recent examples, in which H-atoms were generated in rf or microwave discharges at subatmospheric pressure include the reaction of H with dimethylsuccinic acid, 5,6-dihydrothymine, and methylmaleic acid [178], various derivatives of uracil [179], the aromatic rings of amino acids, polyamino acids and proteins [180], and the aromatic and sulfur-containing amino acids in ribonuclease [181]. A procedure for using this technique to generate H-atoms at atmospheric pressure has recently been described [182].

Ion-Molecule Reactions

Since ions are present in electrical discharges, it would be expected that reactions of ions with neutral molecules could be involved to some extent in the discharge processes. Most of the early studies on ion-molecule reactions have dealt with those occurring in radiation chemistry and in the ion source of a mass spectrometer. Recent research has, however, been stimulated by the rapidly expanding interest in the physics and chemistry of the ionosphere and gas discharges. Much new quantitative information on ion-molecule reactions is becoming available with the development of new experimental techniques. Lampe et al. [183] have presented a review on the kinetics of reactions of ions with molecules, and Franklin et al. [184] have reviewed reactions and reaction rates of ions with molecules, including several studies of ion-molecule reactions in electrical discharges. The recent literature includes a volume of symposium papers [185] on ion-molecule reactions in the gas phase, and reviews by Cermak et al. [186a], Knewstubb [186b], Griese [187], Ferguson [188], Friedman [189], and Futrell and Tiernan [190].

In an electrical discharge primary ions produced by electron bombardment of neutral gas molecules may further collide with the parent neutral molecule to undergo simple charge-exchange processes or collide with a different molecule to form secondary ions. The charge-exchange processes change the energy distribution within the system, while the latter processes, designated as ion-molecule reactions, change the nature of the charge carriers. Study of ion-molecule reactions in gas discharges is complicated by the simultaneous occurrence within the system of other gaseous electronic processes such as electron-ion recombination and ion diffusion to the walls. Nevertheless, the pulsed afterglow technique [191–196], a dc glow discharge [197], a dc corona discharge [197, 198], and an rf discharge [199] have been used successfully in these studies. Mass spectrometers were used to sample the ionic and the intermediate species from the system.

Some ion-molecule reactions known to occur in discharges are mentioned briefly below.

Discharges in Hydrogen

In a glow discharge [200] and in a high-frequency discharge [201], the reaction $H_2^+ + H_2 \rightarrow H_3^+ + H$ occurs very readily to produce the species H_3^+. H^+ and H_2^+ are also present in discharges through H_2, and the ions $H_3O^+(H_3^+ + H_2O \rightarrow H_3O^+ + H_2)$, $H_5^+(H_3^+ \cdot H_2)$, and $H_5O^+(H_3O^+ \cdot H_2)$ have been reported in a dc glow discharge [202].

Discharges in Nitrogen

N^+, N_2^+, N_3^+, and N_4^+ have been observed in electrical discharges in N_2. Dreeskamp [203] suggested that formation of N_3^+ takes place according to

$$N^+ + N_2 + N_2 \rightarrow N_3^+ + N_2 \tag{11.10}$$

and Shahin [197] attributed the formation of N_4^+ to the reaction:

$$N_2^+ + N_2 \rightarrow N_4^+ \tag{11.11}$$

Shahin also explained that the ion N^+ is produced at the expense of the molecular ion by the reaction:

$$N_2^+ + N_2 \rightarrow N^+ + N + N_2 \tag{11.12}$$

Franklin et al. [184] discuss other modes of forming N_3^+, N_4^+, and N^+, including the charge-exchange reaction

$$N_2^+ + N \rightarrow N^+ + N_2 \tag{11.13}$$

Shahin [198] has shown that in a dc corona discharge in N_2 containing 2.2×10^{-2} mole % H_2O vapor, H_2O^+, H_3O^+, $H_5O_2^+(H_3O^+ \cdot H_2O)$, N_2H^+ are present, the latter probably being formed by the reaction

$$N_2^+ + H_2O \rightarrow N_2H^+ + OH \tag{11.14}$$

Discharges in Oxygen

Detection of O^+, O_2^+, O_3^+, and O_4^+ has been reported in glow discharges in O_2. The important charge-exchange reaction is [184, 204]

$$O^+ + O_2 \rightarrow O_2^+ + O \tag{11.15}$$

The finding of the negative ions O^-, O_2^-, and O_3^- in an O_2 discharge is of considerable interest (e.g., Ref. 191), and measurements of the endothermic negative ion reaction

$$O^- + O_2 \rightarrow O_2^- + O \tag{11.16}$$

have also been carried out [205, 206]. When CO_2 is present, O_2^- and O^- are converted to CO_4^- and CO_3^-, respectively [206].

Discharges in H_2O

Knewstubb and Tickner [207] measured the distribution of various positive ions in a dc glow discharge in water vapor (0.6 torr) as a function of the distance from the cathode. The ions are presumably derived from the ion H_2O^+ followed by the very rapid reaction

$$H_2O^+ + H_2O \rightarrow H_3O^+ + OH \qquad (11.17)$$

$H_5O_2^+$, $H_7O_3^+$, and so on are the hydrated ion clusters of H_3O^+. Different ions predominate in different regions of this nonuniform discharge.

Discharges in Hydrocarbons

Knewstubb [208] has described the observation of a wide variety of ions in a glow discharge in methane. The predominant ions are $C_2H_5^+$ and CH_5^+, and the remaining ions are widely distributed in a weaker spectrum of hydrocarbon ions extending to over 100 amu.

Studniarz and Franklin [199] have studied ion-molecule reactions in an rf-generated (50-MHz) discharge in CH_4 at pressures of 0.02 to 0.4 torr. CH_4^+ and CH_3^+ were the principal ions found in the plasma at pressures below 0.05 torr, but as the pressure was increased CH_5^+ and $C_2H_5^+$ were formed via the reactions

$$CH_4^+ + CH_4 \rightarrow CH_5^+ + CH_3 \qquad (11.18)$$

$$CH_3^+ + CH_4 \rightarrow C_2H_5^+ + H_2 \qquad (11.19)$$

Other ions of appreciable intensities ($<2\%$) found were $C_2H_6^+$, $C_2H_4^+$, $C_2H_3^+$, $C_2H_2^+$, and CH_2^+. These authors conclude that the results of sampling ions from the plasma were generally similar to the results obtained from mass spectrometric ion sources, which is surprising in view of the drastic differences in conditions and ion environment in the two ion sources.

As more work is done on ion-molecule reactions in discharges in hydrocarbons, much more information should become available on the mechanisms of organic reactions in discharges.

Kinetics of Discharge Reactions

Complex reactions occur in discharges owing to the presence of various chemically excited species. These reactions undoubtedly occur via mechanisms that consist of multistep reactions, but they can in theory be traced back to an (original) initiation step involving an inelastic electron-molecule or electron-atom collision process.

For an electron-molecule collision process such as

$$X + e_{fast}^- \rightarrow X^* + e_{slow}^- \qquad (11.20)$$

that gives rise to an excited species X^*, the rate of reaction can be written as

$$\text{Rate} = k_{20}n_e n_x, \tag{11.21}$$

where k_{20} is the rate constant for (11.20) in units of cm^3 sec^{-1}, n_e is the number density of electrons in units of cm^{-3}, and n_x is the number density of molecules of X in units of cm^{-3}.

Physicists describe a collision process in terms of a cross section σ. The collision cross-section for (11.20) can be defined in terms of the attenuation of a beam of electrons as they travel through and interact with (and are scattered by) a gas containing molecules of X. The decrease in intensity I of the electron beam as a function of path length l is

$$-dI = \sigma I n_x \, dl. \tag{11.22}$$

Equation (11.22) can be integrated to give

$$I/I_0 = \exp\left(-\sigma n_x l\right), \tag{11.23}$$

where I_0 is the initial intensity of the electron beam, I is the intensity after traveling through 1 cm of gas containing n_x molecules cm^{-3}, and σ is expressed in square centimeters.

The relationship between k and σ for an electron traveling with constant speed c is

$$k \ (cm^3 \ sec^{-1}) = c \ (cm \ sec^{-1})\sigma \ (cm^2). \tag{11.24}$$

(This is as if an electron were to travel in a straight line for 1 sec with a speed c and collide with all molecules that lie in a cylinder of cross section σ and length c.) However, for almost all electron-molecule collision processes, σ is a function of c, that is, of the electron energy. In addition, in a discharge the electrons do not have a constant speed, but instead have a distribution of speeds and energies. Equation (11.24) can be rewritten to take this into account,

$$k = \int_0^\infty c\sigma(c)f(c) \, dc, \tag{11.25}$$

where $f(c)$ is the function that describes the distribution of electron speeds in the discharge, and $\sigma(c)$ shows the dependence of σ on the speed of the electron. This method of deriving equations for k in terms of σ and the distribution of electron speeds (energies) in the discharge is very similar to Greene and Kuppermann's discussion of chemical reaction cross sections [209].

Discussions concerning the nature of the electron energy distribution in discharges are given in various texts (see also Ref. 210). Even though it may not result in an exact treatment, the energy E of the electrons in a discharge is usually assumed to be given by the Maxwell distribution,

$$f(E) \, dE = 2\pi \left(\frac{1}{\pi kT}\right)^{3/2} E^{1/2} \exp\left(-E/kT\right) dE. \tag{11.26}$$

Since σ is measured experimentally as a function of the electron energy, that is, $\sigma = \sigma(E)$, (11.25) can be rewritten using E as the variable,

$$k = \int_0^\infty \left(\frac{2E}{m}\right)^{1/2} \sigma(E) 2\pi \left(\frac{1}{\pi kT}\right)^{3/2} E^{1/2} \exp\left(-E/kT\right) dE \tag{11.27}$$

Here, the substitution $c = (2E/m)^{1/2}$, where m = electron mass, has also been made.

Equation (11.27) can be simplified to

$$k = \left(\frac{1}{\pi m}\right)^{1/2} \left(\frac{2}{kT}\right)^{3/2} \int_0^\infty \sigma(E) E \exp\left(-E/kT\right) dE. \tag{11.28}$$

For the Maxwell distribution, $kT = 2\bar{E}/3$, where $\bar{E}$ is the average electron energy. Accordingly,

$$k = 3 \left(\frac{3}{\pi m}\right)^{1/2} \bar{E}^{-1.5} \int_0^\infty \sigma(E) E \exp\left(-1.5E/\bar{E}\right) dE. \tag{11.29}$$

Thus the rate constant for an electron-molecule collision process, such as (11.20), can be calculated from (11.28) or (11.29) if experimental values have been measured for the cross section as a function of energy for the electron-molecule collision process and if one assumes that the electron energy in the discharge is distributed in a known way.

Several examples of this approach to calculating the rates of reactions in discharges are in the recent literature. Kaufman [31] discusses in detail the production of H-, O-, and N-atoms from the parent gases as they flow through microwave discharges. H-atom production rates of 40 to 200 torr sec^{-1} were calculated from (11.29). These values were based on dissociative electron impact data estimated from the dissociation cross section of H_2, using values for the average electron energy of 2 or 3 eV. Similarly, O-atom production rates of about 200 torr sec^{-1} and N-atom production rates of 6 to 60 torr sec^{-1} can be calculated in the corresponding discharges. For the O_2 and N_2 discharges, there are no other production terms of comparable magnitude, but for the H_2 discharge, H-atoms are also produced by electron-ion recombination at the wall [see (11.4) and (11.5)] and by an ion-molecule reaction [see (11.6)] in the gas phase. However, the net production of H- or O-atoms as measured downstream from the discharge is far lower than the calculated values.

Surface recombination of H-atoms provides the only comparably large loss term in the discharge, and the rate of this recombination appears to be of the same order of magnitude as the rate of production of H-atoms. "One is thus led to the interesting conclusion that the net dissociation yield of such H_2 discharges is mainly controlled by surface recombination and the surface in the discharge must be moderately to highly efficient for atom recombination. Moreover, the effect of small amounts of added gases such as H_2O or O_2 in increasing the yield must be through their influence on the surface efficiency . . ." [31]. Also, for the O_2 discharge, the O-atom yield is principally controlled by surface recombination in the discharge. However, for the N_2 discharge, the rate of surface recombination may be lower, and the yield of N-atoms appears to be controlled by the rate of dissociation.

Lunt [135] performed similar calculations for the reaction $2H_2 + O_2 \rightarrow 2H_2O$ in the positive column of a dc cold-cathode glow discharge. The rate of production of H-atoms in the discharge was calculated from (11.29) and compared with experimental values for the rate of production of water vapor in the discharge. From these results he concludes that two molecules of water are formed per molecule of H_2 initially dissociated into atoms. This is only the basic idea of his discussion, which is very detailed, but it is definitely a most interesting conclusion. It is important that more work of this type be done in an effort to calculate the rates of chemical reactions in discharges, starting from the most probable initial electron-molecule collision process.

Cooper et al. [211] studied the reaction $4HCl + O_2 \rightarrow 2Cl_2 + 2H_2O$ in a microwave-generated (2450-MHz) discharge in a flow system. Using the experimental cross-section data available for the dissociative attachment reaction,

$$HCl + e^- \rightarrow H + Cl^- \qquad (11.30)$$

which they assumed to be the initiation step, they calculated the rate of oxidation R using a slightly modified form of (11.29). Their calculations showed that R increases with increasing values of E/p (ratio of electric field strength to gas pressure) up to a maximum near $E/p = 18$ V cm^{-1} torr^{-1} and then decreases slowly at still higher values of E/p. This theoretical calculation of R versus E/p was in qualitative agreement with their experimental data, which showed that the percent conversion to Cl_2 increased with increasing values of the parameter $W^{1/2}$ torr^{-1} up to a maximum and then decreased at higher values. They used the variable $W^{1/2}$ torr^{-1} because they could not measure E directly but assumed that under their conditions the power absorbed in the discharge was proportional to E^2.

Bell [115] studied the oxidation of HCl in a rf-generated (20-MHz) discharge. As the rate-determining step for the overall reaction, he also used (11.30), for which he calculated the rate constant using (11.27) and the cross-section data for (11.30). This, together with other measurements, allowed him to show that the theoretical model for the reaction system correctly predicted a maximum in the graphs of conversion versus power and the displacement of these maxima in the curves to higher powers as the pressure was increased.

4 PHYSICAL AND CHEMICAL METHODS OF CHARACTERIZING GAS DISCHARGES

Studies of electrical discharges have sought increasingly to elucidate the nature of the ions, atoms, and free radicals responsible for discharge properties. Gas discharge phenomena are part of the general field of plasma physics. Various diagnostic techniques [212–214] are employed for measuring plasma parameters such as electron density and temperature, and ion density and temperature, as well as for analyzing the characteristic electromagnetic radiation emitted by a plasma. Chemists, however, are more interested in learning the identity of atomic, free-radical, and charged species in the discharge system and measuring their concentrations so as to understand the mechanism of the chemical reactions if possible. Specific methods for these measurements include chemical methods, such as gas-phase titration, and physical methods, such as pressure change, the Wrede gauge, calorimetric probe, mass spectrometry, optical spectroscopy, and electron spin resonance spectroscopy (ESR).

Bass and Broida [168, 169] have edited studies on the stabilization and measurement of free radicals, and Jennings [215a] has reviewed the detection and estimation of atoms in the gas phase. Thomas [171] and Mile [172] have also reviewed methods for the preparation and characterization of free radicals. McTaggart [15] has referred to more recent work, in particular to various species produced in electrical discharges. In many instances the methods used may be suitable only for measurements of relative concentrations of energetic species or for measurement of monatomic and diatomic species produced from gas discharges; the detection of polyatomic species in the gas phase is more difficult. For reactions involving larger molecules, it is often just as important and much less difficult to obtain accurate product analyses as it is to trap and/or otherwise identify the intermediates or radicals in the reaction.

Gas-Phase Titration

Chemical methods based on the high reactivity of atoms are frequently used in fast-flow systems to measure atom concentrations. Figure 11.16 shows an apparatus designed for this type of study [215b].

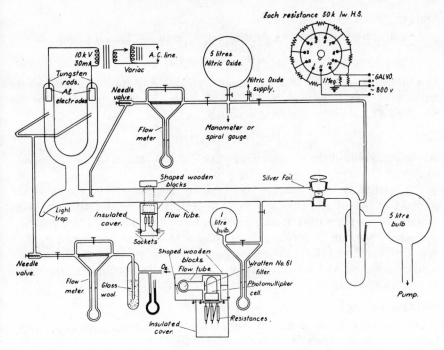

Fig. 11.16   Discharge flow system used by Thrush [215a].

Hydrogen Atoms

The concentration of atomic hydrogen has been determined by titration with NO_2 [216]. Nitric oxide was produced stoichiometrically in the rapid reaction

$$H + NO_2 \rightarrow OH + NO \tag{11.31}$$

The red glow observed in the reaction was caused by the emission of excited HNO according to $H + NO + M \rightarrow HNO + M$. The concentration of H-atoms can then be determined from the intensity of the emission.

It was assumed that one NO_2 molecule was consumed per H-atom, but a later study [217] and the mass spectrometric study of the $H + NO_2$ reaction [218] indicated that the overall stoichiometry was $NO_2:H = 3:2$, presumably because (11.31) is rapidly followed by

$$OH + OH \rightarrow O + H_2O \tag{11.32}$$

$$O + OH \rightarrow H + O_2 \tag{11.33}$$

$$O + NO_2 \rightarrow NO + O_2 \tag{11.34}$$

Oxygen Atoms

Atomic oxygen can be measured by NO_2 titration [219, 220]

$$O + NO_2 \to NO + O_2 \tag{11.35}$$

If a little NO_2 is added to a gas stream containing O-atoms, an equivalent amount of NO is formed by (11.35). A greenish-yellow air afterglow is observed as a result of the recombination

$$O + NO \to NO_2 + h\nu \tag{11.36}$$

At the end point of the gas titration, when the flow rate of the NO_2 is equal to that of O-atoms, the glow is extinguished.

The relative O-atom concentration can be determined by following the intensity of the air afterglow according to (11.36). If a small amount of NO is added to a stream of O-atoms, any NO_2 formed in (11.36) or in the faster three-body reaction $O + NO + M \to NO_2 + M$ is rapidly destroyed by the very fast reaction (11.35) to regenerate NO. Thus the NO concentration remains constant and the intensity of the glow is proportional to the concentration of O-atoms.

Nitrogen Atoms

Two chemical methods that have been used for measuring the concentration of nitrogen atoms in active nitrogen are titration with nitric oxide [221–223] and with ethylene [154, 224].

The NO method is based on the very fast reaction

$$N + NO \to N_2 + O \tag{11.37}$$

in which NO reacts with N-atoms to form O-atoms. If NO is added slowly, the excess N-atoms will react with O-atoms, giving blue NO afterglow. If NO is added in excess, the greenish $O + NO$ afterglow is produced [see (11.36)]. At the end point, at which the flow rate of NO equals that of N-atoms, there is no afterglow and the gas is practically colorless. Thus the N-atom concentration can be titrated simply by observing the sharp change of the color of the afterglow.

The second method [154, 224] is based on the HCN yield from the reaction of N-atoms with an excess of ethylene or other olefin, assuming a 1:1 relation between HCN:N. This method consistently gives lower values by a factor of 1.5 to 2 than the NO method. It has been suggested that NO titration gave higher values because NO might also be decomposed by reaction with the excited nitrogen molecules present in active nitrogen. However, various mass spectrometric studies of the $N + NO$ reaction by following the disappearance of NO [221, 225], the appearance of N_2 (using ^{15}NO) [226], and the formation of O-atoms [227] indicated the compatibility of these data with the simple mechanism of (11.37). The validity of the NO titration method is further supported by quantitative conversion of consumed ^{15}NO into $^{14}N^{15}N$ but no $^{15}N^{15}N$ [226], good agreement with ESR technique [228, 229], the pressure change method [230], and the result of vacuum ultraviolet absorption measurements [231]. It was also shown recently [232] that the reaction with ethylene involves recombination of N-atoms with intermediate radicals, and that addition of H-atoms increases the HCN yield and removes the discrepancy between the NO and the ethylene titration methods (see Section 5).

Pressure Measurements

Wrede-Harteck Gauge

This is suitable for measurement of absolute atom concentration in simple systems at low pressures [233–235]. The method has recently been modified [236, 237]. It depends on the steady-state pressure difference between the discharged gas and an enclosed space connected by a small orifice. Molecules and atoms effuse through the orifice into the closed volume, but atoms recombine on an enclosed catalyst and only molecules diffuse back. If the pressure of the discharged gas is p, the pressure difference Δp is related to the volume fraction of atoms α by

$$\alpha = \Delta p/p(1 - \sqrt{2}/2).$$

The method is not affected by the presence of excited species but is used only with very low pressures in pure gases.

Pressure Change

Absolute atom concentrations can be determined by measuring the pressure change that results when atoms recombine in low-pressure flow systems [230, 238, 239]. A portion of the discharged gas stream is rapidly isolated in a section of the flow line. If isothermal conditions prevail, the pressure loss Δp of the gas sample as a result of recombination is related to the atomic concentration c by $c = 2\,\Delta p/RT$.

Calorimetry

The heat liberated when atoms or radicals recombine can be used for their detection and estimation. The catalytic probe consists of a wire or a small piece of metal having a highly active catalytic surface. Relative atom concentrations were determined by silver-coating the junction of a thermocouple and measuring the emf produced [240a,b]. The emf readings attributable to the temperature rise of the catalytic probe were found to be proportional to the absolute concentration obtained from a Wrede-Harteck gauge [236].

The isothermal calorimetric probe [241] offers an improved way of measuring the absolute atom concentration. A platinum coil forming one arm of a bridge is maintained at a constant temperature by varying the current through the bridge. The drop in electrical power to produce the same coil temperature is a measure of the heat supplied to the calorimeter from the discharged gas. Thus the absolute atom concentrations can be calculated if the flow rate of the gas and the heat of recombination of the atoms are known. The method appears to be reliable for H-atoms [241] and Cl-atoms [242, 243] but is somewhat unreliable for O-atoms [141] or N-atoms, which may be accompanied by appreciable concentrations of active molecular species. These excited molecules in their metastable states produce excessive heat release owing to their deactivation on the catalytic surface.

Mass Spectrometry

There has been much interest in studying free radicals and other species present in electrical discharges by mass spectrometry [244–246b]. The method has assumed still greater importance because it provides a highly sensitive means of detection and an extremely rapid analysis for free radicals, as well as for the other stable chemical species present.

Mass spectrometric studies of free radicals commonly have been limited to species that can survive in the gas-sampling system and ionization chamber. The sampling systems generally use a pinhole as the inlet point and provide one or more stages of differential pumping between the pinhole and the ionization chamber, so as to reduce the sample gas to the required low pressure of about 10^{-5} torr.

For highly reactive free radicals or metastable species, Foner and Hudson [247, 248] used a collision-free modulated molecular beam sampling system to eliminate, or at least minimize, the free-radical loss by wall collisions. The time required for the sample to reach the ionization chamber from the exit slit of the discharge tube was of the order of a few hundred microseconds. More recently [159], they reported satisfactory observation of the vibrationally excited N_2^* species produced by pulsed electrical discharges when the time delay in sampling was reduced.

As reviewed by Knewstubb [186b, 208], ions produced from electrical discharges have also been investigated. Knewstubb and Tickner [249, 250] used a dc glow discharge in noble gases to study the ions formed. Knewstubb and his co-workers also studied H_2O vapor [207], O_2 [251], NH_3 [252], and N_2 and its mixtures with H_2 and O_2 [253]. The interpretation of analyses of ions from discharges is generally quite complicated, for the results depend considerably on the electrical field conditions at the sampling apertures, electron energy, and regions of the plasma where samplings are made. Ion sampling of N_2 afterglows from a microwave discharge to a quadrupole mass spectrometer have been described [254]. Recent works concerning the identification of ionic precursors of the products or study of ion-molecule reactions in electrical discharges include those by Shahin [197, 198, 255, 256], Evans and Jennings [257–259], Franklin et al. [184, 199], and Ferguson et al. [260].

Mass spectrometric studies of free radicals and ions offer convenient means to explain the mechanism of discharge reactions. A mass spectrometer with a high scanning rate is used with two systems: (1) a discharge-flow system in which samples are continuously introduced into the ionization chamber of the mass spectrometer at various points downstream from the reaction zone, and (2) a discharge-static system in which a sampling probe is used.

Studies of free-radical reactions in the discharge-flow system are too numerous to be listed and are mostly concerned with simple atom-molecule reactions and reactions of H-, N-, O-, and halogen atoms with hydrocarbons and other organic compounds. With the development of instruments with an extremely high scan rate, such as time-of-flight and quadrupole mass spectrometers and oscillographic display of the output from the secondary electron multiplier, the static system may gain increasing attention in the future.

The time-of-flight mass spectrometer achieves resolution of the ion beam by measuring the velocity or flight time of ions of each mass. Ions produced from the sample are given equal kinetic energy in an electrostatic field and the time of their travel over a fixed distance varies with their mass. Thus those ions with lighter mass reach the ion detector in a shorter period of time. Ions are collected by an electron multiplier, which has the extremely fast response time needed to record a complete spectrum in about 100 μsec.

The quadrupole mass spectrometer uses a high-frequency field produced by four long, parallel electrodes for mass analysis. The opposite pairs of electrodes are coupled together, and an rf voltage superimposed on a dc voltage is applied to the quadrupole array. Ions entering the field have trajectories which are solutions to Mathieu's differential equation. For a given charge-to-mass ratio, and for a specific frequency and set of voltages, ions of only one mass have oscillatory trajectories and are transmitted through the instrument to an appropriate detector. Mass scanning is accomplished by varying the rf and dc voltage while keeping their ratio constant.

Optical Spectroscopy

The absorption spectra of ground state atoms of most nonmetallic elements lie in the vacuum ultraviolet region where most other substances absorb strongly. For this reason absorption spectroscopy has not been widely used to detect the presence of atoms. Despite the difficulties involved, concentrations of H-, N-, and O-atoms have been determined by vacuum ultraviolet absorption measurements of their resonance lines [231]. Indirect methods have also been used to estimate N- and O-atom concentrations [261]. The concentration of atomic O was established by adding sufficient NO_2 to extinguish the afterglow and making spectroscopic determinations of the NO produced. The concentration of atomic N was measured by titrating with NO, and afterward determining the amount of NO by spectral absorption when the discharge was extinguished.

The absorption spectra of free radicals lie mainly in the more accessible ultraviolet region of the spectrum, but this method has been applied to only a very limited extent in discharge work. Studies of OH [262a,b, 263] and ClO [261, 264] radicals in discharge-flow systems have been made. Absorption spectra of OH, SH, CS, and CN radicals produced in a microwave-pulse discharge have also been observed [103]. However, absorption spectroscopy has been used rather extensively in the study of radicals trapped in solid matrices at low temperatures [168–172] and in the investigation of radicals formed from flash photolysis, for example, OH [265], CN [266], CH [267], and so on. In addition, absorption spectra of various excited atoms and vibrationally excited diatomic molecules were observed during and following a microwave-pulse gas discharge [103, 104]. Recently, infrared spectra of free radicals have been obtained successfully by the photolysis method [268, 269].

Emission spectroscopy is also used to identify the chemical species and the state of these species in gas discharges. For example, atoms such as H, N, O, C, and so on exhibit their characteristic line spectra, and diatomic molecules or radicals such as C_2, CN, CO, and so on exhibit their characteristic band spectra. Various polyatomic free radicals observed in emission from gaseous electrical discharges have been reviewed by Ramsay [173].

While emission spectra can be conveniently used for detection and identification of the species produced in gas discharges, quantitative applications of this technique have been lacking because of profound effects of pressure, temperature, impurities, diluent gases and so on. This technique has found extensive application in characterizing properties of discharge plasmas such as temperature and electron or ion densities, as reviewed recently by Margoshes and Scribner [270].

Emission spectra have also been used to identify species and to follow chemical reactions. The emission produced by the association of atomic O and N has been studied in a fast-flow system by photoelectric and spectroscopic methods [271]. The behavior of the CN radical in active nitrogen has been examined by following the intensity of the CN violet emission [272]. The concentration of OH in its specific rotation-vibration states has been determined by observing its emission in a fast-flow $H–O_3$ system diluted with helium [273]. The emission intensity of N_2^+ and O_2^+ bands has been followed when active species of helium produced by a microwave discharge reacted with nitrogen or oxygen downstream from the discharge [274].

Electron Spin Resonance

The use of ESR for the detection and the quantitative measurement of paramagnetic atoms and radical species in the gas phase is a recent development. The method is highly specific and sensitive and depends on the fact that free radicals contain unpaired electrons and thus exhibit paramagnetism.

Studies on H-, N-, and O-atoms produced in discharge-flow systems were first carried out by Beringer and his co-workers [275–277]. Since then many other atoms and free radicals have been detected in the gas phase by the ESR technique, including F, Cl, Br, I, OH, SH, SeH, TeH, SO, NF_2, and so on. Quantitative measurements of atom and radical concentrations became successful with the use of gaseous O_2 as a calibrating material [278]. Recently, absolute concentrations of N and O [228], and H and OH [279], were determined, although in the case of OH radical NO rather than O_2 was used as the reference gas.

The ESR technique is becoming a valuable quantitative analytical tool in elucidating gas-phase reactions such as those of H- and/or O-atoms with simple hydrocarbons [280–282a]. Up to now, measurements in the gas phase relate principally to monatomic and diatomic species, mainly because the nature of the gas phase ESR spectra of polyatomic free radicals makes them difficult to detect.

5 REACTIONS OF H, N, AND O ATOMS WITH ORGANIC COMPOUNDS

One of the most important applications of electrical discharges in organic chemistry is the production of free atoms for reactions with organic compounds. The studies can be conducted in a discharge-flow system in which atoms produced in an electrical discharge are allowed to react with organic molecules at some point downstream from the discharge zone. A review of atomic reactions in discharge-flow systems has recently appeared [77], and Kaufman [282b] has reviewed many H-atom, O-atom, and N-atom reactions, although neither of these reviews is restricted to reactions with organic compounds.

Reactions of Hydrogen Atoms

Thrush [283] has discussed the reactions of H-atoms, particularly those for which at least relative rate constants have been determined. Unlike the production of O-atoms and active nitrogen in the discharge, metastable states of H and H_2 are not known in the low-pressure H_2 discharge and do not complicate the results.

H + Olefins

Cvetanovic [284] has reviewed this topic, but much of the work has involved H-atoms produced by other techniques such as mercury photosensitization, photolysis, radiolysis, and hot-filament techniques.

Addition of an H-atom to an olefin yields a vibrationally excited alkyl radical which may undergo either fragmentation to form different products or deactivation by collision with other molecules. In the latter processs a stabilized alkyl radical is formed, which is normally removed by combination and disproportionation.

The ethyl radical formed from the reactions of H-atoms with ethylene,

$$H + C_2H_4 \rightarrow C_2H_5{}^* \xrightarrow{M} C_2H_5 \tag{11.38}$$

may react with another ethyl radical in either of two ways:

$$C_2H_5 + C_2H_5 \rightarrow C_4H_{10} \tag{11.39}$$

$$C_2H_5 + C_2H_5 \rightarrow C_2H_6 + C_2H_4 \tag{11.40}$$

Thrush and co-workers [281, 285], using H-atoms produced in a discharge in an argon carrier for the reaction with ethylene, showed that the ethyl radicals formed are removed mainly by

$$H + C_2H_5 \rightarrow C_2H_6{}^* \rightarrow CH_3 + CH_3 \tag{11.41}$$

where the initial concentrations are $[H]_0 \geqq [C_2H_4]_0$. For very low initial ethylene concentrations ($[H]_0 > 5[C_2H_4]_0$), the predominant reaction is the formation of methane by

$$H + CH_3 \rightleftharpoons CH_4{}^* \xrightarrow{M} CH_4 \tag{11.42}$$

When the initial ethylene concentration is increased to a level comparable to that of H-atoms ($[H]_0 \sim [C_2H_4]_0$), formation of ethane by

$$CH_3 + CH_3 \rightarrow C_2H_6 \tag{11.43}$$

and the combination and disproportionation of ethyl radicals [see (11.39) and (11.40)] become more important. Toby and Schiff's [286] study of the reaction of deuterium atoms with ethylene in an argon carrier under similar conditions supports this mechanism. The second-order rate constant for addition of H-atoms to ethylene in reaction (11.38) was found [281] to be $(8.8 \pm 0.4) \times 10^{10}$ cm^3 mole^{-1} sec^{-1} at 298°K, assuming that an average of 3.5 H-atoms is removed per ethylene molecule initially present (4 H-atoms per ethylene molecule would be removed if CH_4 were the only product).

Rabinovitch and co-workers used H- and D-atoms produced in a water-cooled Wood-Bonhoeffer discharge tube for studies of reactions with various olefins. Addition of H-atoms to trans-ethylene-d$_2$ [287] and cis-2-butene [288], and of H- or D-atoms to 1-butene [289, 290] and *trans*-2-butene [290] resulted in the formation of excited alkyl radicals by reactions similar to reaction (11.38). Radicals produced from higher-molecular-weight olefins may decompose into smaller fragments or be stabilized. From the relative rates of stabilization and decomposition of the excited alkyl radicals, Rabinovitch et al. found rate constants for the decomposition of the order of 10^7 to 10^8 sec^{-1}.

H + Acetylenes

When atomic H is produced in electrical discharges, its reaction with C_2H_2 results in the recombination of the H-atoms without any consumption of C_2H_2 [291–293]. The addition of H-atoms to C_2H_2 proceeds initially in a manner analogous to their addition to olefins.

$$H + C_2H_2 \rightleftharpoons C_2H_3{}^* \xrightarrow{M} C_2H_3 \qquad (11.44)$$

$$C_2H_3 + H \rightarrow C_2H_4{}^* \rightarrow C_2H_2 + H_2 \qquad (11.45)$$

The vibrationally activated vinyl radical is stabilized by collision with other molecules but does not undergo any measurable combination or disproportionation. The intermediate $C_2H_4{}^*$ is not stabilized in the pressure range of 0.6 to 3.5 torr [292], apparently because the $C_2H_4{}^*$ possesses an excess energy above its dissociation limit and decomposes into C_2H_2 and H_2. The second-order rate constant for H + C_2H_2 has been reported [292, 294, 295] to be about 10^{10} to 10^{11} cm^3 mole^{-1} sec^{-1} at room temperature.

The reaction of H-atoms with methylacetylene also proceeds according to a similar mechanism, resulting in a catalytic removal of H-atoms with conservation of methylacetylene [281].

$$H + C_3H_4 \rightleftharpoons C_3H_5{}^* \xrightarrow{M} C_3H_5 \qquad (11.46)$$

$$C_3H_5 + H \rightarrow C_3H_6{}^* \longrightarrow C_3H_4 + H_2 \qquad (11.47)$$

The rate constant for (11.46) is 2.4×10^{11} cm^3 mole^{-1} sec^{-1} at room temperature.

H + Alkanes

The initial step of the reaction of H-atoms with alkanes (RH) can be represented by

$$H + RH \rightarrow H_2 + R \qquad (11.48)$$

and for methane, the extent of the attack by H-atoms is hard to detect at temperatures up to 180°C [291]. Some ethane is produced at temperatures near 500°C [296] by the combination of CH_3 radicals formed from methane

$$CH_3 + CH_3 \rightarrow C_2H_6 \qquad (11.49)$$

For higher alkanes the reaction products are usually alkanes and olefins with the same or a lower number of carbon atoms. For example, reaction of H-atoms with isobutane gives isobutene and traces of ethane, ethylene, propane, and propene, but no higher hydrocarbons [297]. The product yield is equivalent to only 4% of the H-atoms consumed. Since the isobutene concentration remains constant, whereas the concentration of H-atoms decreases steadily, it is likely that isobutene catalyzes the removal of H-atoms. This suggests that the mechanism of H + olefins is also applicable here. Thus the olefin formed in (11.50) would yield a vibrationally excited alkyl radical via (11.51).

$$H + R \rightarrow A + H_2 \quad (A = \text{olefin}) \tag{11.50}$$

$$H + A \rightleftharpoons R^* \tag{11.51}$$

As discussed earlier, the excited alkyl radical may be fragmented to form lower hydrocarbons or may be deactivated and removed subsequently by disproportionation or combination.

An activation energy of 7.4 kcal mole^{-1} and a frequency factor of about 10^{11} cm^3 mole^{-1} sec^{-1} have been reported [296] for methane in reaction (11.48). LeRoy et al. [298], however, have reported a much higher frequency of about 10^{14} cm^3 mole^{-1} sec^{-1} and an activation energy of 8.2 kcal mole^{-1} for the H + propane reaction.

H + Aromatic Hydrocarbons

H-atoms are known to react with benzene [291] in the gaseous phase and with various aromatic hydrocarbons in the liquid phase [299, 300]. The reaction with benzene produces methane together with some acetylene, ethylene, and ethane. In addition, recent work of Mulcahy et al. [301] shows that the main liquid products are cyclohexane and n-hexane in comparable amounts.

Mulcahy et al. [301] have reported that the main product of the reaction between H-atoms and toluene at room temperature is methylcyclohexane, accompanied by C_3 to C_7 acyclic alkanes and cycloalkanes. They propose that the addition of an H-atom to the toluene is followed by successive additions of H-atoms to unsaturated radicals to form intermediates of methylcyclohexadiene (I) and methylcyclohexene (II) in highly reactive triplet states.

$$\tag{11.52}$$

In the final step vibrationally excited methylcyclohexane is formed, and it may either be deactivated or disrupted according to

$$(11.53)$$

$$(11.54a)$$

or

$$\text{and so on}\quad (11.54b)$$

Other plausible mechanisms for ring opening and fragmentation are also available; a better understanding of the reaction mechanism will require more detailed studies.

The reaction of H-atoms with toluene at 390°C produces predominantly low-molecular-weight products, methane, ethane, and ethylene, with a small amount of benzene. This can be attributed to the effect of temperature on the rates of activated bond-breaking reactions such as (11.54a) and (11.54b).

H + O-Containing Compounds

Early works on reactions of H-atoms with aldehydes, ketones, alcohols, and acids have been discussed by Steacie [302]. It is suggested that these reactions, similar to those involving alkanes, proceed by hydrogen abstraction as the initial step. Some recent studies in discharge-flow systems are cited here as examples.

The reaction with formaldehyde [303] has been found to be first order in both atomic H and formaldehyde concentrations and can be represented by

$$H + H_2CO \rightarrow H_2 + HCO \tag{11.55}$$

$$H + HCO \rightarrow H_2 + CO \tag{11.56}$$

Reaction (11.56) is fast compared with (11.55), and CO is the only major product observed.

For acetaldehyde, Steacie et al. [304] found that the products were CH_4, CO, and C_2H_6 and assumed the following mechanistic steps initiated by

H abstraction:

$$H + CH_3CHO \rightarrow H_2 + CH_3CO \tag{11.57}$$

$$H + CH_3CO \rightarrow CH_3 + CHO \tag{11.58}$$

$$H + CH_3CO \rightarrow CH_4 + CO, \text{ and so on} \tag{11.59}$$

Recently, however, in a mass spectrometric study of this reaction, Lambert et al. [305] reported that the major products were CH_4, CO, and a substance yielding $m/e = 43$ ions, and that the formation of CH_4 was strictly first-order in acetaldehyde. The amounts of CH_4 and CO were approximately equal, but the paths of their formations were not the same. They suggested that the main course of the reaction is

$$H + CH_3CHO \rightarrow CH_4 + CHO \tag{11.60}$$

$$CHO + CH_3CHO \rightarrow CO + H_2 + CH_2CHO \tag{11.61}$$

When H-atoms react with unsaturated compounds, the most probable primary step is hydrogen addition rather than hydrogen abstraction, owing to the higher activation energy expected for the latter process. For example, the reaction of atomic H with ketene [306, 307] may proceed via the initial addition of H-atoms to the olefinic bond of CH_2CO

$$H + CH_2CO \rightarrow CH_3CO^* \tag{11.62}$$

This is followed by [307]

$$CH_3CO^* \rightarrow CH_3 + CO \tag{11.63}$$

$$CH_3 + H \xrightarrow{\text{wall}} CH_4 \tag{11.64}$$

to give the principal products, CH_4 and CO. The initial addition of H-atoms on the other carbon atom of the olefinic bond in (11.62) would lead to the formation of CH_2CHO and may account for the formation of the minor products CH_2O and C_2H_4. However, the CH_3CO is favored thermochemically over CH_2CHO, based on the H—CH_2CO and CH_2CO—H bond energies of 43.5 and 35 kcal $mole^{-1}$, respectively [308].

H + N-Containing Compounds

As in most other reactions of H-atoms, hydrogen abstraction is the most probable primary step for the reactions of H-atoms with amines, ethylen-imines, and other similar compounds. The mechanism is somewhat compli-cated, however, by the possible occurrence of hydrogen abstraction from both carbon and nitrogen atoms because of nearly equal magnitudes of C—H and N—H bond energies [308].

The reaction of H-atoms with methyl- and ethylamine [309] produces hydrogen cyanide, methane, and ethane as the main products. Winkler et al. [309] assumed that radicals containing N are produced in successive H-atom reactions with amines, and that these radicals decompose to form HCN under suitable conditions.

The reactions of H-atoms with ethylenimine and N-methylethylenimine [310], 2-methylethylenimine, and azacyclobutane [311] are assumed to involve the attack of H-atoms giving rise to cyclic radicals which subsequently decompose or react with H-atoms to form HCN. For example,

$$H + CH_3\text{—}CH\text{—}CH_2 \overset{\diagdown\diagup}{\underset{\substack{N \\ H}}{}} \rightarrow H_2 + CH_3\text{—}CH\text{—}CH_2 \overset{\diagdown\diagup}{\underset{N}{}} \tag{11.65}$$

Jamieson et al. [311] further suggested that at high temperatures (about 300°C) and high imine flow rates the imino radicals may combine with each other to form ethane and cyanogen as the major products.

$$CH_3\text{—}CH\text{—}CH_2 + CH_3\text{—}CH\text{—}CH_2 \rightarrow 2C_2H_6 + C_2N_2 \tag{11.66}$$

They observed that the reaction was rapid and complete and that the disappearance of the cyclic imine under these conditions could be regarded as a satisfactory measure of atomic H flow rates.

Reactions of Nitrogen Atoms

The most extensive studies of the reactions of active nitrogen with organic molecules have been carried out by Winkler and co-workers. The subject has recently been reviewed and discussed comprehensively [18, 37].

As discussed earlier (Section 3), active nitrogen produced from a discharge contains appreciable quantities of $N(^4S)$ atoms, vibrationally excited ground state N_2^* molecules, together with a small quantity of electronically excited $N_2(A\ ^3\Sigma_u^+)$ molecules. The interaction of this complicated mixture with organic compounds results in extensive fragmentation of the organic molecules and conversion of nitrogen mainly to HCN and to polymers which have not been well characterized. Most chemical reactions of active nitrogen have been ascribed to $N(^4S)$ atoms, and mechanisms for most of the reactions with organic compounds have been proposed on the assumption that atomic N is the only reactive species in active nitrogen [154, 312, 313]. In spite of much study, the mechanism of these reactions is little understood because of the apparently very fast reaction of N-atoms with free radicals to yield HCN, H-atoms, and more free radicals.

N + Unsaturated Hydrocarbons

The reaction of ethylene with active nitrogen has been used as a means of measuring the N-atom concentration [154], but the result gives consistently lower values because N_2 and C_2N_2 are formed in addition to the principal product, HCN. Herron [232] has shown that the reaction cannot be described adequately by the simple mechanism [154, 224]

$$N + C_2H_4 \rightarrow HCN + CH_3 \qquad (11.67)$$

$$N + CH_3 \rightarrow HCN + 2H \qquad (11.68)$$

but probably also involves H-atoms and hydrocarbon radicals in the following additional chain reactions

$$H + C_2H_4 \rightarrow C_2H_5 \qquad (11.69)$$

$$H + C_2H_5 \rightarrow CH_3 + CH_3 \qquad (11.70)$$

$$N + C_2H_5 \rightarrow NH + C_2H_4 \qquad (11.71)$$

$$N + NH \rightarrow N_2 + H \qquad (11.72)$$

Competition between H- and N-atoms for C_2H_5 radicals in (11.70) and (11.71) determines the relative extent to which N-atoms produce HCN or are lost as molecular N_2. Addition of H-atoms favors reaction (11.70), hence increases the yield of HCN and removes the discrepancy between the NO and C_2H_4 titration methods for the measurement of N-atom concentrations. This was accomplished by adding H_2 to the N_2 before it went through the discharge. Formation of C_2D_4 in the reaction of active nitrogen with C_2D_3H has been interpreted as further evidence for the involvement of H-atoms in the ethylene reaction [314].

More recently, reactions of hydrocarbons with mixtures of active nitrogen and H-atoms have been studied by using active nitrogen and H-atoms produced in separate discharges [315]. This work confirmed that HCN production was increased by adding H-atoms but suggested that disproportionation of NH radicals, rather than (11.72) produces N_2.

$$NH + NH \rightarrow N_2 + H + H \qquad (11.73)$$

When H-atoms are added, N_2 formation is suppressed because NH radicals are consumed by

$$H + NH \rightarrow H_2 + N \qquad (11.74)$$

The N-atoms regenerated then form enough additional HCN to agree with the NO titration.

The general features of the reactions of N-atoms with higher alkenes are similar [316]. For propene [316–319] the major products are C_2H_4, HCN, and CH_3CN, together with small amounts of C_2H_6, C_3H_8, and a trace of C_2H_2. The presence of other N-containing products such as C_2N_2 [318] and C_2H_3CN (cyanoethylene) [316, 318] was also reported. The mechanisms proposed by these authors differ in detail, but the main feature of the reaction probably is the formation of a radical intermediate which may undergo subsequent rearrangement and decomposition reactions.

$$HCN + C_2H_4 + H \qquad (11.75a)$$

$$C_3H_6 + N \rightarrow C_3H_6N$$

$$CH_3CN + CH_3 \qquad (11.75b)$$

The C_2H_4 and CH_3 formed can be further attacked by N-atoms to produce more HCN. If H-atoms are assigned an important role, the following reactions may be considered

$$C_3H_6 + H \rightarrow C_3H_7 \qquad (11.76)$$

$$C_3H_7 + H \rightarrow C_3H_8{}^* \rightarrow C_2H_5 + CH_3 \qquad (11.77)$$

$$C_3H_7 + N \rightarrow CH_3CN + CH_3 + H \qquad (11.78)$$

The alkyl radicals formed in these reactions can undergo recombination and disproportionation or can be attacked by N-atoms, but the details of the mechanism as regards the relative importance of the various steps are not well established.

In the study of the reaction of 1,3-butadiene with N-atoms by Lichtin et al. [320, 321], numerous products such as HCN, C_2N_2, C_2 to C_4 hydrocarbons, and cyanohydrocarbons were separated and identified. Consumption of butadiene varied from 20 to 90% as the molecular ratio $(C_4H_6)/(N)$ was varied from 6.7 to 0.12; between 6.7 and 0.25 the conversion of N to HCN, the major product, remained essentially constant at approximately 30%. The data appeared to support a mechanism in which the rate-determining addition of N-atoms to C_4H_6 is followed by several parallel modes of uni-molecular decomposition,

$$C_4H_6 + N \rightarrow C_4H_6N \qquad (11.79)$$

$$C_4H_6N \rightarrow HCN + NH + C_pH_q \text{ (radicals)} + C_xH_y \text{ (stable molecules)}$$

$$+ \text{ pyrrole} + CN + H \text{ and so on} \qquad (11.80)$$

where C_4H_6N may not be a single species. Some products undergo further rapid reaction

$$N + C_pH_q \rightarrow HCN + NH \text{ and so on} \qquad (11.81)$$

As in the olefin reactions, NH presumably disappeared by (11.72) and/or (11.73).

Lichtin et al. [322] also reported that the reaction of isoprene with active nitrogen yielded products qualitatively similar to those obtained from the 1,3-butadiene reaction. The nondegradative products identified were β-methylpyrrole, 1-cyanoisoprene, and 2-methyl-1-butene.

N + Saturated Hydrocarbons

Reactions of N-atoms with saturated hydrocarbons are probably very complex and are generally much slower than reactions with olefins. The mechanisms, particularly that of the primary step, are as yet uncertain. In accordance with the mechanism proposed by Winkler et al. [224], it is assumed that the N-atoms attack one of the carbon atoms in the hydrocarbon molecule and that the resulting complex decomposes to form HCN as the primary product, together with organic radicals. The radicals subsequently react rapidly with N-atoms to form more HCN. For example, the propane reaction can be represented as follows:

$$N + C_3H_8 \rightarrow C_3H_8N \rightarrow HCN + C_2H_5 + H_2 \tag{11.82}$$

$$N + C_2H_5 \rightarrow C_2H_5N \rightarrow HCN + CH_3 + H \tag{11.83}$$

However, Safrany and co-workers [315, 323] consider that the initial reactions of lower alkanes or alkenes with N-atoms form alkyl radicals by reacting with H-atoms, which are always present in any discharge. Alkyl radicals can be produced from alkanes by abstraction and from alkenes by addition. These alkyl radicals then react rapidly with N-atoms to produce HCN by degradation and NH by abstraction.

$$C_nH_{2n+1} + N \rightarrow HCN + C_{n-1}H_{2n-1} + H \tag{11.84}$$

$$C_{n-1}H_{2n-1} + N \rightarrow HCN + C_{n-2}H_{2n-3} + H \tag{11.85}$$

$$C_nH_{2n+1} + N \rightarrow NH + C_nH_{2n} \tag{11.86}$$

As in the olefin reactions, NH radicals disproportionate to give N_2 or can further react with H-atoms to form NH_3.

Recently, Hinde and Lichtin [324] studied the competition of ethylene and propane for active nitrogen and found that some ethylene is generated from propane. They also reported that in the competitive reactions the rate of attack of N-atoms on ethylene is more than five times the value for propane. The literature data for the individual steps show that the rate constant for ethylene at 70°C is 1.0×10^7 cm^3 mole^{-1} sec^{-1} [316] and that for propane at 50°C is 1.0×10^6 cm^3 mole^{-1} sec^{-1} [325].

Zabolotny and Gesser [326] reported that HCN and NH_3 were the major gaseous products from the reactions of CH_4 and C_2H_6 with active nitrogen in an argon atmosphere and that excited Ar atoms from the discharge increase the chemical reactivity of the active nitrogen by augmenting the percentage of excited species.

Reactions with Other Organic Compounds

There are many other organic compounds whose reactions with active nitrogen have been studied. A common feature of these reactions is the formation of HCN usually as the major product, but NH_3, nitriles, and various new N-containing compounds are often produced. In a few cases appreciable amounts of products corresponding to the mild degradation of the original molecules are formed: benzonitrile, phenyl isocyanide, and pyridine in the reaction of active nitrogen with benzene, and quinoline and isoquinoline in the reaction with naphthalene [327, 328]. The formation of nondegradative products has also been reported by Lichtin and co-workers, as mentioned earlier, in the reactions of active nitrogen with isoprene and 1,3-butadiene.

Reactions of Oxygen Atoms

Recently, Cvetanovic [284] has discussed the addition of O-atoms to olefins, and Avramenko and Kolesnikova [263] have discussed the reactions of O-atoms with various organic molecules. Cvetanovic and co-workers used, almost exclusively, mercury-photosensitized decomposition of N_2O and photolysis of NO_2 as a means of generating O-atoms, and Avramenko and Kolesnikova generated them with discharges. The latter workers claimed that discharges in H_2O produce only O-atoms, whereas those in O_2 produce mixtures of O-atoms and O_2 molecules. Thus they expected to distinguish between those products formed by the reaction with organic compounds of the different discharge gases produced by these two methods. However, as Kaufman [220] has pointed out, the assumption that only O-atoms are produced in an H_2O discharge is an oversimplification.

Ground state O_2 and excited species such as $O_2(^1\Delta_g)$ present in the O_2 discharge might be expected to contribute to the reaction. Therefore when studying reactions of O-atoms with organic compounds by discharge techniques, it is preferable that O-atoms be produced in an O_2 discharge in the presence of excess He [329] or Ar [330] or by titrating N-atoms generated in a N_2 discharge with NO (see Section 4).

O + Olefins

Avramenko et al. [331] studied the reactions of O-atoms with C_2H_4, C_3H_6, and iso-C_4H_8. They found that at high flow rates of the olefins formaldehyde is the main product for every reaction. With ethylene, they also obtained CO and CO_2 and small quantities of acetaldehyde and acetylene. Since formaldehyde was formed by using the O-atoms produced in the H_2O discharge, its formation via (11.87) was regarded as the primary reaction.

$$C_2H_4 + O \rightarrow CH_2O + CH_2 \qquad (11.87)$$

This is in disagreement with the result of Cvetanovic [332], who concluded that the primary process is a direct addition of an O-atom to the double bond to form an energy-rich intermediate which then undergoes further reactions.

$$C_2H_4 + O \rightarrow C_2H_4O^* \rightarrow CH_3 + CHO \qquad (11.88)$$

The products formed were CO, H_2, C_1–C_4 paraffins, CH_3CHO, small amounts of C_2H_4O, and traces of HCHO. This distribution is similar to that observed in the photolysis of ethylene oxide [333] and the mercury-photosensitized decomposition of ethylene oxide [334].

Reaction (11.88) is supported by recent ESR studies [281] and mass spectrometric studies [335] of the O—C_2H_4 reaction in the discharge-flow system. The rate constant, k_{88}, is reported to be 3.2 × 10^4 cm^3 mole^{-1} sec^{-1} at room temperature [281, 335], although other values have been reported [336–338]. Various mechanisms have been proposed for the subsequent reactions to account for the formation of H-atoms, CO, and HCHO. The reaction O + CH_3 is regarded as an important step following the primary process, (11.88); the suggested products are HCHO + H [335], CO + H_2 + H [281], CHO + H_2 [281] or CH + H_2O [282a].

Avramenko and Kolesnikova [263] also studied the reactions of O-atoms with propylene and 1,3-butadiene and concluded that an O-atom can disrupt a C=C double bond as well as a C—C single bond and insert into CH bonds, forming aldehydes. However, this is different from the conclusions of Cvetanovic and his co-workers, who considered that the active species produced by discharges give complicated results because of consecutive reactions, fragmentation of addition products at the low pressures used, and other reactions attributable to excess molecular O_2. Jarvie and Cvetanovic [329] compared the results of the reaction between 1-butene and O-atoms using electrical discharge, N_2O, and NO_2 techniques and found that the discharge technique resulted in more complicated O-containing compounds. They found also that when O-atoms were generated by a discharge in the presence of a large amount of helium and reacted with 1-butene at not too low partial pressures, the products were similar to those obtained with the N_2O and NO_2 techniques; the main ones were α-butene oxide and n-butyraldehyde.

Thus Cvetanovic [284] concluded that the reaction of O-atoms with an olefin proceeds via addition to the double bond to form a biradical intermediate, which in turn converts to epoxide by ring closure, rearranges by internal migration to form carbonyl compounds, or decomposes to give various degradation products.

O + Acetylenes

In the use of the discharge-flow technique for the study of O—C_2H_2 reaction [281, 339, 340], ground state O-atoms were produced by titrating N-atoms generated in microwave discharges with nitric oxide [see (11.37)]. In this manner the reaction could be studied in the absence of molecular O_2.

Although there is disagreement on the detailed mechanism of the O + C_2H_2

reaction, it is generally accepted that the initial step is

$$C_2H_2 + O \rightarrow C_2H_2O^* \rightarrow CH_2 + CO \tag{11.89}$$

The addition of O-atoms to C_2H_2 in the same way as that observed in the O—C_2H_4 reaction indicates that the rate constant is probably of similar magnitude. Values of $k_{89} = 5 \times 10^{10}$ to 9×10^{10} cm^3 mole^{-1} sec^{-1} have been reported [281, 339, 340].

The dominant second step must be the reaction of O-atoms with CH_2 radicals produced,

$$O + CH_2 \rightarrow HCO + H \tag{11.90}$$

or

$$O + CH_2 \rightarrow CO + 2H \tag{11.91}$$

Observation of HCO emission in the $O + C_2H_2$ reaction led Arrington et al. [339] to suggest (11.90). Brown and Thrush [281], however, consider that this emission is a minor process and that excited HCO probably dissociates to H and CO, giving a result kinetically indistinguishable from (11.91). The H-atoms formed would undergo the acetylene-catalyzed recombination.

The initial step of the reaction of O-atoms with methylacetylene, by analogy to (11.89), is thought to be [281, 339]

$$CH_3C{\equiv}CH + O \rightarrow C_3H_4O^* \rightarrow CH_3CH + CO \tag{11.92}$$

and is a much faster reaction than with acetylene. Since large amounts of C_2H_2 were observed early in the reaction, it could be assumed that the ethylidene radicals, similar to those produced in the photolysis of diazoethane [341], methyl ketene [342], or 3-methyldiazirine [343], rapidly isomerize to excited ethylene molecules which decompose to C_2H_2 and H_2.

$$CH_3CH \rightarrow C_2H_4^* \rightarrow C_2H_2 + H_2 \tag{11.93}$$

O + Alkanes

In the reactions of O-atoms with saturated hydrocarbons, hydrogen abstraction rather than oxygen addition is assumed to be the initial reaction and the reaction rate is usually lower than that of O-atom addition to olefins. However, only some scattered reports are available concerning the chemistry of O-atoms with saturated hydrocarbons [302].

The initial step in the reaction of O-atoms with methane is

$$O + CH_4 \rightarrow CH_3 + OH \tag{11.94}$$

The rate constants obtained from the ESR technique [281, 282a] in the discharge-flow system, the mass spectrometric analysis [344] in a stirred-flow reactor, and the NO titration technique [330] in the discharge-flow system are in reasonable agreement. Cadle and Allen [330], using an O_2 discharge, also found that much more atomic O was removed per mole of CH_4 and that the rate constants were greatly increased. Brown and Thrush [281] consider that formaldehyde is not an important intermediate in the absence of O_2 molecules based on H-atom yields. The suggested steps are

$$O + CH_3 \to CO + H_2 + H \tag{11.95}$$

$$O + OH \to O_2 + H \tag{11.96}$$

The ESR study of the reaction of C_2H_6 with O-atoms by Westenberg and de Haas [282a] showed that the rate was greater than the reaction with CH_4 near room temperature. The initial step is again thought to be the hydrogen abstraction

$$O + C_2H_6 \to C_2H_5 + OH \tag{11.97}$$

and the OH produced probably undergoes (11.96). The C_2H_5 radical may react further with an O-atom to form C_2H_4.

The conclusions presented by Avramenko and Kolesnikova [263] regarding the chemistry of O-atoms with saturated hydrocarbons are quite different. They considered that the reaction of O-atoms with CH_4 proceeds by two parallel steps to form CH_2O or CH_2, the latter reacting with O_2 to form CO. For C_2H_6, C_3H_8, and n-C_4H_{10}, they suggested that the primary step occurs by scission of C—C bonds to form lower aldehydes.

Wright has studied the reactions of O-atoms with isobutane [345], neopentane, and other alkanes [346] and has proposed that the main reaction is a displacement of two groups (CH_3 and/or H) on the parent hydrocarbon by the O-atom with the attendant formation of a carbonyl bond. He considered that hydrogen abstraction by the O-atom to yield an alkyl radical plays only a minor role because the observed reaction products could not be accounted for quantitatively by assuming an intermediate alkoxy radical presumably formed by subsequent addition of an O-atom to the alkyl radical. For isobutane he concluded that some of the possible displacement reactions following are responsible for the products, rather than isobutoxy radicals $(CH_3)_3CO$ and $(CH_3)_2CHCH_2O$.

$$(CH_3)_3CH + O \to (CH_3)_2CO + CH_3 + H \tag{11.98}$$

$$(CH_3)_3CH + O \to CH_3CHO + 2CH_3 \tag{11.99}$$

$$(CH_3)_3CH + O \to (CH_3)_2CHCHO + 2H \tag{11.100}$$

O + O-Containing Compounds

Recent work on the reactions of O-atoms with acetaldehyde [347] and with ketene [307] using the discharge-flow technique are examples. These reactions, similar to those involving H-atoms, apparently proceed initially either by hydrogen abstraction or oxygen addition, depending on the degree of saturation of the substrate.

Thus reaction with CH_3CHO [347] proceeds according to the following sequence

$$CH_3CHO + O \rightarrow CH_3CO + OH \qquad (11.101)$$

$$CH_3CHO + OH \rightarrow CH_3CO + H_2O \qquad (11.102)$$

$$CH_3CO + O \rightarrow CH_3CO_2 \qquad (11.103)$$

$$CH_3CO_2 \rightarrow CH_3 + CO_2 \qquad (11.104)$$

$$CH_3 + CH_3CHO \rightarrow CH_4 + CH_3CO \qquad (11.105)$$

which is essentially similar to that proposed by Cvetanovic [348, 349] using mercury-photosensitized decomposition of N_2O and the photolysis of NO_2. The initial step in the reaction with CH_2CO [307] is

$$O + CH_2CO \rightarrow [C_2H_2O_2]^* \rightarrow \text{Products} \qquad (11.106)$$

and the excited adduct is expected to decompose rapidly to form various products and radicals, which in turn would react further with additional O-atoms. Various modes of decomposition of the adduct could account for the reaction products—CO_2, CO, H_2O, H_2CO, H_2, and H—but the details are still uncertain.

6 REACTIONS AND FORMATION OF SIMPLE HYDROCARBONS IN DISCHARGES

Hydrocarbons undergo extensive rearrangements in discharges and a great many can be formed via discharge reactions, although not in a pure state [15, 25, 350].

Reactions of Methane

The reactions of methane have been studied by so many workers under such a wide variety of conditions [1, 23, 113, 350, and papers cited therein] that a reasonable reaction mechanism can be postulated. The reaction of CH_4 in a discharge produces H_2, hydrocarbons, polymers, and carbon. The principal products vary depending upon the reaction conditions; they can be C_2H_2, C_2H_6, $C_2H_6 + C_3H_8$, C_4, and higher hydrocarbons, or polymers. Some workers report that addition of H_2 or Ar increases the rate of reaction of CH_4 in a discharge [351–354].

Bois d'Enghien and co-workers [1] caused CH_4 to react in an inductively coupled rf discharge (10 to 23 MHz) at pressures of 5 to 20 torr and flow rates of 500 to 2000 ml/min. With low power input, decomposition of CH_4 was only a few percent; C_2H_6 was the main product, and small amounts of C_2H_4, C_2H_2, C_3H_8, and C_3H_6 were formed. This discharge was violet, of low luminosity, and with a maximum temperature of 270°C. At a higher power input, attained by varying the frequency of the input power, decomposition of CH_4 was much greater (up to 42%); the principal products were C_2H_2 and carbon, with small amounts of C_2H_4 and C_2H_6; the discharge was characterized by an intense white emission.

Sieck and Johnsen [354] treated CH_4 in a spark discharge with fused-silica windows adjacent to the discharge to allow the emission to be analyzed on a spectrograph. The apparatus was equipped with a cold-finger trap for condensing products. They also studied the radiolysis of CH_4 in a concurrent series of experiments. The decomposition of CH_4, both with and without added Ar, formed H_2 and C_2 or higher hydrocarbons. Yields of C_2H_6, C_2H_4, and C_3H_8 were small, but increased, relative to the acetylene produced, as the pressure in the system was lowered from 760 to 0.02 torr. An excess of Ar accelerated the specific rate of decomposition of CH_4, giving essentially the same product distribution.

At 760 torr, emission from CH_4 and the Ar–CH_4 mixture in the discharge consisted of bands arising from CH, C_2, and (probably) atomic carbon, but no luminescence was observed from the Ar in the mixture. As the pressure in the system was decreased, spectra from excited H-atoms (Balmer series) appeared both in CH_4 and Ar–CH_4 and spectra from the radiative de-excitation of Ar and singly ionized argon appeared. The spectral distribution at very low pressures in the discharge resembled that obtained from the mixture under 2-MeV electron bombardment at 1 atm.

These results indicate that for the spark discharge at 1 atm the initial decomposition of methane must be by nonionic processes. Since no emission is obtained from Ar in a 9:1 mixture although the CH_4 decomposes nine times faster, the CH_4 molecule must be excited via energy transfer processes involving the lowest metastable state in Ar (11.5 eV) which is below the ionization potential of CH_4 (13.0 eV) [355]. The absence of Ar luminescence indicates that only the lowest-lying excited rare gas states are populated; these states eventually transfer their excitation energy in a quenching process, leading to decomposition of the CH_4 via a free-radical mechanism. In a CH_4 discharge (without Ar) at 760 torr, the products resemble those obtained from the photolysis of CH_4 with subionization photons [267, 356, 358]. This latter process is also described by the initial production of free radicals.

At 760 torr the maximum electron energies are quite low owing to the short mean free paths at this pressure. As the pressure in the discharge is lowered, the electrons have increasingly higher average energies, as evidenced by the gradual appearance of transitions from the higher excited states of Ar and Ar^+. At very low pressures the spectrum differs only slightly from that obtained from the high-energy radiolysis, and the product distribution is also similar. At 760 torr, where the spark discharge-induced decomposition is ascribed to excitation and free-radical processes, acetylene and hydrogen are the major products. At lower pressures the spectra indicate an increasing contribution from ionic processes, the relative yield of acetylene becomes vanishingly small, and the product distribution approaches that found in high-energy radiolysis.

The reactions of CH_4 in cooled discharge reactors have been investigated [81, 132b, 359, 360]. If the initial products can be quenched immediately, rather than undergoing secondary reactions in the discharge, the product distribution will often be different and may provide information on the reaction mechanism. Tickner [81] passed CH_4 through a dc glow discharge at low pressures in a reactor cooled with either liquid or solid N_2. The main product was a solid polymer, with the empirical formula $C_{1.00}H_{1.01}$, which formed on the cathode. Hydrocarbons up to C_5 were also formed.

The amount of C_2H_4 recovered at about 1% CH_4 decomposition increased nearly 10-fold when the discharge tube temperature was lowered from that of liquid N_2 ($-196°C$) to the triple point of N_2 ($-210°C$). The amount of C_2H_6 (the main gaseous product) recovered increased by about one-third; the yield of C_3H_6 and C_4H_8 decreased. Approximately the same amount of C_2H_2 formed as of C_2H_4. Yields of the C_2 products decreased while yields of the higher hydrocarbons increased with increasing current. These facts indicate that the higher hydrocarbons are formed at the expense of the C_2 products.

Most of the C_2H_2, and possibly part of the C_2H_4, appeared to form in those regions of the discharge where the number of high-energy electrons is fairly large. Tickner interprets this to mean that C_2H_2 formation depends on ionization processes. With regard to the solid polymer $(CH)_n$, it is possible that C_2H_2 formed near the cathode becomes ionized and perhaps dissociated, and then polymerized in a series of ion-molecule reactions.

Kawahara [357] studied the formation of C_2 hydrocarbons from CH_4 flowing through a microwave discharge. The yields of C_2H_6 and C_2H_4 reached maximum values of 8 and 9%, respectively, while the yield of C_2H_2 kept on increasing with residence time to exceed 40% based on CH_4. The product distribution indicates differences between the microwave discharge reaction of CH_4 and those in electrode discharges.

Kraaijveld and Waterman [83] studied the decomposition of CH_4 flowing through a high-voltage, low-frequency, ac glow discharge. Using two reactors in series at a pressure of 10 torr they achieved a maximum conversion of 91%. The products consisted of 23% C_2H_2, 39% C_4 and higher-molecular-weight hydrocarbons, H_2, C_2H_6, C_2H_4, and C_3 hydrocarbons.

Kawahata et al. [361] studied the decomposition of CH_4 flowing through electrodeless concentric-tube reactors at 760 torr. The discharge (a blue glow) was generated by high-voltage 10-kHz alternating current. A typical product, for a residence time of approximately 60 sec and an external reactor wall temperature of 200 to 230°C, consisted of 68% CH_4, 20% H_2, 6% C_2H_6, 2% C_3H_8, and approximately 2.5% C_4 and higher-molecular-weight hydrocarbons. In some runs small amounts of C_2H_4 and C_3H_6 formed. This is of interest since significant conversions of CH_4 were obtained under conditions in which apparently no C_2H_2 was formed.

Ponnamperuma and co-workers [362, 363] examined the hydrocarbons, up to C_9 and higher, produced from CH_4 in different discharges. Unsaturates and aromatics predominated in the products from higher-current-density ac glow discharges; saturated hydrocarbons including branched-chain compounds predominated in the products from the lower-current-density glow and high-voltage semicorona discharges. In one semicorona run results similar to those of Kawahata et al. were obtained: C_2H_6 and C_3H_8 were the major gaseous products, some C_2H_4 and C_3H_6 (but no C_2H_2) were also formed.

Burton and co-workers [351, 364, 365] studied the formation of C_2H_2 from CH_4 flowing through a dc glow discharge at atmospheric pressure. In runs made with mixtures of $CH_4 + D_2$ and $CH_4 + CD_4$, CH_2D_2 was by far the most abundant deuterated methane formed. These results indicate that the concentration of CH_2 in the discharge is relatively high, compared with other radicals. In experiments on CH_4–H_2 mixtures, the rate constant for reaction of CH_4 appeared to increase with increasing dilution by H_2. Also, less carbon (believed to come from decomposition of C_2H_2) was formed with H_2 initially present.

Mechanism of Reaction of CH_4

The reactions of CH_4 in a discharge are usually discussed in terms of free-radical mechanisms even though ions are formed from CH_4 and have been shown to be present in discharges [199, 208], and ion-molecule reactions in CH_4 could form the principal products observed. The ionization potential for CH_4 is 13.0 eV, but the distribution of the energies of the electrons in a discharge is such that there are very few high-energy electrons ($>$10 eV). This limits ionization as an initiation mechanism for reactions.

It has been shown [366] that energetic electrons can undergo inelastic collisions with CH_4, transferring 10.12 eV of energy to the molecule, thus causing it to become electronically excited. Bois d'Enghien et al. [1] assume that this same process occurs in discharges and that

$$CH_4 + e^- \rightarrow CH_4{}^* \,(10.12\,eV) + e^- \qquad (11.107)$$

is the initiation step for reactions of CH_4. The electronically excited $CH_4{}^*$ is assumed to dissociate, by analogy with photochemical studies, by the process

$$CH_4{}^* \rightarrow CH_2 \,(singlet) + H_2 \qquad (11.108)$$

Singlet CH_2 then inserts into another CH_4 (present in large excess) to produce $C_2H_6^*$

$$CH_2 \text{ (singlet)} + CH_4 \rightarrow C_2H_6^* \tag{11.109}$$

which is deactivated by collision or at the wall. This series of reactions is assumed to occur in low energy discharges where C_2H_6 is the main product, and little or no C_2H_2 is formed. The work of Burton and co-workers [351, 364, 365], when CH_2 was postulated as an important intermediate in the discharge, is in line with this.

Manton and Tickner [367] also provide evidence for a free radical mechanism for the reaction of CH_4 by electron bombardment. The decomposition of CH_4 by electrons having energies between 15 and 100 eV gave products similar to those from a discharge, and the rate of formation of products varied only slightly with electron energy. If the products were formed mainly by a process depending on ion formation, then the rate of formation would have fallen off rapidly below 50 eV because of the rapid decrease in the ionization cross section of CH_4 [368]. Thus although some ions are undoubtedly formed by collisions with the few very energetic electrons, there is no evidence that they play an important role in the formation of products in a discharge.

Since CH_3 is present in a discharge through CH_4 [369], $C_2H_6^*$ could also form by

$$CH_3 + CH_3 \rightarrow C_2H_6^* \tag{11.110}$$

$C_2H_6^*$, if not deactivated, could dissociate

$$C_2H_6^* \rightarrow C_2H_4^* + H_2 \tag{11.111}$$

$C_2H_4^*$, if not deactivated, could then dissociate

$$C_2H_4^* \rightarrow C_2H_2^* + H_2 \tag{11.112}$$

to produce $C_2H_2^*$, which would either be deactivated or might polymerize.

A mechanism similar to that described above is discussed by Kondrat'ev [23]. Additional evidence for the formation and reaction of $C_2H_6^*$ and $C_2H_4^*$ is furnished by Tickner [81] and McCarthy [132b]. In his study of the production of C_2H_2 from CH_4 in a microwave discharge, McCarthy obtained C_2H_6 and C_2H_4 in the products only when the effluent from the discharge impinged directly on a wall cooled by liquid N_2.

In higher-energy discharges, where C_2H_4 and, more importantly, C_2H_2 are the principal products, Bois d'Enghien et al. [1] assume that the concentration of CH_2 increases and the reaction

$$CH_2 + CH_2 \rightarrow C_2H_4^* \tag{11.113}$$

can then occur, perhaps followed by (11.112). Alternatively, in higher energy discharges, CH_4^* can be assumed to dissociate by

$$CH_4^* \rightarrow CH + H_2 + H \tag{11.114}$$

to give relatively high concentrations of CH. Some aspects of its chemistry are discussed in the recent work on photolysis of CH_4 [267, 356, 358]. There, rates of reactions such as

$$CH + CH_4 \rightarrow C_2H_4 + H \qquad (11.115)$$

$$CH + CH \rightarrow C_2H_2 \qquad (11.116)$$

$$CH + H_2 \rightarrow CH_3 \qquad (11.117)$$

have been measured. More recent studies by the same workers [370] have shown that atomic C can react with CH_4 to form mixtures of C_2H_2 and C_2H_4.

Concerning the formation of C_2H_2, there is general agreement only on the point that higher-energy conditions in a discharge favor its formation. Clarke [371] discusses the high temperature reactions of graphite, H_2, and various C_nH_x species, and points out that various workers have postulated species such as C_2H, C_3H, C_4H, CH, and CH_2 as precursors for the formation of C_2H_2 to explain the experimental results.

C_3H_6 and C_3H_8 could be formed in a discharge via insertion reactions such as

$$CH_2 + C_2H_4 \rightarrow C_3H_6 \qquad (11.118)$$

$$CH_2 + C_2H_6 \rightarrow C_3H_8 \qquad (11.119)$$

and likewise for C_4H_{10}, and so on. These reactions would be in accord with Tickner's data that the yield of C_2 compounds decreased when the yield of C_3 compounds increased. In another study of the photolysis of CH_4 [372], reactions such as

$$CH_2 + CH_4 \rightarrow C_2H_6{}^* \rightarrow CH_3CH + H_2 \qquad (11.120)$$

$$CH_3CH \rightarrow C_2H_4{}^* \rightarrow C_2H_2 + H_2 \qquad (11.93)$$

and the insertion reaction

$$CH_3CH + CH_4 \rightarrow C_3H_8 \qquad (11.121)$$

have been postulated.

Variables Affecting Production of C_2H_2 from CH_4

In an arc discharge, where gas temperatures are usually in excess of $2000°K$, C_2H_2 is produced commercially from CH_4 and other hydrocarbons. Here, the effluent gases from the arc must be quenched rapidly to avoid thermal decomposition of the C_2H_2. Miller [42] reviews in detail both arc and low-temperature discharge processes for making C_2H_2. In addition to the usual C_2 to C_4 hydrocarbons formed by reaction of CH_4, arc-produced C_2H_2 has been shown to contain traces of many higher-molecular-weight unsaturated hydrocarbons [373, 374].

In one of the first papers on chemical reactions in microwave discharges, McCarthy [132b] discussed the synthesis of nitrogen oxides and the decomposition of CH_4. When CH_4 flowed through a microwave discharge, up to

100% of the CH_4 could react; as much as 95% of the reacted CH_4 formed C_2H_2. (No polymers were reported formed.) McCarthy correlated his results in terms of a parameter $\beta = pZ_s/E^2t$, where p is the pressure, Z_s is the shunt impedance, E is the electric field strength, and t is the time the molecules spent in the discharge. The yield of C_2H_2 increased with increasing values of β. This parameter may be useful for correlating the yield of a discharge reaction with the experimental variables.

In the production of C_2H_2 in an arc, and wherever large-scale production in discharges is considered, it is important that the specific energy consumption (SEC, kilowatt-hour per kilogram product) be as low as possible. For C_2H_2 from CH_4, the minimum theoretical value of SEC is 6.45 kW-hr/kg C_2H_2; commercial arc processes operate at as low as 10 kW-hr/kg C_2H_2 [42].

In very detailed studies of several process variables, Hesp and co-workers [74, 113] caused CH_4 to react in anomalous glow discharge reactors (50 Hz ac, maximum potential 2000 V, maximum current 300 mA, graphite electrodes, 4 cm apart). High yields of C_2H_2 were obtained (up to 82 wt % on a C basis); H_2, C_2H_6, C_2H_4, a polymer, and a carbon-black-like material also formed.

Gas temperatures were measured with a thermocouple at the center of the discharge and increased from 815°C at 20 torr to 1050°C at 150 torr. The experimental yields of C_2H_2 were considerably higher than the calculated yields based on the thermodynamic equilibrium

$$2CH_4 \rightarrow C_2H_2 + 3H_2$$

over this range of temperatures and pressures.

Figure 11.17 shows the effects of flow rate and power input on the yield of C_2H_2 in a spherical reactor (see Fig. 11.18) at 60-torr CH_4 pressure [74]. C_2H_2 yields were higher in this reactor than for the same nominal conditions in the cylindrical reactor, owing to intrinsic differences in the flow and temperature patterns. Studies employing -300 B.S.-mesh coke particles indicated that radial forces—probably resulting from thermal and electrical effects—caused the particles to move away from the discharge toward the walls. In the spherical reactor, the coke particles formed a well-defined ring on the wall in line with the lower part of the discharge.

The mean distance d diffused by acetylene molecules in one contact time is $d = (2Dt)^{1/2}$, where $D =$ diffusion coefficient and $t =$ contact time (in seconds). In most of the experiments, d was greater than the reactor diameter, that is, C_2H_2 molecules were able to reach the walls in both reactors. The wall temperature in the spherical reactor, however, was lower. For this reason, wall reactions—which may involve deactivation of active species, their polymerization leading to carbon formation, and decomposition of C_2H_2—were less pronounced in the spherical reactor, and acetylene yields were

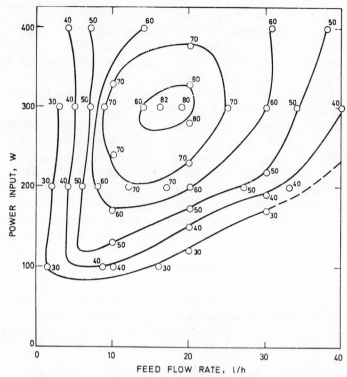

Fig. 11.17 Optimization curves for yield of acetylene from methane in spherical reactor used by Hesp and Rigby [74]. Numbers against points are yields of acetylene (wt. % C basis).

higher. A further reason for higher acetylene yields in the spherical reactor may be that radicals moving from the discharge to the walls have longer to react in the gas phase, where acetylene formation is more likely than carbon-forming reactions.

Kobozev et al. [375] have shown that Hg may catalyze the formation of C_2H_2 from CH_4. To check this interesting possibility, Hesp and co-workers placed about 8 gm of Hg in a hollow disk at the top of the lower electrode where some was evaporated into the CH_4 by the heat from the discharge. Their results showed that Hg, in addition to promoting the overall conversion of CH_4, selectively catalyzed C_2H_2 formation in preference to the carbon-forming reactions. They also investigated the effect of several variables on SEC, the minimum value of which (16.7 kW-hr/kg C_2H_2) is observed when CH_4 preheated to 350°C reacts at low power in the spherical reactor. In largescale operations and with the use of heat exchangers, it may be possible to reduce SEC values further. Also, other feedstocks such as *n*-heptane,

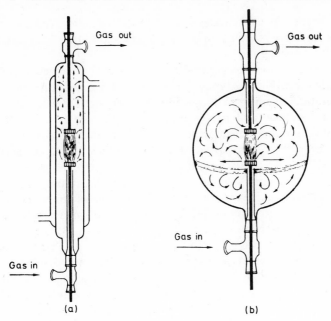

Fig. 11.18 Typical flow patterns in the (*a*) cylindrical and (*b*) spherical reactors used by Hesp and Rigby [74]. Surface/volume ratio (*a*) 1.67:1; (*b*) 0.53:1.

cyclohexane, or benzene can react to form acetylene [41]. A pilot plant to evaluate the process is being constructed [376].

The Russians have done much work on the production of acetylene [23, 377–381]. Most of the papers in the volume edited by Pechuro [20] discuss this subject.

Reactions of Other Aliphatic Hydrocarbons

By comparison with CH_4, the amount of work reported on the reactions of any other hydrocarbon is sparse. The reaction products are complex mixtures. Miquel and co-workers studied the reactions of CH_4, C_2H_6, C_3H_8, n-C_4H_{10} [382, 383], and C_2H_4 [384, 385]. Reddy and Burton also studied the glow discharge reaction of C_2H_4 [386]. Borisova and Eremin have many publications on discharge chemistry [20, 23, 381] including recent papers on the reactions of C_2H_6 [387], C_2H_4 [388], and C_2H_2 [389]. Kupperman and Burton also studied n-C_4H_{10} [390], as did Badereu et al. [391]. Callister and Thornton studied the reactions of isoprene [392], and Coates has passed n-C_6H_{14} through a microwave discharge [393].

In a series of papers, Schüler and Arnold [394–398] postulated various molecular bond-breaking schemes initiated by molecular activation upon electron impact to explain the lower-molecular-weight products obtained from the discharge reactions of n-C_4H_{10} and cyclo-C_6H_{12}. They also studied the effects of varying the frequency in the low ac range.

Breukink and co-workers [399–403a] investigated the reactions of several C_4 to C_8 hydrocarbons as liquid foams; they used a concentric-tube reactor at temperatures from -75 to $-150°C$ and H_2 or Ar as the carrier gas. Isobutene, 1-butene, and styrene polymerized extensively under these conditions; cracking to lower-molecular-weight hydrocarbons also occurred.

When propylene was passed through a high-voltage, concentric-tube reactor, at least 82 peaks were observed in the gas chromatogram of the product; the main products consisted of C_6 hydrocarbons (principally 4-methyl-1-pentene, 2,3-dimethylbutane, 1,5-hexadiene, and 1-hexene), H_2, and C_1 to C_4 hydrocarbons [403b]. Cyclohexene, in a similar reaction, produced small amounts of 3-cyclohexylcyclohexene, 3,3'-bicyclohexenyl, bicyclohexyl, cyclohexane, C_1 to C_4 hydrocarbons, H_2, polymer, an unidentified C_{12} compound, and cyclohexadiene. The authors speculate that the dimeric compounds formed by free-radical reactions and that C_2H_4 and butadiene formed from excited cyclohexene by a reverse Diels-Alder reaction.

In a study concerned primarily with the reactions of aromatic hydrocarbons in a microwave discharge, Rodemeyer [404] has shown that acetylene, 1-butyne, and cis-2-butene, in either H_2 or He carrier gas, formed small amounts of benzene, toluene, ethylbenzene, styrene, and phenylacetylene. Trace amounts of naphthalene and indene were also produced from C_2H_2.

In general, in a high-temperature arc or plasma jet, any hydrocarbon undergoes extensive thermal cracking and forms principally C_2H_2. However, Stokes, who studied the reactions of terpenes [405], found that by feeding the liquid terpene downstream into a helium plasma flame, he obtained a 26% yield of myrcene from β-pinene, and 1 to 2% yields of α-pinene and p-cymene from α-terpinene, and limonene from α-pinene.

Formation of Hydrocarbons from H_2 + Carbon Oxides

Hydrocarbons and other organic compounds can be formed in discharges in high yields from H_2 + CO_2 and H_2 + CO mixtures. Fischer and Peters [406] circulated gas at 10-torr pressure through a glow discharge (50-Hz), a mercury vapor pump, a liquid-air-cooled trap, and back to the discharge. The yield of hydrocarbons from CO was very low for one pass, but almost total conversion was achieved by recirculating the gases for 100 min.

Lunt [56] and Epple and Apt [57] worked with capacitively coupled rf (2- to 110-MHz) discharges in concentric-tube reactors containing static gas at pressures up to 300 torr. Conversions of H_2 + CO and H_2 + CO_2 to

CH_4 were quite high for reaction times of several minutes; no other hydrocarbons were formed. McTaggart [407] and Vastola et al. [408], working with microwave discharges in flow systems at pressures of a few torr, formed only traces of hydrocarbons from $H_2 + CO$. Here, the gas passed through the discharge only once, and the residence time was a fraction of a second.

More recent work [4] has shown that in a microwave discharge in static gas, initial pressures of $H_2 + CO$ (5:1) of 12 and 50 torr gave conversions of CO to $CH_4 + C_2H_2$ of approximately 17 and 22% for reaction times of $\frac{1}{2}$ to 4 min. H_2O and CO_2 are also formed in these reactions. When H_2O vapor was added to the reactants, hydrocarbon formation was repressed. With $H_2 + CO_2$, no hydrocarbons were formed unless H_2O was frozen out as it formed. Conversion of CO or CO_2 to hydrocarbons was increased to as high as 90% when the reaction products were removed, as they formed, by a liquid nitrogen trap. The principal products were $C_2H_6 + C_2H_2$, plus small amounts of CH_4, C_3, and C_4 hydrocarbons.

The different conversions of CO and CO_2 under varying conditions are explained by assuming that the reaction in the discharge reached a stationary state or pseudoequilibrium where production of hydrocarbons was limited by the back reaction with H_2O and/or CO_2. When reaction products were removed from the discharge by being frozen out, the stationary state shifted according to Le Chatelier's principle and more hydrocarbons formed. Addition of H_2O to the reactants shifted the stationary state so as to inhibit hydrocarbon formation.

Martinotti et al. [409] passed $H_2 + C_3O_2$ through a microwave discharge under conditions in which C_3O_2 fragments form $C + 2CO$. As much as 38% of the C-atoms produced reacted to form gaseous hydrocarbons, principally C_2H_2 and CH_4, but small amounts of C_2H_6, C_2H_4, C_3H_8, and C_3H_6 were also formed [410].

7 REACTIONS OF CARBONS AND COALS WITH ACTIVE SPECIES PRODUCED IN ELECTRICAL DISCHARGES

The gasification of carbon and coal involves atomic and free-radical species that are usually produced at high temperatures. Various methods such as resistively heated graphite, high-intensity arcs, and plasma jets have been employed for the studies of the gasification reactions, but the mechanisms are not fully understood. Atoms and other active species can be readily produced in a discharge at temperatures much lower than those attained in an arc or a plasma jet and therefore studies of the interactions of atomic species with carbon and coal by this means should improve our understanding of the gasification processes. In general, such atoms may undergo two basic types of reaction with the solid carbon: (1) recombination of atoms on the catalytic surface, and (2) atom-solid chemical reaction resulting in the formation of C-containing compounds, both volatile and nonvolatile. The reactive collisions between gaseous atoms and solids (metals, semiconductors, and carbons), which result in the formation and rupture of chemical bonds, have recently been discussed by Wise and Wood [411].

Reaction of Carbons

Hydrogen Atoms

H-atoms produced in a discharge react with carbon black. The reaction yielded mainly CH_4, with small amounts of C_2 and C_3 hydrocarbons [412]; spectral evidence indicates that CH radicals are involved [413]. The reaction with wood chars also formed CH_4 as the main product [414].

Vastola et al. [408] and Shahin [415] found that in a microwave discharge in hydrogen carbon forms CH_4 and C_2H_2 as the major products with smaller amounts of other gaseous and polymeric hydrocarbons, and that the reaction occurs appreciably only when carbon is in the discharge zone. This suggests that when carbon is in the dischaige zone the reaction involves reactive species other than H-atoms. Thus it is thought that in a hydrogen discharge transport of carbon from the solid to the vapor phase takes place because of the bombardment of the carbon by energetic ions and electrons and that the gaseous carbon species react with H-atoms or CH species to form hydrocarbons. In fact, a kinetic study of the reaction of H-atoms with carbon located downstream from a discharge indicated that the reaction forming hydrocarbons was much slower than the catalytic recombination of H-atoms in the temperature range 90 to 230°C [416]. The activation energies of these competing reactions are about 9 and 2 kcal mole^{-1}, respectively.

The low reactivity of H-atoms with carbon outside the luminous discharge zone contrasts with the high reactivity of atomic O which attacks carbon even when far removed from the discharge zone. Although the reaction of carbon in a hydrogen discharge probably occurs via electrons and ionic species, one suspects that the temperature of carbon may also need to be elevated. Shahin [415] observed a faint glow on the carbon and estimated the surface temperature to be about 700°C.

Oxygen Atoms

Carbon reacts readily with O-atoms in or downstream from an oxygen discharge to form CO and CO_2. The reaction appears to be complicated and the results are contradictory despite the extensive studies that have been carried out. The complication is attributable, in part, to the sources and impurities of the carbons and to the type of discharge employed.

Streznewski and Turkevich [417] treated carbon films and a carbon black produced by igniting benzene with atomic O in the temperature range 20 to 100°C. The rate of reaction was temperature independent and first order with respect to O-atom concentration; CO_2 was the only reaction product. Blackwood and McTaggart [418], studying the reaction of graphite, wood charcoal, and industrial diamonds, suggested CO as the primary product.

A further point of controversy concerns the activation energy for the reaction of O-atoms with carbon. Values of activation energy between 0 and 10 kcal mole^{-1} have been reported at various temperature ranges [417, 419–422]. Marsh et al. [421] found that the rate of oxidation is not influenced appreciably by the carbon used, and that the activation energy (about 10 kcal mole^{-1}) diminishes above 200°C, becoming almost 0 at 350°C. Based on the observation that the activation energy for gasification by molecular O_2 is several times that for atomic O, they concluded that the rate-controlling step is the formation of carbon-oxygen surface complexes rather than the desorption of such surface complexes. Evidence was given to show that surface oxides retard the rate of oxidation.

Studies using microwave discharges [408, 423] showed that the percentage of reacted O-atoms decreased, as did the $CO:CO_2$ product ratio (always greater than 1) with increasing distance between the carbon and the discharge. Further, between 0.03 to 0.11 torr, the concentration of atomic O decreased with increasing O_2 pressure at a given distance from the discharge. These observations are consistent with the finding of Blackwood and McTaggart [418] that the $CO:CO_2$ ratio in the product stream increases as the pressure is lowered.

These workers seem to agree that CO is the primary product but differ as to the possible modes of formation of CO_2: a direct combination of CO with atomic O on the carbon surface [418], reaction between electronically excited molecular O_2 and carbon [408], and a homogeneous reaction of CO with atomic O [423].

Marsh et al. [424] used an electron microscope to examine the surface changes on carbons and graphites caused by oxidation with atomic O. While molecular O_2 preferentially attacks certain active sites, which may be the defect structure of graphite [425], atomic O produces a general background of conical pits over the entire surface.

Nitrogen Atoms

Zinman [426] studied the reaction of carbon rods with activated nitrogen at 800°C and found that HCN was the principal product. Presumably the hydrogen originated from impurities in the carbon. Giberson [427] studied the reaction of graphite in a N_2 discharge and obtained paracyanogen as the principal product deposited on the reactor wall. Some HCN was also observed.

In Goldstein's study [428] the graphite was carefully outgassed and treated in the temperature range 1400 to 2100°C with active nitrogen produced in a microwave discharge. C_2N_2, HCN, and CO_2 resulted from this reaction, but the production of HCN and CO_2 is believed to be the result of impurities in the N_2 or graphite. Activation energies of 17.6 and 19.2 kcal mole^{-1} were calculated for the production of C_2N_2 for two different graphites.

Reactions of Coals

Fu and Blaustein [429] pyrolyzed coals of different ranks in a microwave discharge. Various reactive species such as H-species, O-species, gaseous C, and hydrogenated carbon fragments (CH, C_2H, or C_xH_y) could be produced from coal in the discharge, and these in turn decompose or combine with each other to form the products—H_2, H_2O, CO, CO_2, and hydrocarbons (mainly C_2H_2). Fast quenching of the primary products by a liquid nitrogen trap gave higher yields of C_2H_2 and other hydrocarbons (up to C_6), but no significant amounts of H_2 and CO. The initial presence of low pressures of gases such as argon increased the rate of volatilization of coal and yielded greater amounts of lower hydrocarbons (below C_4), C_2H_2, H_2, and CO. Over 30% of the carbon in a high-volatile bituminous coal could be recovered as hydrocarbons from the discharge pyrolysis.

Reactions of coals in microwave discharges in H_2 and H_2O vapor [430] gave greater gasification and yielded more hydrocarbons than the discharge pyrolysis in the presence or absence of Ar, indicating that H, OH, and O-species attack the coal surface and interact with the active species derived from the coal. In the H_2O discharge, in addition to large amounts of H_2 and CO, C_2H_2 and CH_4 also formed. In the H_2 discharge over 40% of the carbon in the bituminous coal could be converted to hydrocarbons, mainly C_2H_2.

If O_2 is passed through an rf discharge [431, 432], the active O-species generated will oxidize the carbon in coal and the mineral matter can be recovered in a relatively unaltered state. This process is called low-temperature ashing. Gluskoter [431] reported that with an ashing temperature between 150 and 200°C the residues of the bituminous coals are composed of clay minerals rather than the oxides obtained by high-temperature ashing. This technique has been successfully applied to the low-temperature ashing of many other materials [28].

8 REACTIONS AND FORMATION OF AROMATIC COMPOUNDS

Benzene and Alkylbenzenes

Several recent papers have appeared on reactions of benzene and alkylbenzenes [8, 9, 85, 404, 433–435, 437, 442a, 443–445]. Each contains many references to earlier work, which is abundant. The recent papers have detailed product analyses, reflecting improvement in experimental technique and aiding understanding of the mechanism of reactions in discharges. In general, the products formed depend markedly on the experimental conditions.

Benzene was allowed to react in a 15-kV, 60-Hz semicorona reactor consisting of a threaded steel rod electrode positioned down the center of a long Pyrex tube (annular gap spacing 4 mm), around which was a helical copper-tubing cooling coil which served as the outer electrode [85]. The benzene in a reservoir vaporized into a stream of He (100 ml/min) and the mixture passed through the reactor at atmospheric pressure with an 8.5% conversion to benzene-soluble polymer (6%), benzene-insoluble polymer (0.7%), dimer and trimer (0.7%), and acetylene (1%); the recovered unreacted benzene (bright yellow) contained traces of 1,4- and 1,3-cyclohexadiene, fulvene, and cyclohexene.

Very detailed spectral analyses showed that the dimer and trimer fractions were mostly biphenyl plus compounds believed to be C_{18} phenylbenzyl-cyclopentenes and phenylbenzylcyclopentadienes, smaller amounts of o-, p-, and m-terphenyl, and C_{12} benzyl- and methylphenylcyclopentenes or cyclopentadienes. The benzene-insoluble polymer on the reactor glass surface had an infrared spectrum and C/H ratio (1.01) essentially the same as those of the benzene-soluble polymer. The benzene-soluble polymer was fractionated into three molecular-weight ranges (4400, 1600, and 300); these fractions were similar to the benzyl and methylphenyl-substituted cyclopentenes in the dimer and trimer fractions.

Ranney and O'Connor state [85]:

"In the corona discharge many types of energy transfer occur, varying from photolysis to relatively high energy electrons responsible for fragmentation. The low yield of biphenyl suggests that phenyl radical production may not be the primary reaction route leading to polymer formation. Considerable energy should be available to excite benzene to relatively high vibrational levels which would be somewhat below that energy required actually to separate the H radical. At any given time the number of these excited benzene molecules should greatly exceed the phenyl radical population. Fulvene is produced from benzene by ultraviolet energy . . . . Thus, the formation of this isomer with a resonance energy (11–12 kcal/mole) intermediate between benzene and 1,3-cyclohexadiene may be energetically favorable in the corona. Fulvene has been shown to polymerize rapidly under similar conditions with no reversion to benzene.

"The uniformity of the phenyl(benzyl)-cyclopentene ratio throughout all polymer fractions makes it difficult to accept a mechanism based solely on random attack by phenyl radicals on a growing fulvene polymer. The initial synthesis of a monomeric unit comprised of the benzylcyclopentadienyl system with subsequent diene type polymerization is consistent with all our observations."

Stille et al. [433] allowed benzene to react in an inductively coupled rf discharge (14-MHz) in a flow system at 0.2 torr and collected the products in a series of cold traps. Typically, 10% of the benzene vapor reacted to give polymer (5%), biphenyl (2%), fulvene (1%), allene (1%), acetylene (1%), and methylacetylene (trace). Infrared and ultraviolet spectra indicated that the polymers were predominantly poly(p-phenylenes). When D_2 was introduced just downstream from the discharge, or mixed with benzene prior to entering the discharge, 85% of the recovered benzene was benzene-d_1, with only traces of $C_6H_4D_2$. By comparison, reaction of benzene + D_2 in a microwave discharge [404] produced mostly benzene-d_4, -d_5, and -d_6.

When benzene vapor flowed through a capacitively coupled rf discharge (3.7-MHz), depending on conditions, the reaction yielded either total conversion to a solid, nearly white, fluffy polymer, or 30% conversion to liquid polymer and some biphenyl [434]. A high-energy dose (in watt-seconds per mole) and/or low benzene partial pressure favored the former, while a low dose and high partial pressure favored the latter. Spectral data suggest that both polymers are similar to polystyrene, the liquid having an average molecular weight of 617, the solid having a higher molecular weight and being highly cross-linked, high-melting, insoluble, and amorphous, with a high surface area, high electron spin density, and able to chemisorb O_2.

When benzene was passed through a microwave (3000-MHz) discharge at low pressure [435], about 5% reacted to form low-molecular-weight materials (50%), toluene (30%), ethylbenzene (5%), and phenylacetylene (15%). As the authors state, formation of toluene requires a series of severe rearrangements. Schüler and co-workers [10] obtained small amounts of similar products plus cis-1-phenyl-1,3-butadiene and naphthalene by causing benzene to react in a dc glow discharge; large amounts of polymer and biphenyl also formed. Bryce-Smith and Gilbert [436] also formed polymer from benzene in a microwave discharge.

Kraaijveld and Waterman [8, 9, 83] made an extensive study of the reactions of alkylbenzenes in N_2 at low pressure in an ac glow discharge. Yields and product distribution (dimers, polymers, and low-molecular-weight hydrocarbons) varied markedly depending on the experimental conditions. Reaction of benzene produced as much as 11% biphenyl. Toluene was converted (30% reacted) to 1,2-diphenylethane as one main product, plus smaller amounts of phenyltolylmethane, dimethylbiphenyl, and a pentane-insoluble, benzene-soluble polymer, light hydrocarbons (including acetylene), benzene, and H_2. In the total product there were approximately equal amounts of dimer biaryls, polymer, and low-molecular-weight hydrocarbons plus benzene; the ratio diphenylethane/benzene was almost 4:1. (No ethylbenzene was reported.) Reactions of ethylbenzene, xylenes, and n- and isopropylbenzene were also studied by these workers.

Toluene vapor, when passed through an inductively coupled rf discharge

(28-MHz) at low pressure, was converted to products in 12 to 16% yield with 75 to 82% of the toluene recovered unchanged [437]. The liquid products were ethylbenzene, benzene, 1,2-diphenylethane, diphenylmethane, biphenyl, and xylenes. Noncondensable gases and polymer accounted for 6 to 16% of the original toluene, the amount of polymer varying, unaccountably, over a wide range. Experiments with helium carrier gas showed no substantial difference in the products.

Formation of large amounts of dimer biaryls indicates that free radicals are important reaction intermediates. Dinan [437] ran experiments with $C_6H_5CD_3$ and the products were separated by chromatography. Spectral techniques showed that the side chain of the recovered ethylbenzene was heavily deuterated. This presumably forms via the reaction $C_6H_5CD_2 + CD_3$. Toluene + I_2 passed through the discharge produced benzyl iodide, iodobenzene, benzene, ethylbenzene, and methyl iodide. Dinan explains these results by a series of radical combination and H-abstraction reactions involving benzyl, phenyl, and methyl radicals, and gives spectroscopic evidence for the formation of benzyl radical in the discharge. Other workers have also studied the spectra of the benzyl radical in detail [438–441].

Reaction of toluene vapor in a microwave discharge (3000-MHz) in carrier gas (usually He, but Ar gave essentially the same results) gave benzene, ethylbenzene, phenylacetylene, and styrene as principal products [435]. (Reaction of xylenes or ethylbenzene gave similar products.) Approximately 90% of the toluene was recovered unchanged. Minute amounts of xylenes, and low-molecular-weight compounds containing 4 to 6 carbon atoms, H_2, CH_4, C_2H_4, C_2H_2, and tar also formed. Trace amounts of diphenylethane, diphenylmethane, biphenyl, dihydroanthracene, and dihydrophenanthrene were isolated from special runs under conditions in which 90% of the toluene reacted.

The use of CH_4–He and H_2–He mixtures as carrier gases did not affect the product distribution but did reduce tar formation drastically. Use of H_2 as a carrier gas also reduced tar formation and increased the proportion of benzene (as much as 19% of the starting toluene) and decreased the proportion of C_8 aromatics. Rodemeyer [404] studied the effect of other carrier gases; the reaction of toluene and ethane was interesting in that no tar was formed and 25% of the toluene was converted to benzene. Here, since dimer biaryls were formed in, at most, trace amounts, radicals are not important intermediates in the reactions of toluene in the microwave discharge. Also, reaction of toluene + I_2 did not produce any iodoaromatics, which would be expected if radicals were present in the discharge [404].

Suhr and co-workers have studied in detail the reactions of toluene and other alkylbenzenes in an ac glow discharge [442a] and in an rf discharge generated at 10 MHz [443]; in the latter paper he discusses in detail the possible mechanisms for the many products formed. Le Goff has also published recently on the reactions of toluene [444] and ethylbenzene [445] in an rf discharge.

The results for benzene and toluene show that the products formed from them depend markedly on the reaction conditions. There appear to be at least three principal reaction pathways following the initial excitation of the parent molecule but the relative importance of each depends in some as yet unknown way on reaction conditions. These reaction pathways are (1) rupture of one bond in the excited molecule to produce free radicals, for example, formation of $C_6H_5 + H$ from benzene, (2) reaction of the excited parent molecule with another molecule, for example, $C_6H_5CH_3^* + C_6H_5CH_3$ to give $C_6H_6 + C_6H_5CH_2CH_3$, as discussed by Suhr [443], and (3) rearrangement of the excited parent molecule (for example, benzene to fulvene [85, 433] or its fragmentation, followed by reaction of the new intermediates formed.

Formation of Aromatic Compounds

When 1,4-cyclohexadiene was passed at low pressure through an inductively coupled rf discharge (28-MHz), 6% was converted to benzene; 2% of 1,3-cyclohexadiene was converted to benzene under similar conditions. Passage of 1,3-cyclopentadiene through the discharge produced an emission spectrum assigned to cyclopentadiene radicals and the cyclopentadienide anion. Passage of either indene or indan through the discharge produced an emission spectrum attributed in part to the indenide anion. Approximately 4% of the product recovered from indan was shown to be indene [6].

Formation of aromatics from C_1, C_2, and C_4 hydrocarbons has been mentioned in Section 6 [362, 363, 404]. Schüler produced small amounts of naphthalene from *trans*-1-phenyl-1,3-butadiene in a dc glow discharge [10], and fluorene, dihydrophenanthrene, phenanthrene, pyrene, chrysene and coronene have been detected in discharge products [443, 446].

Reaction of Aromatics with Maleic Anhydride

Solutions of maleic anhydride in benzene, toluene, ethylbenzene, and cumene in a discharge produce adducts as shown in Fig. 11.19 [447]. The reaction mixture circulated through a thermostated concentric-tube reactor and flowed down both the inner wall of the outer tube and the outer wall of the inner tube while carrier gas (N_2 or He) passed through the discharge at atmospheric pressure. High-voltage, 3.6- or 8.0-kHz power maintained the discharge.

Production of the type-II adducts of Fig. 11.19 (previously, these have been prepared photochemically) ranged from 8 to 23% of the converted maleic anhydride; type-I adducts and related telomeric polyanhydrides (usually

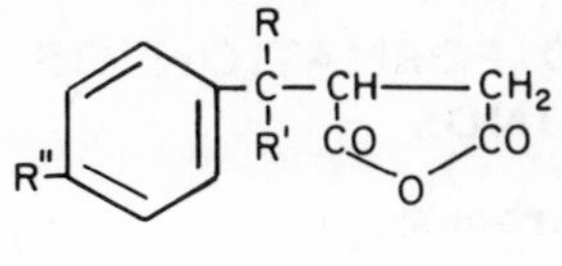

TYPE I

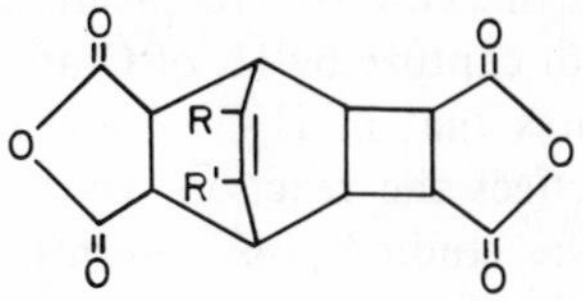

TYPE II

Fig. 11.19   Adducts formed from maleic anhydride + alkylbenzenes [447].

prepared via peroxide-catalyzed chain reactions) formed the balance of the product. From these results the authors concluded that the great majority of active species in the liquid in contact with the discharge are excited molecules and not free radicals.

Reactions of Heterocyclic Compounds

Bittman [7] studied the reactions of several heterocyclics when passed through a microwave discharge in H_2. From each run material was trapped out at $-196°C$ and the products were analyzed by gas chromatography, infrared, and mass spectrometry. As much as 40% of the pyridine that reacted formed benzene; toluene, acetonitrile, benzonitrile, and HCN were other products. Picolines formed pyridine in addition to the above compounds. The product formed from 2,6-lutidine contained 2-methylpyridine and pyridine; 2,4-lutidine formed smaller amounts of these and 4-methylpyridine. The chief gaseous products in each case were C_2H_2 and CH_4.

Quinoline reacted in the discharge to form small amounts of benzene, benzonitrile, toluene, ethylbenzene, and styrene, but no pyridine or isoquinoline. 2-Methylpyrrole formed pyrrole, acetonitrile, and pyridine. Piperidine gave small amounts of acetonitrile and pyridine.

Pyridazine reacted to give a substantial amount of pyrimidine. Pyrazine isomerized in the discharge to give pyrimidine and a trace of pyridazine, but pyrimidine itself is unreactive in the discharge. No benzene or pyridine was detected in the discharge products of any of the diazabenzenes. Bittman discusses in detail the mechanisms of the reactions of these heterocyclic compounds.

9 REACTIONS AND FORMATION OF OTHER ORGANIC COMPOUNDS

Oxidation of Hydrocarbons

Takahashi [448] showed that $CH_4 + H_2O$ vapor at pressures of 10 to 90 torr in an rf-generated (40-MHz) semicorona discharge produced HCHO in yields of about 5%. When H_2 is added to the reactants, decomposition of HCHO is inhibited, and its yield is increased. Reaction of $CH_4 + CO_2$ gave lower yields of HCHO. In this case HCHO production decreased with added H_2, presumably because of capture by H_2 of O-atoms or O_2 produced in the discharge. Takahashi states that in H_2O vapor oxidation was affected by OH; in CO_2, O-atoms effect the reaction. Oxidation of CH_4 by O_2 in a concentric-tube reactor was studied [449] and a marked increase in HCHO yield was found on changing from glass to a copper metal reactor.

Methane-water vapor and CH_4–air mixtures were reacted in an rf discharge (2.6-MHz) in a modified concentric-tube reactor in which the center electrode was in the discharge [2]. As it formed, the HCHO produced was absorbed by a stream of H_2O droplets falling through the discharge. Thus the partial pressure of HCHO in the gas and its decomposition in the discharge was minimized. Efficiency of production (in grams per kilowatt-hour) of HCHO increased dramatically with increasing water flow rates. Reaction of $CH_4 + H_2O$ was also studied in a gas-liquid discharge reactor [3]; the efficiency of production of HCHO was lower than in the rf reactor. In both systems CH_3OH, H_2O_2, acidic compounds, CO, CO_2, H_2, and C_2 and C_3 hydrocarbons also formed. Allen and Ponnamperuma [450] subjected $CH_4 + H_2O$ mixtures to a high-voltage 60-Hz semicorona discharge to form acetic and propionic acids and smaller amounts of C_4 to C_{12} acids.

A mixture of C_2H_4 (580 gm) and air was passed through a concentric-tube reactor at atmospheric pressure; 96 gm of light-yellow liquid was obtained by trapping the products at $-20°C$. Approximately one-third of this product was diformylperoxide. Ethylene oxide, HCHO, CH_3CHO, CH_3OH, C_2H_5OH, water, propargyl alcohol, CO_2, CH_4, and H_2 also formed [451]. Ruppel et al. [452] studied the reaction of C_2H_4–steam mixtures flowing through a high-voltage, 10-kHz, concentric-tube reactor. In one pass as much as 70% of the C_2H_4 was converted to H_2, CO, CO_2, CH_4, C_2 to C_6 hydrocarbons, and a complex liquid product containing paraffins, olefins, and alcohols.

Cyclohexene + air mixtures, when passed through a concentric-tube reactor and the products collected in traps at 0 and $-78°C$, formed cyclohexanol, cyclohexanone, cyclohexenol, cyclohexenone, and cyclohexene oxide, plus CO_2, C_1 to C_4 hydrocarbons, H_2, and small amounts of hydroperoxides. At low ratios of cyclohexene/O_2, as much as 21% of the cyclohexene was oxidized. Product formation is discussed in terms of a mechanism involving alkyl and alkylperoxy radicals [403b]. Propylene + O_2, when reacted similarly, formed small amounts of iso-C_3H_7OH, acetone, acrolein, CH_3OH, CH_3CHO, CH_3CH_2CHO, allyl alcohol, n-C_3H_7OH, hydrocarbons, and a trace of propylene oxide.

O_2, after passing through an ac glow discharge between Al electrodes, was mixed downstream in a heated reactor with benzene vapor. At oxygen pressures of about 10 torr and benzene throughputs of about 0.1 gm/min, conversion rates per pass of 10 to 12.5 mole % of benzene, reacting to form phenol, were achieved [453]. One can speculate that this reaction occurs by insertion of O into the C—H bond:

$$C_6H_5—H + O \rightarrow C_6H_5—OH \tag{11.123}$$

Small amounts of phenol have also been produced by the reaction of benzene + H_2O vapors in a glow discharge [454].

Reactions of Hydrocarbons with Nitrogen Compounds

A high-frequency, high-voltage spark passed through a $CH_4 + N_2$ mixture at atmospheric pressure formed low-molecular-weight hydrocarbons including C_2H_2 and diacetylene, and cyanoacetylene, HCN, and benzene. The cyanoacetylene concentration was maximum after about 25 min (equal to 8.4% of the HCN formed) and slowly decreased thereafter; the HCN concentration eventually equaled 42% of the original CH_4. Sparking of a $CH_4 + NH_3$ mixture also resulted in a high conversion to HCN, but cyanoacetylene was present in only trace amounts; it would have been destroyed rapidly in the presence of NH_3 [455].

Blanton et al. [456] reviewed the work by Miyazaki and Takahashi on the reactions of $CH_4 + N_2$ mixtures to produce HCN as the main product. In a series of 13 papers, the latter authors studied the reaction in batch and flow systems, at very low and near-atmospheric pressures, at various voltages, currents, and frequencies, and with different types of reactors. Miyazaki and Takahashi propose that the main formative reaction is CH + N → HCN, where CH is produced in the discharge by breakdown of CH_4, and N from N_2.

When a high-current (0.5-mA) corona discharge was passed through an equimolar mixture of $CH_4 + NH_3$ at 0.5 atm, gases, a colorless distillate, and ruby-colored residue were produced [363]. Separation of the distillate by gas chromatography and identification by retention time, mass spectrometry, and NMR, established the identity of NH_4CN, CH_3CN, C_2H_5CN, H_2NCH_2CN and its C-methyl and N-methyl homologs.

In a 5-liter corona reactor with tungsten electrodes, $CH_4 + NH_3$ mixtures were circulated so that the volatile products passed repeatedly through the spark [457]. The reactants were previously dried over NaOH to exclude H_2O

and thus maximize vapor phase polymerization and to demonstrate that oxygen species are not essential intermediates. Volatile compounds detected during reaction were mainly H_2, N_2, and HCN, with smaller amounts of CH_4, C_2H_6, C_2H_4, and C_2H_2. Nonvolatile products were accumulated for up to 60 hr, when nearly all of the CH_4 had been consumed. Hydrolysis of this polymeric residue (a peptide precursor) and analysis showed the presence of lysine, histidine, aspartic acid, threonine, serine, glycine, alanine, and isoleucine. This NH_3-catalyzed polymerization of HCN in the absence of H_2O is believed to occur via formation of aminocyanomethylene as a key intermediate.

Emission spectral band intensities during reaction of CH_4–NH_3–Ar mixtures in an rf discharge were compared with the yield of HCN measured by chemical methods [458]. The results were interpreted in terms of CH formed from the decomposition of CH_4 and HCN formed via the reactions:

$$CH + NH_3 \rightarrow CN + 2H_2 \tag{11.124}$$

$$CN + H_2 \rightarrow HCN + H \tag{11.125}$$

A kinetic study of the formation of HCN from $CH_4 + NH_3$ in a microwave discharge has also been made [459].

$C_2H_4 + HCN$ was passed through a concentric-tube reactor at atmospheric pressure forming acrylonitrile as the main product (about 8 % of the C_2H_4), plus saturated C_3 to C_7 nitriles, C_1 to C_4 hydrocarbons, and H_2 [460]. When $C_2H_4 + HCN$ reacted in a concentric-tube reactor containing metals or cyanide salts, the amount of product formed per gram of ethylene reacted decreased markedly but the acrylonitrile concentration in the product increased [461]. Similar reaction of $C_3H_6 + HCN$ produced crotononitrile, methacrylonitrile, and n-propylcyanide as main products, plus smaller amounts of other cyanides and C_5 and C_6 hydrocarbons [461].

Reaction of $C_2H_4 + C_2N_2$ in a concentric-tube reactor formed acrylonitrile in a yield of 40%, plus smaller amounts of propionitrile and valeronitrile, a trace of adiponitrile, C_1 to C_4 hydrocarbons, HCN, and H_2 [462].

Cyclohexane + HCN were reacted in a concentric-tube reactor, as either a mixture of gases and/or in the presence of liquid cyclohexane. Small amounts of cyclohexyl cyanide formed; the main products were cyclohexene and bicyclohexyl [463].

Reaction of 1-hexene, 1-octene, and cyclohexene with NH_3 in a concentric-tube reactor formed the corresponding 2-amino derivatives as principal products. Dimeric compounds bound in the 2-position also formed as by-products. Maximal output of basic compound (20%, 11.6 gm/kW-hr) was attained with short reaction time and an NH_3 excess of at least 16 moles [464]. Reaction of NH_3 with vapors of n-hexane, n-heptane, n-octane, 1-hexene, or 1-heptene in a concentric-tube reactor at atmospheric pressure and 200 to 250°C yielded mixtures containing small amounts of primary, secondary, and tertiary amines [465]. In the glow discharge reaction of benzene + N_2, C_6H_5CN, $CH_3C_6H_4CN$, and HCN were formed. Reaction of C_6H_6 with NH_3 produced $C_6H_5NH_2$ in addition to the above compounds [466].

Addition of Amino and Carboxyl Groups

In a gas-liquid discharge reactor similar to that shown in Fig. 11.15, but sparked from an ac high-voltage source at atmospheric pressure in an air stream for 2 hr, glycine was produced in a 10% aqueous solution of acetic acid. When acetic acid was sparked under N_2, glycine and (probably) aspartic acid were produced. Sparking an aqueous glycerol solution produced fractions which had the properties of reducing groups, amino groups, and amino sugars [5].

By the same technique, an aqueous solution of 0.01 M L-alanine was sparked for 1 hr with $H_2 + CO_2$ (1:1) flowing through a cooled reaction vessel. The yield of aspartic acid was 5% and a trace of α,β-diaminopropionic acid also formed. When a solution of α-aminobutyric acid was sparked, aspartic acid was produced, presumably from a carbon–carbon cleavage yielding a methyl radical and an alanyl radical which then reacted with CO_2; glutamic acid was also produced [467].

Hollahan et al. [468] added NH_2 groups to the surfaces of several types of polymers by passing NH_3 or 1:2 $N_2 + H_2$ mixtures at low pressures through capacitively coupled rf discharges (13.56-MHz) and exposing the polymer samples to the excited gases downstream from the discharge. The mechanism of addition is presumably via the combination of radicals on the polymer surface with the NH_2 species produced in the discharge

$$R\cdot + \cdot NH_2 \rightarrow R\text{—}NH_2 \tag{11.126}$$

or perhaps via insertion [469] of nitrene :NH produced in the discharge

$$R\text{—}H + :NH \rightarrow R\text{—}NH_2 \tag{11.127}$$

Formation of Organic Compounds from Mixtures of Simple Gases

$H_2 + CO$ and $H_2 + CO_2$ mixtures react in a high-frequency electrodeless discharge to produce low-molecular-weight hydrocarbons (see Section 6). Under different conditions $H_2 + CO$ mixtures react to form oxygenates. Passage of a $H_2 + CO$ mixture through a concentric-tube reactor formed HCHO, acids, and some unsaturated hydrocarbons [470–473]. When H_2 was passed through a glow discharge and mixed downstream with CO, the products identified in the mass spectrograph were HCHO, CH_3COOH,

CH_3OH, C_2H_5OH, CH_4, C_2H_6, C_3H_8, H_2O, and CO_2 [474]. Reaction of H_2 + CO flowing at 1-torr pressure through a microwave discharge produced mainly carbon deposits and polymeric material, plus H_2O and traces of CO_2, HCHO, CH_4, and C_2H_6 [407].

Passage of H_2 + CO + N_2 mixtures (essentially free of H_2O vapor) at about 0.4 torr pressure through an inductively coupled rf discharge (13.6-MHz) produced polymeric films having spectral properties similar to those of polyacrylamides and proteins. The films were recovered from a dry ice-cooled trap downstream from the discharge. Analysis showed aspartic acid, glutamic acid, glycine, and alanine to be hydrolysis products of the polymer (elemental analysis: 55.9% C, 7.8% H, 18.4% O, and 17.6% N) produced in one of the runs [475].

As part of the study of the origin of life, a great many organic compounds have been synthesized in discharges from mixtures of CH_4, NH_3, H_2, and H_2O (see Section 1), the so-called primitive earth atmosphere. These include many amino acids and amino acid derivatives, carboxylic acids and their derivatives, aldehydes, urea, and methylurea. Trace quantities of porphyrins have also been produced in discharges [476]. Keosian [38] lists the compounds produced abiotically by the action of discharges, ultraviolet and ionizing radiation, and heat. Other recent reviews of the abiotic formation of organic compounds are available [39, 477–480].

Reactions of Various Oxygenates

Reaction of 2-propanol was studied in two concentric-tube reactors, one of conventional design, the other having the inside wall made of copper or its salts. The products formed (approximately 5% of the propanol) were mainly acetone, C_5 and C_6 hydrocarbons, and CH_3CHO, plus C_4 to C_6 alcohols and ketones, CH_4, C_2 to C_4 hydrocarbons, CO, CO_2, and H_2. A reaction mechanism was written in terms of excited propanol molecules forming hydroxypropyl, hydroxyethyl, and isopropyl radicals, which in turn react to form the products [481].

m-Cresol vapor in H_2 carrier gas (total pressure = 300 torr) reacted in a high-voltage, 10-kHz, concentric-tube reactor at 300°C to form phenol, toluene, benzene, aliphatic hydrocarbons (mostly unsaturated), CO_2, H_2O, and polymer [482]. (More phenol was formed than toluene; the C—OH bond is probably stronger than the C—CH_3 bond, and the latter breaks preferentially.)

Vuillermoz [483, 484a] caused aryl aldehydes and ketones to react at low pressures in a capacitively coupled rf (50-MHz) discharge. Reaction of C_6H_5CHO yielded benzophenone, acetophenone, biphenyl, benzene, toluene, ethylbenzene, and xylenes. Reaction of acetophenone yielded toluene and benzene as major products, plus smaller amounts of ethylbenzene, C_6H_5CHO, biphenyl, diphenylmethane, benzophenone, xylene, and bibenzyl. Reaction of phenylacetaldehyde gave similar products, except that C_6H_5CHO and benzophenone were not formed. Reaction of butyrophenone under conditions in which 88% of the condensed product was butyrophenone gave aceto-phenone as the major product, plus phenyl-1-cyclobutanol, α-tetralone, phenylacetophenone, C_6H_5CHO, trans-stilbene, biphenyl, and other products. (The first three above were also those formed by photolysis of butyrophenone in benzene.) Reaction of butyrophenone under more severe conditions gave benzene, toluene, and acetophenone mainly, plus biphenyl, C_8 aromatics, C_6H_5CHO and other products. In both of these papers, Vuillermoz discusses the mechanisms involved in these discharge reactions.

Suhr and collaborators [442a] passed anisole vapor through a glow discharge at low pressure to form mainly phenol and o- and p-cresol (no m-cresol), plus small amounts of 2,4-xylenol, CH_3-C_5H_5, C_6H_6, toluene, and CH_3OH. Similarly, phenyl ethyl ether formed phenol, o- and p-ethylphenol, and cresol; p-methylanisole formed p-cresol and 2,4-xylenol. The authors argue that in the products observed the extraordinary selectivity in migration of the alkyl groups militates against a free-radical mechanism; sole formation of ortho- and para-substituted alkylphenols suggests that the products form via rearrangement of molecule ions formed from the parent ether molecule. A later paper [442b] gives further details on these reactions.

A single-step synthesis of biphenylene from 9-fluorenone in an rf discharge plasma has been reported [484b].

Reactions and Formation of Organic Halogen Compounds

CCl_4 vapor at a reduced pressure was passed through an inductively coupled rf discharge (14-MHz) and the products were collected in cold traps. As much as 95% of the CCl_4 reacted to yield approximately equal amounts by weight of C_2Cl_6, C_2Cl_4, C_2Cl_2, Cl_2, and polymer. The CCl_3 radical is believed to be the primary reactive species; attempts to detect $:CCl_2$ as an intermediate were unsuccessful. In one experiment products collected at $-196°$ were aged at room temperature in the absence of air for 1 month. Gas chromatographic analysis of this mixture showed the presence of C_2Cl_6 and hexachlorobenzene [485].

By comparison, reaction of CCl_4 in a high-temperature Ar plasma flame [442a] produced C_2Cl_4 in high yields, much smaller amounts of C_2Cl_6, C_6Cl_6, and hexachlorobutadiene, and traces of chlorinated C_5 to C_8 compounds. Under the same conditions C_2Cl_4 and hexachlorobutadiene reacted to form similar C_5 to C_8 compounds. Reaction of $CHCl_3$ produced $C_2H_2Cl_2$, C_2HCl_3, C_2HCl_5, and similar compounds up to $C_8H_2Cl_6$.

Passage of chlorofluorocarbons + Ar through an inductively coupled rf arc (6-MHz) and collection of the products in cold traps produced principally

C, Cl_2, and/or F_2 [116] and small yields of the following: C_2Cl_4 and C_2Cl_6 from CCl_4 as a reactant; C_2Cl_3F, CCl_3–$CClF_2$, C_2Cl_6, C_6Cl_6, and C_6Cl_5F from CCl_3F; C_2Cl_3F, C_2Cl_4, $C_2Cl_4F_2$, C_6Cl_6, and C_6Cl_5F from CCl_2F_2; C_2Cl_4, C_2Cl_3F, $C_2Cl_2F_2$, $C_2Cl_4F_2$, $C_2Cl_3F_3$, C_6Cl_6, C_6Cl_5F, $C_6Cl_4F_2$, and $C_6Cl_2F_4$ from $CClF_3$; and COF_2 and SiF_4 from CF_4. In each case the major products were the benzene derivatives.

When CF_4 was added to a high-temperature N_2 plasma, small amounts of NF_3, CF_3NF_2, C_2F_6, N_2F_4, and cis- and trans-N_2F_2 were formed [486]. Bronfin [486] also summarizes numerous other studies on fluorine compounds in arcs and discharges. CF_4, rather than F_2, has been used as the source of fluorine in the formation of XeF_2 in a discharge [487]. Reaction of CF_4 with organic compounds in discharges might be used to produce organic fluorine compounds under rather mild conditions.

Passage of C_6H_5Cl at reduced pressure through an inductively coupled rf discharge (14-MHz) at the rate of 6.5 gm/hr and collection of the products in cold traps produced principally C_6H_6, polymer, and gas (mainly HCl and C_2H_2), plus $C_6H_4Cl_2$ (o-, m-, p- ratio = 53:35:11), biphenyl, 1,3,5-, 1,2,4-, and 1,2,3-trichlorobenzene, o-, m-, and p-chlorobiphenyl, and dichlorobiphenyls. No biphenylene was detected [488].

When C_6H_5Cl was passed through the discharge (0.44 gm/hr) and Br_2 added downstream, the percent of C_6H_5Cl reacting increased and the products were principally C_6H_5Br, C_6H_6, and o-$C_6H_4Br_2$, plus o-, m-, and p-C_6H_4BrCl, m-, and p-$C_6H_4Br_2$, and o-$C_6H_4Cl_2$. Stille and Rix state that "The ratio of introduced bromine to chlorine available from the conversion of chlorobenzene to chlorine atoms and phenyl radicals was exactly the ratio of bromobenzene-chlorobenzene in the products. This suggests that C—Cl bond scission is relatively selective in this reaction." The C_6H_5—Cl bond dissociation energy can be estimated at approximately 90 to 95 kcal [489], compared with 112 kcal for C_6H_5—H [490]. Thus one might expect that the C—Cl bond in C_6H_5—Cl breaks before the ClC_6H_4—H bond.

Stille and Rix propose the reaction pathway shown in Fig. 11.20 to account for the various products and the high percentage of o-$C_6H_4Cl_2$ from the reaction of C_6H_5Cl. The presence of benzyne as an intermediate would also explain the large amount of o-$C_6H_4Br_2$ formed when Br_2 was added downstream from C_6H_5Cl in the discharge. However, in trying to isolate benzyne by reaction with furan, no 1,4-dihydronaphthalene-1,4-endoxide could be detected. Reactions of the dichlorobenzenes were also studied. Except for greatly increased amounts of polymers, the compounds formed were the same as for C_6H_5Cl. Again, the ratios of the dichlorobenzenes produced can be explained on the basis of a benzyne intermediate.

The fact that aromatic carbon–halogen bonds can apparently be broken with facility in an rf discharge was used by Fridmann and Dinan [11] to

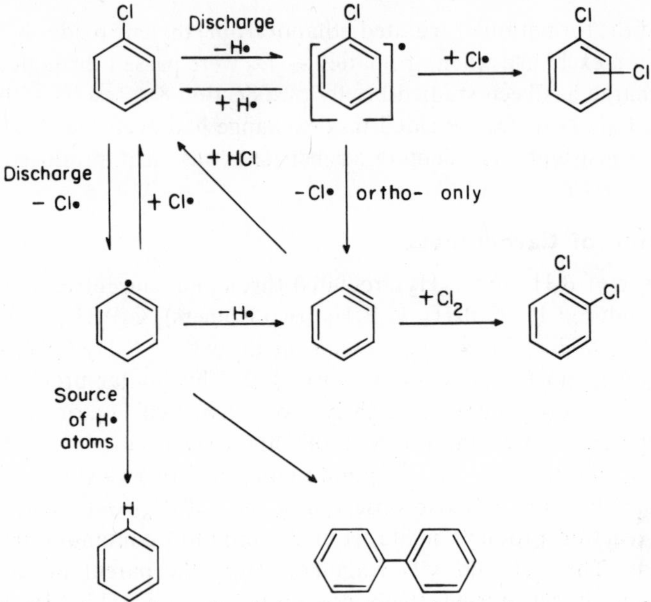

Fig. 11.20 Reaction pathway for rf decomposition of chlorobenzene, as adapted from Stille and Rix [448].

prepare C_6D_5Cl from $Cl_2 + C_6D_5Br$. When a mixture of $Cl_2 + C_6H_5Br$ was passed through an inductively coupled rf discharge (28-MHz), a 1:1 mixture of $C_6H_5Cl + C_6H_5Br$ was produced in high yield. Experiments in which C_6D_5Br was used and the products were separated by preparative gas chromatography afforded chlorobenzene, shown by mass spectrometry to be fully deuterated; the recovered bromobenzene and benzene were also fully deuterated.

Isotopic Labeling of Organic Compounds

When an organic compound is exposed to tritium gas, radiation-induced exchange occurs and H-atoms in the molecule are replaced by T-atoms [491]. If the compound is exposed to T_2 in a discharge, exchange is greatly accelerated because of the much higher concentration of the active species which bring about exchange. Preparation of tritium-labeled compounds has been reviewed by Evans [40], who gives extensive tables of labeled compounds, including those labeled in discharges.

In addition to tritium-labeling the original molecule, reactions in a discharge can give rise to other (labeled) products. Examples are: formation of chlorobenzene, benzene, and lower-molecular-weight hydrocarbons from $C_6H_4Cl_2 + T_2$; formation of tetrahydronaphthalene, *trans*-decalin, benzene, toluene, ethylbenzene, and other hydrocarbons from naphthalene $+ T_2$

[492]; and the formation of tritiated ethanol from ethylene oxide + T_2 [493].

Deuterium exchange when aromatics + D_2 were passed through a microwave discharge has been studied briefly (see Section 8). Results with C_5H_5N + D_2 and C_6H_7N + D_2 indicated that exchange had occurred, but the data were not consistent [7]; deuterated benzene was also produced in this reaction.

Preparation of Carboranes

A mixture of B_5H_9 and C_2H_2 circulated through a concentric-tube reactor for 1 hr produced $1,5\text{-}C_2B_3H_5$, $C_2B_4H_6$ (two isomers), $C_2B_5H_7$, and diacetylene in small yields. From experiments made with a $B_5D_9\text{-}C_2H_2$ mixture, $C_2B_3D_3H_2$ with no C—D bonds was isolated. The similar product from a $B_5H_9\text{-}C_2D_2$ mixture contained slightly more than two D-atoms, while the infrared spectra showed the presence of only a small amount of the B—D bond (thus, presumably, the compound contained two C—D bonds). This same type of labeling was also observed in the $C_2B_4H_6$ compounds isolated from the reaction products made from the mixtures containing deuterated compounds. The BH and CH fragments from the parent molecules appear to stay intact during these discharge reactions [13, 14]. Reaction of 2,3-dicarbahexaborane(8) circulated in He carrier gas through a concentric-tube reactor also produced $1,5\text{-}C_2B_3H_5$, $1,6\text{-}C_2B_4H_6$, and $1,2\text{-}C_2B_4H_6$ [494].

Rapid circulation of $B_2H_6\text{-}C_2H_2$ mixtures diluted with helium through a high-voltage ac discharge between copper disk electrodes yielded small amounts of volatile products of which 62 to 99 mole % were carboranes [495]. When B_2H_6 was initially in excess, approximately 10 to 15% of the C_2H_2 consumed was converted into volatile carboranes, most of the remainder forming nonvolatile solids. B_5H_9, B_4H_{10}, and some hydrocarbons condensed out during the reaction when the mixture was continuously circulated through a cold trap. In the absence of such a trap, however, few noncarborane volatile products were obtained; for the most part, only the closed-cage carboranes survive repeated passage through the discharge.

The products obtained were $1,5\text{-}C_2B_3H_5$, $1,6\text{-}C_2B_4H_6$, $2,4\text{-}C_2B_5H_7$, the five B-monomethyl derivatives of these parent carboranes, $C,3\text{-dimethyl-}1,2\text{-}C_2B_3H_3$, and perhaps 2,3-dimethyl-$1,5\text{-}C_2B_3H_3$. Experiments made with a concentric-tube reactor replacing the copper-disk electrode reactor gave smaller yields of fewer carboranes and B_5H_9 as the major product. The occurrence of many methylated species (most B-methyl) among the products, even though the only carbon compound initially present was C_2H_2, was postulated as perhaps being the result of hydroboration of acetylene as an important early step in the reaction.

In a discussion [496] of the possible reaction mechanisms involved in the vapor-phase C_2H_2-borane interactions, a distinction is made between low-energy reactions (thermal), in which the nature of the products is strongly dependent on the specific borane starting material, and high-energy reactions (discharge and "flash" conditions), in which the products are closed-cage carboranes or their methyl derivatives (mostly B-methyl); it appears that the products are largely determined by the relative thermodynamic stabilities of the carborane cage systems. Preparations of various other borane-related compounds via reactions in discharges are also discussed in two recent books [497, 498].

Formation and Reactions of Organosilicon Compounds

Two recent reviews of this subject [43, 499] and the patent by Akerlof [500] discuss various reactions: (1) reaction of a 5:1 mixture of $CH_4 + SiCl_4$ flowing through a concentric-tube reactor to give CH_3SiCl_3, $(CH_3)_2SiCl_2$, $(CH_3)_3SiCl$, and higher-boiling material; (2) reactions of CH_3SiCl_3 or $(CH_3)_2SiCl_2$ entrained in H_2 and flowing through a concentric-tube reactor to give mixtures of various methylchlorodisilalkanes and methylchloropoly-silalkanes; and (3) similar types of products from the reactions of $SiCl_4$ with cyclohexane or benzene.

Shaw made a detailed study of the reactions of hexamethyldisiloxane and tetramethylsilane in a concentric-tube reactor [43, 86]. In this apparatus up to 500 gm of starting material could be converted to products in yields as high as 90% by running for several days; however, the yield of any one compound in the product mixtures was usually low. $(CH_3)_3SiOSi(CH_3)_2OSi-(CH_3)_3$ and $(CH_3)_3SiOSi(CH_3)_2C_2H_5$ were the major products isolated from the reaction of $(CH_3)_3SiOSi(CH_3)_3$. $(CH_3)_3SiC_2H_5$, $(CH_3)_3SiSi(CH_3)_3$, $(CH_3)_3SiSi(CH_3)_2H$, and $(CH_3)_3SiCH_2Si(CH_3)_2H$ were the major products isolated from the reaction of $Si(CH_3)_4$. Various radicals, ions, and excited molecules are considered to be the active species in the discharge, and a detailed discussion is given of the possible mechanisms responsible for the products.

Methyldisilane, Si_2H_6, and Si_3H_8, have been isolated from the products obtained by passing $SiH_4 + CH_3OCH_3$ through a concentric-tube reactor [12] in which the gas issuing from the reactor continuously passed through two traps at $-96°C$ to remove products having a lower volatility than the reactants.

Preparation of Oxamide

Oxamide has been prepared by oxidation of formamide in a two-compart-ment gas-liquid discharge reactor (see Section 2) in which a frit separated the anode and cathode parts of the cell. Formamide was dissolved in 0.8 N H_2SO_4 in the anode part of the cell and reacted in a stream of O_2 at 30 torr total pressure to form oxamide at an efficiency of 1.5 moles oxamide/faraday. Reaction of formamide alone also produced oxamide but at a lower efficiency and with considerable decomposition of the formamide [501]. Oxamide has also been produced from alkaline solutions of HCN by reaction in a gas-liquid discharge reactor [502]. The mechanism of formation of oxamide probably occurs via formation of H_2O_2 and/or OH radicals by the action of the discharge on the solution [503].

Reactions of Sulfur-Containing Compounds

Sulfur-containing compounds were allowed to react in a high-voltage, semicorona reactor to effect their partial desulfurization [504]. In the most effective example (43 % S removed, mostly as H_2S), a dilute solution of C_2H_5SH in petroleum spirit was refluxed so that the vapors were in the discharge between a center copper electrode and a cylindrical condenser tube surrounded by an aluminum-foil electrode. When thiophene itself was refluxed in the discharge, there was some evidence for the formation of α-poly-thienyls.

Formation of Organophosphorus Compounds

Reactions of active phosphorus in a discharge with various hydrocarbons have been studied briefly [505]. Phosphine, methylphosphine, and ethane were formed.

Formation of Polymers

Formation of polymeric materials in discharge reactions is extremely common. From the point of view of synthesizing nonpolymeric molecules, this is usually a drawback since polymer formation uses up both reactants and electrical energy. Perhaps the magnetically focused rf discharge glow system [91] shown in Fig. 11.11 could be adapted so as to minimize polymer formation in organic reactions. Sometimes, however, polymers, especially in the form of films, can be the desired product and increasing attention is being given to this type of synthesis. The reviews by McTaggart [15], Spedding [29], and Kolotyrkin et al. [36] discuss formation of polymers and in the discussion of various reactions in Sections 6 through 9 of this chapter, repeated mention has been made of polymer formation in the products of reaction.

Some other papers on polymers are concerned with deposition of films in rf glow discharges [75, 91, 506], polymerization in a gas-liquid discharge reactor [507], polymerization of hydrocarbons [508, 509], polymerization of liquid styrene at $-20°C$ by reaction with H-atoms [182], deposition of boron, silicon, and various oxides, carbides, and nitrides [510–517], and other polymerizations [518–519].

10 OTHER ASPECTS OF DISCHARGES

Temperature and Equilibrium

The concept of temperature in a discharge was mentioned previously in Sections 2 and 3, and the distinction was made between "low-temperature" discharges and "high-temperature" arcs. In an arc, where the current is higher than in a discharge (see Fig. 11.4) and where the gas pressure is usually higher, the temperature of the neutral species is about 2000°C or higher. Since conditions in an arc may approach thermal equilibrium, Reed [47a] refers to this as a "thermal plasma" or "chemist's plasma, because the temperature is a meaningful concept which can be used to predict other properties of the plasma." However, Reed refers to low-temperature discharges as a "cold plasma" or "physicist's plasma" since mean free paths are relatively long, kinetic processes are very important, and electronic excitation processes are relatively much more important. There is no equilibrium between the hot electrons and the cold atoms, and temperature is a meaningless concept."

Even though the different species in a discharge have different temperatures and thermal equilibrium does not hold, chemical equilibrium concepts can still be useful. This has been demonstrated experimentally, at least for some reactions. For example, it has been shown that Le Chatelier's principle can be applied to the shifting of the reactions producing hydrocarbons from $H_2 + CO$ and $H_2 + CO_2$ mixtures in a microwave discharge (Section 6). Another example is the study of the $H_2O + CO \rightarrow H_2 + CO_2$ reaction in a concentric-tube reactor [520] where the conversion of CO approached the thermodynamic limit (calculated on the basis of reactor wall temperature) as the space velocity decreased.

Bell [115] studied the reaction $4HCl + O_2 \rightarrow 2Cl_2 + 2H_2O$ in an rf discharge. With increasing pressure at constant power input, for both the forward and reverse reactions, the percent Cl_2 in the product converged to the same value at a pressure of 15 torr. He concluded that the appearance of such a steady-state value of conversion was characteristic of a reaction that approaches equilibrium.

Lippincott and co-workers [446, 521, 522] studied the reactions of hydrocarbons and organic oxygen compounds in an rf discharge and attempted to apply equilibrium concepts to the formation of various compounds after removal of the energizing power, which allows the plasma to tend toward a state of equilibrium, although the rapid rate of cooling may prevent its complete attainment.

These studies suggest that chemical equilibrium concepts, or at least the balancing of forward and reverse reactions to reach a steady state in a discharge, are useful in interpreting discharge reactions. Manes [523] and Potapov [524] have developed statistical-mechanical arguments showing that a law of mass action can be written for reactions in a discharge. However, one cannot calculate a value for an equilibrium constant since thermal equilibrium does not exist under these conditions.

By way of contrast, it should be pointed out that for at least three cases, the formation of C_2H_2 from CH_4, O_3 from O_2, and N_2H_4 from NH_3, the concentration of the product in each case is higher than one would expect from equilibrium at the gas temperature in the discharge.

Surface Effects and Catalysis

Surfaces both in and downstream from a discharge affect reactions occurring there. However, it is one thing to say this and another to measure the effect quantitatively (or even consistently in a qualitative way). Metal electrodes act as efficient surfaces for recombination of radicals and one advantage of electrodeless reactors for radical production is the absence of electrodes in the gas (Section 2). Recombination on metal surfaces also forms the basis for calorimetric determination of radicals in a discharged gas (Section 4). Electron-ion recombination processes at surfaces in a discharge is another factor affecting discharge reactions. McTaggart [15], Venugopalan and Jones [17], and Shaw [73] discuss these topics.

Kaufman calculated [31] the rates of production of H-atoms and O-atoms in microwave discharges (Section 3) and concluded that the net dissociation in such discharges is mainly controlled by surface recombination and the surface in the discharge must be moderately to highly efficient for atom recombination. Moreover, the effect of small amounts of added gases (such as H_2O) in increasing the yield must be through their influence on the surface efficiency. He recommended that experiments be done to characterize the surface in and immediately downstream from the discharge, as important chemical effects appear to occur there.

NH_3 can be produced in a discharge from $N_2 + H_2$ mixtures [15, 29]. Various metals have been tested as catalysts for NH_3 production in an ac glow discharge between stainless-steel electrodes, where the concentration of NH_3 in the product was about 1% [525]. Films of Pt and Fe were the most effective in increasing the yield of NH_3. Under different conditions NH_3 decomposes in a dc glow discharge to produce N_2H_4, N_2, and H_2. N_2 is produced uniformly throughout the discharge, while N_2H_4 is produced significantly only in the positive column region. The N_2H_4 yield is limited, at least in part, by the back reaction:

$$H + N_2H_4 \rightarrow NH_3 + NH_2 \tag{11.128}$$

Thus catalysis of H-atom removal by platinum-coating the wall of the discharge tube increased the overall N_2H_4 yield [80].

In the decomposition of NH_3 in an ac glow discharge with aluminum electrodes in recessed ports perpendicular to the reactor, the size of the electrode port openings appeared to have no effect on NH_3 decomposition, but the N_2H_4 yield increased with the larger opening [526], which may indicate a decrease in the atomic hydrogen present owing to increased accessibility of the electrode surface and rapid hydrogen recombination there.

Rubtsova and Eremin [527, 528] studied the reaction of NH_3 flowing through a glow discharge with a metal-coated quartz insert placed between the electrodes. Of several active metals tested, platinum was most effective in increasing the N_2H_4 yield. A similar effect of Pt films was found in the production of N_2H_4 from NH_3 recirculated through a concentric-tube reactor. Spedding discusses in detail these and other factors affecting the production of N_2H_4 from NH_3 [29, 529].

However, when Sahasrabudhey and Deshpande [473] investigated the influence of wall catalysts on the production of HCHO from $CO + H_2$ in a concentric-tube reactor, the reaction giving rise to HCHO was not affected by the catalysts employed. Also, Ruppel et al. [520] could not detect any effect on the conversion in the reaction $H_2O + CO \rightarrow H_2 + CO_2$ in a concentric-tube reactor when the annular space was packed with quartz wool and the surface-to-volume ratio increased from 4.85 to 6.45 cm^2/cm^3.

Morinaga and Suzuki [530] studied the effect on ozone production of filling the space between the electrodes of a reactor with granular packings. The rate of ozone production increased markedly. However, this effect may be attributable, at least in part, to a decrease in the effective gap length between electrodes, which has been shown to increase efficiency of ozone production [531].

The possible importance of wall reactions in the reaction $CO_2 \rightarrow CO + \frac{1}{2}O_2$ has been studied at low pressures in an rf discharge [532]. Connell and Gregor [91] also discuss wall reactions in an rf discharge and show experimentally how they can be minimized by the use of an external magnetic field to focus the discharge and thus keep it away from the walls (Section 2).

In their study of the production of C_2H_2 from CH_4 in an anomalous glow discharge (Section 6), Hesp and Rigby [74] discussed the possible effects of wall reactions—deactivation of active species, their polymerization leading to carbon formation, and decomposition of C_2H_2. In separate experiments they also showed that mercury vapor, in addition to promoting the overall conversion of CH_4, selectively catalyzed C_2H_2 formation in preference to the carbon-forming reactions. Lebedev and co-workers [533, 534] also reported catalytic effects of Hg vapor on the synthesis and decomposition of NH_3 in a glow discharge. Table 11.2 shows some results obtained by Rodemeyer [404]. It is difficult to draw conclusions based on only two runs, but these results suggest that Hg vapor does influence the reactions of toluene in a microwave discharge. In the presence of Hg, twice as much toluene reacted and the amounts of ethylbenzene, styrene, and phenylacetylene formed were greater, when compared with the run made in the absence of Hg (by removing the Hg manometer from the flow system). Argon may also have an effect on discharge reactions, as shown by its ability to accelerate the decomposition of CH_4 (Section 6).

Table 11.2   The Microwave Glow Discharge Reaction of Toluene in the Presence and Absence of Mercury Vapor [404]

Run	Toluene*	Benzene†	Ethyl-benzene†	Styrene†	Phenyl-acetylene†
Mercury present	30	89	7	2	2
Mercury absent	68	98	2	0.3	0.2

* Percent of volatiles distilled from trap containing discharge products collected at $-196°C$.

† Percent of volatiles, normalized to exclude toluene and low boilers.

Photochemical Effects in Discharge Reactions

Arcs and discharges have been used as spectral light sources for some time [535]. Electronically excited atoms and molecules are present in significant concentrations in discharges and the light that they emit upon de-excitation could photolyze other molecules present in the discharge.

Gesser and Hussain's study on the reactivity of active nitrogen led them [536] to state that: "The results would seem to indicate that the discharge glow can act as a photochemical source which can photolyze reactants introduced further down the tube. If precautions are not taken to break the light path between discharge glow and reactant, then spurious results are possible. In view of the absence of any windows between source and reactant, such photochemical effects may extend into the vacuum ultraviolet where very low-intensity light sources in the discharge can still be very effective . . . ." In discharge flow systems, it has long been quite common to place a "Wood's horn" light trap between the discharge and any reactor downstream in order to avoid photolytic reactions as complicating factors. Campbell and Thrush show an example of such an apparatus [537].

Dougherty [538] studied the effects on fluorocarbon polymers of the short-wavelength ultraviolet light (<165 nm) produced by high-frequency, electrodeless discharges in argon, helium, or nitrogen. Electron spin resonance measurements on the irradiated polymer samples after exposure to air gave a sharp singlet (presumably peroxy radicals) in approximately one-half the concentration previously found when the polymers had been exposed directly to the discharge. Thus neither direct interaction with the excited inert gas atoms nor with H-atoms from the discharge is required for radical formation in the polymer; the short-wavelength ultraviolet light generated in all gas discharges is sufficient to account for the results.

Benzene and its alkyl derivatives react with maleic anhydride to form adducts (Section 8). Considering both the location of the liquid reaction mixture in the discharge and the type of products formed, it appears quite probable that at least part of the product is formed by a photochemical reaction mechanism.

Industrial Applications and the Engineering of Discharge Processes

There are some industrial applications of low-temperature discharge processes. Ozone is produced on a large scale from oxygen [539]. The Société des Huiles de Cavel et Roegiers, S.A., Ghent, Belgium, uses a glow-discharge ("Elektrion") process to upgrade lubricating oil by reaction with H_2 [540]. Spedding [29] describes a pilot plant discharge process used for the production of H_2O_2 in Germany during World War II. Work is being done in Australia to develop a pilot plant to produce C_2H_2 from CH_4 and other low-molecular-weight hydrocarbons in a glow discharge [376]. A considerable amount of work has been done on the production of N_2H_4 from NH_3, with the idea of achieving commercial production via a discharge process [29, 45, 529].

Surface treatment of polymers and the deposition in discharges of thin films, both organic and inorganic, show considerable promise for widespread application [468, 541; also see Section 9). The use of discharged O_2 to oxidize semiconductor surfaces [542, 543], to remove carbonaceous films from surfaces, and to "ash" carbonaceous materials at low temperature are growing applications [28, 431, 544]. Discharges have also been used to sinter ceramic compacts [98] and to machine ceramic and glass materials [545]. Because of increasing industrial interest in discharge processes, the chemical engineering aspects of discharges are receiving more attention [47a, b, c, 546]. Recently, there have been several reviews of the economic aspects of discharge and arc processes [29, 547–550].

From an engineering point of view, Thornton [45, 46] states that at least three requirements are necessary for an economically acceptable process: (1) a high energy yield (in grams of product per kilowatt-hour); (2) a high percentage conversion per pass; and (3) a high degree of selectivity for the desired product, that is, side reactions should be reduced to a minimum.

The term "specific energy consumption" or SEC (in kilowatt-hours per kilogram of product) is used more frequently than "energy yield" to express the energy requirements of a discharge process; the former phrase is preferable because it is less likely to be misinterpreted. A low value of SEC is obviously a major factor governing the economics of the process even though the cost of electrical power is very likely to decrease in the future. Lunt [135] suggests that an approximate minimum attainable value of SEC for many discharge reactions will be $[\varphi_s(0.03 \pm 0.01)]^{-1}$ eV per molecule of product or $0.9/\varphi_s$ kw-hr/mole product, where φ_s is the number of product molecules formed per molecule of the parent (reactant) species decomposed or reacted.

Thornton and co-workers discuss various approaches to achieve selectivity and to minimize decomposition of a product once it has formed in the discharge. In their study of the formation of N_2H_4 from NH_3 [45, 529], the residence time and degradation of the N_2H_4 was minimized and the SEC value lowered by absorption of the N_2H_4 in the discharge zone by a spray of ethylene glycol, which is itself substantially inert in the discharge. This technique was also used in their study of the formation of HCHO from $CH_4 + H_2O$, in which the yield of HCHO was increased by absorbing it in the water spray [2].

In situations in which it is impractical to use selective absorption of the product or high gas flow rates to achieve low residence times and product concentrations, one alternative is to use a pulsed discharge in which the effective residence time in the discharge is controlled by the pulse duration and the time interval between pulses. The use of such a pulsed discharge for the $NH_3 \rightarrow N_2H_4$ conversion decreased the value of SEC for the reaction [45, 529].

Another basic problem in the engineering of discharges is to scale up the size of the reactor. Thornton discusses this [45, 46] and proposes somewhat tentatively that instead of scale-up, a more attractive possibility might be to step up the laboratory reactor until the desired through-put was achieved, that is, putting a sufficient number of small-scale reactors in parallel to handle the required gas flow. Bell [551] and Spedding [29] also discuss the engineering problem of reactor scale-up.

Operation of a discharge at less than atmospheric pressure is one of the difficulties in scaling-up to commercial operation, but several types of discharge reactors can be operated at atmospheric pressure or higher. These are (1) the concentric-tube reactor[520], (2) corona and semicorona discharges, (3) an autoclave-type reactor [552] designed for high-pressure operation, (4) the adjection discharge described by Bryner and Coleman [553], (5) the microwave discharge with hydrogen at atmospheric pressure [182], and (6) the contact glow discharge electrolysis technique [108].

Acknowledgment

The authors would like to thank Dr. Irving Wender for his helpful comments and encouragement and Miss Wanda Andrews for her most careful typing of the manuscript.

References

1. A. -P. Bois d'Enghien, J. Vrebosch, and A. Van Tiggelen, *Bull. Soc. Chim. France*, **1968**, 2315, 2321.
2. J. D. Thornton and R. Sergio, *Nature*, **213**, 590 (1967).
3. R. Sergio and J. D. Thornton, *J. Appl. Chem.*, **17**, 325 (1967).
4. B. D. Blaustein and Y. C. Fu, *Advan. Chem. Ser.*, **80**, 259 (1969).
5. G. D. Steinman and H. A. Lillevik, *Arch. Biochem. Biophys.*, **105**, 303 (1964).
6. F. J. Dinan and W. D. Cooke, *J. Org. Chem.*, **31**, 3025 (1966).
7. A. Streitwieser, Jr., and R. Bittman, Abstracts 148th National Meeting, American Chemical Society, Chicago, Illinois, August 30–September 4, 1964, p. 17S; R. Bittman, *Studies of Microwave Discharge Reactions of Heterocyclic Compounds*, Ph.D. Thesis, University of California, Berkeley, 1966.
8. H. J. Kraaijveld and H. I. Waterman, *Brennstoff-Chem.*, **43**, 1 (1962).
9. H. J. Kraaijveld and H. I. Waterman, *Brennstoff-Chem.*, **43**, 33 (1962).
10. H. Schüler, K. Prchal, and E. Kloppenburg, *Z. Naturforsch.*, **15A**, 308 (1960).
11. S. Fridmann and F. J. Dinan, *J. Org. Chem.*, **33**, 1253 (1968).
12. M. Abedini and A. G. MacDiarmid, *Inorg. Chem.*, **5**, 2040 (1966).
13. I. Shapiro, C. D. Good, and R. E. Williams, *J. Am. Chem. Soc.*, **84**, 3837 (1962).
14. I. Shapiro, B. Keilin, R. E. Williams, and C. D. Good, *J. Am. Chem. Soc.*, **85**, 3167 (1963).
15. F. K. McTaggart, *Plasma Chemistry in Electrical Discharges*, Elsevier, Amsterdam, 1967.
16. R. F. Baddour and R. S. Timmins, Eds., *The Application of Plasmas to Chemical Processing*, M.I.T. Press, Cambridge, Massachusetts, 1967.
17. M. Venugopalan and R. A. Jones, *Chemistry of Dissociated Water Vapor and Related Systems*, Interscience, New York, 1968.
18. A. N. Wright and C. A. Winkler, *Active Nitrogen*, Academic, New York, 1968.
19. M. Venugopalan, Ed., *Chemical Reactions under Plasma Conditions*, Interscience, New York, in press.
20. N. S. Pechuro, Ed., *Organic Reactions in Electrical Discharges*, English Transl., Consultants Bureau, New York, 1968.

21. *Properties and Applications of Low Temperature Plasma, Plenary Lectures from the International Symposium, Moscow, July 1965*, Butterworths, London, 1967.
22. R. F. Gould, Ed., *Chemical Reactions in Electrical Discharges, Advan. Chem. Ser.*, **80**, Am. Chem. Soc., Washington, D.C., 1969.
23. "Chemical Reactions in Electrical Discharges," in V. N. Kondrat'ev, *Chemical Kinetics of Gas Reactions*, J. M. Crabtree, Transl., and S. N. Carruthers and N. B. Slater, Eds., Pergamon, Oxford, 1964.
24. W. L. Jolly, "The Use of Electric Discharges in Chemical Syntheses," in *Technique of Inorganic Chemistry*, H. B. Jonassen and A. Weissberger, Eds., Vol. I, Interscience, New York, 1963, p. 179.
25. A. S. Kana'an and J. L. Margrave, "Chemical Reactions in Electric Discharges," in *Advances in Inorganic Chemistry and Radiochemistry*, H. J. Emeleus and A. G. Sharpe, Eds., Vol. VI, Academic, New York, 1964, p. 143.
26. A. von Engel, "Electric Discharges and Excited Species," in *The Molecular Designing of Materials and Devices*, A. R. von Hippel, Ed., M.I.T. Press, Cambridge, Massachusetts, 1965, p. 173.
27. J. A. Coffman and W. R. Browne, *Sci. Amer.*, **212**, 90 (June 1965).
28. J. R. Hollahan, *J. Chem. Educ.*, **43**, A401, A497, 392 (1966).
29. P. L. Spedding, *Chem. Eng. (London)*, CE17 (1969).
30. W. L. Fite, *Advan. Chem. Ser.*, **80**, 1 (1969).
31. F. Kaufman, *Advan. Chem. Ser.*, **80**, 29 (1969).
32. W. L. Jolly, *Advan. Chem. Ser.*, **80**, 156 (1969).
33. A. G. Massey, *J. Chem. Educ.*, **40**, 311 (1963).
34. M. Venugopalan and R. A. Jones, *Chem. Rev.*, **66**, 133 (1966).
35a. E. J. Mezey, G. J. Falkenbach, and J. H. Oxley, *Battelle Tech. Rev.*, **14**, 3 (November 1965).
35b. M. Burton and K. Funabashi, *Advan. Chem. Ser.*, **80**, 140 (1969).
36. V. M. Kolotyrkin, A. B. Gil'man, and A. K. Tsapuk, *Russ. Chem. Rev. (English Transl.)*, **36**, 579 (1967).
37. O. K. Fomin, *Russ. Chem. Rev. (English Transl.)*, **36**, 725 (1967).
38. J. Keosian, *The Origin of Life*, 2nd Ed., Van Nostrand Reinhold, New York, 1968.
39. C. Ponnamperuma and N. W. Gabel, *Space Life Sci.*, **1**, 64 (1968).
40. E. A. Evans, *Tritium and Its Compounds*, Van Nostrand Reinhold, New York, 1966, p. 99.
41. J. D. Brooks, W. R. Hesp, and D. Rigby, *J. Appl. Chem.*, **17**, 225 (1967).
42. S. A. Miller, *Acetylene—Its Properties, Manufacture and Uses*, Vol. I, Academic, New York, 1965.
43. R. A. Shaw, *Pure Appl. Chem.*, **13**, 297 (1966).
44. J. E. Flinn and W. M. Goldberger, *Advan. Chem. Ser.*, **80**, 441 (1969).
45. J. D. Thornton, *Advan. Chem. Ser.*, **80**, 372 (1969).
46. J. D. Thornton, *Rev. Pure Appl. Chem.*, **18**, 197 (1968).

47a. T. B. Reed, "Plasmas for High Temperature Chemistry," in *Advances in High Temperature Chemistry*, L. Eyring, Ed., Vol. I, Academic, New York, 1967, p. 259.

47b. V. J. Ibberson and M. W. Thring, *Ind. Eng. Chem.*, **61,** 48 (November 1969).

47c. F. B. Vurzel and L. S. Polak, *Ind. Eng. Chem.*, **62,** 8 (June 1970).

48. S. L. Miller, *Science*, **117,** 528 (1953).

49. S. L. Miller, *J. Am. Chem. Soc.*, **77,** 2351 (1955).

50. S. L. Miller, *Biochim. Biophys. Acta*, **23,** 480 (1957).

51. S. L. Miller, *Ann. N.Y. Acad. Sci.*, **69,** 260 (1957).

52. S. L. Miller, "Formation of Organic Compounds on the Primitive Earth," in *Proceedings of the First International Union of Biochemistry Symposium on Origin of Life on the Earth, Moscow, 1957*, A. I. Oparin et al., Eds., Pergamon, Oxford, 1959, p. 123.

53. S. L. Miller and H. C. Urey, *Science*, **130,** 245 (1959).

54. P. H. Abelson, *Carnegie Inst. Wash. Yearbook*, **55,** 171 (1955).

55. P. H. Abelson, *Carnegie Inst. Wash. Yearbook*, **56,** 179 (1956).

56. R. W. Lunt, *Proc. Roy. Soc. London*, **108A,** 172 (1925).

57. R. P. Epple and C. M. Apt, *The Formation of Methane from Synthesis Gas by High-Frequency Radiation*, Am. Gas Assoc., New York, 1962.

58. G. Francis, "The Glow Discharge at Low Pressure," in *Gas Discharges II* (*Encyclopedia of Physics*, Vol. XXII), S. Flügge, Ed., Springer, Berlin, 1956, p. 53.

59. J. D. Cobine, *Gaseous Conductors*, corrected ed., Dover, New York, 1958.

60. L. B. Loeb, *Basic Processes of Gaseous Electronics*, 2nd rev. ed., Univ. of California, Press, Berkeley, 1960.

61. G. Francis, *Ionization Phenomena in Gases*, Academic, New York, 1960.

62. A. M. Howatson, *An Introduction to Gas Discharges*, Pergamon, Oxford, 1965.

63. C. G. Morgan, "Fundamentals of Electric Discharges in Gases," in *Physical Electronics* (*Handbook of Vacuum Physics*, Vol. II, Part I), A. H. Beck, Ed., Pergamon, Oxford, 1965.

64. L. B. Loeb, *Electrical Coronas—Their Basic Physical Mechanisms*, Univ. of California Press, Berkeley, 1965.

65. A. von Engel, *Ionized Gases*, 2nd ed., Oxford Univ. Press, London, 1965.

66. F. Llewellyn-Jones, *The Glow Discharge and an Introduction to Plasma Physics*, Methuen, London, 1966.

67. S. C. Brown, *Introduction to Electrical Discharges in Gases*, Wiley, New York, 1966.

68. F. Llewellyn-Jones, *Ionization and Breakdown in Gases*, Methuen, London, corrected ed., 1966.

69. W. B. Kunkel, "Laboratory Plasma Production," in *Plasma Physics in Theory and Application*, W. B. Kunkel, Ed., McGraw-Hill, New York, 1966, p. 299.

70. S. C. Brown, *Basic Data of Plasma Physics, 1966*, 2nd ed., rev., M.I.T. Press, Cambridge, Massachusetts, 1967.

71. R. Papoular, *Electrical Phenomena in Gases*, Iliffe, London, 1965.

72. A. V. Phelps, *Advan. Chem. Ser.*, **80**, 18 (1969).
73. T. M. Shaw, "Techniques of Electrical Discharge for Radical Production," in *Formation and Trapping of Free Radicals*, A. M. Bass and H. P. Broida, Eds., Academic, New York, 1960, p. 47.
74. W. R. Hesp and D. Rigby, *J. Appl. Chem.*, **18**, 313 (1968).
75. A. R. Denaro, P. A. Owens, and A. Crawshaw, *European Polymer J.*, **4**, 93 (1968).
76. R. W. Wood, *Proc. Roy. Soc. (London)*, **102A**, 1 (1922).
77. I. M. Campbell and B. A. Thrush, *Ann. Rept. Chem. Soc.*, **62**, 17 (1965).
78. A. K. Brewer and J. W. Westhaver, *J. Phys. Chem.*, **34**, 153 (1930).
79. A. K. Brewer, *Chem. Rev.*, **21**, 213 (1937).
80. J. C. Devins and M. Burton, *J. Am. Chem. Soc.*, **76**, 2618 (1954).
81. A. W. Tickner, *Can. J. Chem.*, **39**, 87 (1961).
82a. E. F. Logan and J. M. Marchello, *J. Chem. Phys.*, **49**, 3929 (1968).
82b. A. G. Streng, A. D. Kirshenbaum, L. V. Streng, and A. V. Grosse, "Preparation of Rare-Gas Fluorides and Oxyfluorides by the Electric-Discharge Method and Their Properties," in *Noble-Gas Compounds*, H. Hyman, Ed., Univ. Chicago Press, Chicago, 1963, p. 73.
83. H. J. Kraaijveld and H. I. Waterman, *Brennstoff-Chem.*, **42**, 369 (1961).
84. G. Wehner, *Sci. Technol.*, 32 (September 1968).
85. M. W. Ranney and W. F. O'Connor, *Advan. Chem. Ser.*, **80**, 297 (1969).
86. R. C. Golesworthy and R. A. Shaw, *Proc. Roy. Soc. (London)*, **A292**, 489 (1966).
87. M. Suzuki, *Mem. Defense Acad. Japan*, **7**, 1023 (1967).
88a. T. Aiba and M. P. Freeman, *J. Chem. Phys.*, in press.
88b. M. McInally, *Nature*, **216**, 259 (1967).
89. *Sci. Amer.*, **209**, 146 (July 1963).
90. A. G. Prodell and P. Kusch, *Phys. Rev.*, **106**, 87 (1957).
91. R. A. Connell and L. V. Gregor, *J. Electrochem. Soc.*, **112**, 1198 (1965).
92. P. D. Davidse and L. I. Maissel, *J. Appl. Phys.*, **37**, 574 (1966).
93. P. D. Davidse and L. I. Maissel, *Transactions of the Third International Vacuum Congress, 1965*, Vol. 2, Part III, Pergamon, Oxford, 1966, p. 651.
94. P. D. Davidse, *Vacuum*, **17**, 139 (1967).
95. P. R. Rony, *Rev. Sci. Instr.*, **37**, 532 (1966).
96. R. F. Baddour and P. H. Dundas, "Chemical Reactions in Microwave Discharge," in *The Applications of Plasmas to Chemical Processing*, R. F. Baddour and R. S. Timmins, Eds., M.I.T. Press, Cambridge, Massachusetts, 167, p. 87.
97. H. P. Broida and M. W. Chapman, *Anal. Chem.*, **30**, 2049 (1958).
98. C. E. G. Bennett, N. A. McKinnon, and L. S. Williams, *Nature*, **217**, 1288 (1968).
99. Varian Industrial Microwave Operation, San Carlos, California.
100. F. C. Fehsenfeld, K. M. Evenson, and H. P. Broida, *Rev. Sci. Instr.*, **36**, 294 (1965); NBS Report 8701, U. S. Dept. Commerce, 1964.
101. K. E. Zacha, M. P. Bratzel, Jr., J. D. Winefordner, and J. M. Mansfield, Jr., *Anal. Chem.*, **40**, 1733 (1968).

102. C. A. Bache and D. J. Lisk, *Anal. Chem.*, **40**, 2224 (1968).
103. A. B. Callear, J. A. Green, and G. J. Williams, *Trans. Faraday Soc.*, **61**, 1831 (1965).
104. A. B. Callear and R. E. M. Hedges, *Nature*, **215**, 1267 (1967).
105. A. B. Callear and R. E. M. Hedges, *Nature*, **218**, 163 (1968).
106. A. Hickling and M. D. Ingram, *J. Electroanal. Chem.*, **8**, 65 (1964).
107. K. O. Hough and A. R. Denaro, *J. Sci. Instr.*, **43**, 488 (1966).
108. A. Hickling and M. D. Ingram, *Trans. Faraday Soc.*, **60**, 783 (1964).
109. A. Yokohata, K. Harakon, and S. Tsuda, *Bull. Chem. Soc. Japan*, **41**, 2292 (1968) and the preceding papers in this series.
110. A. R. Denaro and P. A. Owens, *Electrochim. Acta*, **13**, 157 (1968).
111a. A. R. Denaro, private communication, 1967.
111b. S. I. Reynolds, Test Methods for Measuring Energy in a Gas Discharge, ASTM Special Tech. Publ. No. 198, 28 (1957).
112. D. Rutenberg, "Measurement of Electrical Power and Energy," in *Encyclopaedic Dictionary of Physics*, J. Thewlis, Ed.-in-Chief, Vol. 2, Macmillan, New York, 1962, p. 668.
113. W. R. Hesp, I. Halasz, and H. O. Gerlach, *J. Appl. Chem.*, **17**, 306 (1967).
114. J. C. Fraser, *Advan. Chem. Ser.*, **80**, 361 (1969).
115. A. T. Bell, *Chemical Reaction in a Radiofrequency Discharge. The Oxidation of Hydrogen Chloride*, Sc.D. Thesis, Massachusetts Institute of Technology, Cambridge, Massachusetts, 1967.
116. C. P. Beguin, J. B. Ezell, A. Salvemini, J. C. Thompson, D. G. Vickroy, and J. L. Margrave, "Chemical Syntheses in Radio-Frequency Plasma Torches," in *The Application of Plasmas to Chemical Processing*, R. F. Baddour and R. S. Timmins, Eds., M.I.T. Press, Cambridge, Massachusetts, 1967, p. 35.
117. D. Waller, Ph.D. Thesis, Department of Chemical Engineering, The University, Newcastle-upon-Tyne, England.
118. M. Zelikoff and P. Wyekoff, *J. Opt. Soc. Am.*, **42**, 818 (1952).
119a. A. T. Forrester, R. A. Gudmundsen, and P. O. Johnson, *J. Opt. Soc. Am.*, **46**, 339 (1956).
119b. O. P. Bochkova and E. Ya. Shreyder, *Spectroscopic Analysis of Gas Mixtures*, Academic, New York, 1965.
120. *Microwave Radiation Hazards*, Bureau of Occupational Health, Technical Information Service, California State Department of Public Health, Berkeley, California, 1964.
121. W. Moore, Jr., *Biological Aspects of Microwave Radiation· A Review of Hazards, TSB4*, National Center for Biological Health, Public Health Service, U.S. Department of Health, Education, and Welfare, July, 1968.
122. H. M. Hoffart, *Electro-Technol.*, 52 (November 1968).
123. *Narda Electromagnetic Radiation Monitor*, The Narda Microwave Corporation, Plainview, New York.
124a. Radio and Microwave Radiations—Applications and Potential Hazards, An International Symposium, January 1969. Proceedings of this symposium are published in Vol. I of *Non-Ionizing Radiation*, Iliffe, Guildford, Surrey, England.

124b. E. Gross, *Science News*, **96**, 382 (1969).

125. C. M. Cade, *New Scientist*, **39**, 588 (1968).

126. "Part 18—Industrial, Scientific, and Medical Equipment," in *Title 47—Telecommunication, Code of Federal Regulations*, revised as of January 1, 1968.

127. D. R. Bates, Ed., *Atomic and Molecular Processes*, Academic, New York, 1962.

128. J. B. Hasted, *Physics of Atomic Collisions*, Butterworths, London, 1964.

129. H. S. W. Massey, E. H. S. Burhop, and H. B. Gilbody, *Electronic and Ionic Impact Phenomena*, 2nd Ed. Oxford Univ. Press, New York, 1969.

130. A. V. Phelps, *Rev. Mod. Phys.*, **40**, 399 (1968).

131a. E. E. Muschlitz, Jr., *Science*, **159**, 599 (1968).

131b. B. L. Moiseiwitsch and S. J. Smith, *Rev. Mod. Phys.*, **40**, 238 (1968).

132a. L. J. Kieffer and G. H. Dunn, *Rev. Mod. Phys.*, **38**, 1 (1966).

132b. R. L. McCarthy, *J. Chem. Phys.*, **22**, 1360 (1954).

133. K. R. Jennings and J. W. Linnett, *Nature*, **182**, 597 (1958).

134. B. Bak and J. Rastrup-Andersen, *Acta Chem. Scand.*, **16**, 111 (1962).

135. R. Lunt, *Advan. Chem. Ser.*, **80**, 452 (1969).

136. A. A. Bergh, *Bell System Tech. J.*, **44**, 261 (1965).

137. P. R. Rony and D. N. Hanson, *J. Chem. Phys.*, **44**, 2536 (1966).

138. V. I. Svettsov, I. N. Sikolova, and A. I. Naksimov, *Russ. J. Phys. Chem. (English Transl.)*, **40**, 1415 (1966).

139. F. Kaufman and J. R. Kelso, *J. Chem. Phys.*, **32**, 301 (1960).

140. R. L. Brown, *J. Phys. Chem.*, **71**, 2492 (1967).

141. L. Elias, E. A. Ogryzlo, and H. I. Schiff, *Can. J. Chem.*, **37**, 1680 (1959).

142. M. A. A. Clyne, B. A. Thrush, and R. P. Wayne, *Nature*, **199**, 1057 (1963).

143. S. N. Foner and R. L. Hudson, *J. Chem. Phys.*, **25**, 601 (1956).

144. J. T. Herron and H. I. Schiff, *Can. J. Chem.*, **36**, 1159 (1958).

145. S. J. Arnold, E. A. Ogryzlo, and H. Witzke, *J. Chem. Phys.*, **40**, 1769 (1964).

146. L. W. Bader and E. A. Ogryzlo, *Discussions Faraday Soc.*, **37**, 46 (1964).

147. S. J. Arnold, N. Finlayson, and E. A. Ogryzlo, *J. Chem. Phys.*, **44**, 2529 (1966).

148. A. M. Winer and K. D. Bayes, *J. Phys. Chem.*, **70**, 302 (1966).

149a. M. L. Kaplan and P. G. Kelleher, *Science*, **169**, 1206 (1970).

149b. A. Mathias and H. I. Schiff, *Discussions Faraday Soc.*, **37**, 1 (1964).

150. A. Mathias and H. I. Schiff, *J. Chem. Phys.*, **40**, 3118 (1964).

151. H. S. Johnston, *Gas Phase Reaction Kinetics of Neutral Oxygen Species*, NSRDS-NBS 20, National Bureau of Standards, U.S. Dept. Commerce, Washington, D.C., 1968.

152. G. G. Mannella, *Chem. Rev.*, **63**, 1 (1963).

153. A. N. Wright and C. A. Winkler, *Can. J. Chem.*, **40**, 5 (1962).

154. A. N. Wright, R. L. Nelson, and C. A. Winkler, *Can. J. Chem.*, **40**, 1082 (1962).

155. R. A. Young, R. L. Sharpless, and R. Stringham, *J. Chem. Phys.*, **40**, 117 (1964).

156. F. Kaufman and J. R. Kelso, *J. Chem. Phys.*, **28**, 510 (1958).

157. K. Dressler, *J. Chem. Phys.*, **30**, 1621 (1959).

158. R. E. Huffman, J. C. Larrabee, and Y. Tanaka, *J. Chem. Phys.*, **45**, 3205 (1966).

159. S. N. Foner and R. L. Hudson, *J. Chem. Phys.*, **45**, 40 (1966).

160. R. A. Young, *Can. J. Chem.*, **44**, 1171 (1966).

161. S. N. Foner and R. L. Hudson, *J. Chem. Phys.*, **37**, 1662 (1962).

162. J. F. Noxon, *J. Chem. Phys.*, **36**, 926 (1962).

163. P. G. Wilkinson and R. S. Mulliken, *J. Chem. Phys.*, **31**, 674 (1959).

164. E. C. Zipf, *J. Chem. Phys.*, **38**, 2034 (1963).

165. N. P. Carleton and O. Oldenburg, *J. Chem. Phys.*, **36**, 3460 (1962).

166. W. Brenner, *J. Chem. Phys.*, **44**, 1793 (1966).

167a. J. S. Shirk and A. M. Bass, *J. Chem. Phys.*, **49**, 5156 (1968).

167b. L. W. Sieck, "The Fragmentation of Highly Excited Neutral Molecules," in *Fundamental Processes in Radiation Chemistry*, P. Ausloos, Ed., Interscience, New York, 1968, p. 119.

168. A. M. Bass and H. P. Broida, Eds., *Formation and Trapping of Free Radicals*, Academic, New York, 1960.

169. A. M. Bass and H. P. Broida, Eds., *Stabilization of Free Radicals at Low Temperatures*, NBS Monograph 12, U.S. Department Commerce, Washington, D.C., 1960.

170. G. J. Minkoff, *Frozen Free Radicals*, Interscience, New York, 1960.

171. A. Thomas, "Trapped Radicals and Combustion," in *Oxidation and Combustion Reviews*, C. F. H. Tipper, Ed., Vol. 2, Elsevier, Amsterdam, 1967, p. 257.

172. B. Mile, *Angew. Chem. Intern. Ed. Engl.*, **7**, 507 (1968).

173. D. A. Ramsay, "The Spectra of Polyatomic Free Radicals," in *Advances in Spectroscopy*, H. W. Thompson, Ed., Vol. 1, Interscience, New York, 1959, p. 1.

174. T. F. Bindley, A. T. Watts, and S. Walker, *Trans. Faraday Soc.*, **58**, 849 (1962).

175. T. F. Bindley, A. T. Watts, and S. Walker, *Trans. Faraday Soc.*, **60**, 1 (1964).

176. T. F. Bindley, A. T. Watts, and S. Walker, *J. Chem. Soc.*, **1964**, 2345.

177. A. T. Watts and S. Walker, *J. Chem. Soc.*, **1964**, 2348.

178. H. C. Heller, S. Schlick, and T. Cole, *J. Phys. Chem.*, **71**, 97 (1967).

179. J. N. Herak and W. Gordy, *J. Am. Chem. Soc.*, **89**, 3818 (1967).

180. F. G. Liming, Jr., and W. Gordy, *Proc. Natl. Acad. Sci.*, **60**, 794 (1968).

181. B. E. Holmes, G. Navon, and G. Stein, *Nature*, **213**, 1087 (1967).

182. C. L. Currie, S. J. and B. A. Thrush, *Trans. Faraday Soc.*, **64**, 390 (1968).

183. F. W. Lampe, J. L. Franklin, and F. H. Field, "Kinetics of the Reactions of Ions with Molecules," in *Progress in Reaction Kinetics*, G. Porter, Ed., Vol. 1, Pergamon, Oxford, 1961, p. 67.

184. J. L. Franklin, P. K. Ghosh, and S. Studniarz, *Advan. Chem. Ser.*, **80**, 59 (1969).

185. R. F. Gould, Ed., *Ion-Molecule Reactions in the Gas Phase*, *Advan. Chem. Ser.*, **58**, (1966).

186a. W. Cermak, A. Dalgarno, E. E. Ferguson, L. Friedman, and E. W. McDaniel, *Ion-Molecule Reactions*, Wiley, New York, 1968.

186b. P. F. Knewstubb, *Mass Spectrometry and Ion-Molecule Reactions*, Cambridge Univ. Press, London, 1969.

187. C. F. Griese, *Advan. Chem. Phys.*, **10**, 247 (1966).

188. E. E. Ferguson, *Advan. Electronics Electron Phys.*, **24**, 1 (1968).

189. L. Friedman, *Ann. Rev. Phys. Chem.*, **19**, 273 (1968).

190. J. H. Futrell and T. O. Tiernan, *Science*, **162**, 415 (1968); "Ion-Molecule Reactions," in *Fundamental Processes in Radiation Chemistry*, Interscience, P. Ausloos, Ed., New York, 1968, p. 171.

191. W. L. Fite and J. A. Rutherford, *Discussions Faraday Soc.*, **37**, 192 (1964).

192. W. L. Fite, J. A. Rutherford, W. R. Snow, and V. A. J. VanLint, *Discussions Faraday Soc.*, **33**, 264 (1962).

193. M. J. Copsey, D. Smith, and J. Sayers, *Planetary Space Sci.*, **14**, 1047 (1966).

194. P. H. Batey, G. R. Court, and J. Sayers, *Planetary Space Sci.*, **13**, 911 (1965).

195. J. Sayers and D. Smith, *Discussions Faraday Soc.*, **37**, 167 (1964).

196. G. F. O. Langstroth and J. B. Hasted, *Discussions Faraday Soc.*, **33**, 298 (1962).

197. M. M. Shahin, *Advan. Chem. Ser.*, **58**, 315 (1966).

198. M. M. Shahin, *Advan. Chem. Ser.*, **80**, 48 (1969).

199. S. A. Studniarz and J. L. Franklin, *J. Chem. Phys.*, **49**, 2652 (1968).

200. H. D. Beckey and H. Dreeskamp, *Z. Naturforsch.*, **9a**, 735 (1954).

201. I. B. Ortenburger, M. Hertzberg, and R. A. Ogg, *J. Chem. Phys.*, **33**, 579 (1960).

202. P. H. Dawson and A. W. Tickner, *J. Chem. Phys.*, **37**, 672 (1962).

203. H. Dreeskamp, *Z. Naturforsch.*, **12a**, 876 (1958).

204. P. H. G. Dickinson and J. Sayers, *Proc. Phys. Soc.*, **A76**, 137 (1960).

205. D. S. Burch and R. Geballe, *Phys. Rev.*, **106**, 188 (1957).

206. J. L. Moruzzi and A. V. Phelps, *J. Chem. Phys.*, **45**, 4617 (1966).

207. P. F. Knewstubb and A. W. Tickner, *J. Chem. Phys.*, **38**, 464 (1963).

208. P. F. Knewstubb, "Mass Spectrometry of Ions from Electric Discharges, Flames, and Other Sources," in *Mass Spectrometry of Organic Ions*, F. W. McLafferty, Ed., Academic, New York, 1963, p. 255.

209. E. F. Greene and A. Kuppermann, *J. Chem. Educ.*, **45**, 361 (1968).

210. J. L. Franklin, S. A. Studniarz, and P. K. Ghosh, *J. Appl. Phys.*, **39**, 2052 (1968).

211. W. W. Cooper, H. S. Mickley, and R. F. Baddour, *Ind. Eng. Chem. Fund.*, **7**, 400 (1968).

212. M. A. Heald and C. B. Wharton, *Plasma Diagnostics with Microwaves*, Wiley, New York, 1965.

213. R. Huddleston and S. H. L. Leonards, Eds., *Plasma Diagnostic Techniques*, Academic, New York, 1965.

214. J. C. Ingraham and S. C. Brown, "Plasma Diagnostics," in *The Application of Plasmas to Chemical Processing*, R. F. Baddour and R. F. Timmins, Eds., M.I.T. Press, Cambridge, Massachusetts, 1967, p. 54.

215a. K. R. Jennings, *Quart. Rev. (London)*, **15**, 237 (1961).

215b. B. A. Thrush, *J. Chem. Educ.*, **41**, 429 (1964).

216. M. A. A. Clyne and B. A. Thrush, *Trans. Faraday Soc.*, **57**, 2176 (1961).
217. M. A. A. Clyne, *9th Symposium on Combustion, Cornell University, 1962*, Academic, New York, 1963, p. 211.
218. L. F. Phillips and H. I. Schiff, *J. Chem. Phys.*, **37**, 1233 (1962).
219. F. Kaufman, *Proc. Roy. Soc. London*, **A247**, 123 (1958).
220. F. Kaufman, "Reactions of Oxygen Atoms," in *Progress in Reaction Kinetics*, G. Porter, Ed., Vol. 1, Pergamon, Oxford, 1961, p. 1.
221. G. B. Kistiakowsky and G. G. Volpi, *J. Chem. Phys.*, **27**, 114 (1957).
222. F. Kaufman, *J. Chem. Phys.*, **28**, 992 (1958).
223. P. Harteck, R. R. Reeves, and G. Mannella, *J. Chem. Phys.*, **29**, 608 (1958).
224. H. G. V. Evans, G. R. Freeman, and C. A. Winkler, *Can. J. Chem.*, **34**, 1271 (1956).
225. J. T. Herron, *J. Chem. Phys.*, **35**, 1138 (1961).
226. R. A. Back and J. Y. P. Mui, *J. Phys. Chem.*, **66**, 1362 (1962).
227. J. E. Morgan, L. Elias, and H. I. Schiff, *J. Chem. Phys.*, **33**, 930 (1960).
228. A. A. Westenberg and N. de Haas, *J. Chem. Phys.*, **40**, 3087 (1964).
229. H. Von Weyssenhoff and M. Patapoff, *J. Phys. Chem.*, **69**, 1756 (1965).
230. L. Elias, *J. Chem. Phys.*, **44**, 3810 (1966).
231. F. A. Morse and F. Kaufman, *J. Chem. Phys.*, **42**, 1785 (1965).
232. J. T. Herron, *J. Phys. Chem.*, **69**, 2736 (1965).
233. E. Wrede, *Z. Physik*, **54**, 53 (1929).
234. E. Wrede, *Z. Instrumentenku.*, **48**, 201 (1928).
235. P. Harteck, *Z. Phys. Chem.*, **A139**, 98 (1928).
236. W. Groth and P. Warneck, *Z. Phys. Chem.*, **10**, 323 (1957).
237. J. C. Greaves and J. W. Linnett, *Trans. Faraday Soc.*, **55**, 1338 (1959).
238. L. Elias, *J. Chem. Phys.*, **42**, 4311 (1965).
239. H. M. Smallwood, *J. Am. Chem. Soc.*, **56**, 1542 (1934).
240a. J. W. Linnett and D. G. H. Marsden, *Proc. Roy. Soc. (London)*, **A234**, 489 (1956).
240b. J. W. Linnett and D. G. H. Marsden, *Proc. Roy. Soc. (London)*, **A234**, 504 (1956).
241. E. L. Tollefson and D. J. LeRoy, *J. Chem. Phys.*, **16**, 1057 (1948).
242. E. A. Ogryzlo, *Can. J. Chem.*, **39**, 2556 (1961).
243. L. W. Bader and E. A. Ogryzlo, *Nature*, **201**, 491 (1964).
244. F. P. Lossing, "Mass Spectrometry of Free Radicals," in *Mass Spectrometry*, C. A. McDowell, Ed., McGraw-Hill, New York, 1963, p. 442.
245. A. G. Harrison, "Mass Spectrometry of Organic Radicals," in *Mass Spectrometry of Organic Ions*, F. W. McLafferty, Ed., Academic, New York, 1963, p. 207.
246a. S. N. Foner, "Mass Spectrometry of Free Radicals," in *Advances in Atomic and Molecular Physics*, D. R. Bates and I. Estermann, Eds., Vol. 2, Academic, New York, 1966, p. 385.
246b. F. J. Fletcher, *Chem. Eng. Fuel Sci. Newcastle*, 27 (December 1968).
247. S. N. Foner and R. L. Hudson, *J. Chem. Phys.*, **21**, 1374 (1953).
248. S. N. Foner and R. L. Hudson, *J. Chem. Phys.*, **36**, 2681 (1962).
249. P. F. Knewstubb and A. W. Tickner, *J. Chem. Phys.*, **36**, 674 (1962).
250. P. F. Knewstubb and A. W. Tickner, *J. Chem. Phys.*, **36**, 684 (1962).

251. P. F. Knewstubb, P. H. Dawson, and A. W. Tickner, *J. Chem. Phys.*, **38**, 1031 (1963).
252. P. H. Dawson and A. W. Tickner, *J. Chem. Phys.*, **40**, 3745 (1964).
253. P. F. Knewstubb and A. W. Tickner, *J. Chem. Phys.*, **37**, 2941 (1962).
254. G. N. Spokes and B. E. Evans, *10th Symposium on Combustion*, The Combustion Institute, Pittsburgh, Pennsylvania 1965, p. 639.
255. M. M. Shahin, *J. Chem. Phys.*, **43**, 1798 (1965).
256. M. M. Shahin, *J. Chem. Phys.*, **45**, 2600 (1966).
257. H. E. Evans and P. P. Jennings, *Trans. Faraday Soc.*, **61**, 2153 (1965).
258. H. E. Evans and P. P. Jennings, *J. Phys. Chem.*, **70**, 1265 (1966).
259. H. E. Evans and P. P. Jennings, *Carbon*, **6**, 695 (1968).
260. E. E. Ferguson, F. C. Fehsenfeld, and A. L. Schmeltekopf, *Advan. Chem. Ser.*, **80**, 83 (1969).
261. H. P. Broida, H. I. Schiff, and T. M. Sugden, *Nature*, **185**, 759 (1960).
262a. F. P. Del Greco and F. Kaufman, *Discussions Faraday Soc.*, **33**, 128 (1962).
262b. F. P. Del Greco and F. Kaufman, *9th Symposium on Combustion, Cornell University, 1962*, Academic, New York, 1963, p. 659.
263. L. I. Avramenko and R. V. Kolesnikova, *Advan. Photochem.*, **2**, 25 (1964).
264. M. A. A. Clyne and J. A. Coxon, *Trans. Faraday Soc.*, **62**, 1175 (1966).
265. N. Basco, *Advan. Chem. Ser.*, **36**, 26 (1962).
266. N. Basco, J. E. Nicholas, R. G. W. Norrish, and W. H. J. Vickers, *Proc. Roy. Soc. (London)*, **A272**, 147 (1963).
267. W. Braun, J. R. McNesby, and A. M. Bass, *J. Chem. Phys.*, **46**, 2071 (1967).
268. K. C. Herr and G. C. Pimentel, *Appl. Opt.*, **4**, 25 (1965).
269. G. A. Carlson and G. C. Pimentel, *J. Chem. Phys.*, **44**, 4053 (1966).
270. M. Margoshes and B. F. Scribner, *Anal. Chem.*, **40**, 223R, April 1968.
271. R. A. Young and R. L. Sharpless, *J. Chem. Phys.*, **39**, 1071 (1963).
272. I. M. Campbell and B. A. Thrush, *Proc. Chem. Soc.*, **1964**, 410.
273. F. Kaufman, *Ann. Geophys.*, **20**, 106 (1964).
274. M. Cher and C. S. Hollingsworth, *Advan. Chem. Ser.*, **80**, 118 (1969).
275. R. Beringer and E. B. Rawson, *Phys. Rev.*, **87**, 228 (1952).
276. E. B. Rawson and R. Beringer, *Phys. Rev.*, **88**, 677 (1952).
277. M. A. Heald and R. Beringer, *Phys. Rev.*, **96**, 645 (1954).
278. S. Krongelb and M. W. P. Strandberg, *J. Chem. Phys.*, **31**, 1196 (1959).
279. A. A. Westenberg and N. de Haas, *J. Chem. Phys.*, **43**, 1550 (1965).
280. J. M. Brown, B. A. Thrush, and A. F. Tuck, *Proc. Roy. Soc. (London)*, **A302**, 311 (1968).
281. J. M. Brown and B. A. Thrush, *Trans. Faraday Soc.*, **63**, 630 (1967).
282a. A. A. Westenberg and N. de Haas, *J. Chem. Phys.*, **46**, 490 (1967).
282b. F. Kaufman, *Ann. Rev. Phys. Chem.*, **20**, 45 (1969).
283. B. A. Thrush, "Reactions of Hydrogen Atoms in the Gas Phase," in *Progress in Reaction Kinetics*, G. Porter, Ed., Vol. 3, Pergamon, Oxford, 1965, p. 63.
284. R. J. Cvetanovic, "Addition of Atoms to Olefins in the Gas Phase," in *Advances in Photochemistry*, W. A. Noyes, Jr., G. S. Hammond, and J. N. Pitts, Jr., Eds., Vol. 1, Interscience, New York, 1963, p. 115.
285. J. M. Brown, P. B. Coates, and B. A. Thrush, *Chem. Commun.*, **1966**, 884.

286. S. Toby and H. I. Schiff, *Can. J. Chem.*, **34**, 1061 (1955).
287. B. S. Rabinovitch, D. H. Dills, W. H. McLain, and J. H. Current, *J. Chem. Phys.*, **32**, 493 (1960).
288. B. S. Rabinovitch and R. W. Diesen, *J. Chem. Phys.*, **30**, 735 (1959).
289. R. E. Harrington, B. S. Rabinovitch, and H. M. Frey, *J. Chem. Phys.*, **33**, 1271 (1960).
290. R. F. Kubin, B. S. Rabinovitch, and R. E. Harrington, *J. Chem. Phys.*, **37**, 937 (1962).
291. E. W. R. Steacie, *Atomic and Free Radical Reactions*, Vol. 1, Reinhold, New York, 1954.
292. G. G. Volpi and F. Zocchi, *J. Chem. Phys.*, **44**, 4010 (1966).
293. J. V. Michael and H. Niki, *J. Chem. Phys.*, **46**, 4965 (1967).
294. J. R. Dingle and D. J. LeRoy, *J. Chem. Phys.*, **18**, 1632 (1950).
295. J. V. Michael and R. E. Weston, Jr., *J. Chem. Phys.*, **45**, 3632 (1966).
296. J. W. S. Jamieson and G. R. Brown, *Can. J. Chem.*, **42**, 1638 (1964).
297. D. G. Dalgleish and J. H. Knox, *Chem. Commun.*, **1966**, 917.
298. H. A. Kazmi, R. J. Diefendorf, and D. J. LeRoy, *Can. J. Chem.*, **41**, 690 (1963).
299. T. J. Hardwick, *J. Phys. Chem.*, **66**, 117 (1962).
300. T. J. Hardwick, *J. Phys. Chem.*, **66**, 291 (1962).
301. M. F. R. Mulcahy, R. J. Harrison, and J. R. Wilmshurst, *Australian J. Chem.*, **19**, 1431 (1966).
302. E. W. R. Steacie, *Atomic and Free Radical Reactions*, Vol. 2, Reinhold, New York, 1954.
303. W. R. Brennen, I. D. Gay, G. P. Glass, and H. Niki, *J. Chem. Phys.*, **43**, 2569 (1965).
304. W. R. Trost, B. deB. Darwent, and E. W. R. Steacie, *J. Chem. Phys.*, **16**, 353 (1948).
305. R. M. Lambert, M. I. Christie, and J. W. Linnett, *Chem. Commun.*, **1967**, 388.
306. N. Demchuk and H. Gesser, *Can. J. Chem.*, **42**, 1 (1964).
307. R. W. Carr, Jr., I. D. Gay, G. P. Glass, and H. Niki, *J. Chem. Phys.*, **49**, 846 (1968).
308. S. W. Benson, *J. Chem. Educ.*, **42**, 502 (1965).
309. A. N. Wright, J. W. S. Jamieson, and C. A. Winkler, *J. Phys. Chem.*, **62**, 657 (1958).
310. J. W. S. Jamieson and C. A. Winkler, *J. Phys. Chem.*, **60**, 1542 (1956).
311. J. W. S. Jamieson, G. R. Brown, and W. K. Hancock, *Can. J. Chem.*, **43**, 1973 (1965).
312. C. A. Winkler and H. I. Schiff, *Discussions Faraday Soc.*, **14**, 63 (1953).
313. N. N. Lichtin, "Some Aspects of the Reaction of Active Nitrogen with Organic Substrates," in *The Chemistry of Ionization Excitation*, G. R. A. Johnson and G. Scholes, Eds., Taylor & Francis, London, 1967, p. 181.
314. K. D. Foster, P. Kebarle, and H. B. Dunford, *Can. J. Chem.*, **44**, 2691 (1966).
315. D. R. Safrany and W. Jaster, *J. Phys. Chem.*, **72**, 518 (1968).
316. J. T. Herron, *J. Phys. Chem.*, **70**, 2803 (1966).

317. Y. Shinozaki, R. Shaw, and N. N. Lichtin, *J. Am. Chem. Soc.*, **86,** 341 (1964).
318. G. Paraskevopoulos and C. A. Winkler, *J. Phys. Chem.*, **71,** 947 (1967).
319. Y. Titani and N. N. Lichtin, *J. Phys. Chem.*, **72,** 526 (1968).
320. A. Tsukamoto and N. N. Lichtin, *J. Am. Chem. Soc.*, **84,** 1601 (1962).
321. A. Fujino, S. Lundsted, and N. N. Lichtin, *J. Am. Chem. Soc.*, **88,** 775 (1966).
322. T. Hanafusa and N. N. Lichtin, *Can. J. Chem.*, **44,** 1230 (1966).
323. D. R. Safrany, P. Harteck, and R. R. Reeves, Jr., *J. Chem. Phys.*, **41,** 1161 (1964).
324. P. T. Hinde and N. N. Lichtin, *Advan. Chem. Ser.*, **80,** 250 (1969).
325. W. E. Jones and C. A. Winkler, *Can. J. Chem.*, **42,** 1948 (1964).
326. E. R. Zabolotny and H. Gesser, *J. Phys. Chem.*, **66,** 854 (1962).
327. P. M. Aronovich and B. M. Mikhailov, *Izv. Akad. Nauk SSSR, Otd. Khim. Nauk*, **1956,** 544; *Chem. Abstr.*, **51,** 1892 (1957).
328. P. M. Aronovich, N. K. Belsky, and B. M. Mikhailov, *Izv. Akad. Nauk SSSR, Otd. Khim. Nauk*, **1956,** 696; *Chem. Abstr.*, **51,** 1893 (1957).
329. J. M. S. Jarvie and R. J. Cvetanovic, *Can. J. Chem.*, **37,** 529 (1959).
330. R. D. Cadle and E. R. Allen, *J. Phys. Chem.*, **69,** 1611 (1965).
331. L. I. Avramenko, R. V. Kolesnikova, and G. I. Savinova, *Izv. Akad. Nauk SSSR, Otd. Khim. Nauk*, **1,** 36 (1963).
332. R. J. Cvetanovic, *J. Chem. Phys.*, **23,** 1375 (1955).
333. R. Gomer and W. A. Noyes, Jr., *J. Am. Chem. Soc.*, **72,** 101 (1950).
334. R. J. Cvetanovic and L. C. Doyle, *Can. J. Chem.*, **33,** 1684 (1955).
335. H. Niki, E. E. Daby, and B. Weinstock, *Twelfth Symposium (International) on Combustion*, The Combustion Institute, Pittsburgh, Pennsylvania, 1969, p. 277.
336. L. Elias and H. I. Schiff, *Can. J. Chem.*, **38,** 1657 (1960).
337. L. Elias, *J. Chem. Phys.*, **38,** 989 (1963).
338. D. Saunders and J. Heicklen, *J. Phys. Chem.*, **70,** 1950 (1966).
339. C. A. Arrington, W. Brennen, G. P. Glass, J. V. Michael, and H. Niki, *J. Chem. Phys.*, **43,** 525 (1965).
340. J. D. Sullivan and P. Warneck, *J. Phys. Chem.*, **69,** 1749 (1965).
341. H. M. Frey, *J. Chem. Soc.*, **1962,** 2293.
342. D. P. Chang and G. B. Kistiakowsky, *J. Phys. Chem.*, **68,** 1793 (1964).
343. H. M. Frey and I. D. R. Stevens, *J. Chem. Soc.*, **1965,** 1700.
344. E. L. Wong and A. E. Potter, *Can. J. Chem.*, **45,** 367 (1967).
345. F. J. Wright, *J. Chem. Phys.*, **38,** 950 (1963).
346. F. J. Wright, *Tenth International Symposium on Combustion*, The Combustion Institute, Pittsburgh, Pennsylvania, 1965, p. 387.
347. R. D. Cadle and J. W. Powers, *J. Phys. Chem.*, **71,** 1702 (1967).
348. R. J. Cvetanovic, *Can. J. Chem.*, **34,** 775 (1956).
349. H. E. Avery and R. J. Cvetanovic, *J. Chem. Phys.*, **43,** 3727 (1965).
350. C. L. Thomas, G. Egloff, and J. C. Morrell, *Chem. Rev.*, **28,** 1 (1941).
351. H. Wiener and M. Burton, *J. Am. Chem. Soc.*, **75,** 5815 (1953).
352. A. B. Tsentsiper, E. N. Eremin, and N. I. Kobozev, *Russ. J. Phys. Chem. (Engl. Transl.)*, **37,** 433 (1963).

353. A. B. Tsentsiper, E. N. Eremin, and N. I. Kobozev, *Russ. J. Phys. Chem.* (*Engl. Transl.*), **37**, 558 (1963).
354. L. W. Sieck and R. H. Johnsen, *J. Phys. Chem.*, **67**, 2281 (1963).
355. J. M. Williams and W. H. Hamill, *J. Chem. Phys.*, **49**, 4467 (1968).
356. W. Braun, K. H. Welge, and J. R. McNesby, *J. Chem. Phys.*, **45**, 2650 (1966).
357. Y. Kawahara, *J. Phys. Chem.*, **73**, 1648 (1969).
358. R. Gorden, Jr., and P. Ausloos, *J. Chem. Phys.*, **46**, 4823 (1967).
359. A. K. Brewer and P. D. Kneck, *J. Phys. Chem.*, **35**, 1293 (1931).
360. L. M. Yeddanapalli, *J. Chem. Phys.*, **10**, 249 (1942).
361. M. Kawahata, J. C. Fraser, and J. A. Coffman, Preprints Div. Fuel Chem., *Am. Chem. Soc.*, **8**(2), 33 (1964).
362. C. Ponnamperuma and F. Woeller, *Nature*, **203**, 272 (1964).
363. C. Ponnamperuma, F. Woeller, J. Flores, M. Romiez, and W. Allen, *Advan. Chem. Ser.*, **80**, 280 (1969).
364. M. Burton and J. L. Magee, *J. Chem. Phys.*, **23**, 2194 (1955).
365. M. Burton and J. L. Magee, *J. Chem. Phys.*, **23**, 2195 (1956).
366. E. N. Lassettre and S. A. Francis, *J. Chem. Phys.*, **40**, 1208 (1964).
367. J. E. Manton and A. W. Tickner, *Can. J. Chem.*, **38**, 858 (1960).
368. B. A. Tozer, *J. Electron. Control*, **4**, 149 (1958).
369. S. N. Foner and R. L. Hudson, *J. Chem. Phys.*, **45**, 49 (1966).
370. *Chem. Eng. News*, January 6, 1969, p. 37.
371. J. T. Clarke, "Reaction of Graphite and Hydrogen Above 2000°K," in *The Application of Plasmas to Chemical Processing*, R. F. Baddour and R. S. Timmins, Eds., M.I.T. Press, Cambridge, Massachusetts, 1967, p. 132.
372. E. M. Magee, *J. Chem. Phys.*, **39**, 855 (1963).
373. T. Böhm-Gössl, W. Hunsmann, L. Rohrschneider, W. M. Schneider, and W. Ziegenbein, *Chem. Ber.*, **96**, 2504 (1963).
374. E. A. Nevmerzhitskaya, A. N. Belyaeva, V. A. Poprotskaya, and N. A. Kudryavtseva, *Khim. Prom.*, **41**, 895 (1965); *Chem. Abstr.*, **64**, 10992h (1966).
375. N. I. Kobozev, S. S. Vasil'ev, and E. E. Gal'braikh, *Dokl. Akad. Nauk SSSR*, **2**, 236 (1935); *Chem. Abstr.*, **29**, 6152[9] (1935).
376. *Anon.*, *New Scientist*, **40**, 715 (1968).
377. S. V. Starodubtsev, Sh. A. Ablyaev, and L. G. Keitlin, *Izv. Akad. Nauk Uz. SSR, Ser. Fiz.-Mat. Nauk*, **6**(5), 50 (1962).
378. S. V. Starodubtsev, Sh. A. Ablyaev, F. Bakhramov, Sh. Ziyatdinov, and L. G. Keitlin, *Izv. Akad. Nauk Uz. SSR, Ser. Fiz.-Mat. Nauk*, **6**(5), 58 (1962).
379. S. V. Starodubtsev, Sh. A. Ablyaev, F. Bakhramov, Sh. Ziyatdinov, and L. G. Keitlin, *Izv. Akad. Nauk Uz. SSR, Ser. Fiz.-Mat. Nauk*, **6**(6), 53 (1962).
380. S. V. Starodubtsev, Sh. A. Ablyaev, L. Ya. Alimova, and Yu. B. Sokolova, *Izv. Akad. Nauk Uz. SSR, Ser. Fiz.-Mat. Nauk*, **6**(6), 61 (1962).
381. E. N. Borisova and E. N. Eremin, *Russ. J. Phys. Chem.* (*Engl. Transl.*), **41**, 69 (1967).
382. R. Miquel and M. Chirol, *Bull. Soc. Chim. France*, **283**, 1677 (1962).
383. R. Miquel and J. Bonnet, *Bull. Soc. Chim. France*, **1965**, 2770.

384. G. Mignonac, R. Miquel, and H. Lecouls, *Bull. Soc. Chim. France*, **1966**, 2161.

385. G. Mignonac, R. Miquel, and H. Lecouls, *Bull. Soc. Chim. France*, **1966**, 2168.

386. M. P. Reddy and M. Burton, *J. Am. Chem. Soc.*, **79**, 813 (1957).

387. E. N. Borisova and E. N. Eremin, *Russ. J. Phys. Chem.* (*Engl. Transl.*), **41**, 395 (1967).

388. E. N. Borisova and E. N. Eremin, *Russ. J. Phys. Chem.* (*Engl. Transl.*), **40**, 1459 (1966).

389. E. N. Borisova and E. N. Eremin, *Russ. J. Phys. Chem.* (*Engl. Transl.*), **40**, 1273 (1966).

390. A. Kupperman and M. Burton, *Radiation Res.*, **10**, 636 (1959).

391. E. Badereu, D. Stefanescu, and C. Popovici, *Comun. Acad. Rep. Populare Romine*, **9**, 1141 (1959); *Chem. Abstr.*, **54**, 16126i (1960).

392. J. D. Callister and E. R. Thornton, *Nature*, **206**, 504 (1965).

393. A. D. Coates, U.S. Dept. Commerce OTS AD 419–618; *Chem. Abstr.*, **61**, 2056 (1964).

394. H. Schüler and G. Arnold, *Z. Naturforsch.*, **17a**, 670 (1962).

395. H. Schüler and G. Arnold, *Z. Naturforsch.*, **18a**, 15 (1963).

396. H. Schüler and G. Arnold, *Z. Naturforsch.*, **18a**, 604 (1963).

397. H. Schüler and G. Arnold, *Z. Naturforsch.*, **19a**, 771 (1964).

398. G. Arnold, *Z. Naturforsch.*, **20a**, 435 (1965).

399. C. J. Breukink, P. Havenaar, T. Hoekstra, H. I. Waterman, and J. B. Westerdijk, *Brennstoff-Chem.*, **41**, 273 (1960).

400. C. J. Breukink, H. J. Pasman, and J. C. Vlugter, *Brennstoff-Chem.*, **46**, 161 (1965).

401. H. J. Pasman, J. C. Vlugter, and C. J. Breukink, *Brennstoff-Chem.*, **46**, 241 (1965).

402. H. J. Pasman, J. C. Vlugter, and C. J. Breukink, *Brennstoff-Chem.*, **46**, 271 (1965).

403a. H. J. Pasman, J. C. Vlugter, and C. J. Breukink, *Brennstoff-Chem.*, **46**, 358 (1965).

403b. N. Sonoda, S. Yamamoto, K. Okumura, S. Noda, and S. Tsutsumi, *Advan. Chem. Ser.*, **76**, 352 (1968).

404. S. A. Rodemeyer, *Studies of Reactions of Aromatic Hydrocarbons Within a Microwave Discharge*, Ph.D. Thesis, University of California, Berkeley, 1966; A. Streitwieser, Jr., and S. A. Rodemeyer, Abstracts 148th National Meeting, American Chemical Society, Chicago, Illinois, August 30–September 4, 1964, p. 18U.

405. C. S. Stokes, *Advan. Chem. Ser.*, **80**, 390 (1969).

406. F. Fischer and K. Peters, *Brennstoff-Chem.*, **12**, 260 (1931).

407. F. K. McTaggart, *Australian J. Chem.*, **17**, 1182 (1964).

408. F. J. Vastola, P. L. Walker, Jr., and J. P. Wightman, *Carbon*, **1**, 11 (1963).

409. F. F. Martinotti, M. J. Welch, and A. P. Wolf, *Chem. Commun.*, **1968**, 115.

410. A. P. Wolf, private communication.
411. H. Wise and B. J. Wood, "Reactive Collisions Between Gas and Surface Atoms," in *Advances in Atomic and Molecular Physics*, D. R. Bates and I. Estermann, Eds., Vol. 3, 1967, p. 291.
412. G. M. Harris and A. W. Tickner, *Nature*, **160**, 871 (1947).
413. L. I. Avramenko, *Zh. Fiz. Khim.*, **20**, 1299 (1946); *Chem. Abstr.*, **41**, 2998 (1947).
414. J. D. Blackwood and F. K. McTaggart, *Australian J. Chem.*, **12**, 533 (1959).
415. M. M. Shahin, *Nature*, **195**, 992 (1962).
416. A. B. King and H. Wise, *J. Phys. Chem.*, **67**, 1163 (1963).
417. J. Streznewski and J. Turkevich, *Proceedings Third Carbon Conference*, Pergamon, Oxford, 1959, p. 273.
418. J. D. Blackwood and F. K. McTaggart, *Australian J. Chem.*, **12**, 114 (1959).
419. G. R. Henning, *Proceedings of the Fourth Carbon Conference*, Pergamon, Oxford, 1960, p. 145.
420. C. E. Gleit, W. D. Holland, and R. C. Wrigley, *Nature*, **200**, 69 (1963).
421. H. Marsh, T. E. O'Hair, and W. F. K. Wynne-Jones, *Trans. Faraday Soc.*, **61**, 274 (1965).
422. D. E. Rosner and H. D. Allendorf, *Carbon*, **3**, 153 (1965).
423. R. C. Melucci and J. P. Wightman, *Carbon*, **4**, 467 (1966).
424. H. Marsh, T. E. O'Hair, and R. Reed, *Trans. Faraday Soc.*, **61**, 285 (1965).
425. E. E. G. Hughes, B. R. Williams, and J. M. Thomas, *Trans. Faraday Soc.*, **58**, 2011 (1962).
426. W. Zinman, *Planetary Space Sci.*, **3**, 46 (1961).
427. R. C. Giberson, HW-68380 UC-4, Chemistry, Office of Technical Services, Dept. of Commerce, Washington, D.C., 1961.
428. H. W. Goldstein, *J. Phys. Chem.*, **68**, 39 (1964).
429. Y. C. Fu and B. D. Blaustein, *Ind. Eng. Chem.*, *Proc. Design Develop.*, **8**, 257 (1969).
430. Y. C. Fu and B. D. Blaustein, *Fuel (London)*, **47**, 463 (1968).
431. H. J. Gluskoter, *Fuel (London)*, **44**, 285 (1965).
432. H. J. Gluskoter, *J. Sediment. Petrol.*, **37**, 205 (1967).
433. J. K. Stille, R. L. Sung, and J. Vander Kooi, *J. Org. Chem.*, **30**, 3116 (1965); R. L. Sung, *Reactions of Organic Compounds in a Radiofrequency Discharge*, Ph.D. Thesis, State University of Iowa, Ames, Iowa, 1965.
434. D. D. Neiswender, *Advan. Chem. Ser.*, **80**, 338 (1969).
435. A. Streitwieser, Jr., and H. R. Ward, *J. Am. Chem. Soc.*, **85**, 539 (1963).
436. D. Bryce-Smith and A. Gilbert, *Chem. Commun.*, **1966**, 643.
437. F. J. Dinan, *Advan. Chem. Ser.*, **80**, 289 (1969).
438. M. Vacher and Y. Lortie, *J. Chim. Phys.*, **56**, 732 (1959).
439. T. F. Bindley and S. Walker, *Trans. Faraday Soc.*, **58**, 217 (1962).
440. A. T. Watts and S. Walker, *J. Chem. Soc.*, **1962**, 4323.
441. J. Ripoche, *J. Phys.*, **27**, 686 (1966).
442a. H. Suhr, G. Rolle, and B. Schrader, *Naturwissenschaften*, **55**, 168 (1968).
442b. H. Suhr and R. I. Weiss, *Z. Naturforsch.*, **25b**, 41 (1970).

443. H. Suhr, Z. Naturforsch., 23b, 1559 (1968).
444. F. Le Goff, J. Chim. Phys., 65, 883 (1968).
445. F. Le Goff, J. Chim. Phys., 66, 385 (1969).
446. R. V. Eck, E. R. Lippincott, M. O. Dayhoff, and Y. T. Pratt, Science, 153, 628 (1966).
447. S. Sifniades, D. Jerolamon, and R. Fuhrmann, Advan. Chem. Ser., 80, 332 (1969).
448. S. Takahashi, Shinkyu Kagaku, 9, 55 (1961).
449. E. Otsuka and H. Watanabe, Nenryo Kyokaishi, 42, 523 (1963).
450. W. V. Allen and C. Ponnamperuma, Currents Mod. Biol., 1, 24 (1967).
451. K. Sugino, E. Inoue, K. Shirai, T. Koseki, and T. Gomi, Nippon Kagaku Zasshi, 86, 1200 (1965).
452. T. C. Ruppel, P. F. Mossbauer, M. F. Ferrer, and D. Bienstock, Ind. Eng. Chem. Prod. Res. Develop., 9, 369 (1970).
453. J. C. Chu, H. C. Ai, and D. F. Othmer, Ind. Eng. Chem., 45, 1266 (1953).
454. H. Schüler, E. Lutz, and G. Arnold, Naturwissenschaften, 48, 426 (1961).
455. R. A. Sanchez, J. P. Ferris, and L. E. Orgel, Science, 154, 784 (1966).
456. J. R. Blanton, J. Grunwald, and K. H. Gayer, Record Chem. Prog., 27, 269 (1966).
457. C. N. Matthews and R. E. Moser, Proc. Natl. Acad. Sci., 56, 1087 (1966).
458. A. Topouzkhanian, J. d'Incan, and J. Janin, J. Chim. Phys., 64, 506, 1299 (1967).
459. N. F. Brockmeier and T. Juul-Dam, Preprints Div. Fuel Chem., Am. Chem. Soc., 13(4), 331 (1969).
460. K. Kawamoto, Bull. Chem. Soc. Japan, 41, 2161 (1968).
461. K. Kawamoto and Y. Nishimura, Bull. Chem. Soc. Japan, 42, 1105 (1969).
462. T. Isshiki, N. Sonoda, and S. Tsutsumi, Bull. Chem. Soc. Japan, 41, 2180 (1968).
463. K. Kawamoto, N. Sonoda, and S. Tsutsumi, Bull. Chem. Soc. Japan, 41, 1376 (1968).
464. U. Müller and A. Greiner, Chem. Tech. (Berlin), 18, 327 (1966).
465. N. G. Pilyugina and O. I. Zakharov-Nartsissov, High Energy Chem. (Engl. Transl.), 2, 153 (1968).
466. S. Matsuda, S. Kikkawa, S. Oka, and Y. Tanaka, Kogyo Kagaku Zasshi, 71, 1499 (1968); Chem. Abstr., 70, 37311y (1969).
467. G. Steinman, Science, 154, 1344 (1966).
468. J. R. Hollahan, B. B. Stafford, R. D. Falb, and S. T. Payne, J. Appl. Polymer Sci., 13, 807 (1969).
469. A. J. Osteraas and D. A. Olsen, Nature, 221, 1140 (1969).
470. R. H. Sahasrabudhey and A. Kalyanasundaram, Proc. Indian Acad. Sci., 27A, 366 (1948).
471. R. H. Sahasrabudhey and S. M. Deshpande, Proc. Indian Acad. Sci., 31A, 317 (1950).
472. R. H. Sahasrabudhey and S. M. Deshpande, J. Indian Chem. Soc., 27, 361 (1950).

473. R. H. Sahasrabudhey and S. M. Deshpande, *J. Indian Chem. Soc.*, **28**, 377 (1951).
474. M. F. Nagiev, R. M. Efendiev, and I. G. Ismailzade, *Dokl. Akad. Nauk Azerb. SSR.*, **14**, 347 (1958); *Chem. Abstr.*, **52**, 17080i (1958).
475. J. R. Hollahan and R. P. McKeever, *Advan. Chem. Ser.*, **80**, 272 (1969).
476. G. W. Hodgson and C. Ponnamperuma, *Proc. Natl. Acad. Sci.*, **59**, 22 (1968).
477. S. W. Fox, Ed., *The Origins of Prebiological Systems and of Their Molecular Matrices*, Academic, New York, 1965.
478. J. de Rosnay, *Ann. Chim.*, **2**, 57, 133 (1967).
479a. A. I. Oparin, *Genesis and Evolutionary Development of Life*, Academic, New York, 1968.
479b. R. M. Lemmon, *Chem. Rev.*, **70**, 95 (1970).
480. M. Calvin, *Chemical Evolution*, Oxford Univ. Press, London, 1969.
481. T. Hiraki, *Bull. Chem. Soc. Japan*, **42**, 470 (1969).
482. M. Kawahata, *Advan. Chem. Ser.*, **80**, 316 (1969).
483. B. Vuillermoz, *J. Chim. Phys.*, **63**, 1486 (1966).
484a. B. Vuillermoz, *J. Chim. Phys.*, **66**, 382 (1969).
484b. H. Suhr and R. I. Weiss, *Angew. Chem. Intern. Ed. Engl.*, **9**, 312 (1970).
485. F. Swift, R. L. Sung, J. Doyle, and J. K. Stille, *J. Org. Chem.*, **30**, 3114 (1965).
486. B. R. Bronfin, "Fluorine Reactions in Plasma," in *The Application of Plasmas to Chemical Processing*, R. F. Baddour and R. S. Timmins, Eds., M.I.T. Press, Cambridge, Massachusetts, 1967, p. 157.
487. D. E. Milligan and D. R. Sears, *J. Am. Chem. Soc.*, **85**, 823 (1963).
488. J. K. Stille and C. E. Rix, *J. Org. Chem.*, **31**, 1591 (1966).
489. J. A. Kerr, private communication, 1969.
490. A. S. Rodgers, D. M. Golden, and S. W. Benson, *J. Am. Chem. Soc.*, **89**, 4578 (1967).
491. K. E. Wilzbach, *J. Am. Chem. Soc.*, **79**, 1013 (1957).
492. L. M. Dorfman and K. E. Wilzbach, *J. Phys. Chem.*, **63**, 799 (1959).
493. N. A. Ghanem and T. Westermark, "Extensions of the Techniques for the Accelerated Unspecific Isotopic Labelling of Organic Compounds," in *Radioisotopes in the Physical Sciences and Industry*, Intern. Atomic Energy Agency, Vienna, 1962, p. 43.
494. T. Onak, R. P. Drake, and G. B. Dunks, *Inorg. Chem.*, **3**, 1686 (1964).
495. R. N. Grimes, *J. Am. Chem. Soc.*, **88**, 1895 (1966).
496. R. N. Grimes and C. L. Bramlett, *J. Am. Chem. Soc.*, **89**, 2557 (1967).
497. R. L. Hughes, I. C. Smith, and E. W. Lawless, *Production of the Boranes and Related Research*, R. T. Holzmann, Ed., Academic, New York, 1967.
498. E. L. Muetterties and W. H. Knoth, *Polyhedral Boranes*, Marcel Dekker, New York, 1968.
499. V. Bažant and V. Chvalovsky, *Chemistry of Organosilicon Compounds*, Vol. I, Academic, New York, 1965.
500. G. C. Akerlof, U.S. Patent, 2,899,371 (1959).
501. E. H. Brown, W. D. Wilhide, and K. L. Elmore, *J. Org. Chem.*, **27**, 3698 (1962).

502. E. H. Brown, W. D. Wilhide, and K. L. Elmore, *J. Electrochem. Soc.*, **111**, 123 (1964).

503. R. C. Sheridan and E. H. Brown, *J. Org. Chem.*, **30**, 668 (1965).

504. P. K. Allt, P. Datta, W. A. T. Macey, and B. Semmens, *J. Appl. Chem.*, **18**, 213 (1968).

505. E. R. Zabolotny and H. Gesser, *J. Am. Chem. Soc.*, **81**, 6091 (1959).

506. A. R. Denaro, P. A. Owens, and A. Crawshaw, *European Polymer J.*, **5**, 471 (1969).

507. J. F. Woodman, U.S. Patent, 2,632,729 (1953).

508. F. J. Vastola and B. Greco, Preprints Div. Fuel Chem., Am. Chem. Soc., **8**(2), 51 (1964).

509. K. Jesch, J. E. Bloor, and P. L. Kronick, *J. Polymer Sci. A-1*, **4**, 1487 (1966).

510. H. F. Sterling, J. H. Alexander, and R. J. Joyce, *Le Vide, Special A.V.I. Seminar*, 80 (October 1966).

511. R. C. G. Swann, R. R. Mehta, and T. P. Cauge, *J. Electrochem. Soc.*, **114**, 713 (1967).

512. B. A. Probyn, *Vacuum*, **18**, 253 (1968).

513. O. A. Weinreich and A. Ribner, *J. Electrochem. Soc.*, **115**, 1090 (1968).

514. H. F. Sterling, J. H. Alexander, and R. J. Joyce, *Special Ceramics*, **4**, 139 (1968).

515. A. E. Hultquist and M. E. Sibert, *Advan. Chem. Ser.*, **80**, 182 (1969).

516. R. D. Wales, *Advan. Chem. Ser.*, **80**, 198 (1969).

517. D. R. Secrist and J. D. Mackenzie, *Advan. Chem. Ser.*, **80**, 242 (1969).

518. J. P. Wightman and N. J. Johnston, *Advan. Chem. Ser.*, **80**, 322 (1969).

519. P. M. Hay, *Advan. Chem. Ser.*, **80**, 350 (1969).

520. T. C. Ruppel, P. F. Mossbauer, and D. Bienstock, *Advan. Chem. Ser.*, **80**, 214 (1969).

521. C. K. Weiffenbach, P. R. Griffiths, P. J. Schuhmann, and E. R. Lippincott, *J. Phys. Chem.*, **73**, 2526 (1969).

522. P. R. Griffiths, P. J. Schuhmann, and E. R. Lippincott, *J. Phys. Chem.*, **73**, 2532 (1969).

523. M. Manes, *Advan. Chem. Ser.*, **80**, 133 (1969).

524. A. V. Potapov, *High Temp. (Engl. Transl.)*, **4**, 48 (1966).

525. A. N. Mal'tsev, L. A. Churina, and E. N. Eremin, *Russ J. Phys. Chem.*, *(Engl. Transl.)*, **42**, 1235 (1968).

526. D. C. Carbaugh, F. J. Munno, and J. M. Marchello, *J. Chem. Phys.*, **47**, 5211 (1967).

527. E. A. Rubtsova and E. N. Eremin, *Russ. J. Phys. Chem. (Engl. Transl.)*, **42**, 536 (1968).

528. E. A. Rubtsova and E. N. Eremin, *Russ. J. Phys. Chem. (Engl. Transl.)*, **42**, 1099 (1968).

529. J. D. Thornton, W. D. Charlton, and P. L. Spedding, *Advan. Chem. Ser.*, **80**, 165 (1969).

530. K. Morinaga and M. Suzuki, *Bull. Chem. Soc. Japan*, **35**, 429 (1962).

531. Yu. M. Emel'yanov, V. G. Babayan, and Z. G. Aliev, *Russ. J. Phys. Chem. (Engl. Transl.)*, **42**, 1183 (1968).

532. S. S. Barton, S. T. Balke, R. J. Beardmore, R. T. Perry, M. Daniel, and W. Newstead, *J. Phys. Chem.*, **71**, 4573 (1967).

533. V. P. Lebedev, Yu. V. Filippov, and N. I. Kobozev, *Zh. Fiz. Khim.*, **24**, 845 (1950); *Chem. Abstr.*, **45**, 433e (1951).

534. Yu. V. Filippov, V. P. Lebedev, and N. I. Kobozev, *Zh. Fiz. Khim.*, **24**, 1009 (1950); *Chem. Abstr.*, **45**, 1882f (1951).

535. C. R. Masson, V. Boekelheide, and W. A. Noyes, Jr., "Photochemical Reactions," in *Technique of Organic Chemistry, Catalytic, Photochemical, and Electrolytic Reactions*, A. Weissberger, Ed., Vol. 2, 2nd ed., Interscience, New York, 1956, p. 257.

536. H. Gesser and S. Hussain, *Nature*, **201**, 290 (1964).

537. I. M. Campbell and B. A. Thrush, *Proc. Roy. Soc. (London)*, **296A**, 201 (1967).

538. T. J. Dougherty, Div. Phys. Chem., 157th National Meeting, American Chemical Society, April 1969, Paper 77.

539. "Ozone Chemistry and Technology," *Advan. Chem. Ser.*, Vol. 21, Am. Chem. Soc., Washington, D.C., 1959.

540. M. Roegiers, *Petroleum (London)*, 179 (July 1952).

541. J. R. Hollahan, *J. Sci. Instrum. Ser. 2*, **2**, 203 (1969).

542. J. R. Ligenza, *J. Appl. Phys.*, **36**, 2703 (1965).

543. O. A. Weinreich, *J. Appl. Phys.*, **37**, 2924 (1966).

544. C. E. Gleit, *Advan. Chem. Ser.*, **80**, 232 (1969).

545. R. A. Dugdale, *Nature*, **220**, 1179 (1968).

546. "Engineering Aspects of Electrical Discharges as Chemical Reactors," Symposium held at the American Institute Chemical Engineers Meeting in Denver, Colorado, August 30–September 2, 1970.

547. S. A. Gregory, *Chem. Eng. (London)*, CE329 (December 1966).

548. E. J. Mezey and J. H. Oxley, *J. Microwave Power*, **2**, 79 (1967).

549. D. A. Dunn, *Sci. J.*, 3 (June 1967).

550. P. H. Dundas and M. L. Thorpe, *Chem. Eng.*, 123 (June 30, 1969).

551. A. T. Bell, *Ind. Eng. Chem. Fund.*, **9**, 160 (1970).

552. G. Földiák, *Chem. Technik*, **13**, 748 (1961).

553. J. C. Bryner and W. J. Coleman, 21st Annual Gaseous Electronics Conference, Boulder, Colorado, October 1968, Paper B-9.

Chapter **XII**

PHOTOCONDUCTIVITY OF ORGANIC SOLIDS

Richard C. Nelson

1   INTRODUCTION

Photoconductivity was first observed nearly 100 years ago by Willoughby Smith [1], who found that the resistance of bars of selenium was constant in darkness but decreased upon illumination. Some 50 years elapsed before any real progress was made toward understanding the nature of the processes involved. In the early 1920's Gudden and Pohl [2] demonstrated that photoconductivity was a quantum effect: in "primary photocurrents" one electronic charge passed between the electrodes per photon absorbed.

For some time thereafter it was customary to think of photoconductivity much as one thinks of photoemission, as though one electron per photon were liberated to make its way through the solid medium. However, the progress made in the physics of the solid state during the past 20 years has freed us from the simplistic concept of the "internal photoelectric effect" and opened pathways through which considerable progress has been made toward understanding photoconductivity.

The classic photoconductive materials are nonmetallic elements and the oxides, sulfides, and halides of heavy metals. The study of the photoconductivity of organic materials began in the 1930's and has developed into a distinct field of research, owing to the fact that organic solids are in general bound by van der Waals forces, hence are much more weakly bound than the covalent and ionic inorganic solids. Because of this the molecules in the organic solid retain much of their individual character. In addition, a molecule in an organic solid is an entity much larger than an atom, so that interactions extend over a smaller number of structural units.

The study of organic photoconductors is itself further divided into two recognizable branches. One of these deals with the coherent or wavelike transport of excitation and charge carriers in hyperpure crystals of aromatic hydrocarbons. It has a well-developed theory and demands an elegance of technique comparable to that of solid-state research on silicon and germanium, to which it bears a family resemblance. The other broadly recognizable branch is motivated directly by an interest in problems of energy conversion and storage; because of the importance of photosynthesis, it is often concerned with dye-sensitized processes in solid systems, broadly defined.

Since the chlorophyll molecules in photosynthesis and the sensitizer molecules on a photographic emulsion grain occur in two-dimensional arrays without long-range order, the work in this field is less concerned with coherent processes in nearly perfect crystals than with phenomena that can be discussed in localized or quasi-chemical terminology. The two points of view should be thought of as complementary rather than opposing; both are concerned with the formulation of a model sufficiently general to comprehend the whole range of photoconductive phenomena in organic solids. The ultimate model will have in it elements of both the localized and coherent character of phenomena in organic solids; we are not yet sure how to strike a balance between them.

In the following discussion we shall perhaps overemphasize the "localized" point of view because the sort of experiments it suggests do not necessarily require access to hyperpure crystalline material and because it has a more direct appeal to chemical intuition. Gutmann and Lyons *Organic Semiconductors* [3] provides access to the literature dealing with theoretical and experimental studies of nearly perfect crystals.

It is well to bear in mind that while hundreds of organic photoconductors are known only a handful have been studied intensively enough to allow a reasonable certainty as to what elements of the two complementary pictures are applicable to them in particular; the adoption of an eclectic point of view, taking desirable features of each to suit the taste, is not always advisable.

2 THEORETICAL CONSIDERATIONS

An electron in a solid moves in a potential which arises from all the atoms in the solid, and its allowed energies are determined by this potential. There are two general ways to approach the problem of allowed energies. In the tight-binding approximation, one inserts into the solid positive and negative ion radicals and considers the resonance penetration integrals that define the movement of an electron or hole into other sites in the solid. To make useful calculations, the positions and orientations of the neighboring molecules must be known, but the concept of periodicity of arrangement does not enter explicitly into the calculation.

In the weak-binding approximation, one considers the solid as an infinite array of potential wells with periodic spacing, thus incorporating the idea of crystallinity directly into the model. The allowed energies of an electron are found by solving Schrödinger's equation for this case. The solutions take the form of bands of allowed energies; the widths of the bands depend on the dimensions of the potential wells and their separations, as determined by the nature of the entities represented as wells and the strength with which they are bound in the array.

By either method one can, in principle, estimate the widths of the bands of allowed energies for holes and electrons. In general, if the width is large compared with kT, the electrons take on a wavelike character in the periodic lattice, and lattice coherence, hence the crystalline nature of the solid, becomes important. If the width is much less than kT, the free path of an electron is roughly the distance between lattice sites, and it may be thought of as being localized.

The question whether localized or coherent transport of charge carriers dominates in organic solids is still controversial; differences of opinion tend to arise from divergent views of the importance of the simplifying assumptions that must always be made, particularly the π-electron approximation and the neglect of intermolecular vibrations [4]. The simple aromatic hydrocarbons, such as naphthalene and anthracene, seem to lie in a region in which neither a coherent nor a localized model has strict validity [5]. As one considers more complicated molecules, such as dyes, the appraisal becomes more difficult because less pertinent information is available. For solids having only local order or scattered domains of one-dimensional order, the localized picture seems reasonable.

All practical crystals are imperfect, and much of the problem of describing the effects of irradiation on solids in terms of conductivity is concerned with the contribution of imperfections. Any departure from an ideal lattice at absolute zero can be regarded as an imperfection, including the presence of a photon; in addition, we must consider phonons, or quantized lattice vibrations; electrons and holes; excitons; lattice vacancies; lattice dislocations; and foreign molecules, among which we may include a lattice molecule which has trapped an electron by deformation.

The term "exciton" has a somewhat elastic meaning and in the literature it may refer to anything from a localized excitation in a molecule to a collective excitation distributed over a whole crystal. The exciton of covalent and ionic photoconductors is the so-called Wannier exciton, a hydrogenlike bound state of a hole and electron. The Wannier exciton is not known in molecular crystals, but it is sometimes convenient to think of a localized molecular excitation as being similar to a bound hole-electron pair.

In van der Waals solids, the term "exciton" is reserved by some writers for the Frenkel exciton, which is attributable to a strong energy-exchange interaction between molecules. This is basically a coherent or wavelike crystal lattice phenomenon, with a rate of excitation transfer of $\sim 10^{13}$–10^{15}/sec [6]. Both kinds of excitons have the common properties of being mobile, thermally dissociable, and able to collapse with the emission of radiation.

The various types of structural defects of the lattice may give rise to new energy levels localized at the site of the defect. This is particularly true of surfaces and interfaces, which are ever-present, large-scale defects. Useful inorganic photoconductors must ordinarily be crystals that are reasonably free of structural defects, but organic materials may display photoconductivity in glassy specimens without obvious crystal order. In a van der Waals solid composed of large molecules, the molecules themselves are domains of rigorous order which, in first approximation, establish the optical properties of the solid; the charge-transport interactions are greatly attenuated in such disordered systems but can be detected because of the great sensitivity of the operation of current measurement.

Light absorbed by lattice structural defects, and particularly by foreign molecules, may lead directly to charge-carrier generation if the energy-level relationships are favorable. Light absorbed by the principal or nominal constituent does not generally lead directly to the appearance of charge carriers but rather to an excited state with a lifetime of $\sim 10^{-9}$ sec, and the process of charge-carrier generation depends ultimately on an interaction between a crystal defect and the excited state during its lifetime.

The excited molecule may interact with phonons (or dissociate thermally), giving rise to charge carriers. This process contributes to carrier generation even in rather disordered situations. In nearly perfect large crystals, the mobility of the excited state, or exciton, makes possible a variety of additional processes, which greatly increases the effective optical cross section of structural defects able to interact with the exciton; hence the contribution of foreign molecules and surfaces may be much greater than would be possible if it were necessary that the photon be absorbed by, or in the immediate neighborhood of, the defect. The diffusion length of a singlet exciton in anthracene has been measured to be ~ 1000 Å, so a minute concentration of foreign molecules with appropriate energy levels can dominate the photoelectric behavior of the crystal. Singlet excitons may also interact with each other to supply energy for charge-carrier generation, and the same may be true of triplet excitons formed by intersystem crossing [7]. The delocalization of excited states is therefore a phenomenon of great importance in nearly perfect crystals of aromatic hydrocarbon photoconductors.

Another type of excitation transfer process ascribed to Förster is a dipole-dipole resonance transfer, usually used to describe the exchange of excitation energy between well-separated molecules and not necessarily related to crystal structure. Since the resonance is between the fluorescence of the initial molecule and the absorption of the acceptor, the molecules need not be identical. Transfer rates for the Förster process are given as 10^6–10^{11}/sec. The 50% transfer probability distance is ~ 50 Å [6].

In solids having a low degree of order, the role of excitation transfer is not clear. A strong-interaction exciton process is known for linear aggregates of many cyanine dyes (J-band aggregates), but this interaction does not always accompany linear aggregation and is rare or absent in dyes of other classes. In J-band materials, the interaction manifests itself in a new, sharp band in both absorption and fluorescence, and the appearance of such new spectral features is a good indicator of strong excitation transfer interaction. Weigl [8] has interpreted the broadening of the lowest-lying absorption band of dye films (compared with the same absorption in solution) as a result of excitation transfer, but there also seems to be a purely classical explanation of this broadening [9]. There can be no serious doubt that such processes exist in dye solids, but Weigl [10] showed that in the case of tetraphenylporphine they did not contribute to the generation of charge carriers.

Pearlstein [11] studied the transfer of excitation energy in some models of the chlorophyll aggregate in the photosynthetic apparatus. He showed that random transfer of localized excitation by a diffusive process could account for the coupling of the aggregate of ~500 molecules to a few reaction sites.

The principal concern of studies of inorganic photoconductors is the effect of defects of the crystal on the processes of generation and transport of charge carriers as they appear in the behavior of the specimen as a conductive object; the concepts of Fermi level and carrier lifetime are the important unifying ideas. These ideas are basic in studies of organic photoconductors, but the problem of generation of charge carriers assumes a much greater significance in van der Waals solids than in inorganic crystals. Here the absorption can be broadly associated with the molecules of the lattice, and energy absorbed in any electronic transition leads to the appearance of charge carriers; there is no special absorption of the solid associated with photoconductivity. However, the initial excited state of a molecule is a bound state, and it is not at all obvious that enough energy is associated with it to generate mobile holes or electrons.

The energy required to insert a hole and an electron into a solid is its ionization energy or work function minus its electron affinity. Serious difficulties may arise in the measurement of one or both of these quantities on a crystal. If the value of the quantities for the molecular unit are used, a considerable correction for the polarization of the solid must be included, so that it is not simple to compare the energy of the separated hole-electron pair with the molecular excitation energy.

There is generally a temperature dependence of photoconductivity at constant irradiance associated with organic photoconductors which can be represented by a Boltzmann factor $\exp(-E/kT)$, where E is of the order of tenths of an electron volt. This is sometimes ascribed to the shifting of the Fermi level in a logarithmic distribution of traps, but the high degree of reproducibility associated with E in many cases suggests a more fundamental cause. Nelson [12] has shown for some dye photoconductors that E corresponds to the difference between the energy of the hole-electron pair and of the photon that produced them and is thus the dissociation energy of the initial excited state.

The problem of the temperature effect is of more than academic interest because the conductive excited state stores some part of the energy of the photon with a lifetime many orders of magnitude greater than that of the molecular excited state and is thus of great significance for studies of energy storage and conversion. If there is also a thermal dissociation stage requiring energies of ~0.3 eV, a strong implication exists that the quantum yield of holes and electrons will be small.

The quasi-chemical terminology of the localized model is particularly suited to discussion of energy conversion and storage in organic photoconductors. A hole and electron each may be associated with a molecule, and these molecules appear as new chemical species, oxidant and reductant, respectively, so that it is apparent that in terms of the model the energy of the photon has been converted, if only briefly, to chemical free energy.

In considering the possibility of utilizing these species as reactants, one must think not only of the energy stored in them but also of their chemical potentials. That is, for an electron to be transferred exergonically from one molecule to another it must be more strongly bound by the second than by the first. We must thus consider binding energies of electrons and holes on some conventional scale which will make possible comparisons between different systems.

The most suitable scale is that in which the energy of an electron at rest at a distance from the solid is defined as zero. The energy of the highest-lying electron in the ground state, of the optical electron of the excited state, and of an electron in the conductive excited state are all of interest and appear as binding energies. These energies are properly defined by the operations used to measure them, which will be discussed later.

We must now give a more precise meaning to the term "localized" in relation to the spatial extent of the state corresponding to each binding energy. We cannot do this a priori in a general sense, but rather we consider some cyanine dyes which are useful as photographic sensitizers. These materials are carbocyanines and thiacarbocyanines with known energy-level structures [12]. None of them show J-bands, hence we assume that energy transfer occurs by the Förster process. In this case the appropriate excited state is that of a single molecule. The energy of the optical electron is determined by the structure of the dye and the effects of its environment; for the solid dye the environmental effect is attributable to the London dispersion forces. These require an aggregate of many molecules for their full expression and affect the energy of the optical electron rather than the ground state energy [13].

Selsby and Nelson [14] have calculated the ionization energy of adsorbed monolayers of these molecules; this is a measure of the energy of the highest-lying electron in the ground state. They applied the HF-LCAO-MO-SCF method, using the π-reminimization technique and a modification of the semiempirical σ-π-interaction correction of Hoyland and Goodman [15], to take into account intramolecular polarization; they found that all other environmental effects attributable to counterions and nearest-neighbor cations could be introduced into the problem in a classical manner. The polarization energy associated with nearest-neighbor cations and counterions was ∼0.2 eV. The residual difference between experiment and calculation was about 0.1 eV, setting a very low limit to the effects of exchange interactions on the ionization energy. The ionization energy is a highly localized property of these materials.

Similar calculations indicated that exchange effects must probably be considered for the energy of the conduction electron, so that "localized" may mean "spread over a few molecules," although the analysis in this case was less complete than for the ionization energy. It is difficult to say how applicable these results are to dyes in general; these materials may represent special but highly interesting cases [16].

In the localized model, the individual molecules are visualized as potential wells, and charge transport takes place by discrete jumps, by tunneling through the intermolecular barrier. Application of an electric field gives an asymmetry to the barriers associated with any well, so that there is a preferred direction for tunneling. Generation of charge carriers may also take place by an analogous tunneling of the optical electron of the excited state to an adjacent molecule (Fig. 12.1).

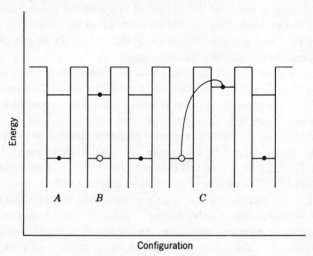

Fig. 12.1   A photoconductive solid as a one-dimensional array of potential wells in a localized model. *A*, A molecule in the ground state; *B*, an optically excited molecule; *C*, a separated hole-electron pair.

3 SOME PHENOMENA IN DYE PHOTOCONDUCTORS

Dye photoconductors may be nonionic, cationic, or anionic. The binding of the solid is in all cases attributable primarily to van der Waals forces, and there are no fundamental differences between ionic and nonionic materials considered as photoconductors. The work of Selsby [16] on the ionization energy of cationic dyes shows that the essential similarity results from charge compensation by the counterion; the ionization energies of cationic and anionic dyes belong to the same statistical population in spite of the charge on the dye ion.

In cationic dyes the ionization energy and the electron affinity of adsorbed monolayers are in first approximation independent of the nature of the counterion, as is also the energy of the lowest singlet excitation. However, the counterion may have large effects on dark conductivity and on the kinetics of photoconductivity [17].

Dye molecules are characteristically planar, unless forced out of planarity by steric effects, either intramolecular or extramolecular. A molecule that has been forced out of planarity by its environment is a lattice defect and may trap an electron. Having done so, it is no longer constrained to planarity and may relax into a strongly nonplanar configuration, trapping the electron more deeply. Dyes of the triphenylmethane type, which depart somewhat from planarity at all times because of crowding around the central carbon atom, have a strong tendency to form disordered solids, and this type of trapping is a prominent phenomenon in many of them.

Since traps of this sort result from the interaction of an electron and a defect, their density can be built up by irradiation. While they may survive the loss of the trapped electron as a frozen-in lattice defect, if the specimen is held in darkness for a sufficient time, ranging from hours to days, the traps decay away but can be regenerated by further irradiation [18, 19].

Electrons trapped in this way can be ejected from the surface of the solid by an external photoelectric effect. Measurements of the threshold show that the energy of the trapped electron is nearly independent of the density of trapped electrons on the surface. The density can be built up by irradiation in the visible and allowed to decay; within the limits imposed by the difficulty of comparing thresholds for the emission at widely varying peak values, the electrons are essentially monoenergetic [18].

If the binding energy of the trapped electron is expressed on the same scale as the energy of the conduction electron, the difference is found to be an energy that appears as an activation energy all though the kinetics of photoconductivity of the dye, representing the effect of temperature on the mobility, the rate of decay of photoconductivity, and the rate of reaching a steady state in irradiation [19, 20].

The density of monoenergetically trapped electrons may be of the order of $10^{17}/cm^3$ under moderate illumination [21], and the electrons appear to be in equilibrium with the conductive level [22]. They are responsible for the pseudointrinsic kinetics observed in dyes of this type.

In principle, microscopic and macroscopic rate equations can be written for an intrinsic photoconductor as follows

$$dn/dt = gI - an^2$$

and

$$d\sigma/dt = \gamma I - \alpha\sigma^2,$$

where n is the density of electrons and of holes, I is the rate of absorption of photons per unit volume, g and γ are quantum yields, a and α are second-order rate constants in appropriate units, and σ is conductivity. The decay is second order because it takes place by recombination of equal numbers of electrons and holes; dn/dt and $d\sigma/dt$ will follow parallel courses if $\sigma/n = \mu e$ is a constant; μ is the mean mobility averaged over all excited carriers, including those in traps.

If there are no traps, μ will be constant; this is the intrinsic case. If there are traps and if the electrons are distributed over them in a classical statistical manner, then μ will vary in time as the traps are emptied because the fraction of electrons in the conductive state will vary, except in the single case in which the traps are monoenergetic. In dyes of this kind, it is sometimes possible to observe dn/dt directly by electron spin resonance (ESR) techniques. The process follows the law:

$$at = \frac{1}{n_t} - \frac{1}{n_0},$$

that is, it is a simple second-order process. Correspondingly, the decay of conductivity follows the analogous law:

$$\alpha t = \frac{1}{\sigma_t} - \frac{1}{\sigma_0}$$

and appears also to be a simple second-order process. A second-order process does not have a characteristic relaxation time, but the two measurements follow similar courses in time. It can be concluded that the conductivity is a constant measure of the carrier density. In dye photoconductors in which this sort of trapping does not take place, the decay is complex and fits no simple scheme.

4 TECHNIQUES AND APPARATUS

Types of Experimental Specimens

An ideal preparation for studying the photoconductivity of a material would be a pure single crystal in the form of a very thin plate with electrically indifferent, optically transparent electrodes on the faces. This ideal cannot ordinarily be realized.

The requirement of purity is very difficult to evaluate. There can be no doubt that in anthracene crystals, for example, the requirement is as stringent as it is for germanium or silicon, of the order of parts in 10^9. It is an over-simplification to say that for other types of preparations and for other sorts of measurements than those ordinarily performed on anthracene crystals the requirement must necessarily be equally stringent.

Much interesting work has been done on sublimed films of organic photo-conductors. Such samples are usually highly disordered, that is, they have a high density of lattice defects. It is by no means obvious that the introduction of additional defects in the form of a few parts in 10^8 of foreign molecules has an appreciable effect on charge transport in the disordered preparation. It is conceivable that there might be an effect on charge-carrier generation; whether or not this is true depends not only on the density of the impurity but also on its effective optical cross section, account being taken of the transport of excitation energy from host to impurity. If the transport of excitation energy in the disordered sample is less efficient than it is in the crystal, which seems inevitable, the effect of impurity will also be diminished.

The properties of the ideal crystal lattice are just those required to enhance the effect of impurities; although the effects of all types of defects are not necessarily precisely equivalent, it must be true that the presence of a high density of one type of defect tends to mask the presence of a low density of another type.

All this would be merely academic if organic photoconductors possessed no properties that could be studied on specimens other than nearly perfect crystals. For the study of strong-interaction excitation transport, there is no substitute for a nearly perfect crystal. The use of crystals is advantageous for the study of charge transport because mobilities are high and because of the greater convenience of charge transport calculations in an ordered lattice, but it would be entirely possible to calculate mobilities in a statistical model of a van der Waals solid with only local order.

Studies of energy-level structures of organic photoconductors can often be carried out on disordered solids, except for details arising from strong excitation-exchange processes. This is particularly true of photographic sensitizing dyes, in which the details of energy-level structure are of great importance. Nelson [13] found that for the dye pinacyanol measurements of the ionization energy were identical, within a small classical correction for the molecular environment, for disordered solvent film preparations, poly-crystalline films, adsorbed monolayers, and very sparsely adsorbed small aggregates. A self-consistency test on an overdetermined energy-level diagram showed that the energy levels were those of pinacyanol and not of an impurity. Each level (Fig. 12.2A) can be deduced in two different ways, one involving the excitation energy, and one without using it. Since the two ways give consistent values, since the four data were obtained by mutually independent methods, and since the excitation energy was determined from the action spectrum for sensitized photoconductivity which agreed with that well known for this dye used as a photographic sensitizer, the levels must be those of pinacyanol. Similar self-consistent overdetermined energy-level diagrams are known for other cyanine dyes [12].

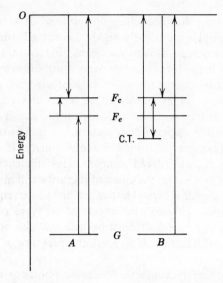

Fig. 12.2 Energy levels and transitions in the localized model: A, the simple case; B, a dye molecule with characteristic trapping. The energy $F_c - F_e$ is the thermal energy for the generation of charge carriers.

Takeda [23] has studied the effect of defects on the properties of the dye auramine hydrochloride as a photoconductor. The starting material was a crude, technical grade of dye which, in solvent films, was photoconductive with a fast response. The dye was purified by several recrystallizations, followed by chemical purification [24], conversion to the free base, further purification by zone melting, and reconversion to the hydrochloride. Comparison of the ends of the zone melted samples with the center section showed that a substantial degree of purification had been achieved in the center.

At each stage of purification, the ionization energy, the energy of the configurationally trapped electron, the thermal activation energy for photoconductivity, and the activation energy for dark conductivity were measured. In addition, the ratio of photoconductivity to dark conductivity was measured, and the density of configurational traps estimated. The ratio of photoconductivity to dark conductivity increased by three orders of magnitude during the whole purification process, with a steady increase in the density of configurational traps.

The various energies were measured for four states of order in the experimental specimen: sublimed disordered, solvent films, polycrystalline samples, and single crystals.

After the chemical purification, further purification had no effect on the energies, which were also independent of state of order. The density of configurational traps was greatest in the single-crystal specimen and least in the sublimed, disordered samples. As might be expected, the largest photo-conductivity was also associated with the single-crystal specimen.

There are no simple universal criteria of purity, and to defend one's work against the imputation that the phenomena observed are attributable to impurities is never easy. In the most general sense, it is never possible to prove for any practical crystal that defects do not exist and are not responsible for some phenomenon in the same way that the counterproposition that a defect does exist and is responsible for a phenomenon, can be proved. At best, one can only attempt by experiment or theoretical argument to render it unlikely that defects are responsible. Part of any such argument must obviously be to show that sensible precautions have been taken to achieve a substantial degree of purity.

It is desirable to use a thin specimen in photoconductivity studies to make possible a reasonably uniform density of photons throughout the thickness during irradiation. While a sample can be fairly uniformly irradiated at a wavelength that is very weakly absorbed, it becomes less certain that the effect observed is attributable to the principal component and not to an impurity. In addition, if the dark conductivity is bulk conductivity, use of a thick specimen increases the dark effect without any compensating increase in sensitivity to radiation.

A more important objection to thick specimens is that if response is to be measured as a function of wavelength the thickness of the specimen that is actually irradiated depends on the extinction coefficient. As a result, the density of carriers and their lifetime will be wavelength dependent and the relative quantum efficiency may be completely obscured.

Since many organic photoconductors have very high extinction coefficients, such effects can never be eliminated completely in films of practical thickness. They may, in fact, be useful under special circumstances in which it is desired to illuminate one face of a film while leaving the other almost dark. Since for many dyes a monomolecular film absorbs 2 to 3 % of incident radiation at the peak of the lowest singlet absorption, a film $\sim 1 \ \mu$ thick gives a very high ratio of front-to-rear photon flux for this wavelength [25].

The desirability of thin specimens makes the use of single crystals of many materials impractical and nearly always eliminates consideration of cast specimens or pellets of compressed powder. With thick specimens there is an ever-present risk that the effects of impurities may be enhanced if one irradiates with weakly absorbed light to allow the radiation to penetrate, since one may inadvertently excite an impurity with strong absorption in this region and obtain a completely false picture of the photoconductive threshold.

Uniform electric fields can generally be obtained only with thin, flat crystals or specimens cast between electrodes. It should be remembered that strip electrodes such as those that must be used with thin films give highly nonuniform fields owing to edge effects. Specimens prepared by pressing powders or small crystals between conductive plates are ordinarily of little use for photoconductivity studies, and the fields in the solid phase may be highly nonuniform.

Preparation of Samples

Thus we are faced not so much with striving for perfection in the preparation of photoconductive specimens as with making prudent compromises to obtain such features as may be important in some particular case. This usually requires the use of thin-film preparations, or what are sometimes called "surface cells," an unfortunate term in that it implies what is not invariably true, that the conductivity observed is surface conductivity.

Thin-film cells are usually made by sublimation of the material or by evaporating a solution of the material over electrodes arranged on the face of an insulating solid. It is possible in either case to manipulate partially the state of order of the specimen by choice of conditions.

The character of a sublimed film depends largely on the geometry of the molecule and of the crystal lattice. If the molecule is compact and symmetrical, so that any molecule approaching the surface is not too far removed in orientation from a possible orientation in the solid, then crystals may be formed. An elongated or asymmetrical molecule has a much smaller chance at first encounter of coming to rest in a position consistent with long-range order. The use of buffering gas favors crystalline order, as does the use of a heated substrate. A cold substrate, high rates of evaporation, and high vacuum favor disordered films.

Sublimation may contribute to the purification of the sample, but there is a chance that the material will be degraded. Care must be taken when molecules of doubtful stability are to be sublimed, and one should always check the deposited film spectroscopically at some point. Especially with dyes, sublimation may lead to the depositing of a different, chemically altered dye in the film. One should also watch the vacuum gauge during the sublimation process for evidence of evolution of gas; quaternary alkyl groups on a heterocyclic nitrogen may split off with the production of an alkyl halide.

It is not easy to make a thin, uniform film by drying a spot of solution, but it can often be done by paying attention to details. If one puts a few drops of solution on a concave cylindrical surface, spreads it over the surface by tilting and rotating, and immediately dries the film by partial evacuation, a very uniform film a few tenths of a micron thick and several square centimeters in area can be formed with a little practice. The solvent should have neither too high a heat of vaporization nor too high a boiling point, and the solid must be soluble to about 1% or greater in it for films of moderate thickness. Absolute ethanol is a satisfactory solvent for many dyes.

The structure of the film obtained in this way is highly dependent on the rate of evaporation. Vartanyan [26] showed that many dyes could be obtained in the form of "continuous films" having a glassy surface luster by sufficiently rapid evaporation of solvent. Weigl [27], in a study of the structure of continuous crystal violet films, found that the x-ray diffraction pattern shows a single, strong, sharp line and several weaker ones. The strong line corresponds to an interplanar distance in a stacked array, and the solid appears to have domains of one-dimensional order.

Polycrystalline films can be made by slower evaporation of the solvent, but this is often accompanied by a tendency to dry at the edges of the pool of solution so that nonuniform films result. In certain cases, of which the dye pinacyanol is a good example, continuous films can be made and then converted to polycrystalline films by treatment with solvent vapor [28].

Electrodes

Making electrical contact between a photoconductive specimen and the external circuitry is a problem with which one must usually deal empirically. A considerable number of conductive pastes and soft metals can be used on massive specimens, but for thin films one must usually use deposited or evaporated metal electrodes. Bube [29] has discussed the theoretical and experimental aspects of the electrode problem for inorganic photoconductive crystals, which are more readily manipulated than organic materials. We shall confine our discussion to the detection of nonohmic contacts, since at best the character of untried electrode-photoconductor systems is unpredictable.

Nonohmic contacts can be recognized by the presence of rectification, photocurrent noise, photovoltaic effects, and space charge effects. Photovoltaic effects are easily recognizable as signals upon illumination in the absence of applied voltage. However, small signals so obtained may be associated with nonuniform thickness or illumination. A diagnosis of photocurrent noise should be made cautiously in view of the innumerable sources of noise detectable by meters with high input impedance. Space charge effects may be very obvious and dramatic, usually appearing as a moderately rapid falling-off of current under constant irradiance and voltage. If the working voltage is removed and illumination is resumed, a current of the opposite sense will be observed, falling off to zero as the field resulting from accumulated space charge disappears. While space charge accompanies nonohmic contacts, it may be found also in situations in which the contacts are ohmic; it is then analogous to the space charge in a thermionic diode. It may also be found at interfaces of any kind, and especially at surfaces [30].

The most convenient electrodes for thin-film samples on a quartz or glass substrate are made with the "liquid platinum" or liquid palladium paint used for decorating ceramic materials. These are solutions of metal salts in an oily medium which are painted on the surface and fired in a furnace at as high a temperature as is possible without risk of distortion of the glass. The resulting metal films make satisfactory ohmic contacts with most ionic dyes. Evaporated metal films using masks to define the electrodes can also be used but are inconvenient to apply to the interior surfaces of tubing.

Electrodes can be ruled on the interior of open cylinders using liquid platinum and a Leroy drawing pen.* The cylinder of glass or quartz is mounted so that it can be rotated on its axis through reproducible angles. The pen is mounted on a micrometer slide so that it can be translated parallel to the axis of the cylinder; by suitable manipulation any set of lines either parallel to the axis or lying in planes perpendicular to the axis can be constructed. This can be done on tubes of 18 mm i.d. or larger using the standard pen.

Electrodes in the form of interlocking combs (Fig. 12.3) are readily made

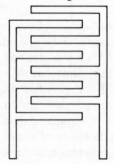

Fig. 12.3   Electrodes in the form of interlocking combs.

in this way for studying photoconductive films of high resistivity. It is difficult to rule lines narrower than 1 mm because of the tendency of the fluid to spread, but with care the interelectrode spacing can be made as little as 0.4 mm. With 10 or 12 electrodes spaced less than 1 mm apart, the conductance of the substrate on which the electrodes are ruled may become unpleasantly noticeable. This is especially true of Pyrex glass, which is not a particularly good insulator; if this shunt conductivity becomes a problem, quartz tubing may be used. Fabricated quartz apparatus with sealed-in electrodes is costly, but a simple trick makes it possible to evade this problem. Electrodes are ruled on the interior of a quartz tube by using liquid platinum, and then with a small brush a streak of platinum is painted from one electrode

* Manufactured by Keuffel and Esser, Hoboken, New Jersey.

to an open end of the quartz tube. A ring about a centimeter wide is then painted over the interior, exterior, and end surfaces of the tube so that after firing the exterior ring is continuous with the interior and is thus connected to one electrode. In the same way the other electrode is connected to a ring on the other end of the tube. The tube may now be incorporated into a piece of glass apparatus with epoxy cement, either making a butt joint at each end to a piece of glass tubing of the same size, or closing one end with a glass or metal plate. Annealed copper wire of small gauge is wrapped around the exterior platinum rings for leads. It is advisable to define the contact and immobilize the wrapping by paiuting over with colloidal graphite. Such cells have extremely high resistance and are fairly dependable. High-vacuum epoxy cement may be used, but the ordinary household variety is almost as good for this purpose even if the system is to be held at high vacuum.

Ambient Gases; Vacuum Technique

It has been recognized for many years that the behavior of organic conductors in air may be different from that *in vacuo*, but recent work has suggested that the sensitivity of many of these materials to oxygen is much greater than had been thought previously. Maruyama and Inokuchi [31] showed that the dark conductivity of quaterrylene was decreased by some three orders of magnitude when the ambient pressure was reduced from 10^{-2} torr to 10^{-8} torr. Other work has shown that for certain anionic dyes whose photoconductivity is enhanced by oxygen, stable, reproducible values of photoconductivity are obtained only at pressures below 10^{-6} torr. It thus becomes desirable in studies of photoconductivity to provide for adequate control of the atmosphere in contact with the specimen.

We have done a good deal of work with cells that could be loaded, pumped, and sealed off at reduced pressure. Such a procedure is convenient but does not provide particularly high vacuum because it is impossible to bake and getter labile materials properly. We now prefer to use a cell with a small ion pump permanently attached to it so that evacuation can be maintained conveniently for an indefinite period. Since the pump also serves as vacuum gauge, one can obtain current, accurate information about the condition of the cell; a 1 liter/sec appendage pump is small enough so that the portability and manipulability of the apparatus are not much diminished.

The sample cell assembly is first attached to a conventional pumping system with mechanical and diffusion pumps by means of a ball joint. The cell may contain the test material in the form of 1 or 2 mg of powder or small crystals, and the system is arranged so that it can be rotated on the cylindrical axis of the cell. With the cell oriented so that the electrodes face upward and the sample on the other side of the tube, the cell is opened to the pumping system and pumped down. A manifold is provided to shut off this part of the vacuum system from the pump and open it to an appendix containing solvent. Solvent vapor diffuses into the cell and is condensed to liquid by applying a bit of ice to the wall. The sample is dissolved with slight warming if necessary. If desired, the resulting solution can be spread on the blank wall of the cell and dried down by opening to the pump. Several repetitions of this procedure greatly reduce the amount of water and other atmospheric gases in the solution.

If the specimen is to be made by sublimation, the dry material is evaporated from the blank wall of the cell to the side having electrodes. If the specimen is to be pnt on from solution, the cell is turned over so that the solution lies on the electrodes, tilted and rotated to spread the solution, and the film is formed by opening to the vacuum system. It is then pumped with the diffusion pump; the sample is warmed to 50 to 60°C or higher with heating tape if so desired, while the appendage pump is baked with an infrared lamp. When the cell system is evacuated to $\sim 10^{-4}$ torr, it is closed off from the diffusion pump with a stopcock, the ion pump is started, and the cell and appendage can be detached completely.

Evacuation of the cell is much faster if its interior is kept under an atmosphere of dry nitrogen while it is being cleaned and reloaded. A 1 liter/sec appendage pump can maintain a small system of this sort, complete with low vapor pressure stopcock grease, black-waxed ground joints, and epoxy cement joints at 10^{-7} torr indefinitely and economically. If lower pressures are needed, a pump of greater capacity may be used. In this case the pump and magnet are heavy enough so that they must be supported separately, and the maneuverability of the whole apparatus is impaired.

Electrical Measurements

In the early days of research on organic photoconductors, the measurement of very small currents was difficult and most of the materials mentioned in the earlier literature are relatively highly conductive. This problem has essentially disappeared with the advent of highly stable, dc current-measuring devices, so that now a specimen with photoconductance of 10^{-14} mho offers no particular difficulties. Typically, the most sensitive scale of such an instrument may be 10^{-13} A full scale. If a 10-V potential is placed across specimen and meter, the full potential may be assumed to be across the specimen, since the input impedance of an electrometer-type of current-measuring instrument is greatly reduced by inverse feedback and the current is a good measure of the photoconductivity. If an electrometer of the vibrating capacitor type is available, it is possible to measure photoconductances of 10^{-16} mho to a few percent.

This range can usually be extended by using higher voltages across the sample, since the free range of a carrier is so small that it never acquires much kinetic energy. However, at applied fields above 10^4 V/cm the current-voltage plot may become markedly supralinear and there is danger of electric breakdown.

Although current-measuring instruments leave little to be desired, problems are still encountered in coupling the cell to the meter. Great care should be taken in shielding the cell, preferably in a metal box, and in arranging the connection between the cell in its shielding and the input connector of the meter. Teflon, polyethylene, or polystyrene insulation should be used at all points. Experience indicates that time spent in doing the best possible job in the circuitry external to the meter is well spent indeed, since in working with very low currents every bit of carelessness or sloppy improvization leads to trouble.

Even with the most painstaking effort, trouble may arise from vibration of coaxial cable; from pickup of extraneous signals from electrical heating devices; from 60-cycle pickup or pulse noises from fluorescent lamps; from electrical coupling between cell and light source, especially at the onset and conclusion of illumination; from noise resulting from extraneous surface conduction under conditions of high humidity and from other causes. The solution of these problems requires time, patience, and resourcefulness.

5 MEASUREMENTS AND OBSERVATIONS ON ORGANIC PHOTOCONDUCTORS

Dark Current

Before illumination, photoconductors exhibit a certain amount of conductivity of problematical origin. This conductivity is ordinarily proportional to the Boltzmann factor, $\exp(-E/2kT)$, where E is often interpreted as the separation between intrinsic ground and conductive states. There is sometimes an element of paradox in data of this sort in that the observed activation energy is so large that if we assume a plausible number of electrons in the lower level and calculate the number of electrons in the upper level in equilibrium with them, an unreasonably high mobility has to be attributed to these carriers to account for the observed current [17]. Attribution of the current to impurities only intensifies the problem since it implies a smaller number of electrons in the lower level.

However, there are cases in which the thermal activation energy is such that E corresponds reasonably well with the optical excitation energy for photoconductivity and the conductivity is consistent with reasonable mobilities. There is no reason in general why the optical and thermal excitation energies should agree; application of the Franck-Condon principle suggests that thermal energies may be substantially less than optical energies [32].

If additional thermal energy is required in the optical generation of charge carriers, this contribution to the total thermal energy may in part compensate for the lowering attributable to the Franck-Condon effect. Because dark currents in photoconductors are poorly understood, it is usually preferable not to rely on the interpretation of the activation energy for dark conductivity as a direct measurement of an energy-level separation in the solid.

Spatial Range of Effects

Some fairly simple experiments can be performed which are instructive in relation to the general character of organic photoconductors. If one prepares a square thin film and illuminates it with the image of a bright slit, first in an area removed from the electrodes, with the slit oriented parallel to them and then transverse to the electrodes, so that the film is illuminated continuously from electrode to electrode, one can form an idea of how nearly localized the effect of irradiation is by comparing the photoconductance associated in each case with the same radiant flux.

If the product of carrier lifetime and mobility is large enough, then carriers will drift over nonilluminated parts of the film for distances comparable to its dimensions, and there may be only a small effect on the conductivity owing to changing the orientation of the slit. This is true of some inorganic thin-film photoconductors such as cadmium sulfide and lead sulfide. In crystal violet, however, almost no detectable photoconductivity is present for the case in which no continuously illuminated path from electrode to electrode exists.

An equivalent experiment is that in which a small spot of light is traversed across the cell from electrode to electrode. For a material with a large lifetime mobility product, what one sees may be largely traceable to nonuniform fields and thickness of the film. With crystal violet the result is a very slowly rising current as one traverses the cell until the far electrode is closely approached, when the current begins to rise very rapidly [33]. The resistance of the part of the film illuminated by the light spot is lowered, and since the decay of photoconductivity is very slow it remains low while the spot traverses the cell; hence a strip of conductive material is built up and reaches out from the first electrode toward the second. The resistance of the cell measured is the sum of the resistance of this conductive strip and that of the dark part of the cell. The latter dominates the behavior until the spot of light comes close to the second electrode, when the resistance falls very rapidly and a flush of current results.

One type of dye photoconductor gives surprising and deceptive results in such an experiment; this phenomenon illustrates both the fact that unexpected things sometimes happen with organic photoconductors and the occasional need to make a thorough analysis of a superficially simple situation [34].

A film of this kind on glass shows photoconductivity almost independently of whether the illuminated portion is contiguous with both electrodes or not, but if there is not a continuous illuminated path from electrode to electrode, space charge appears. The dye film need not touch the electrodes at all for photoconductivity to be observed.

One tends to think of a dye film as a sort of two-dimensional system in which all the charge transport takes place. In this kind of film, part of the transport takes place in the glass substrate through charge carriers, probably electrons, injected into the glass by the dye. Glass is customarily treated as if all its conductivity is ionic, but if electrons can be injected into glass, they are mobile. Since the magnitudes of the mobilities in the glass and in the dye probably do not differ greatly, the currents in the glass are not much different from those in the dye.

In the dye phase the relaxation time of photoconductivity is very small, and space charge effects do not appear. Since it is likely that carriers of one sign only are injected into the glass, their lifetime becomes considerable and space charge builds up under irradiation.

In a geometry in which two very thin coplanar electrodes are used, it is incorrect to suppose that the field is confined to the region between the electrodes that lies in the plane. The field is indeed strongest at the edges of the electrodes that face each other, but there is a smaller but not negligible field near the edges that face away from each other, and the field extends into the dielectric upon which the electrodes lie. An electron at any point in this field moves from negative to positive independently of any purely geometrical coordinates, and photoconductivity may be observed as the result of irradiation of any part of the whole dye film in which the field is strong enough to lead to a detectable current.

This behavior has been observed in a variety of photographic sensitizing dyes. It is possible that the measured properties of such a system, such as thermal activation energies, are characteristic of the whole system including substrate rather than specifically of the photoconductor. For this reason the use of fused quartz as substrate is desirable since effects of this type are much smaller or absent in quartz.

Sign of the Charge Carrier

Organic photoconductors may be either *n*-type or *p*-type, in which conduction occurs predominantly by electrons or by holes, respectively. While some generalizations about the relationship between molecular structure and carrier type can be made, the carrier type is not certainly predictable. A number of methods of ascertaining the sign of the carrier have been reported.

The method ordinarily used with inorganic crystals, the Hall effect, is not applicable in the great majority of cases because of the high resistivity of many organic photoconductors and the extremely low mobilities.

The sign of the thermoelectric power appears to be a reliable index of the sign of the charge carrier, although its magnitude is not completely understood [35]. Its measurement on thin-film samples, however, is difficult. The problem of insulating one part of a thin film from the rest both electrically and thermally is solved by using an element consisting of two pieces of platinum foil joined by a thin bead or strip of platinum-sealing lead glass. The two foil parts of the element may be clamped or soldered to copper blocks, the temperatures of which can be measured and controlled. If 10-mil foil is used, the element is quite sturdy, but the sealing of the two pieces requires great care so that the joint is smooth enough to allow a uniform film to be formed on it (Fig. 12.4).

When only the sign of the thermoelectric effect is needed, it is easier to support the measuring element at its edges and to heat the blackened reverse sides of the foils radiatively with a ribbon-filament lamp and a lens or mirror of large aperture. The temperature can be measured with thermocouples cemented to the foils. A difference in temperature of the two sides of 10 to 20°C can be obtained with such heating.

In the measuring circuit, the resistance of the measuring element, that of the glass bead which joins the foils, appears as a shunt across the input resistance of the voltmeter, so that the observed signal will be

$$\frac{Q \, \Delta T R_{IB}}{R_{IB} + R_F},$$

where Q is the thermoelectric power, R_{IB} the resistance of the bead and voltmeter in parallel, and R_F the resistance of the thin film being measured. Since if one attempts to increase the resistance of the bead by making it wider the resistance of the film is increased proportionately, the resistivity of the insulating material of the bead is in practice usually the limiting factor in measuring the thermoelectric power. Since Q is of the order of 1 mV per degree, a voltmeter of high sensitivity and high input resistance is required. The sign of the effect in even rather poor photoconductors can be determined with glass insulation, but the magnitude may be uncertain because of the size of the shunt correction.

It is important to measure the specimen in both senses, first with one side heated, then the other. Some films show inherent asymmetries which may be mistaken for thermoelectric effects if this is not done. If the magnitude of the asymmetry is not much greater than that of the thermoelectric voltage, one can correct for it directly. Asymmetries appear often to be attributable to insufficiently rigorous cleaning of the element.

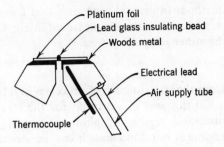

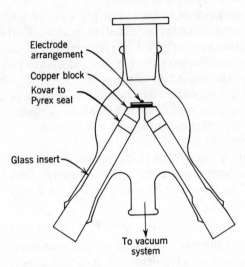

To vacuum
system

Fig. 12.4 Element for measurement of the thermoelectric power of thin-film specimens [22].

A very simple method often used to determine the sign of the charge carrier is to observe the effect of oxygen or air on the magnitude of the photo-conductivity. If it is quenched by oxygen, it is *n*-type; if increased, *p*-type. A localized electron reacts with oxygen and becomes more tightly bound, thus removing mobile electrons from the conductive state; in so doing it may increase the lifetime of the holes. Depending on whether hole or electron conduction is more important in the absence of oxygen, the effect is to increase or decrease the photoconductivity.

Meier [36] has measured a large number of dyes in this way, and his results agree well with those obtained from the sign of the thermoelectric effect. Other more difficult procedures have been described in the literature, but they seem to be less reliable than the oxygen method, as judged by agreement with the thermoelectric method. In general it appears that anionic dyes are always p-type conductors, as are all materials measured in air. Cationic and nonionic materials may be either p-type or n-type.

Kinetics

Much can be learned from the study of rate of processes and the influence of temperature on rates, but this sort of work has for the most part been confined to the pseudointrinsic regime of photoconductivity. In many materials in which this regime is not dominant, it can be separated out by waiting until the faster processes have gone to an end, leaving the slower pseudointrinsic kinetics in control.

It is often possible in such slow processes to wait until the time rate of change of conductivity is very small to measure the thermal activation energy for conduction very simply. If the temperature of the specimen is changed as rapidly as possible, and the log of conductance plotted against $1/T$ in the usual way, the activation energy for mobility can be found directly. The success of this procedure depends on the absence of a temperature effect on the decay rate, as well as on the slowness of decay; better data result from averaging the effect of an increase of temperature with that of a decrease in temperature [20].

Similarly, if one measures the second-order rate constant for decay as a function of temperature, the activation energy found is just that found for mobility. The second-order rate constant for a pseudointrinsic process can be written as

$$a = \text{const. } [F_e \exp\left(-E_1/kT\right)P \exp\left(-E_2/kT\right)]/n_0,$$

where F_e is an effective lattice frequency, E_1 is an activation energy for diffusion of carriers, n_0 a suitably defined unit carrier density, and P the probability that a random electron-hole encounter will result in recombination, subject to the availability of a thermal energy E_2 which may be required if the recombination goes through the conductive state.

Comparison of the effect of temperature on the rate constant for decay of charge density, as measured by ESR techniques, with the effect on the rate of decay of conductivity, shows that $E_1 = E_2$, which is in turn equal to the activation energy for mobility, in the dyes rhodamine-B and crystal violet [19, 21].

The integrated rate equation for the rise of photoconduction in constant illuminance for a pseudo-intrinsic photoconductor is

$$\ln\left[(\sigma_s + \sigma_t)/(\sigma_s - \sigma_t)\right] = 2a\sigma_s t,$$

where σ_s is the steady-state photoconductance and σ_t that at a specified time. Measurement of the effect of temperature on the term at the left shows an activation energy just equal to that for mobility [19].

Since rates in pseudo-intrinsic processes are slow, they can usually be followed with no more sophisticated equipment than a simple electrometer amplifier and fast mechanical recorder. Much faster processes are known in organic photoconductors; the relaxation time for photoconductivity in some dyes is $\sim 10^{-5}$ sec [28]. These pose a more difficult experimental problem. Since the lifetime of a carrier is short, one cannot build up a high density of electrons, and the resistance of the cell in light is large. This necessarily limits the response time of a current-measuring device since its time constant is equal to the product of input resistance and capacitance. The effect of the capacitance may be reduced by feedback, most simply by using a cathode follower as the input stage, with all possible circuit elements having appreciable capacitance to the input connected to the cathode of the input tube. Since their potential now follows that of the input, the effect of capacitance is reduced by the factor $(1 - g)$, where g is the gain of the cathode follower. Some commercially available devices use more complicated circuitry to produce the same effect.

Another problem is modulating the radiation used to excite the cell. Field-modulated devices are satisfactory, but not generally available. Pulse discharge lamps are unsatisfactory in two ways: there is usually a tail on the decay curve of the lamp which interferes with the observation of a tail on the decay curve of the cell, and the electrical interference associated with them may be hard to eliminate. It is often better to use a mechanical interrupter to produce a light pulse. A synchronous motor of 1/75 horsepower can drive a 20-mil magnesium disk 1 m in circumference at 30 rps. A slot 0.3 mm wide at the edge has an equivalent width in time of 11 μsec. It can be illuminated by a ribbon-filament lamp together with a large aperture lens to form a reduced image in the plane of the disk of width $\leqslant$ to that of the slot, together with another lens to form an image of the slot in the plane of the photoconductive cell. The first lens must be of fairly good quality because fuzziness in its image leads to fuzziness on the rise and decay of the light pulse, but since the image field is small, the demands are not very stringent. The quality of the light pulse so obtained is easily tested by using a commercial vacuum-type photoemissive cell or other fast detector. By comparing the pulse obtained with the phototube with that of the photoconductive specimen, one can make estimates of the response time when approaching the limits of time resolution of the apparatus. By using a larger disk and a 60-rps motor, the pulse width can be brought into the neighborhood of 1 μsec, but a motor of $\frac{1}{4}$ hp or more may be needed. A synchronous motor is convenient but not necessary if an additional circuit is provided to trigger the oscilloscope from the rotating disk.

All measurements of photoconductivity of organic materials show some temperature dependence, and the temperature of the film must always be

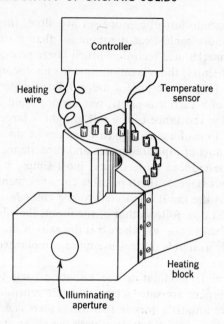

Fig 12.5 Heating block for controlling the temperature of a thin film on the interior surface of a cylindrical cell.

controlled. Usually a precision of 0.1 to 0.2°C is adequate. A fairly satisfactory device is shown in Fig. 12.5. It consists of a split aluminum block which has a cylindrical bore through it at the division into which the cell just fits. Provision should be made for shimming the block so that a practicable range of tube diameters can be accommodated. The block is heated electrically; heating wire is wound through holes drilled through the block and insulated with tightly fitting glass tubing. Cooling is achieved by copper tubing soldered to a copper plate attached to the block with epoxy cement. The highest temperature that can be reached easily is about 90°C; the cooling coil is used principally for hastening the return of the block to room temperature after heating.

The principal disadvantages of this type of device are the possibility of electrical interference, bulkiness and clumsiness in certain situations, slow heating, and slow cooling. Other systems have been used that alleviate these difficulties, but they may introduce others. It is possible to regulate the temperature of a cell by a stream of air passing through a jacket around it, the temperature being monitored by a thermocouple cemented to the critical area of the device, giving a fairly rapid response time. No entirely satisfactory way of performing this necessary function has been devised at present.

The most important effect of temperature on organic photoconductors is that on the steady-state photoconductivity at constant illuminance. The interpretation of the thermal activation energy for generation of charge carriers is a problem of some interest. This energy is probably traceable to intermolecular polarization effects. Let us consider three characteristic processes connected with photoconductivity of a molecular solid in the localized model: taking an electron away from a molecule, adding one to it, and exciting it optically. If we conceive of each of these processes as happening instantaneously then, by Koopmans' theorem [37], the sum of the excitation energy and the electron affinity is equal to the ionization energy. By extension, this should also be true of very small aggregates.

The laboratory values of these energies deviate from this rule because the actual processes are not instantaneous but take place in a time that is long compared with that required for the redistribution of charge in the molecule and its neighbors to minimize the electronic energy. However, this time is short compared with that required for the rearrangement of the atomic framework.

It has been shown [12, 18] for a number of cationic dyes that the ionization energy is greater than the sum of excitation energy and electron affinity by a small amount, ~ 0.06 to 0.5 eV, which is approximately equal to the thermal energy for the generation of charge carriers. Since in a thermal process lattice or molecular framework relaxation processes may participate, the equality of the two energies suggests that charge transfer processes in materials of this type take place very rapidly, so that the Franck-Condon principle must be considered in discussing them.

Mobility and Quantum Yield

The measurement of electric current is an extremely sensitive way to detect the existence of a photoelectric process in a solid, but the observed conductance is not subject to a unique interpretation since it depends on both the quantum yield of carriers and their mobility. To separate these two factors is never easy, and one may well be concerned whether a set of observations of current have real significance or are attributable to changes in both yield and mobility arising from concealed causes. The work of Cho and co-workers is related to this point [21].

In certain photoconductive dyes in which the pseudointrinsic behavior is very marked, a spin density can be measured which is analogous to photoconductivity in that it appears under irradiation and decays in the dark. The kinetics of this spin population were studied in the dye rhodamine-B to test the assumption that the spin signal was a measure of the number of electrons in characteristic traps and that these electrons were in equilibrium with conduction electrons. It was found that the kinetics were just equivalent to the kinetics of changes of conductance. Since in the latter the yield-mobility product appears, and in the former only the yield, the additional implicit assumption that the mobility was constant was also justified.

It is in fact possible to estimate both yield and mobility in cases in which the spin density at steady state can be measured by ESR experiments. The mobility averaged over all the spins, or the mean mobility of an excited electron, is very small because nearly all the electrons are trapped. The free mobility is given by

$$\mu_f = \bar{\mu} \exp (E_t/kT),$$

where E_t is the monoenergetic trap depth; for rhodamine-B and crystal violet μ_f was about 0.1-1 cm²/V sec. The quantum yield γ is

$$\gamma = n/I\tau,$$

where τ is the lifetime of a spin. It is approximately 10^{-4} for rhodamine-B and 10^{-6} for crystal violet.

These estimates are necessarily crude, both because of the difficulty of measuring spin densities and because the sort of sample suitable for ESR work is not well suited for measurements of photoconductivity, so that the final value is a patchwork of measurement and estimate. An additional difficulty is present, associated with the possibility of spins pairing at high densities. Cho [38] provides evidence for this in his observation that in crystal violet sulfate, in which the spins are of chemical rather than optical origin and the density of them is quite high, the spin density shows reversible enhancement during short periods of heating above room temperature, although most of the spins persist to liquid nitrogen temperature. It must be assumed that the population of paired spins interacts very slowly with that of the unpaired and so can be neglected for short-term processes.

ESR experiments can be carried out on material deposited from solution on the walls of 3-mm quartz and Vycor tubing; they require very concentrated solutions since samples of a few cubic millimeters of solid are desirable. Such samples of photoconductive materials should be evacuated and sealed off for stability. The results have been generally disappointing, since no hyperfine structure has been observed either in glassy materials or in single crystals of crystal violet doped with sulfate ion. Exchange narrowing was found by Bohandy where high spin densities can be attained [39]. He also constructed sample tubes having electrodes in which the parallel growth of spin density and photoconductivity could be observed in irradiated dye samples.

For materials in which the short lifetime of an excited electron makes it impossible to measure spin densities, there is no generally satisfactory way to measure mobilities in thin-film samples. A number of experiments have been reported in which mobilities could be estimated in special cases, and the results seem to confirm the impression that mobilities in organic materials are $\leqslant 1$ cm²/V sec [28, 40]. Time of flight measurements on anthracene crystals give similar results. A broadly applicable method for determining mobilities on films is much to be desired.

A similar situation exists with regard to quantum yields. It is probably a safe generalization that quantum yields of carriers per photon are never large and may be very small. The quantum yield in the quasi-chemical model can be calculated and is found to be $\sim (\exp - E/kT)$, where E is the activation energy for generation of charge carriers [13]. Since E is seldom less than 0.1 eV, the yield is ordinarily about 1 % or less. The quantum yields reported by Meier [41], which are larger, refer to number of electrons passing through the circuit per photon absorbed; this quantity is not of great interest in relation to energy conversion or storage problems.

The possibility exists of quantum yields that are dependent on the intensity of irradiation; in anthracene, there is evidence of tandem two-photon processes involving excitons. If the lifetime of the product of the first photon is sufficiently long and its cross section large enough, the steady-state photocurrent may be nearly linearly related to irradiance. The two-photon character of the process can be detected by observing the intensity-current relationship at the very beginning of an irradiation. A linear relationship between the initial slope of current rise and irradiance is good evidence for a one-photon charge-carrier generation process.

Photovoltaic Effects

It is not uncommon to observe a potential difference between parts of a photoconductive system arising from irradiation. This effect is usually associated with the presence of a potential barrier attributable to nonohmic electrode contacts, with a change in the sign of the carrier between two regions, or with a junction between two unlike materials. Gutmann and Lyons [42] list about 60 instances reported in the literature. Those involving electrode contacts are likely to be ill-characterized, but a certain amount of work bearing on the nature of organic photoconductors has been done using a photovoltaic effect.

A common type of photovoltage arises from the Dember effect and is often observed in sandwich-type cells. When such a cell is irradiated on one face, charge carriers are generated and diffuse from the illuminated region. If the rates of diffusion of holes and electrons are not equal, a photovoltage will be observed between the electrodes, from which the sign of the majority carrier can be inferred.

The photovoltaic effect at a junction between a dye and cadmium sulfide has been studied in some detail because of its connection with the mechanism of dye-sensitized photoconductivity [25]. Here the effect arises from radiation absorbed by the dye. Other dye-inorganic photoconductor couples have been studied in both thin-film and sandwich geometries [43]. The results reported do not agree well from laboratory to laboratory and the difficulties of replicating experiments tend to be serious.

The quantity of greatest interest is the open-circuit photovoltage; the photocurrent depends on the resistance of the cell, which is hard to control. The open-circuit photovoltage can be measured with an electrometer voltmeter having an input resistance very much greater than the illuminated resistance of the cell, or by a potentiometer circuit with a variable bucking voltage using an electrometer voltmeter as detector of imbalance. When the first method is used, it is very important to use quartz or Vycor as substrate for overlap cells; with glass rather large potential differences often arise from the weak conductance of the glass and cell asymmetries, which tend to obscure the phenomena in which one is interested.

Nelson [25] has described two forms of behavior in cadmium sulfide–dye cells, one in which the photovoltage is determined by the contact potential difference nearly independently of irradiance and one in which the more common behavior of voltage varying with log of irradiance is observed. These cells are for the most part composed of n-type dyes coupled with the n-type cadmium sulfide.

There is a broad, imprecise, but significant relationship in dye photoconductors between dark conductivity and rate of response to irradiation. Using the dye pinacyanol and preparing films in various ways, one can obtain films that are very fast and extremely resistive in the dark, or films with response times and dark conductivities several orders of magnitude greater. The latter are typical of films prepared without the use of special techniques and display the logarithmic dependence of photovoltage on irradiance. This behavior is "normal," but the striking phenomenon of sensitization of photoconductivity of cadmium sulfide with a thick dye film is seen only with fast resistive films [25].

Petruzzlla et al. treat these two types of behavior as follows [44]. If the dye is not highly insulating in the dark, it is assumed that when the dye–cadmium sulfide interface is formed charge passes across it from dye to cadmium sulfide until equilibrium is established between the two sides. The conduction levels on the two sides approach each other and a macropotential difference exists between the sides which is equal to $\Delta E - E_0$, where E_0 is the difference in electron energy across the junction and ΔE is the contact potential difference between dye and substrate. When the junction is illuminated with open circuit, the macropotential difference becomes $\Delta E - E$, where E is less than E_0 if electrons again move from dye to cadmium sulfide. The open-circuit photovoltage is just the difference between the macropotentials in light and dark, or $(\Delta E - E) - (\Delta E - E_0) = E_0 - E$. We assume that in the steady state the net flow of carriers of either sign is just zero, which implies that the density of electrons in the dye, n_d, and n_s, the density in the substrate, satisfy the relationship $n_d = n_s \exp(-E/kT)$. Then the photovoltage is

$$V_p = \frac{kT}{e}\left[\ln\left(\frac{n_d}{n_s}\right) - \ln\left(\frac{n_d}{n_s}\right)_0\right].$$

a relationship analogous to that found for a p-n junction.

In the case in which the dye has a very large dark resistance, it is assumed that there is negligible transfer of charge from dye to substrate in the dark and thus no macropotential difference. In light, electrons move from dye to substrate, and the open-circuit photovoltage is now given by $\Delta E - E$. Again assuming no net flow of either carrier, $n_d = n_s \exp(-E/kT)$ and the photovoltage is

$$V_p = \frac{\Delta E}{e} + \frac{kT}{e}\ln\left(\frac{n_d}{n_s}\right).$$

In many cases the first term dominates the behavior completely, and the photovoltage is determined by the contact potential difference.

These two cases have been presented in extreme forms, and the assumption that the net current for either carrier separately is zero may not be true. However, it is possible to arrive at the two cases in terms of kinetic arguments in which the governing factor is rate of recombination across the interface, a fast rate leading to a photovoltage independent of irradiance and equal to the contact potential difference. As a result of this, the assumption of zero net current for the carriers separately does not seem to be crucial. Real dye films for the most part lie toward one extreme or other of the formalism, but with very highly conductive films the voltage is nearly zero and occasionally the ideal of photovoltage equal to contact potential difference and independent of irradiance is realized.

6 ELECTRON INTERCHANGE PROCESSES

In sensitization processes that involve only excitation transfer, it is sufficient to know the excitation and fluorescence energies of the molecules between which the transfer takes place. When electron transfer is involved, it also becomes necessary to know where the ground state and the excited state of each molecule lie with respect to each other on a common scale of energies. This common scale of energies is defined in terms of a conventional standard, the energy of an electron at rest and removed at a distance from the system being taken as zero. We make the fundamental assumption that the excited state of a molecule can be represented as a paired hole and electron having an energy with respect to recombination that is just that of the least energetic photon that causes them to appear. We assign as the energy of the hole the binding energy of an electron in the ground state of the molecule as measured by its ionization energy. The excited electron, or optical electron, is assigned the energy $F_e = G - E_e$, where G refers to the energy of the ground state electron and E_e is the excitation energy. Similarly, the energy of a conduction electron, or a supernumerary electron in a molecule, is given a value F_e, which is measured by the electron affinity, or the work done in taking an electron at rest at a distance and placing it in the molecule. These energies and the transitions that define them are shown in Fig. 12.2.

Under the terms of our fundamental assumption, an excited molecule has an electron less tightly bound than any electron in the ground state, as well as an electron vacancy more deeply bound than any in the ground state. It is thus a more effective electron donor or electron acceptor than a molecule in the ground state, which is to say that it is both a more powerful reductant and a more powerful oxidant.

Ionization Energy

Ionization energy is measured as an external photoelectric effect and is roughly the energy of the least energetic photon that is able to eject an electron from the solid into the vacuum. Since there is no sharply defined threshold, it is necessary to set an arbitrary cutoff point in order to establish a reproducible numerical value. This might be set at some standard quantum yield or at some fraction of the quantum yield for wavelengths at which the variation of quantum yield with energy is small. While it is probable that a more satisfactory basis for defining the threshold exists, our present knowledge of the details of the photoelectric emission from organic surfaces does not suffice to inform us of it.

Two basic methods are available to measure photoelectric ionization energies. One may use a source of photons of continuously variable energy and plot current as a function of energy, or one may use a source of photons of a single energy and plot the yield of electrons of given kinetic energy against the kinetic energy. Both methods have been used in recent years [45, 46], and the second is usually chosen only when an ultraviolet monochromator is not available. It is not an easy or convenient method, and accuracy is hard to achieve. However, in recent years good small monochromators with reflective optics have become relatively common; the high-pressure xenon arc is a good continuous source in the ultraviolet down to 2000 Å.

For solids having ionization energies <5 eV, the measurement of this quantity to within 0.1 to 0.2 eV is not difficult. A cell with a window of fused

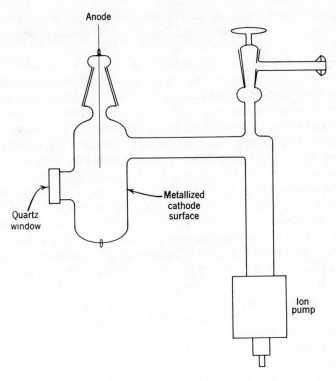

Fig. 12.6 Apparatus for measurement of the external photoelectric effect of a film specimen.

quartz is required, as shown in Fig. 12.6. With a small monochromator and a 150-W xenon arc, a photon flux $\sim 10^{11}$/sec at 2500 Å and $\sim 10^{12}$/sec at 2700 Å is not unrealistic. With a current meter reading 10^{-13} A full scale, the threshold current would correspond to a quantum yield of $\sim 10^{-7}$ electrons per incident photon and it would be possible to make meaningful comparisons among a series of similar materials.

Some problems need a much higher precision, and attaining it reduces to a matter of achieving a much higher sensitivity in terms of current per photon at equal noise level. This permits reduction of slit widths in the monochromator, making it unnecessary to attempt the very difficult slit-width correction in the typical situation in which the photon flux as a function of wavelength is decreasing rapidly, the quantum yield is increasing rapidly, and the brightness of the source is very nonuniform. In addition, if the threshold is defined in terms of some fraction of the maximum response, for a larger scale reading corresponding to that fraction there will be less influence of random irregularities on its location since one can use information about the yield curve at both higher and lower wavelengths to locate it more precisely.

The sensitivity of current measurement can be greatly improved by the use of a particle multiplier between the photocathode and the current amplifier. This is a device made familiar by its application to photomultiplier detectors. A primary photoelectron is accelerated in an electric field and upon striking the surface of the first dynode of the multiplier causes more than one electron to be ejected. The secondary electrons in turn are accelerated into the second stage, and so on. A 10-stage Dumont particle multiplier with copper-beryllium dynodes is desirable for this purpose. It requires a well-regulated power supply capable of about 1 mA at 3000 V. The progression of voltages is obtained from cascaded resistors giving a series of equal voltage intervals to which the dynodes are tapped. A current gain of 100 is adequate; this is obtained with no loss in response time and with only a little additional noise attributable to surface leakage on the base of the multiplier and a certain amount of gain instability arising from the fact that the gain of the multiplier increases somewhat during the early stages of an experiment as an effect of the current passing through it.

Cathodes of hemicylindrical form with the cylindrical axis on the long axis of the multiplier structure are satisfactory. The diameter of the cathode cylinder should be less than the smallest dimension of the aperture of the first multiplier stage and the cathode should be brought as close to the entrance of the multiplier as possible. The yield of photoelectrons from the cathode to the first dynode falls off rapidly as a function of distance on the cathode surface measured from the end closest to the multiplier. It is thus desirable to form an image of the exit slit of the monochromator on its surface and transverse to its axis for most efficient utilization of the photon flux. Great care is necessary to assure that none of the radiation falls directly on the first dynode since it may give rise to photoelectrons indistinguishable from those arising from the cathode.

Ordinarily one proceeds by applying a thin coating of the material on the cathode, pumping down, usually overnight, placing the apparatus in a preset holder so that it has the proper position in relation to the irradiating beam, and exposing it to photons of increasing energy starting below the threshold. Upon entering the threshold region, the quantum yield begins to increase exponentially and continues to do so while the photon energy increases by about 0.5 eV, after which the increase becomes rather slow. Since the photon flux ordinarily decreases toward higher energies, there is a current in the saturation region that is typically a few hundred times that near the threshold, but this represents an increase in quantum yield of 10^4 to 10^5 over that at threshold.

If a high-pressure xenon arc is used as source, the distribution of brightness in the column is far from uniform either as a function of position or of wavelength. There is thus some value in using a magnified image of the arc column at the entrance slit so that as much of the slit as possible is illuminated by the brightest part of the arc. Since magnification also magnifies the instability of the arc, a compromise must be made; three to six times magnification is usually tolerable. The arc is appreciably more stable when operated from a regulated dc power supply than when a motor-generator is used.

A phenomenon is seen with some organic photoconductors that makes it difficult to obtain satisfactory values of ionization energy. This is a tandem two-photon ionization process in which the first photon leads to a metastable excited state which is ionized by the second. In several cases the intermediate state has been shown on the basis of the energy relationships to be the characteristically trapped electron [18]. The photocurrent attributable to it may in some cases exceed that attributable to the intrinsic one-photon process, and since it occurs at lower energy it ordinarily obscures the threshold for the latter. One can cope with this problem to some extent by avoiding exposure of the cathode to extraneous radiation before and during the measurement process.

Electron Affinity

The only satisfactory method of measuring the electron affinity of an organic solid is the electron beam retardation method in which a source of electrons, such as a hot tungsten wire, is used to spray electrons on its surface; the work done in taking an electron out of the metal with zero kinetic energy and bringing it to rest within the surface of the solid is inferred from the relationship between electron current and potential difference between source and target. Since the electrons coming from the hot wire have a Maxwellian distribution of energies, the log of the target current is proportional to the potential difference up to the point at which the latter is just sufficient to bring an electron of zero kinetic energy at the source into the target, after which increasing the potential difference leaves the current unchanged. The inflection point corresponds to the contact potential difference between source and target; if the effective work function of the source is known, the electron affinity of the target differs from it by the contact potential difference [47].

The measurement is one of considerable difficulty. To avoid space charge around the tungsten wire, it must be operated at a fairly low temperature, perhaps 1200 to 1300°C, which in turn requires a rather high vacuum, $\sim 10^{-8}$ torr for constant emission current. This is because the ability of a tungsten wire to maintain itself clean and free from oxide film is diminished at low temperature. The electron gun must be constructed with great care in order to realize even approximately the desired condition of Maxwellian distribution of electron energies; it is important that the portion of the filament being sampled be very close to the aperture in the anode (Fig. 12.7). If the gun is properly constructed and operated, its effective work function will be very nearly that of the tungsten filament, about 4.55 eV; poor design and construction can cause it to vary by many tenths of an electron volt from this value.

The effective work function of the gun can be determined by using a clean metal surface as a transfer standard; gold is particularly suitable. Its work

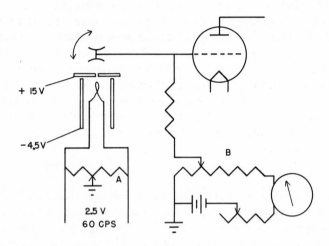

Fig. 12.7 Circuit for measurement of the contact potential difference by the electron beam retardation method [47].

function is measured optically from the threshold of the external photoelectric effect, after which the contact potential difference between it and the gun is determined by the electron beam retardation method.

The electron affinity apparatus is usually constructed so that a series of samples can be presented to the beam by rotation of a holder. It is necessary that all construction of the gun and in its neighborhood be nonmagnetic if an ion pump is used, since the stray field of the pump magnet can cause large derangements of the electron beam; magnetic shielding is desirable and may be essential.

A possible cause of error is the existence of a nonohmic contact between the organic material being measured and its metallic backing, since a rectifying contact or the buildup of space charge could cause the potential at the organic surface to differ greatly from that at the metal backing.

Since the excitation of an organic solid may involve molecules plus extra electrons in either planar or distorted configuration, one must know in which state the electron affinity is measured by the beam retardation method. In principle, the measurement deals with the work done in bringing an electron to rest at the surface of the solid, but, in practice, the data deal not with a single electron but with a population of electrons of varying energies, and for a single value of the retarding field some are rejected, a few just come to rest at the surface, and some have an appreciable kinetic energy as they approach the surface. The current associated with any point on the current-voltage plot is mostly electrons with small kinetic energies as they approach the surface. If we take as a conservative value for this energy the precision of setting of the retarding voltage, about 0.01 eV, the electrons approach the surface at $\sim 10^6$ cm/sec. The influence of the electron on the molecule is not significant until it is closer than ~ 10 Å distant, so that the effective approach time is about 10^{-13} sec. Since the effective molecular vibration frequency for large-scale framework vibrations is probably no greater than 10^{11}/sec, the electron affinity measured must be for the planar molecule. This conclusion is confirmed by the fact that the electron affinity is less than the ionization energy of the electron in the distorted molecule (free radical) by an amount approximately equal to the characteristic trap depth in cases in which both can be measured.

Typically, the saturation current from a simple electron gun operated under conditions in which space charge can be neglected is in the range 10^{-8} to 10^{-10} A. It is usually possible to obtain a satisfactory linear plot of log current against retarding voltage over two decades or more of current. There is a transition region between the logarithmic and saturation regions of the curve which with good geometry is small; extrapolation of the data in the linear region to the saturation current gives the contact potential difference between gun and target. The saturation region may not be perfectly constant; current increasing with voltage indicates poor geometry, a large resistance in the circuit, or stray magnetic fields, and decreasing current may be attributable to the emission of secondary electrons from the target.

Measurement of the difference in retarding potential at a chosen current for two targets of similar geometry measured successively in the same experiment gives the contact potential difference between them. If a suitable standard of electron affinity were available, most of the critical difficulties of construction and geometry could be eliminated by such a procedure. The only well-established standard is a pure tungsten surface freshly cleaned by heating to a high temperature. This is not suitable for use in the presence of labile materials, but the possibility exists that certain dyes might make suitable internal standards [12].

Energy of the Optical Electron

The energy of the optical electron F_0 is the ionization energy minus the threshold excitation energy. Since both of the latter are measured as thresholds,

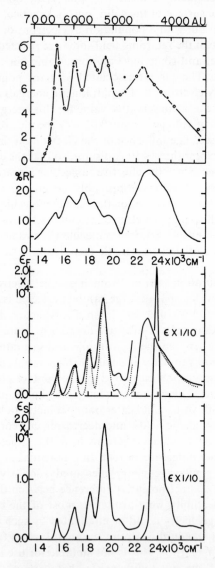

Fig. 12.8 Properties of a film of tetraphenylporphine: σ, steady-state photoconductivity in arbitrary units; $\%R$, specular reflectivity; ϵ_F, $\log_{10}$ extinction coefficients at room temperature (solid line) and 77°K. ϵ_s shows $\log_{10}$ extinction coefficient of a benzene solution.

there is an element of the arbitrary in the assignment of an exact value. This is especially true of thin-film specimens because many of the rather imposing difficulties of measuring the action spectrum for photoconductivity are felt near the threshold. This problem is discussed by Weigl [8, 48]. The nonuniform reflectivity of the sample as well as the variation of the lifetime of carriers attributable to the variation in charge density as a function of wavelength are especially troublesome.

By contrast with the interpretation, the measurements themselves are simple and require nothing but a sensitive current meter and a monochromator. The type of results obtainable is illustrated by Weigl's [10] data for tetraphenylporphine in which the series of peaks of increasing absorption is matched nicely in wavelength by a series of peaks of nearly constant photoconductance (Fig. 12.8). For materials having complex absorption spectra, it is to be expected that the location of the bands, but not their relative intensities, will be reproduced.

Sensitized Photoconductivity

The fact that dyes adsorbed on a substrate may be able to induce effects in the substrate resulting from light absorbed by the dye has been known for nearly 100 years, and the mechanism is still the subject of vigorous controversy. This phenomenon is widely applied in conventional photography and electrophotography, where it is called spectral sensitization and where it makes possible materials sensitive throughout the visible and into the near infrared based on substrates that absorb only in the blue or near ultraviolet.

There may be two types of mechanisms involved in spectral sensitization. One of these is a resonant transfer of energy of excitation from the sensitizing dye to surface states of the substrate. The other is a transfer of a charge carrier from the excited dye molecule to the substrate. This is of particular interest in connection with problems of energy conversion and storage because it represents a simple model system in which photooxidations and photoreductions by excited dye molecules can be investigated, since the injection of an electron from an excited molecule is formally a reduction of the crystal by the molecule (Fig. 12.7).

The primary effect of the sensitized process is an increase in the conductivity of the substrate; this is accounted for by either mechanism, but a resonant transfer does not imply an oxidation-reduction process. The useful secondary process in silver photography is the formation of a development center; in electrophotography it is the dissipation of a surface charge on the sensitive sheet. The sensitization process can be studied in terms of a device such as a photographic film, but is often investigated on a thin film or powder of a pure substrate by direct observation of the sensitized photoconductivity.

A rather large number of substrates show this effect, among them the silver halides, thallous halides, zinc oxide, and cadmium sulfide. The sensitized photoconductivity of glass has already been mentioned; glass differs from the above materials in that it has no intrinsic photoconductive process of its own to which excitation can be transferred, so that transfer of a charge carrier must be involved.

Because of the importance of zinc oxide in electrophotography, a great deal of work has been done on its sensitization [49]. Zinc oxide has the disadvantage that a photodesorption of oxygen is a part of the photoconductive process, so that the electrical properties of the substrate depend strongly on the ambient atmosphere; zinc oxide irradiated *in vacuo* is quite a different system from zinc oxide in air [50]. Cadmium sulfide shows similar behavior to a minor extent, but it is nearly enough insensitive to atmosphere so that the behavior of sensitization is the same in air or *in vacuo*.

Powdered substrates may be studied by the Bergmann condenser method, which has been fully exploited by Terenin's group [51]. They may also be briquetted under high pressure before sensitizing. Since the optimal thickness of sensitizer on the substrate is less than a monolayer, such preparations have the advantage of giving a substantial absorption of light by piling up monolayers. In the work of Nelson on cadmium sulfide films, only a single layer of sensitizer is available for absorption, so that at most some 2 or 3 % of the incident radiation is utilized. The excellent signal-to-noise ratio of the cadmium sulfide films makes possible the observation of thresholds at $\sim 10^{-4}$ of the peak signal, so that good work can still be done with it. The use of films of substrate has the additional advantage that preparations can be made in which the interface between sensitizer and substrate can be made part of a circuit and thus studied [52].

There are distinct quantitative and qualitative differences between the behavior as substrates of zinc oxide, on the one hand, and silver halides and cadmium sulfide, on the other. The best single sensitizer for zinc oxide is eosin, which is an indifferent photographic sensitizer, while many excellent photographic sensitizers in the red and near infrared perform poorly on zinc oxide. There is thus a division in both character and methodology between the principal types of substrates, which is not easily bridged; we discuss the sensitization of cadmium sulfide here not because of its usefulness, which is not notable, but because of the relatively straightforward experiments that can be performed on it.

Since cadmium sulfide still has appreciable photoconductive sensitivity at wavelengths absorbed by many interesting sensitizers, measurements are made using two-part cadmium sulfide cells in which both parts are incorporated into a resistance bridge circuit and illuminated, but only one part is sensitized so that ideally the effect of the sensitizer is displayed quite apart from the characteristics of the substrate. The measurement can be made by interrupting the illumination and using ac amplification with phase-sensitive detection, so that the tendency of the adsorbed material to diminish or quench the photoconductivity of the substrate can also be detected. An alternative scheme is to measure the effect with an operational amplifier, using the unsensitized portion of the cell as feedback resistor [53].

Cadmium sulfide photoconductive cells can be prepared on microscope slide glass. Electrodes are ruled with liquid platinum and fired, after which the cadmium sulfide is sublimed on under high vacuum. Pure crystalline cadmium sulfide should be used, and the deposited film should be about three fringes thick. It is desirable to heat the glass to 200 to 250°C during the deposition process, but the temperature of the glass must be very uniform over its surface since small local variations in temperature may affect the uniformity of the film. After removal from the vacuum chamber, the cell is washed with high-purity chloroform to remove traces of pump oil and heated at 350°C in air to stabilize it, the heating being carried on as long as necessary to give a high dark resistance that is not affected by further heating.

The cell is mounted in an evacuable envelope and exposed to monochromator illumination and the bridge circuit is balanced so as to give the minimal response to the range of wavelength of irradiation to be used. The cell is sensitized by allowing 1 or 2 drops of solution to flow over and drain from one of its parts; it is again evacuated, and its response measured as a function of wavelength. For an effective sensitizer, the resulting curve resembles the absorption spectrum of the dye in solution, somewhat broadened and displaced toward the red. Such a technique is probably also applicable to zinc oxide films, although in this case it might be preferable not to evacuate the cell since the dark conductivity of zinc oxide may be undesirably increased by so doing; it is not easily applicable to silver halides because of their large ionic dark conductivity at room temperature. The technique can be used to study many of the characteristic phenomena of photography, such as the effect of density of adsorbed molecules on efficiency of sensitization, supersensitization, desensitization, and so on.

A more important aspect of this technique may be that it provides the means for studying the properties of dyes in a well-specified state, in which the dye is adsorbed on a substrate in mean thickness equal to or less than a monolayer. The ionization energies of such adsorbates are easily measured, and the sensitized photoeffect gives a measure of the energy of the optical electron free from effects of reflectivity and carrier density. The electron affinity of the adsorbate can also be measured even though the coverage of the surface by the dye may not be complete. This is because the electron affinities of dyes are usually substantially less than that of, for example, cadmium sulfide, so that the correction for electrons going to the substrate is small.

It is indeed possible to measure the ionization energies of dyes adsorbed on a variety of substrates. Pyrex glass is a (peculiarly) desirable one, since there is only a small current arising from photoejection of electrons from the glass itself. It has been found for several dyes that there is a simple relationship between the dielectric constant κ of the substrate and the ionization energy of the dye

$$E_{\mathrm{ion}} = E_0 - C(\kappa - 1)/(\kappa + 1)$$

The proportionality constant C is often small, <0.3 eV. E_0. The ionization energy when $\kappa = 1$, thus resembles the vacuum ionization energy of the molecule itself, which in dyes is often otherwise unmeasurable [54].

By procedures of this kind, one can estimate the ionization energy of a dye molecule in some particular specified environment. This is important in connection with the mechanism of dye-sensitized processes, since the possibility of a hole or electron transfer process rests on the relative positions of energy levels of donor and acceptor on a binding-energy scale, which is established to fair approximation by the value of the ionization energy.

The energy levels measured for adsorbed dye films are not much different from those measured on solid dyes [13]; whereas the techniques for working on adsorbed films are necessarily more elaborate than those for working on solid dyes, the extra trouble is justified by the fact that not only are measurements more reproducible but also the adsorbed dye film is either of actual interest to the problem, or in the case of biological problems, in a much better approximation to it than the solid massive dye.

While the term "sensitization" is properly reserved for the effect of adsorbed dyes, two-part systems involving a thick dye film and a conductive substrate are also of interest. A film of cadmium sulfide with a film of pinacyanol in contact with it, considered as a detector of radiation at 7000 Å, is a combination of a material with a relatively high quantum yield, the dye, with one in which carriers have a relatively high mobility, the cadmium sulfide, in such a way as to exploit the advantages of both [25].

7 SIGNIFICANCE OF PHOTOCONDUCTIVITY FOR PROBLEMS OF ENERGY CONVERSION

It is characteristic of the extreme form of the localized model that it views the phenomena of sensitization and photoconductivity as completely analogous, either being representable as a one-electron oxidation-reduction process involving an excited molecule and a substrate. In photoconductivity the substrate is another molecule of the same type; in the case of sensitization, the process takes place across an interface between dissimilar molecules or between a molecule and a crystal.

It was first pointed out by implication in Gurney and Mott's classic paper on the primary photographic process [55] that processes of this kind have the potentiality of converting radiant energy into chemical free energy because they provide a machine in which oxidizing power can be separated from reducing power. The generation of charge carriers does just this since the electron is formally a reductant and the hole an oxidant. Since they may diffuse independently of each other, if one is able to trap them out at different sites, one has done chemical work. In its simplest form such a system is metastable and dissipates its stored energy in a fairly short time. It is not difficult to conceive of a system only slightly more complicated in which further processes interpose a physical barrier or a high activation barrier between the trapped charges in such a way as to give the excitation an indefinitely long lifetime.

Upon examination it appears that a process based upon generation of charge carriers in a pure dye phase is inherently inefficient because there is always a thermal activation energy associated with the optical generation of charge carriers; the problem of supplying this energy within the lifetime of the excited state is the factor that limits the yield.

Several possibilities exist in principle for carrying out an efficient long-lived conversion in heterogeneous systems. One of these is typified by the kind of process in which an adsorbed dye sensitizes photoconductivity in a crystal substrate by electron transfer. Figure 12.9 shows the type of energy-level relationship found at an interface between cadmium sulfide and an efficient sensitizer. We may visualize the excited dye molecule as having a potential energy equal to the threshold excitation energy.

The unexcited molecule can be characterized to good approximation as

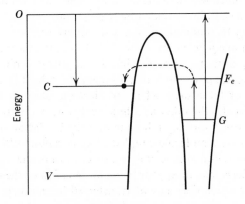

Fig. 12.9 Energy relationships at sensitizer-substrate interface as determined by the transitions indicated. C and V are the conduction and valence bands of the substrate, respectively.

an oxidant or reductant on the binding-energy scale by the midpoint between G and F_e; when the molecule is excited, the electron lies above this level and the hole below and it is thus both a better oxidant and a better reductant than the molecule in the dark. However, this state has a lifetime of only $\sim 10^{-9}$ sec, and if the molecule does not undergo reaction in that time, its energy is lost by internal conversion or by reradiation.

If, however, we can initiate the process of separation of oxidant within this time, we may be able to give an arbitrarily long relaxation time to the whole excited system. We shall assume that the donor and acceptor stand in fixed spatial relationship to each other and that there is a potential barrier between them; we deal only with systems that are ordered to this extent at least.

When the donor is an excited dye molecule it is possible to set an upper limit to the height of the barrier; it cannot be higher than about 3.5 eV, the binding energy of the optical electron. A not unreasonable value for the thickness of an intermolecular barrier might be 5 to 8 Å. Taking the semi-classical transparency of the barrier to be

$$t = \exp\,[-2a(2ME_b/\hbar^2)^{1/2}],$$

where a is its thickness and E_b is its height, we find a transparency of roughly 10^{-3}. The probability of tunneling the barrier during the lifetime of the excited state is then

$$P = tf_c\tau/(1 + tf_c\tau),$$

where f_c, the classical frequency of the electron in the potential well, is $\sim 10^{15}$/sec; P is substantially unity since the tunneling requires on the average about 10^{-12} sec, much less than the lifetime of the excited state. If the electron is transferred to a cadmium sulfide film, the relaxation time for this excitation is about 1 sec, by recombination across the interface.

A second example is given by Arnold [56] as part of a mechanism for the primary process in photosynthesis. Here the sensitizer, chlorophyll, forms a two-dimensional domain, on the periphery of which are two kinds of molecules. One of these may act as an electron acceptor from an excited chlorophyll molecule, the other as a hole acceptor. A photon is absorbed by any molecule in the chlorophyll domain and the excitation migrates through it until it encounters a molecule coupled to an acceptor. When this happens, a hole or electron is donated, leaving a carrier of opposite sign in the chloro-phyll domain. These may disappear by recombination or they may eventually diffuse to sites at which they may be transferred to an acceptor. Since we are not attempting to generate holes and electrons by intrinsic processes in a pure chlorophyll domain, it is now possible in principle that the transfer processes may be exergonic (Fig. 12.10).

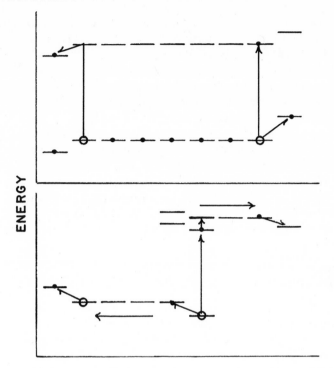

Fig. 12.10 Two types of molecular apparatus for separation of carrier-mediated oxidation and reduction processes. Above, transfers at the periphery of a domain, after Arnold [56]; below, carrier generation at an interface between domains.

In a final example we choose two materials, each to be placed in its own two-dimensional domain, with these domains in contact with each other. If excitation can be carried to the interface by resonance processes, then the possibility of exergonic generation of charge carriers at the interface arises. Such a process leads to electrons trapped in one domain and holes trapped in the other. Each migrating in its own domain, the carriers may encounter acceptors on the periphery, as in the previous example [57].

In the context of biological processes there seems to be no difficulty in making the relaxation time of such a collective excitation arbitrarily long.

As long as we confine our discussion to single molecules and pairs of molecules, we can use the terminology of the completely localized model. However, excitations of the bulk solid dye exist and are of interest. For instance, in materials having a large density of characteristic traps, the trap plus electron is equivalent to a free radical in its ground state; it is not a localized excitation but an excitation of the whole body of the solid because there is potential energy associated with it and a hole, which is dissipated as the solid returns to its preillumination ground state. The same is true of spin-paired adjacent free radicals. While such a system has nothing in common with the band model, it should be possible to describe its chemical potential as a Fermi level. The Fermi level energy is measurable by the thermoelectric power, but the problem of accounting for its value in terms of these excitations has proved difficult [22].

In crystal violet, in which the lifetime of the conductive excited state is great, an appreciable amount of energy is stored in the dye solid after prolonged illumination. If holes are not trapped, this might be ∼0.1 eV per molecule. If holes are trapped deeply, it would be an order of magnitude less; it is very difficult to obtain detailed information about the state of the minority carrier, but the fact that the photoconductivity of crystal violet is reduced several orders of magnitude by the effects of oxygen suggests that holes are deeply trapped.

8 CONCLUSION

In this chapter we have attempted to open one of several possible doorways into the field of organic photoconductive phenomena. The approach described here is not necessarily the best, but it has the merit of allowing the neophyte to come to the subject with simple techniques, apparatus, and point of view. Since the field is one in which it is almost impossible to make a nontrivial statement that is also entirely noncontroversial, the reader is urged most strongly to acquaint himself with other viewpoints. The volumes listed in the general reference list are useful either for basic theory, introduction to the literature, or both.

References

1. W. Smith, *Nature* **7**, 303 (1873).
2. B. Gudden and R. W. Pohl, *Z. Phys.*, **17**, 334 (1923).
3. F. Gutmann and L. E. Lyons, *Organic Photoconductors*, Wiley, New York, 1967.
4. R. M. Glaeser and R. S. Berry, *J. Chem. Phys.*, **44**, 3797 (1966).
5. S. H. Glarum, *J. Phys. Chem. Solids*, **24**, 1577 (1963).
6. Ref. 3, p. 310.
7. Ref. 3, p. 394.
8. J. W. Weigl, *J. Chem. Phys.*, **24**, 364 (1956).
9. N. G. Bakhshiev and V. N. Korovina, *Opt. Spectr.*, **22**, 17 (1967).
10. J. W. Weigl, *J. Mol. Spectr.*, **1**, 216 (1957).

11. R. M. Pearlstein, Tech. Note BN-453, Institute for Fluid Dynamics and Applied Mathematics, University, of Maryland, College Park, Maryland, 1966.

12. R. C. Nelson, *J. Phys. Chem.*, **71**, 2517 (1967).

13. R. C. Nelson, *J. Chem. Phys.*, **47**, 4451 (1967).

14. R. G. Selsby and R. C. Nelson, *J. Mol. Spectr.*, **33**, 1 (1970).

15. J. R. Hoyland and L. Goodman, *J. Chem. Phys.*, **33**, 946 (1960).

16. R. G. Selsby, Ph.D. Dissertation, Ohio State University, Columbus, Ohio, 1969.

17. R. C. Nelson, *J. Chem. Phys.*, **39**, 859 (1963).

18. R. C. Nelson, *J. Mol. Spectr.*, **7**, 439 (1961).

19. R. C. Nelson, *J. Chem. Phys.*, **22**, 885 (1954).

20. Ref. 19, p. 892.

21. B. -Y. Cho, R. C. Nelson, and L. C. Brown, *J. Chem. Phys.*, **39**, 499 (1963).

22. N. Petruzzella and R. C. Nelson, *J. Chem. Phys.*, **42**, 3922 (1965).

23. S. Takeda, Ph.D. Dissertation Ohio State University Columbus, Ohio, 1969.

24. G. N. Lewis, T. Magel, and D. Lipkin, *J. Am. Chem. Soc.*, **64**, 1774 (1942).

25. R. C. Nelson, *J. Opt. Soc. Am.*, **51**, 1182 (1961).

26. A. T. Vartanyan, *Zh. Tekh. Fiz.*, **20**, 847 (1950); *Chem. Abstr.*, **44**, 9799 (1950).

27. J. W. Weigl, unpublished work.

28. R. C. Nelson, *J. Mol. Spectr.*, **7**, 449 (1961).

29. R. H. Bube, *Photoconductivity of Solids*, Wiley, New York, 1960, pp. 110–118.

30. Ref. 29, pp. 120–126.

31. Y. Maruyama and H. Inokuchi, *Bull. Chem. Soc. Japan*, **39**, 1418 (1966).

32. N. F. Mott and R. W. Gurney, *Electronic Processes in Ionic Crystals*, 2nd ed., Dover, New York, 1948, pp. 160–162.

33. R. C. Nelson, *J. Chem. Phys* , **23**, 1550 (1955)

34 R. C. Nelson, *J. Opt. Soc. Am.*, **50**, 1029 (1960).

35. N. Petruzzella and R. C. Nelson, *J. Chem. Phys.*, **37**, 3010 (1962).

36. H. Meier, *Z. Wiss. Phot.*, **53**, 1 (1958).

37. T. Koopmans, *Physica*, **1**, 104 (1934).

38. B. -Y. Cho, Ph.D. Dissertation, Ohio State University, Columbus, Ohio, 1962.

39. J. Bohandy, Ph.D. Dissertation, Ohio State University, Columbus, Ohio, 1965.

40. J. W. Weigl, *J. Chem. Phys.*, **24**, 883 (1956); D. R. Kearns and M. Calvin, *J. Chem. Phys.*, **34**, 2022 (1961).

41. H. Meier, *Phot. Sci. Eng.*, **6**, 236 (1962).

42. Ref. 3, pp. 790–795.

43. H. Meier, *J. Phys. Chem.*, **69**, 719 (1965).

44. N. Petruzzella, J. Ferrier, M. Schaer, and R. C. Nelson, *J. Chem. Phys.*, **50**, 3527 (1969).

45. B. L. Kurbatov and F. I. Vilesov, *Soviet Phys. "Doklady,"* **6**, 1091 (1962).

46. R. C. Nelson, *J. Opt. Soc. Am.*, **51**, 1186 (1961).

47. R. C. Nelson, *J. Opt. Soc. Am.*, **46**, 1016 (1956).

48. J. W. Weigl, *J. Chem. Phys.*, **24**, 883 (1956).

49. H. Frieser and M. Schlesinger, *Phot. Korr.*, **101**, 69 (1965).

50. S. J. Dudkowski and L. I. Grossweiner, *J. Opt. Soc. Am.*, **54**, 486 (1964).

51. A. Terenin, E. Putseiko, and I. Akimov, *J. Chim. Phys.*, **1957**, 716.
52. R. C. Nelson, *J. Opt. Soc. Am.*, **46**, 13 (1956).
53. H. Kuhn, personal communication.
54. R. C. Nelson, *J. Mol. Spectr.*, **23**, 213 (1967).
55. R. W. Gurney and N. F. Mott, *Proc. Roy. Soc. (London)*, **A164**, 151 (1938).
56. W. Arnold, *J. Phys. Chem.*, **69**, 788 (1965).
57. R. C. Nelson, *J. Photochem. Photobiol.*, **8**, 441 (1968).

General

Bube, R. H., *Photoconductivity of Solids*, Wiley, New York, 1960.

Craig, D. P., and S. H. Walmsley, *Excitons in Molecular Crystals*, W. A. Benjamin, New York, 1968.

Fox, D., M. M. Labes, and A. Weissberger, Eds. *Physics and Chemistry of the Organic Solid State*, Interscience, New York, 1967.

Gutmann, F., and L. E. Lyons, *Organic Semiconductors*, Wiley, New York, 1967.

Rose, A., *Concepts in Photoconductivity and Allied Problems*, Interscience, New York, 1963.

Chapter XIII

ORGANIC ELECTROLUMINESCENCE*

David M. Hercules

* This work was supported in part through funds provided by the U. S. Atomic Energy Commission under Contract AT(30-1)-905 to the Laboratory for Nuclear Science, Massachusetts Institute of Technology, Cambridge, Massachusetts.

4 Electroluminescence in Solution: Radical Ion Reactions   286

I INTRODUCTION

Electroluminescence from organic systems has been known for a number of years, but fewer examples are known than for inorganic systems. Both applications and basic processes have been studied more extensively for inorganic systems. Organic electroluminescence can occur under conditions of excitation analogous to inorganics or under very different conditions. Inorganic electroluminescence is generally observed in the solid state, while organics electroluminesce both in the solid state and in solution.

When excitation occurs under "classic" conditions, inorganic systems generally electroluminesce more brightly than their organic analogs, probably accounting for the fact that inorganic systems have been more extensively studied. Intrinsically, organics offer a wide variety of possibilities for producing electroluminescence because of the diversity of compounds available and the variety of excitation conditions that can be used. One of the important goals of electroluminescence research is to produce a variety of colors—the possibility for variation of color is much greater in organic systems. Generally, the efficiency of organic electroluminescence is less than that of comparable inorganic systems although, recently, considerable effort has been directed toward improving efficiency. The difference in efficiencies results from the vastly different mechanisms in the two types of systems. In the long run, it may be simpler to interpret organic crystal electroluminescence because the electroluminescent process is intrinsic to the crystal and does not require the presence of an impurity site as in many inorganic cases.

Investigation of organic electroluminescence often proves to be quite exciting since it combines a number of research areas such as electronic spectroscopy, electrochemistry, and photochemistry, both in the solid state and in solution. Several known excitation mechanisms include recombination processes, glow discharge, and generation of reactants for known chemiluminescent systems. There are definite analogies between solid-state and liquid electroluminescence; hole-electron recombination processes have been shown to produce electroluminescence in crystalline aromatic hydrocarbons, while radical ion recombination processes are known for aromatics in solution. Also, it appears that triplet-triplet annihilation is responsible for electroluminescence in both fluid and solid systems.

The present chapter deals with three aspects of organic electroluminescence: comparison of organic and inorganic electroluminescence processes; solid-state electroluminescence both in crystals and in thin films in which different excitation mechanisms operate; and solution electroluminescence both for some "classic" chemiluminescent systems and for ion-radical recombination reactions. Greater emphasis is placed on organic electroluminescence in solution, reflecting the greater number of publications on solution electroluminescence as well as the author's own personal bias. This chapter deals only with organic EL, discussing inorganic systems only where necessary for purposes of comparison. A detailed discussion of inorganic EL can be found in several references [1, 4, 6]. Electroluminescence is abbreviated EL and electrochemically generated electroluminescence is abbreviated ECL throughout this review.

2 ELECTROLUMINESCENCE IN ORGANIC SOLIDS

EL in organic systems falls into two categories, that occurring in the solid state and that occurring in solution. Inorganic EL, however, is observed almost entirely in the solid state. Therefore a direct comparison of EL mechanisms between organic and inorganic systems is not always possible. There are several basic differences between solid-state and solution EL.

For example, solid-state photoluminescence processes are multimolecular in that they often involve the entire crystal lattice, whereas luminescence processes in solution are monomolecular. In solution, EL is produced by a chemical reaction attributable to electrochemically generated species, whereas in the solid state, for both organic and inorganic systems, the excitation mechanism is related to the band structure of the solid and occurs by one of several possible mechanisms.

The discussion in this section compares luminescence and excitation mechanisms for organic and inorganic EL in solids, realizing that solution EL processes are quite different.

Comparison of Photoluminescence Processes

Because light emission processes are different in solutions and in solids, and often different in organic and inorganic solids, it is well to point out some general characteristics of each. A detailed discussion of these processes is beyond the scope of the present treatment, particularly because several fairly comprehensive treatments are available [1–5].

Organic Solution Luminescence

Photoluminescence in fluid solution is characterized by emission from an isolated species usually involving an excited singlet state, although in some cases emission from triplet states is known. There is a direct correlation between the emission spectrum observed for an electroluminescent reaction and the fluorescence spectrum of the emitting species excited in the same environment. The excitation mechanism for solution EL must be such that it can cause a large amount of energy to concentrate on a single site in a very short period of time. This is usually accomplished by a chemical reaction in which the emitting species is produced either directly in an excited state or by one of several well-known energy transfer processes.

Inorganic Solid Luminescence

Inorganic solids showing EL are either semiconductors or insulators with appropriate band gaps. EL from inorganics is observed not only in the visible region of the spectrum but in the infrared region as well. The luminescence is usually associated with some impurity site in the lattice for an electric insulator—a good example being copper-doped zinc sulfide. Photo-excitation involves raising one of the valence band electrons to the conduction band where it is free to move about the crystal until trapped by an impurity site in the lattice. The luminescence observed, then, is characteristic of the trap, and modifying the trap site also modifies the luminescence. Intrinsic emission from pure inorganic solids is known, but it is much less common than that from a lattice impurity.

Organic Crystal Luminescence

Photoluminescence from organic crystals is similar to that from inorganic crystals except that most emission observed is from the crystal itself rather than from impurities. However, photoluminescence in doped organic crystals is known. The mechanism of excitation of organic crystals is similar to that of inorganic crystals, except that band gaps in the former are much larger. Photoexcitation of organic crystals causes an "exciton" to be produced which allows excitation energy to migrate throughout the crystal prior to emission. The photoluminescence spectrum for an organic crystal is not necessarily identical to the solution photoluminescence of the same molecule because of effects such as solvent-solute interactions, reabsorption effects, and splitting of energy levels as a result of bimolecular interactions.

Electrical Excitation Processes in Crystalline Solids

Although the EL of crystalline inorganic materials has been extensively studied, there are still many questions concerning the mechanism of EL in any particular case. Theoretically, it can be considered that there are five possible excitation mechanisms that can occur, although not all five of these mechanisms have been authenticated. The mechanisms are: glow discharge excitation, field ionization, impact ionization, charge-carrier injection, and radiative recombination. Again, a detailed discussion of each of these processes is beyond the scope of the present text, and more details on each can be found in the excellent treatments by Ivey [1] and Piper and Williams [6].

Glow Discharge Excitation

In many respects, this mechanism should not be consider true EL. In a cell having a high ac voltage (10^5 V/cm or greater) applied between the two electrodes, breakdown of the gas surrounding the cell can occur, resulting in light emission from the gas. If a fluorescent material is present, the light emitted by the gas can cause photoexcitation of the material in the cell. This is a particularly common mechanism of "EL" for organic films in which high quantum efficiencies of fluorescence prevail along with intense absorption bands. The details of this process are discussed in Section 2, pages 265–270.

Field Ionization

For the case in which an impurity is present in the lattice, direct ionization of the impurity by an applied field is possible. If such ionization can occur, then electroluminescence can also occur by a recombination reaction between the electron and the hole at the activator site. The major difficulty associated with excitation of EL by field ionization is competition from dielectric break-down of the matrix either by an avalanche mechanism or by Zener break-down. Generally, if field ionization is to occur, it would be more likely in the high field region where quantum mechanical tunneling can occur.

Generally, the breakdown of crystalline inorganic materials occurs in the vicinity of 10^6 V/cm by either the avalanche or Zener mechanisms. Cal-culations on the field necessary to excite EL by field ionization [6] have shown that fields in the order of 10^7 V/cm are required, an order of magnitude greater than those required for breakdown. Therefore, the occurrence of direct field excitation seems unlikely, and the unambiguous identification of such a mechanism in EL has not yet been established. However, the possibility does exist of direct field excitation for an activator system that can be per-turbed by the applied potential to an energy low enough to permit a reason-able probability of excitation from the ground state.

Impact Ionization

EL excitation can occur if an electron is injected into the conduction band of a crystal and experiences a sufficiently strong electric field that it is acceler-ated to a kinetic energy capable of ionizing an activator atom by collision. The electrons may be injected into the conduction band directly from the surface of the crystal or may arise from deep traps within the crystal lattice. Similar excitation processes can occur for positive holes accelerated through the lattice.

In order to produce EL by electron collision, three conditions are essential. First, high field regions capable of accelerating charge carriers must be produced. Second, electrons or holes must be injected into this high field region; and third, activator sites in the lattice must be situated such that they can absorb a major fraction of the energy produced by collision. Calculations show that the field necessary for excitation by electron impact is lower than that for breakdown, ca. 10^5 V/cm [1]. It has generally been considered that EL excitation of the zinc sulfide–copper system occurs by this mech-anism [1].

Charge-Carrier Injection

Injection of charge carriers into a particular region of a crystal is an EL mechanism that occurs in semiconductors. It can occur by injection into either p- or n-type material or at a p-n junction. For n-type material the activator center has its ground state occupied. Therefore a hole injected into the valence band can be trapped by the activator and cause ionization of the center. The ionized center can attract a conduction band electron with the subsequent emission of radiation. For p-type material, free holes are available for the activator system in the ground state. Therefore injection of electrons into the conduction band causes these electrons to be captured by the activator center and likewise results in EL.

For a *p-n* junction with no applied potential, thermal excitation can lead to some injection and therefore to light emission. With small potentials applied across the *p-n* junctions, the injection process is temperature dependent, the luminescence efficiency depending on the carrier lifetime. The EL of SiC has been attributed to charge-carrier injection [1].

Radiative Recombination

For crystalline materials not containing activator centers, it is possible for holes and electrons to combine directly to give rise to photon emission. This process involves introduction of an electron into the conduction band of the material and introduction of a hole into the valence band and diffusion of the holes and the electrons until they combine. The efficiency of such a process depends on the rate of radiative combination versus the rate of radiationless combination. Radiative combination of holes and electrons is favored by materials of high purity and the presence of high carrier concentrations. Such a mechanism has been proposed for the infrared emission in germanium [6] and appears to be operative in a number of crystalline organic electroluminescent materials.

Space-Charge Limited Currents

EL in organic crystals results from recombination of holes and electrons injected into the crystals by electrodes. A complete description of this process requires a detailed discussion of space charge-limited currents (SCL currents) in organic crystals, which is beyond the scope of this review. The reader is referred to a discussion such as that by Lampert [7]. The present treatment consists of a brief discussion of hole injection into organic crystals and a summary of the processes specifically related to EL production.

Current flow through insulators is limited by space charge when carriers in excess of those generated thermally can be injected into the insulator. For anthracene crystals in contact with an iodine-iodide electrode, Kallmann and Pope [8] showed that iodine extracts an electron from the anthracene crystal, injecting a positive hole into the anthracene. The positive hole travels under the action of the applied field through the crystal to the negative electrode. They found that although the reaction takes place in the dark a much greater current is observed when the iodine is illuminated on its absorption band. Typical of the apparatus used for such studies is the photoconductivity cell described by Kallmann and Pope [9] which permits single crystal studies, both with and without irradiation.

Mark and Helfrich have studied SCL currents [10] for biphenyl, *p*-terphenyl, *p*-quaterphenyl, napthalene, and anthracene. They observed hole injection for p-terphenyl, p-quaterphenyl, and anthracene, but not for napthalene and biphenyl; the ionization potentials of napthalene and biphenyl are sufficiently high that an electron can not be removed by the iodine-iodide couple. They concluded that the acceptor electrode forms an ohmic contact for hole injection into the crystals and that the steady-state current through such crystals is trap-limited as long as the injecting contact is ohmic. Initial transient currents can approach trap-free SCL current flow.

Mark and Helfrich performed both steady-state and transient current measurements [10]. Steady-state currents result from holes injected in excess of the thermal equilibrium density through the ohmic contact. When traps are present, most of the injected holes are localized; the magnitude and voltage dependence of the current are both dictated by the energy and distribution of the trapping states. For transient currents, when a voltage is applied and traps are empty, the initial current is attributable to the flow of holes forced into the crystal through the electrode, limited only by space charge. As the free holes are trapped, the current decays to the steady-state value dictated by the density and energy distribution of the trapping states. When the voltage is removed, the holes condensed in the traps are thermally into the released valence band. Current-voltage measurements on p-terphenyl and anthracene indicated different behavior for these two crystals. p-Terphenyl showed idealized behavior, while anthracene deviated, the deviation in anthracene being attributable to impurity carriers, probably tetracene.

The best interpretation for currents in organic crystals measured below saturation is that they are space-charge-limited and that the current carriers are positive holes. Some supporting observations follow. The steady-state current and the peak of the initial transient current saturated at the same current level. This indicates that the transient current carriers are positive holes supplied by the anode. The peak transient current depends on the number of holes present in the crystal before the field is applied. The peak transient current through p-terphenyl varies as the square of the voltage and gives a reasonable value for hole mobility when fitted to Child's law [10]. From two independent time constant measurements and from the assumption that the steady-state current is space charge-limited under the influence of an exponential trap distribution and that the hole mobility is field independent, the effective lattice frequency can be obtained in two different ways. The two values are in good agreement. The interpretation requires the assumption of hole-trapping states in organic crystals; this, however, is not unreasonable [10].

EI in Aromatic Crystals

Probably the first report of EL in organic crystals in attributable to Pope et al. [11], who performed measurements on single crystals of anthracene and anthracene doped with tetracene. Two electrode configurations were used, giving different results, In one case silver paste electrodes were epoxied onto the crystal while in the other ohmic contacts of 0.1 M sodium chloride solutions on opposite sides of the crystal were used. For the small silver paste electrodes, dc EL was observed at about 400 V applied across a 10 to 20-μ-thick crystal. When a slowly varying ac field was applied to the crystal, luminescence appeared in phase with the applied voltage. The current density through the crystal was about 100 $\mu A/cm^2$. Anthracene crystals doped with tetracene behaved similarly.

When the electrolyte electrode was used, light appeared only when square waves were applied and only during the rising and falling portions of the wave; no light appeared during times when the voltage was constant. A current surge was observed as the EL appeared. The intensity of the light emitted was frequency dependent, being greater per cycle at lower frequencies. The brightness depended only on the peak-to-peak square-wave voltage. A typical voltage change was 2000 V in 10^{-3} sec, and EL could not be observed when the duration of the applied voltage was less than 10 msec.

Sano et al. [12] observed delayed EL from anthracene at silver-epoxied paste electrodes. Light was emitted only when the point electrode was negative in the voltage range studied. When an anthracene crystal was pulsed with a 10^{-7} sec voltage spike, a delayed luminescence appeared, a large fraction of which could be observed after the voltage pulse had disappeared. Sometimes EL occurred in the form of a second peak of light emission, the first peak occurring with the application of the pulse. The delayed EL was shown to arise from an excited singlet state. These authors [12] interpreted their results to indicate that delayed EL was produced by carrier recombination between holes and electrons, either in the lowest conduction band or released from traps. They further concluded that the holes were not produced by direct electron injection but arose from electron acceleration.

Helfrich and Schneider [13] also have observed recombination luminescence in anthracene crystals. They used 1- to 5-mm-thick crystals approximately 1 cm in diameter sandwiched between two liquid electrodes contained in glass tubes. When generating positive holes, an electrode of anthracene positive ions in nitromethane was used, and saturation currents of approximately 3×10^{-6} A were observed. Electron injection was accomplished by using an electrode containing anthracene negative ions in tetrahydrofuran, and electron currents as high as 10^{-5} A could be produced without observing saturation. They showed that the currents were space charge-limited. Two carrier currents were obtained when the electron-injecting electrode was combined with the hole-injecting electrode, resulting in higher currents than with either electrode alone. During the flow of the doubly injected current, fluorescence of anthracene was produced *within* the anthracene crystal. The intensity correlated linearly with the current through the crystal down to currents as low as 10^{-10} A.

The observation of fluorescence within the interior of the crystal indicated that the luminescence must arise from recombination within the crystal rather than at the surface of either electrode. The mechanism was interpreted as SCL electron current flowing through the crystal to meet positive hole current in front of the positive electrode. The process appeared to be highly efficient, approximately one photon emitted for every electron injected. The singlet emitter was thought to be formed directly from carrier recombination rather than by a triplet-triplet annihilation mechanism.

Later, Helfrich and Schneider [14] studied the recombination rate processes for hole-electron-produced luminescence in anthracene and were able to distinguish between singlets produced directly from recombination and by annihilation processes. The overall carrier recombination rate constant was determined to be $k = 1.05 \times 10^{-6}$ cm sec^{-1}, which agreed well with their theoretical model.

The recombination luminescence from anthracene was found to consist of two components having vastly different rise times. The component of luminescence having the fast rise time was attributed to excited singlet states produced directly by carrier recombinations as proposed earlier [13]. The component of luminescence showing a slow rise time was found to be anthracene fluorescence as well. It was interpreted as arising from carriers producing triplet excitons which subsequently underwent triplet-triplet annihilation to produce an excited singlet state. The ratio of the intensity of the slow fluorescence component to the fast fluorescence component was established as 0.65, indicating that about 60% of the photons emitted arise from singlet states produced directly and that about 40% of the photons are produced by a triplet-triplet annihilation process. Helfrich and Schneider were also able to estimate the rate constant for triplet-triplet processes in anthracene crystals which was determined to be $4-8 \times 10^{-12}$ cm^3 sec^{-1}.

It is interesting to compare the studies of Helfrich and Schneider on organic crystals with the results from cation-anion annihilation reactions occurring in solution to be discussed later. Evidence is also presented that both direct singlet formation and triplet-triplet annihilation processes occur when radical anions and radical cations combine to produce luminescence in solution.

Johnson et al. [15] have reported electrophotoluminescence for N-N-N'-N'-tetramethyl-p-phenylenediamene dissolved in an organic glass and cooled to liquid nitrogen temperature. Electrophotoluminescence is the phenomenon of electrical stimulation of luminescence in a sample that has been photolyzed. A quartz electrode coated with a semitransparent coating of chromium and a stainless-steel-back electrode were used.

Rigid solutions were irradiated for 30 sec with 313-nm radiation and then an electric field applied. A sharp enhancement of the luminescence level was noted with the applied electric field, and when the field was reversed, a second electrical stimulation was observed. Following the two-step application of the field, the solid was only slightly sensitive to electrical stimulation and once again had to be sensitized with ultraviolet radiation.

Johnson et al. [15] have presented three possible mechanisms to explain electrophotoluminescence in organic systems: release of *shallowly* trapped electrons by the direct action of the electric field; release of trapped electrons as a result of dielectric relaxation processes in the matrix; and injection of electrons from the electrodes. In all of these processes the electrons would combine with the tetramethyl-*p*-phenylenediamene radical cations to give the observed luminescence. The first explanation, that of releasing shallowly trapped electrons, has been favored by the authors.

Excitation by Gaseous Discharge

The first report of EL from organic phosphors was presented by Bernanose and co-workers who have published a number of studies in this area [16–24]. These authors used electroluminescent cells containing films impregnated with organic dyes which gave off a characteristic luminescence when exposed to a high-voltage ac field. The experimental technique is described below [16, 23].

The emitter was a film of cellophane prepared by dipping it into a fluorescent solution, drying it, and placing it with melted paraffin wax between a plate of aluminum and a sheet of transparent mica. The cell was compressed before cooling to exclude air bubbles. The sheet of mica was wetted on its exterior surface by a saline glycerol solution in order to provide electrical contact. The thickness of the dielectric in the cell was approximately 0.1 mm. EL was excited in the cellophane film by application of a 50- to 500-Hz ac voltage as large as 2000 V. Light emission was measured with a 1P21 photomultiplier tube.

The intensity of EL was found to vary with the applied voltage [48, 55] according to the relationship:

$$I = AV^2 \exp\left(-B/V\right), \qquad (13.1)$$

where A and B are constants.

Equation (13.1) is similar to the relationship observed for inorganic electroluminescent phosphors such as copper–zinc sulfide. Under normal conditions of EL, the cell current was constant, indicating that discharge through the cell was not the excitation mechanism. The light intensity was found to be frequency dependent, a phase shift being noted between the voltage and light emission characteristics. The phase shift was greater at 500 than at 50 cps.

For most of the compounds studied by Bernanose et al., the EL spectrum matched the fluorescence spectrum of the compound contained in the cellophane layer [19, 20, 24]. Typical examples of the compounds studied are acridine orange, cyanine dyes, carbazole, and derivatives of 8-hydroxy-quinoline. In some circumstances a new emission band was observed in addition to the normal fluorescence spectrum. This band occurred in the blue region of the spectrum around 435 nm [20, 23].

Bernanose considered several possible excitation mechanisms for EL produced in the cellophane films [21]. He pointed out that explanations involving structural defects, active centers, or crystal abnormalities were not consistent with his data. He proposed that direct field excitation of the molecules occurred.

Following the work of Bernanose et al., several workers have both confirmed and questioned his results. Namba et al. [25] repeated Bernanose's experiments on acridine orange and auramine dyes. They found that as the concentration of organic phosphors increased the EL spectrum shifted toward a longer wavelength, probably because of self-absorption. They likewise confirmed the relationship between intensity and the square of applied voltage as well as the intensity dependence on frequency. They confirmed that the spectral distribution was affected neither by voltage nor frequency and that it resembled fluorescence of organic dyes. However, Tumerman and Czayanov [26, 27] and Lozykowski and Meczynska [28] unsuccessfully attempted to obtain EL for organic dyes such as acridine, fluorescein, and flavins. Lozykowski and Meczynska prepared their cell in an evacuated tube and were unable to produce any excitation of luminescence by the ac field. They did, in fact, observe a blue emission from all cells independent of whether or not an organic dye was on the cellophane layer [26–28].

Gurnee et al. have studied EL produced by aromatic hydrocarbons in the presence of a finely divided electric conductor [29, 30]. For example, anthracene in the presence of about 1 % carbon black showed a blue EL characteristic of anthracene fluorescence. When a small amount of tetracene was added to the anthracene, the green luminescence of tetracene was observed.

The cells used by Gurnee consisted of a chromium-plated steel-backed electrode upon which a 1-mil polycrystalline layer of the hydrocarbon-conductor mixture was placed. A 1-mil polystyrene film separated the conducting layer from a transparent tin oxide-coated glass electrode. A thin film of silicone oil was used on each side of the dielectric layer in order to displace air present in the cell. A detailed discussion of experimental procedures can be found in Ref. 29. The cells prepared by Gurnee et al. were similar to those used in the technique of Lehmann [31], who excited a number of nonluminescent inorganic materials by mixing them with a finely divided conductive powder. The brightness of such a cell was found to be a function of applied voltage in the same fashion as the cells described by Bernanose. The light output showed two peaks per voltage cycle, usually of different heights. In a symmetrical cell containing two conducting glass electrodes, both separated by a dielectric layer from the conducting mixture, the greater intensity was observed through the positive electrode. It was also observed that at higher frequencies the light output did not fall to zero as the voltage passed through zero. The emission spectrum observed for any given conductive mixture was identical with the fluorescence spectrum observed under the same conditions.

Gurnee concluded [30] that excitation of the organic material originated in the vicinity of the carbon particles, probably by electron injection into the organic material from the conducting particle. He also concluded that the injected electrons were sufficiently energetic to excite the hydrocarbon directly, although hole combination processes were also considered. In the case of tetracene-doped anthracene, Gurnee determined that excitation energy was transferred to the tetracene by the energy transfer normally associated with organic crystals.

Short and Hercules [32] studied the EL of a variety of fluorescent organic compounds by a technique similar to that of Gurnee's except that they found it was not necessary to add the conductive material to the fluorescent organic layer. The cell used in their studies is shown in Fig. 13.1. When an exciting voltage was applied to this cell in the range of 1 to 5 kV, in the

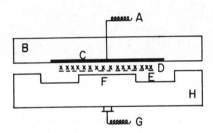

Fig. 13.1 Cross-sectional diagram showing details of EL cell construction: *A*, electrical contact to conducting tin oxide layer; *B*, glass plate; *C*, tin oxide layer; *D*, phosphor layer; *E*, dielectric film; *F*, central platform for confining thicknesses in range 1 to 5 mils; *G*, electrical contact to steel plate; *H*, stainless steel plate electrode [32].

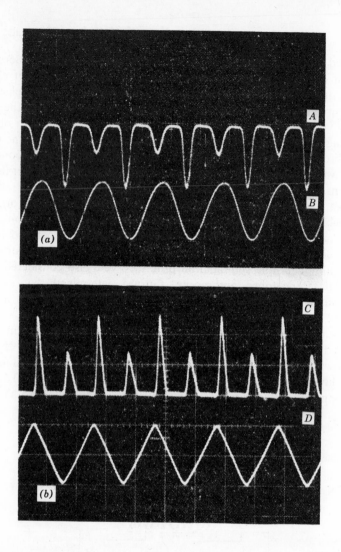

Fig. 13.2 Typical output waveforms for sine and triangular excitation voltages. (a) Cell material, phenanthrene–tetrachlorophthalic anhydride charge transfer complex: A, photomultiplier output, scale 2 V cm^{-1}; B, exciting voltage, sine wave, frequency 500 cps, 2 kV peak to peak. (b) Cell material, hexamethylbenezene–tetrachlorophthalic anhydride charge transfer complex: C, photomultiplier output, scale 2 V cm^{-1}; D, exciting voltage, triangular wave, frequency 700 cps, 2 kV peak to peak [32].

270

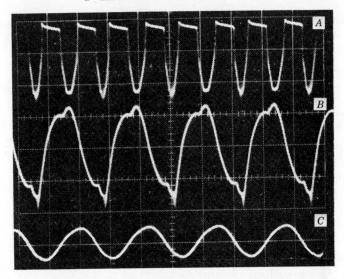

Fig. 13.3 Photograph of waveforms showing relationship between intensity of emitted radiation, cell current, and exciting voltage for a cell containing only a polystyrene film: *A*, photomultiplier output, scale, 5 V cm^{-1}; *B*, cell current; *C*, exciting voltage, sine wave, frequency 230 cps, 2 kV peak to peak [32].

frequency range 50 to 2000 cps, in sine, square, pulse, and triangular wave-forms, light output wave forms were observed similar to those shown in Fig. 13.2. The light output increased with voltage and frequency, and there was evidence of saturation at high voltage. In agreement with Gurnee, it was observed that two peaks of unequal size were obtained for each complete cycle except from those cells that did not contain any fluorescent material. The higher peak corresponded to a cathodic potential on the metal electrode. In general, the ratio of the higher peak to lower peak increased with voltage and with frequency. It was also observed that light emission occurred from the cells even when the fluorescent layer was absent, and that under these circumstances the light peaks were of equal intensity on each half-cycle and coincided with a current surge through the cell as shown in Fig. 13.3. In those cells containing only polystyrene films, the light emitted was blue. The wave forms obtained from such cells showed no difference between anodic and cathodic peaks, and the light outputs were relatively high. A high proportion of the emission in this case was found in the ultraviolet region of the spectrum. Spectroscopic examination of the emitted radiation from such a cell revealed a series of bands in the 300 to 500-nm region which were identified with the second positive series of nitrogen, the spectrum obtained from the positive column of discharge tubes containing air or nitrogen at low pressure. These bands were observed both in the presence and absence of a fluorescent material in the cell. For cells prepared and run in the complete absence of air, *no EL could be observed.*

The authors [32] explained the origin of the radiation emitted by an electroluminescent cell to be the normal fluorescence of the organic compound excited by the ultraviolet radiation from nitrogen. With even a small amount of nitrogen present in the cell, sufficient gaseous discharge could be produced to give fluorescence of the organic material. It was found that when the cell was prepared in an atmosphere of helium no light emission could be observed from an organic layer, although a standard commercial electroluminescent zinc sulfide phosphor produced light.

From Fig. 13.3 it is apparent that the current in a cell consists of two components. The capacitive charging current which is sinusoidal has the wave form of the exciting voltage. The spikes on the current curve coincide exactly with light emission which is the extra current resulting from gaseous discharge in the cell at that point. Since the anode region in a glow tube exhibits the greater light intensity, it would be expected that a higher light output would be obtained from a cell when the transparent electrode was the anode—this was observed to be the case. The fact that no peak height difference was observed in the case in which a transparent dielectric material alone was used to prepare the cell is also consistent with this interpretation.

Another strong point suggesting the validity of the gaseous discharge interpretation is that no emission bands could be observed for any material except for those normally fluorescent in the solid state. This also correlates with some of the spurious emission bands observed by Bernanose, who apparently failed to observe most of the nitrogen bands because of the high optical absorption of his mica layers in the region of nitrogen discharge.

An interesting and somewhat confusing effect is that the glow discharge mechanism has electrical properties similar to those observed for genuine EL. It is doubtless this fact that has been a source of confusion to a number of investigators. It seems, however, that the bulk of EL reported to data in thin cells under high-potential ac excitation probably results from a discharge excitation mechanism.

3 ELECTROLUMINESCENCE IN SOLUTION: "CLASSIC" CHEMILUMINESCENT REACTIONS

The early work on EL of classic chemiluminescent systems is attributable to Harvey [33], who observed chemiluminescence from luminol undergoing electrolysis. Harvey also references several earlier observations of EL worthy of mention. It has been reported that light emission occurred at several metal anodes undergoing oxidation in electrolyte solutions; light has been observed when halides were electrolyzed at mercury and other anodes; and chemiluminescence has been induced in solutions containing oxyluciferin and luciferase when they were reduced at a cathode.

Harvey [24] electrolyzed basic luminol solutions and observed that light could be produced at both the cathode and the anode, depending upon conditions. He attributed anodic light production to a reaction between luminol and nascent oxygen produced at the anode. Chemiluminescence produced at the cathode was attributed to reaction with hydrogen peroxide generated from the oxygen present in solution. It is interesting to note that few workers followed up Harvey's original observations, reported in 1929, even though other literature on the chemiluminescence of luminol is voluminous.

ECL of Luminol

Studies on the ECL of luminol are attributable to Kuwana et al. [34–38]. These have largely been follow-up studies to Harvey's original observations that luminol could be made to chemiluminesce if oxidized in the presence of oxygen. The relationship between the ECL studies and the chemiluminescence of luminol is not immediately apparent, although there are certain conclusions that can be drawn from Kuwana's studies which seem to have bearing on the chemiluminescence mechanism.

These workers have clearly established that luminol in water reacts with oxygen to give light if the luminol is first oxidized. They have also established that the rate of light emission in the luminol reaction appears to be limited by a slow chemical step which probably involves decomposition of a reaction intermediate. Such an intermediate is comparable to the luminol peroxide popularly proposed as an intermediate in the chemiluminescent reaction. The studies of Kuwana et al. show that electrochemical studies can do much to augment photochemical studies in the elucidation of chemiluminescence mechanisms.

Electrochemistry of Liminol

The electrochemistry of luminol and its relationship to light emission are shown in Fig. 13.4. Curve A shows three distinct regions of oxidation with different processes occurring in each. The region F of curve A corresponds to the oxidation of plantinum to platinum oxide. As the oxidation continued, luminol was then oxidized in region G. If oxygen had been present in solution, luminescence would have appeared as soon as region G was reached. Region H corresponds to generation of oxygen from the solution and luminescence was observed in region H even though oxygen was initially excluded from the system. The curve labeled E is the light emission curve corresponding to the oxidation B. Curve A' is a cathodic scan after curve A was run, indicating the reduction of platinum oxide. Cyclic voltammetry indicated that $E_{p/2} = +0.22$ V versus SCE and that the exact location of the peak depends upon

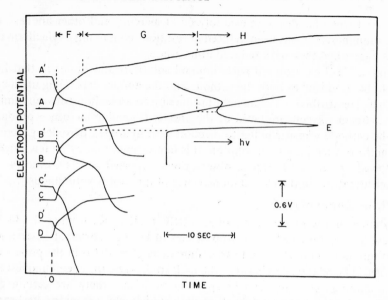

Fig. 13.4 Chronopotentiograms for the oxidation of $10^{-3} F$ luminol in 0.1 F sodium carbonate. Current, 400 μA. A to D are anodic potential-time traces. Traces A' to D' are cathodic chronopotentiograms run after the corresponding A-to-D anodic scans. Solution was stirred between the anodic and cathodic runs. Trace E is light emission versus potential for chronopotentiogram B [35].

scan rate. No evidence of a reduction wave attributable to oxidized luminol could be observed [35, 36]. The electrochemical study of luminol indicates that the electrode reactions are diffusion-controlled without any chemical reaction preceding the electron transfer step [36].

Kuwana et al. made extensive investigations to determine the number of electrons involved in the electron transfer step. A plot of $E_{p/2}$ versus pH for unsubstituted phthalhydrazide could be rationalized in terms of a three-electron transfer involving two protons. This result was viewed with some skepticism by the authors [36] because of the irreversible nature of the phthalhydrazide oxidation wave. In order to obtain a better n value, the authors performed controlled-potential coulometry of the unsubstituted phthalhydrazide and obtained n values of 2.68 and 2.31, respectively, depending upon whether oxygen was absent or present. These results could correlate with either a value of $n = 2$ or $n = 3$, and calculation of diffusion coefficients was more consistent with a value of $n = 3$. However, using $nD^{1/2}$ values obtained from chronopotentiometry to calculate values of αn, it seems more reasonable that a one-electron transfer would be involved in the rate-determining step. Epstein and Kuwana [36] concluded that the electro-chemical results confirm a mixed type of parallel electron transfer in which one or more electrons are transferred with the same activation overpotential.

One upsetting thing about the electrochemistry of luminol is the inconsistency of various parameters calculated by different electrochemical techniques. For example, by the technique of chronocoulometry, βn values of 0.081 and 0.089 are obtained by different plots, whereas from linear sweep voltammetry values of 0.85 and 0.82 are obtained [37]. The high degree of variablility in calculating various electrochemical parameters leads one to the conclusion that none of the reported n values for electrochemical oxidation of luminol is very trustworthy and their relationship to the initial oxidation step in solution is probably somewhat vague.

It was also necessary to establish the nature of the oxidative process in luminol, that is, whether or not the amino group participated in electrooxidation. To do this, the authors compared the oxidation of luminol, unsubstituted phthalhydrazide, and 3-methylphthalhydrazide. Epstein and Kuwana showed quite conclusively that the number of electrons transferred in the overall electrode reaction is similar for luminol and the unsubstituted phthalhydrazide [36]. A comparison of current-voltage curves for the three compounds indicated qualitative similarity and similar irreversibility [37]. On the basis of the large number of electrochemical studies [37], it can be concluded that the nature of the electrooxidative process in all three compounds is similar and that the amino group is not involved in the electrode reaction. Since the amino group comes through the chemical oxidation unscathed as well, this lends support to the idea that the electrochemical studies are, in fact, pertinent to the chemical oxidation.

Light Emission

That light emission is related to the electrochemical oxidation of luminol is readily seen from curves B and E in Fig. 13.4. Upon reaching region G, the light emission increases rapidly, rising to a peak and then slowly decreasing until region H is reached where again light emission increases as a result of the generation of oxygen in solution. A comparison of the spectra for electrochemically and chemically generated chemiluminescence of luminol indicates similar spectral distributions and virtually identical maxima at 425 nm. This establishes with reasonable certainty that the emitting species is the same in both cases [36]. It is also established [36] that the intensity of ECL for the unsubstituted phthalhydrazide was a factor of 10^3 lower than that of luminol. In fact, it is questionable whether or not the unsubstituted phthalhydrazide emits at all, and the light emission observed by Epstein and Kuwana for this compound is probably a result of impurities. A quantum yield of 3×10^{-4} Einsteins/mole for the ECL of luminol was obtained assuming an average n value of 2.5 equiv/mole. Here the quantum efficiency is defined as the ratio of the integrated photocurrent to the electrochemical coulombs passed [36]. Because the ECL efficiency of luminol and the unsubstituted phthalhydrazide are vastly different, yet the electrochemical oxidations are at least qualitatively similar, one may conclude that the effect of substituent on ECL of luminol is correlated more to the substituent effect on the emissive properties of the excited state of the product rather than on the electrochemical oxidation of the starting material.

Kinetics of Luminol ECL

Application of square wave potential pulses to luminol solutions gave light emission-time curves characterized by three regions: the rise portion of the curve-pulse, the faradaic portion of the curve which is the light emission observed while the electrode is at some fixed potential, and the decay part of the curve which is the light emission observed when no faradaic reaction is occurring, after the potential has been returned to 0 V [36, 38]. Analysis of these curves gives information relating to the kinetics and possibly to the nature of the intermediates involved in the luminol light emission reaction.

In the rising portion of the curve, the light intensity I_t follows the relationship [33]

$$I_t = I_0[1 - \exp(-k_r t)], \tag{13.2}$$

where I_0 is the light intensity at the peak, k_r is the rate constant for light emission, and t is time in seconds. If electron transfer is the slow step, it would be anticipated that k_r would be potential dependent because of the known irreversibility of the luminol oxidation reaction.

Application of chronocoulometry to the oxidation of luminol [38] gives a parameter $t_i^{1/2}$, which is related to the kinetics of the heterogeneous electron transfer. Plots of $\ln(1/t_i^{1/2})$ versus E and $\ln(k_r)$ versus E should both have slopes of $\beta n_a F/RT$, assuming k_r is directly proportional to the heterogeneous electron-transfer rate constant. Values of βn_a calculated from the above plots were 0.081 and 0.089, respectively [38], indicating that light emission is at least partially controlled by electron transfer kinetics. Additional evidence for this conclusion comes from the fact that k_r is independent of oxygen concentration in luminol solutions [36]. Using the above techniques, a value of 6.6×10^{-4} cm sec^{-1} was obtained for the heterogeneous electron-transfer rate constant.

In the faradaic region of the light emission–time curve, light intensity appeared to be proportional to electrolytic current in stirred solution. This was verified by stepped potential chronoamperometry for short light pulses. A linear relationship was established between the light intensity and the mass transfer rate.

In the decay portion of the curve, the potential was returned to 0.0 V at the end of the pulse, and after 10 μsec no faradaic processes were observed. Therefore the rate of decay of light emission in this region depends upon the rates of chemical reactions following electron transfer. A rate constant for the decay reaction k_d was calculated to be $1.3 \times 10^3 \ sec^{-1}$ in an oxygen-saturated solution. The rate was found to be independent of luminol concentration over the ranges of pulse duration and oxygen concentration studied. It was also observed that the quantum efficiency of chemiluminescence of luminol was independent of oxygen concentration. These results are consistent with the idea of an intermediate produced after the electrochemical reaction, which undergoes a unimolecular decomposition reaction to give light emission.

ECL Mechanisms

Any mechanism for ECL in the luminol system must explain several observations: how to account for the nonintegral n values observed by Kuwana et al.; how to rationalize all of the electrochemical data presented; and how the ECL mechanism proposed relates to current knowledge of the mechanism of luminol chemiluminescence in solution.

Epstein and Kuwana [37] have suggested three possible mechanisms to account for the nonintegral n-values: regreneration of the starting material after electrooxidation, the consumption of electroactive material by reaction of a product of the electrode reaction, and stepwise electron transfer involving consumption of electroactive material between steps. Although the data are not sufficient to distinguish between the three cases, the authors favor the last mechanism and this is summarized:

$$R \rightarrow O_1 + n_1 e^- \tag{13.3}$$

$$O_1 + Z \rightarrow M \quad \text{(nonelectroactive)} \tag{13.4}$$

$$O_1 + n_2 e^- \rightarrow O_2 \quad \text{(nonelectoactive)} \tag{13.5}$$

The reduced form of luminol, R, is oxidized at the electrode surface in (13.3) and the product, O_1, undergoes a chemical reaction to produce a second product, M, which is not electroactive. In a parallel reaction, a second oxidation step, (13.5) occurs in which O_1 is oxidized to O_2 which is also not electroactive.

The following overall ECL mechanism for luminol has been proposed [36] based on the mechanism for nonintegral n-values presented above:

$$LH^- \xrightarrow{k_1'} L^{n_1-2} + n_1 e^- + H^+ \qquad \text{Initial oxidation} \tag{13.6}$$

$$\Big\downarrow k_2' \qquad \qquad \text{Nonchemiluminescent, parallel} \tag{13.7}$$
$$\text{oxidative route } (n_2 e^-)$$

$$\Big\downarrow_{\substack{k_3' \\ O_2}} \qquad \qquad \text{Intermediate} \tag{13.8}$$

$$\text{Intermediate} \xrightarrow{k_4} APA^{2-*} \qquad \text{Production of excited state} \tag{13.9}$$

$$APA^{2-*} \xrightarrow{k_5} APA^{2-} + h\nu \qquad \text{Fluorescence} \tag{13.10}$$

where LH$^-$ is

and APA^{2-} is

The mechanism presented above is consistent with the idea that luminol is oxidized by two or more parallel reactions, one of which is possibly a one-electron oxidation to a free radical. Although such a mechanism is favored by Epstein and Kuwana, the required free radical has never been observed, although free radical traps have been shown to quench chemiluminescence of the luminol system. The values obtained for k_r by Epstein and Kuwana do not correlate with chemical oxidation rates obtained by other workers for luminol in aqueous solution. However, this did not mean that one-electron oxidation processes do not occur for both cases. There is very often little correlation between an electron transfer reaction of a species in solution and a hetero-geneous electron transfer reaction of the same species at an electrode surface. The proposed intermediate of Epstein and Kuwana, which decomposes to give the light-emitting species, is quite consistent with the bridged peroxide intermediate often proposed in the chemiluminescent oxidation of luminol. Although the rate data for the initial oxidation of ECL and chemiluminescence of luminol would not necessarily be expected to be the same, if the chemi-luminescent and ECL mechanisms are similar, other rate constants should be identical. However, only insufficient kinetic data for both processes are available at present, so that it is not possible to determine how much one mechanism relates to the other.

Electrolysis of Fluorescein Solutions

Shlyapintokh et al. [39] have reported that light emission occurs during the dc electrolysis of fluorescein or eosin in alkaline aqueous solutions at platinum electrodes. The solutions investigated were 5×10^{-5} M in the dye, the applied voltage to the cell was 30 V, and the observed current in the solution was 14 mA at a 1-cm^2 electrode. Light emission was observed only at the anode for dc electrolysis, and the light output was estimated to be between 10^4 and 10^5 photons/cm^2/sec. Under the same conditions of concentration, voltage, and current, luminescence was also observed when pulses of alternating polarity were applied to the cell, the light emission occurring at the moment of switching the potential. Both the intensity and characteristics of light emission under ac electrolysis were reported to be frequency dependent. The authors [39] interpreted the light emission to result from reaction of active intermediates of reduction with active intermediates produced by oxidation.

Because the results reported above were reminiscent of the light emission characteristic of cation-anion annihilation reactions, we endeavored to duplicate the results of Shlyapintokh et al. [40]. However, the production of light by fluorescein electrolysis is apparently either sensitive to extraneous factors or the exact conditions necessary for light emission are not correctly reported in the paper [39], since by duplicating conditions as closely as possible it was not possible to observe light emission. In addition to the attempt to repeat the results of Shlyapintokh et al., we carried out some additional attempts to generate fluorescein ECL at both platinum and mercury electrodes [40]. These are summarized below.

Utilizing two cylindrical, concentric, platinum electrodes in a solution of 10^{-5} M fluorescein in 0.1 M sodium hydroxide, voltages up to 2.3 V were applied and no fluorescence could be observed with the dark-adapted eye. Upon switching polarity after a few minutes of generation, likewise, no light was observed. By using a single platinum electrode as the anode, up to 20 V were applied versus a saturated Ag/AgBr reference electrode degassed by bubbling with nitrogen. Again, no light was observed.

Considering that Shlyapintokh et al. [39] might have been reducing fluorescein at one electrode and oxidizing oxygen to peroxide at another, light generation was attempted at a mercury pool electrode using a platinum counterelectrode and a Ag/AgBr reference electrode. Potentiostatic measurements were used and solution conditions were as before. A fairly reversible reduction peak was observed for fluorescein at −1.1 V. However, no light emission was observed when a triangular wave sweep was made potentiostatically from +1.5 to −1.5 V or when the mercury electrode was held at −1.1 V and then switched positive after a given time of generation, this being equivalent to a low-frequency square wave. When fluorescein was reduced at −1.1 V for ca. 15 sec, the generating potential turned off, and a hydrogen peroxide solution added, still no light was observed.

On the basis of the above experiments, it is reasonable to conclude that light generation from electrolysis of fluorescein under the conditions stated by Shlyapintokh et al. is highly questionable. Our attempts to generate light were made both with a dark-adapted eye and with a photomultiplier tube. Also, it is clear that reduced fluorescein reacting with hydrogen peroxide in basic solution does not give light emission. Since Shlyapintokh et al. were not able to record the emission spectrum, it is possible that the emission they observed did not arise from fluorescein at all but rather from impurities in their solutions.

Solvent Electrolysis

Bader and Kuwana [41] have studied low-level light emission produced during cyclic voltammetry at platinum electrodes immersed in either acetonitrile or dimethyl sulfoxide containing $LiClO_4$ as an electrolyte. It is not possible to estimate the absolute intensity of emission, which was probably very weak, since the authors recorded it with an unfiltered photomultiplier tube.

In dimethyl sulfoxide, light emission is related to anodic solvent decomposition and the reduction of oxygen. For example, if the cathodic limit of a triangular wave scan is -1.2 V versus SCE (oxygen reduction at -0.9 V versus SCE) on scanning toward anodic potentials, light emission is observed at ca. 0.0 V with increasing intensity into the solvent oxidation wave which occurs at $+1.4$ V versus SCE. During the anodic portion of the scan, a new anodic peak develops at -0.2 V.

In degassed solutions of acetonitrile, light emission is observed when the potential is scanned cathodically to -2.9 V where lithium ion is reduced. Also, light is observed anodically at the combined solvent-electrolyte oxidation wave at $+2.1$ V. If anthracene and oxygen are present in solution, light emission seems to correlate with oxygen reduction and anthracene oxidation. In degassed solutions containing anthracene, light emission is observed from a reaction of the anthracene radical anion with some solvent oxidation product.

Bader and Kuwana [41] have indicated a number of possible mechanisms to explain the light-emiting reaction and these are summarized below. Radicals can be formed by the electrooxidation reaction:

$$RH \rightarrow R\cdot + H^+ + e^\ominus \tag{13.11}$$

which may react to produce light and in the presence of oxygen possibly:

$$R\cdot + O_2 \rightarrow ROO\cdot \tag{13.12}$$

$$ROO\cdot + ROO\cdot \rightarrow ROOR + O_2 + h\nu \tag{13.13}$$

Radical production may also be possible if superoxide is generated:

$$O_2 + e^- \rightarrow O_2^-\cdot \tag{13.14}$$

$$O_2^-\cdot + RH \rightarrow R\cdot + HO_2^\ominus \tag{13.15}$$

and radical recombination reactions may be a possible source of light emission:

$$R\cdot + R\cdot \rightarrow R - R \qquad (13.16)$$

The light emission resulting from lithium metal reduction is probably attributable to radicals produced by the reaction of lithium metal either with traces of water present or with the organic solvent, with possible excitation resulting from micro gas pockets of hydrogen gas. The experiments reported with anthracene and many of the other results reported in this communication seem to resemble the preannihilation ECL that is discussed in the next section. A note of caution is warranted in attempting to establish mechanisms for low-level light emission associated with electrolysis of organic solvents. As workers in the field of ECL of radical ions have shown, low-level impurities in the solvent as well as complex reactions attributable to solvent oxidation products can produce significant light intensity even though on a quantum basis relative to radical ion recombination reactions the intensity is low.

Electrolysis of Grignard Solutions

A study by Dufford et al. [42] of luminescence generated on the application of an electrical potential to Grignard solutions is one of the very early ECL studies. These authors applied up to 1500 V to electrodes immersed in Grignard solutions and observed that light emission occurred at one or both electrodes, usually at the anode. The effect was found to be voltage dependent and, interestingly enough, the brightness of the light observed appeared to have little if any relation to the brightness obtained by oxygen oxidation of Grignard solutions. In fact, many of the compounds showing bright oxygen-induced chemiluminescence in Grignards hardly showed any intensity at all when electrolyzed. In a qualitative sense, the more intense light appeared to come from solutions of Grignards derived from phenyl bromide, p-iodo-toluene, and 1,4-chlorobromonaphthalene. It was observed that all of the Grignard compounds deposited magnesium on electrolysis. Dufford et al. also discovered that the potentials of electrodes immersed in a Grignard solution were light dependent, that is, irradiation of an electrode caused a significant change in the emf of the electrode.

It is virtually impossible to interpret the results of Dufford et al. because very little is known about the chemiluminescence of Grignards except that it has recently been shown that the emitter in the oxidation of p-phenyl-magnesium bromide is p-terphenyl [43]. Since electrolysis of arylmagnesium halides quite likely produces aryl radicals, it is very possible that the light emission comes from a radical recombination or possibly even a radical ion reaction. These kinds of systems certainly merit further investigation.

ECL of Lucigenin

The chemiluminescence of lucigenin (LUC) observed on reaction with hydrogen peroxide in basic solutions is well known. The light emission observed is either blue or green, depending upon conditions under which the reaction is run. *N*-Methylacridone (NMA) has been identified as the primary emitter, being responsible for the blue chemiluminescence.

LUC   NMA   DBA

The first report of ECL in the lucigenin system is attributable to Tamamushi and Akiyama [44], who observed that when lucigenin was electrolyzed in alkaline aqueous solutions at a platinum electrode light emission took place at the cathode along the path of hydrogen gas evolution. Recently, Legg and Hercules have reported an extensive investigation of ECL for lucigenin in both aqueous and nonaqueous solvents [45] and have studied the spectral variations in light emission as a function of solvent.

Cyclic voltammetry revealed that the electrochemical reduction of lucigenin is irreversible [45] and that the reduction product can be identified as dimethylbiacridine (DBA). The irreversibility of the reaction implies that lucigenin is reduced in a one-electron step to a free radical which is rapidly reduced by solvent to DBA.

Attempts to generate ECL under conditions described by Tamamushi and Akiyama were unsuccessful [45]. When a mercury pool was used in place of a platinum electrode for the cathode and the solution was buffered at pH 7, light emission was observed. Oxygen was necessary for production of light. It is known that in basic solutions at a platinum electrode oxygen is reduced to OH$^-$, via a multistep process occurring at the same potential, whereas at a mercury cathode in a neutral solution oxygen is reduced by:

$$O_2 + 2H_2O + 2e^- \rightarrow H_2O_2 + 2OH^-$$

Therefore at a mercury cathode hydrogen peroxide and base are produced corresponding to the reagents necessary for production of light, according to the normal chemiluminescent reaction of lucigenin.

ECL for lucigenin was produced in four nonaqueous solvents: ethanol, dimethylsulfoxide, dimethylformamide (DMF), and acetonitrile. In these solvents, however, oxygen is reduced to superoxide and experiments show conclusively that luminescence arises from a reaction of superoxide ion with lucigenin.

The spectral distribution of ECL emission was shown to be both time dependent and solvent dependent [45]. Typical examples of lucigenin ECL in ethanol and dimethyl sulfoxide are shown in Fig. 13.5. In ethanol only blue emission is observed; the spectral distribution does not change with time and matches exactly the fluorescence of NMA as shown by comparison of curves A and B. In dimethyl sulfoxide the initial light emission largely matches the fluorescence of NMA as evidenced by curve C, but as the reaction progresses the spectral distribution changes until toward the end of the reaction it resembles the fluorescence of DBA as shown by curves D and E.

Changes in spectral distribution can be accounted for by singlet-singlet energy transfer between the primary emitter, NMA, the lucigenin and DBA. Since energy transfer occurs between NMA and lucigenin and DBA at

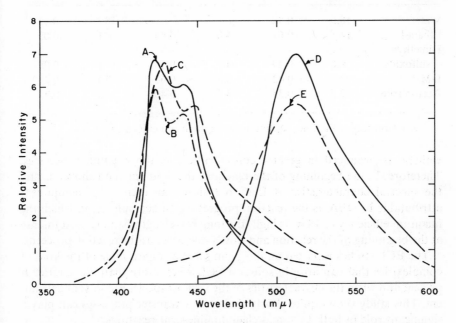

Fig. 13.5 Spectra in dimethyl sulfoxide and ethanol. (*A*) (———) Fluorescence spectrum of $5 \times 10^{-5} M$ NMA in DMSO; (*B*) (— · —) ECL spectrum in ethanol; (*C*) (– – –) ECL spectrum in dimethyl sulfoxide at the beginning of electrolysis; (*D*) (———) Fluorescence spectrum of $1 \times 10^{-4} M$ DBA in dimethyl sulfoxide; (*E*) (– – –) ECL spectrum in dimethyl sulfoxide after 10 min of electrolysis [45].

approximately the same rate, the quantum efficiency and solubility of the acceptors determines the nature of the secondary emitter. In dimethyl sulfoxide and DMF the quantum efficiencies of DBA are greater than those of LUC, as can be seen in Table 13.1, and secondary emission observed in these solvents matches the fluorescence of DBA. In acetonitrile the quantum efficiency of LUC is high and therefore the secondary emission matches its fluorescence. In ethanol DBA is relatively insoluble and the quantum efficiency of LUC is very low, therefore only emission attributable to NMA is observed.

The time dependence of the light emission can also be explained by the data of Table 13.1. In dimethyl sulfoxide and DMF, DBA, being the secondary

Table 13.1   Fluorescent Lifetimes and Quantum Efficiencies* [45]

	NMA		DBA		Lucigenin	
Solvent	$\tau(nsec)$	Φ	$\tau(nsec)$	Φ	$\tau(nsec)$	Φ
Water	18.5	0.82	—	—	18.8	0.43
Ethanol	14.1	0.61	4.0	0.45	<1	0.09
Dimethyl sulfoxide	9.0	0.49	4.9	0.58	<1	0.08
DMF	7.6	0.42	5.3	0.60	3.1	0.24
Acetonitrile	7.2	0.35	3.2	0.40	24.7	0.72

* τ, Fluorescence lifetime; Φ, fluorescence quantum efficiency.

emitter, is produced in greater concentration as the reaction progresses. Therefore, in the beginning of the reaction, the light emission shows mostly the spectral characteristics of LUC but shows an increase in component attributable to DBA as the reaction progresses. In acetonitrile, in which the quantum efficiency of LUC is high, the long wavelength band is most intense at the beginning of the reaction and slowly decreases as the reaction proceeds.

The ECL studies reported on lucigenin serve as an example of the kind of complexities that can arise in solution ECL when more than one emitter is present and when the characteristics of the various species are solvent dependent. This study shows quite clearly that energy transfer processes can play a significant role in both ECL and chemiluminescent reactions.

Kolbe Electrolysis

Ahnstrom [46] has studied the light emission accompanying electrolysis of aliphatic acids in the Kolbe synthesis. In the electrolysis of sodium acetate in water or methanol, the main products of the reaction are ethane and carbon dioxide accompanied by light emission at the anode. Similar results were observed for propionate, citrate, and tartrate salts. In addition, Ahnstrom studied the electrolysis of tyrosine and phenylalanine, although his observations indicated that different mechanisms probably are operative in the case of the amino acids.

Electrolysis of a 1 M sodium acetate solution gave light emission at the anode, having a wavelength maximum in the vicinity of 450 nm. When methanol was used as a solvent, the emission maximum shifted to ca. 500 nm and at pH 14 the maximum appeared to shift even further to approximately 550 nm. The rise and decay of light emission with applied voltage is very rapid; the light emission following the current at least into the millisecond region. When chloride or bromide ions were added, an increase in light intensity was observed. Paramagnetic ions such as copper(II), cobalt(II), iron(II), and iron(III) showed little effect on the intensity of light emission, as did temperature. The addition of radical scavengers was found to completely quench the light emission. In all the experiments with 1 M sodium acetate, the voltage applied to the electrode was not given, but the current flow was in the vicinity of ca. 100 mA.

Electrolysis of ca. 10^{-3} M tyrosine and phenylalanine solutions in 0.2 M sodium sulfate showed light emission having a wavelength maximum at approximately 480 nm. In the case of the amino acids, the light intensity did not follow the applied voltage. After electrolysis was begun approximately 30 sec were required to reach the maximum light intensity. When the current flow was stopped, the half-life of light decay was approximately 1 sec. When electrolysis was started again for the second time, the rise time of light emission was approximately 1 sec instead of longer as before. The form of the intensity time relationship observed was temperature dependent. Also, on prolonged electrolysis, a new, long-lived (ca. 10 sec) light emission appeared. In the case of the long-lived emission in phenylalanine, bromide and chloride showed no effect on its intensity, while the aforementioned paramagnetic ions quenched the long-lived emission.

Several things are apparent from the observations of Ahnstrom reported above [46]. First, light emission from the Kolbe reaction of the aliphatic acid salts must be related to the free-radical reactions known to occur in these salts. Second, since none of the major products of the Kolbe electrolysis is capable of light emission, the light-emitting reaction must be attributable to a side product or a product of a partially unsaturated radical derived from one of the main radicals in the reaction. The rapid kinetics indicate that a possibility would be for light emission to occur from a radical recombination reaction which is also consistent with the observed effect of radical scavengers. The nature of the light-emitting species is only a matter of conjecture until emission spectra can be obtained and the emitter positively identified. The situation seems quite analogous to the chemiluminescence of Grignard reagents [43] in which virtually all of the light emission is observed from a minor product of the reaction. Third, the spectral shifts reported cannot be regarded as significant because the spectra were obtained from concentrated solutions. Again, in the case of Grignard reagents, it was shown that high concentrations of starting materials severely distorted the emission because of self-absorption [43]. Fourth, because of the effect of metal ions, the emission observed in the case of the amino acids may involve decomposition of peroxide intermediates, but this is probably not the case in the simple aliphatic acids, again because of a lack of metal ion catalysis.

4 ELECTROLUMINESCENCE IN SOLUTION: RADICAL ION REACTIONS

Introduction

Historical Perspective

As is often the case in scientific research, the same idea occurs to several investigators at the same time. Such was the case for EL from reactions involving radical ions of aromatic hydrocarbons, four investigators performing similar experiments at about the same time. Three of these groups eventually published their findings within 6 months of each other, the group at Bell Laboratories [48], the University of Texas [52], and our experiments [47], with the Bell Laboratories' group being significantly influenced by the earlier experiments of Hoytink which were never published. It is of interest to summarize some of these earlier experiments at this point.

Professor G. J. Hoytink began studies involving the generation of light by cation-anion annihilation reactions of anthracene in 1960. After several years of experimentation the results were still very doubtful and the results were never published. While visiting Bell Telephone Laboratories, he encouraged Dr. E. A. Chandross to perform similar investigations.

Dr. Chandross had been attempting to generate light from cation-anion reactions by chemically preparing the radicals of 9,10-diphenylanthracene. The cation of 9,10-diphenylanthracene was found to be unstable, but a variety of chemiluminescent reactions was produced by the reaction of the radical anion with reagents such as peroxides or reduced 9,10-dichloroanthracene. Along with Dr. R. E. Visco, he began to study the possibility of electrochemically generating the radical ions, a technique that lead to bright EL and their initial publication [48].

In late 1961 Professor A. J. Bard and a student observed light during studies on the electroreduction on benzyldimethylanilinium bromide. They later noticed chemiluminescence during preliminary studies on the electrochemistry of stilbene in 1962. These observations were incidental to the main course of their study and were not pursued further. Their interest was revived by the appearance of our communication in *Science* [47], and Professor Bard and Dr. Santhanam began conducting experiments which were ultimately published [52].

Our experiments began as a collaboration between Dr. J. P. Paris and myself, in the summer of 1962, in which we attempted to generate light by reaction of chemically produced cation and anion radicals of anthracene. Similar to Hoytink's experiments, these were largely unsuccessful. My interest in this field was renewed early in 1964 when the possibility occurred to me of generating both ions by alternate electrolysis at an electrode surface. Experiments were conducted early in 1964 which ultimately lead to the first communication from our group [47].

The present section summarizes most published research in the area of organic EL from radical ion reactions from 1964 through 1968.

General Description

EL produced by electrochemically generated radical ions in solution is also a form of chemiluminescence. ECL is produced by alternate electrochemical generation of reactive species at an electrode in a solution containing an organic compound with a supporting electrolyte. For example, a widely used system is a solution of the hydrocarbon rubrene in benzonitrile containing tetra-n-butylammonium perchlorate as supporting electrolyte.

In many systems the light emitted in the ECL reaction is identical to the fluorescence of the electroactive organic compound [47, 48], although this is not always the case, differences having been reported [49, 50]. In many systems, ECL results from an annihilation reaction between aromatic radical cations and anions ($A^{.+}$ and $A^{.-}$, respectively) although other light-producing reactions can occur. For example, A^+ can react with other electron donors [51], A^- with other oxidizing agents [48], and light-producing reactions can occur with the anodic dissolution of mercury in the presence of $A^{.-}$ [52]. There is little doubt that aromatic radical ions are involved, their color having been observed visually and their presence detected by electron spin resonance. ECL is not the only process in which recombination luminescence is observed from radical ions; the thermoluminescence of gamma-irradiated organic glasses has been shown to result from a radical ion annihilation reaction [53].

The earliest studies of ECL reported a number of qualitative observations which will be summarized here in order to contrast ECL with other EL processes [41, 48, 52]. The early work was done on aromatic hydrocarbons, but other compounds have been observed to show ECL; in general, the processes are similar. The light emission was observed to occur in solution, not at the electrode surface; in some cases it could be seen streaming away from the electrode. Also, it was established that ECL definitely results from an electrochemically produced species of the aromatic compound rather than from simple solvent reactions. ECL can be produced both by ac and dc electrolysis. By using two electrodes in the dc mode such that positive radicals are generated at one and negative radicals at the other, light emission can be observed to occur between them when the radicals are mixed either by diffusion or by convection. In the ac mode light production is independent of the waveform, triangular, square, and sine waves having been used. The light intensity–time relationship does not parallel the waveform of the exciting voltage. In ac cells frequencies into the kilocycle region have been possible. The frequency of the light is twice that of the frequency of the exciting waveform, with the peaks observed on each half-cycle not necessarily being equally intense. Oxygen must be excluded from cells in order to observe ECL.

Although the above discussion stresses the similarities of ECL processes among different compounds a great many complications exist in specific

Table 13.2 Summary of Processes Contributing to ECL*

(1)	$A + e^- \longrightarrow A^-$	One-electron reduction of A at the electrode surface to produce the radical anion
(2)	$A \longrightarrow A^+ + e^-$	One-electron oxidation of A at the electrode surface to produce the radical cation
(3)	$A^+ + A^- \xrightarrow{k_3} {}^1A^* + A$	Annihilation reaction between the radical anion and cation to generate an excited singlet state
(4)	${}^1A^* \xrightarrow{k_4} A + h\nu_f$	Fluorescence of aromatic hydrocarbon
(5)	$A^+ + A^- \xrightarrow{k_5} {}^3A + A$	Annihilation reaction of cation and anion radicals to generate a triplet state
(6)	${}^3A + A^3 \xrightarrow{k_6} {}^1A^* + A$	Triplet-triplet annihilation to produce an excited singlet state
(7)	$A^+ + X \longrightarrow {}^3A + P$	Reaction of a cation radical with some electron donor to form a triplet state of an aromatic hydrocarbon. The form of the donor may vary considerably and a triplet rather than a singlet is the product based on energy considerations
(8)	$A^- + Y \longrightarrow {}^3A + P$	Reaction of anion radical with an electron acceptor to form a triplet state
(9)	$A^+ + A^- \xrightarrow{k_6} {}^1A_2^*$	An annihilation reaction between cation and anion radicals to form an excimer
(10)	${}^1A_2^* \xrightarrow{k_{10}} 2A + h\nu_e$	Excimer fluorescence of the aromatic molecule

* A is a typical aromatic compound.

cases, some of which are discussed in detail. It is of value at this point to summarize the various processes that contribute to ECL. The mechanisms considered to date can readily be divided into four classes [54]:

1. *Direct formation of the emitting species.* This can be a reaction of aromatic radical ions to form either an excited singlet state directly or an excimer.

2. *Radical ion reaction to form a triplet.* If the initial annihilation reaction forms a triplet rather than a singlet, two triplets can come together in a triplet-triplet annihilation reaction to give an excited singlet or an excimer which can then emit.

3. *Heterogeneous production of triplets.* The production of direct generation of triplets at an electrode surface has been suggested as a possible mechanism for ECL. This could occur either by oxidation of $A\cdot^-$ or the reduction of $A\cdot^+$ under conditions of polarization.

4. *Reaction of radical ions with some other species.* Impurities, solvents, water, solvent decomposition products, and so on have been shown to result in light emission when reacting with radical ions.

Considering for the moment only those processes that occur in homogeneous solution (i.e., not considering process 3), Table 13.2 presents a summary of the chemical reactions that are either known or postulated to contribute to ECL.

Experimental Aspects of ECL

Apparatus

Figure 13.6 shows a block diagram of a typical apparatus used for studying ECL. It consists of two parts, the electrochemical part, located on the left of the figure, and the photoelectric part on the right. The cell contains a conventional three-electrode system used for cyclic voltammetry. The indicator electrode, where the light is generated, usually is located as near to the photodetector as possible. The counter electrode is usually isolated optically and chemically from the cell so that electrode processes occurring at this electrode do not contaminate the bulk of the solution and affect the light emission characteristics. The potentiostat imposes a potential on the indicator electrode relative to the reference electrode by varying the potential at the counter electrode to compensate for the *IR* drop of the solution. Potentiostatic control is particularly important in ECL studies since they are traditionally carried out in organic solvents where the *IR* drop is high. A reference electrode for use in ECL has been described [55]. A function generator is used to supply the desired waveform to the potentiostat. Usually an $X - Y$ recorder or an oscilloscope records the current-voltage curve. A typical current-voltage curve for compounds studied in ECL is that for rubrene shown in Fig. 13.7.

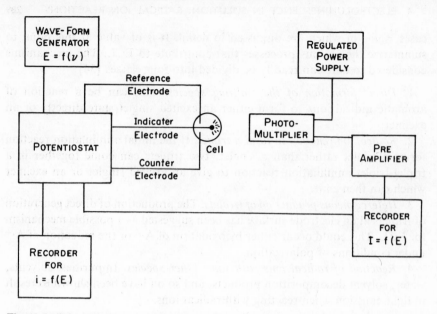

Fig. 13.6 Schematic diagram of apparatus used to study electrochemically generated ECL.

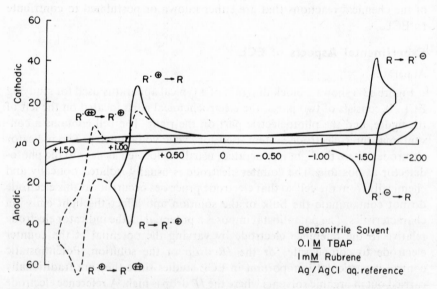

Fig. 13.7 Current-voltage curve for rubrene in benzonitrile versus Ag/AgCl reference. Concentration, $1.00 \times 10^{-3} M$; supporting electrolysis, $0.1 M$ tetrabutyl ammonium perchlorate; residual current shown for identical conditions.

The light emitted from the indicator electrode is picked up by the photo-multiplier, amplified, and recorded. Usually the voltage of the potentiostat defines the axes of both the current and light intensity recorders so that on successive sweeps current and light intensity can be recorded simultaneously. A typical light intensity–time curve for rubrene is shown in Fig. 13.8 along with the waveform of the applied voltage.

Although a more detailed discussion of the electrochemistry relevant to ECL is given later, it is instructive at this point to look at the current-voltage and light intensity–voltage curves shown in Fig. 13.7 and 13.8. The current-voltage curve of Fig. 13.7. follows the usual polarographic convention with cathodic (reductive) processes shown to the right of zero and anodic (oxidative) processes shown to the left. Cathodic current is positive and anodic negative. The current-voltage curve has the form shown only if both

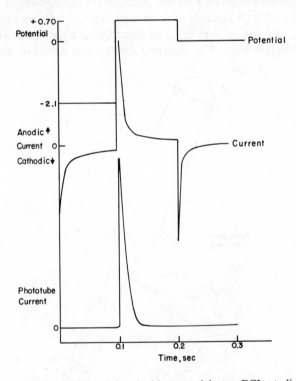

Fig. 13.8 Typical curves obtained for double potential step ECL studies on rubrene. Solvent, benzonitrile; supporting electrolyte, 0.34 M TBAP; rubrene, 9.1 × 10^{-4} M; electrode area, 0.085 cm^{-2}; reference electrode, Ag^+ (0.01 M)/Ag; potential, applied waveform; current, current observed in electrochemical cell; phototube current, light intensity. Data obtained using an apparatus similar to that outlined in Fig. 13.6, and a cell similar to that shown in Fig. 13.9. (Data obtained by Professor D. K. Roe.)

the radical anions and radical cations are stable during the time domain of the sweep. For example, where the rubrene cation is unstable, the cathodic peak at ca. +0.7 V is not be observed. Figure 13.8 shows the voltage, current, and light intensity versus time curves for a single square wave pulse applied to a rubrene solution. Voltage was first applied at −2.1 V for 0.1 sec, then switched to +0.70 V for 0.1 sec, and returned to 0.0 V. ECL emission was observed at 0.1 sec as indicated by the phototube current, which parallels the anodic current pulse in the solution. If repeated square wave pulses were applied between the limits of −2.1 and +0.7 V, a light emission would be observed on each half-cycle. Greater details concerning the practice of the electrochemistry of hydrocarbons can be obtained from Ref. 56 and references therein.

A variety of cells have been employed in ECL studies. Figure 13.9 shows a typical cell used in our laboratories. A complete description of the cell has been provided [57]. It consists of a piece of 2-cm o.d. Pyrex tubing with an optically flat window at one end and joined to a Pyrex bulb and a female 12/30 ground-glass joint. The indicator electrode is a ball of platinum wire

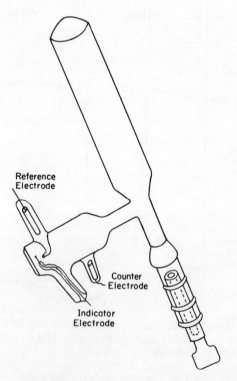

Fig. 13.9   A typical cell used for ECL studies [57].

approximately 0.5 cm behind the window. The indicator electrode is glass coated except for the very tip where it is flattened into a plate. The reference electrode is contained in another arm near the indicator electrode. Perpendicular to these and set back from the window about 2.5 cm is a third arm containing the counter electrode which is a platinum cylinder of large area compared to the indicator electrode. When measurements were being taken, the arms containing the counter electrode and indicator electrodes were usually down. The approximate oxygen content of the cell can be determined by current-voltage measurements. A circular electrode in this cell behaves essentially as a point source of light and with rubrene is sufficiently bright that light from the electrode can be clearly seen in a normally lighted room.

Several cells have been described for use in obtaining ECL spectra. Two platinum helices located in the plane of the spectrometer slit have been used [58, 59]. Another cell has been constructed from a tin oxide-coated glass electrode and a spectrophotometer cell [51]. This cell also features connection to the reference electrode with a salt bridge and an isolated counter electrode. The cell was constructed from a 1-cm² fluorescence cell by cutting off oner face and replacing it with a piece of tin oxide glass, using a silicone rubber gasket. Most of the tin oxide was removed from the glass except for a vertical strip 40 × 1 mm. Another interesting innovation in spectral cells has been the use of a rotating ring disk electrode [60]. Light emitted at the ring disk electrode is reflected into the spectrometer through a totally reflecting prism. This electrode provides for the simultaneous generation of anionic and cationic species and is particularly convenient because it produces a steady-state emission rather than the pulse emission from the other cells. Also, charging currents are negligible and one can employ a larger electrode area resulting in more intense ECL. One way of obtaining ECL spectra to enhance considerably the signal-to-noise ratio has been described [55]. The photomultiplier current is electronically integrated with an operational amplifier and recorded. The procedure used was to set the wavelength and potentiostatically produce the reactants during equal and consecutive time periods so that the time integral of the phototube current was proportional to the energy at the selected wavelength.

Several cells have been described for use in quantum yield studies. The cell shown in Fig. 13.9 has been used in our laboratory to measure the efficiency of ECL [57]. Also, several cells have been described for use in an integrating sphere [61]. In addition to the specialized cells discussed above, a number of cells for general ECL use have been described by Zweig et al. [62, 63] and by Bard et al. [59]. Usually the electrode material for ECL cells has been platinum, although mercury drops, mercury pools, and gold solid electrodes have been used.

Solvents and Supporting Electrolytes

No ideal solvent seems to exist for E3L work. In the earlier work both DMF and acetonitrile were used [47, 48, 52], and DMF still appears to be the most popular solvent. Recently, benzonitrile has been used as a solvent [54, 55] and for most ECL studies appears to be preferable to either DMF or acetonitrile. Studies in other solvents have been reported by the Bell Laboratories group such as N-methylpyrrolidone, acetone, and glyme [48]. The American Cyanimid group has also studied ECL and other solvents such as dimethyl sulfite, propylene carbonate, 1,2-dimethoxyethane, and trimethylacetonitrile [62].

The ideal solvent for ECL should fulfill a number of criteria. First, it should have about a 5-V spread between the solvent oxidation and reduction waves, preferably ± 2.5 V on either side of zero versus SCE. Second, the solvent should be unreactive with the radical anion or radical cation and should exhibit infinite solubility to all organic compounds that electrochemiluminesce. Third, it should be easy to dry and easy to purify or preferably come infinitely pure. Of the two more widely used solvents, acetonitrile usually provides problems because of its poor solubility for many of the high-molecular-weight aromatic hydrocarbons studied, as well as its ease of contamination by small amounts of water. DMF usually shows a greater solubility than acetonitrile but is less ideal because of trace impurities which are very difficult to remove, as well as contamination by water. Benzonitrile seems to combine the better qualities of both and is for most ECL studies the recommended solvent. An interesting point relating to solvents is that the practical anodic and cathodic limits in ECl appear to be set by the water content of the solvent rather than by the decomposition of the solvent or the electrolyte itself.

Electrolytes for ECL are not quite as difficult to come by. Generally, the alkylammonium perchlorates are very good. Difficulties that can arise because of solvent effects are illustrated in Fig. 13.10. This shows the effect of repetitively scanning into the positive potential region for rubrene in DMF. The upper curves are plots of light intensity on successive scans and the lower are current voltage curves; the successive scans are numbered 1, 2, 3, and so on [51]. When scanning over the potential range 0 to $+1.5$ V after four successive scans, no light emission could be observed on subsequent scans. As the potential scan range was decreased, the light emission behavior depended less on the number of previous scans until when scanning over the potential range 0 to $+0.95$ V the light intensity–voltage curves of successive scans were virtually superimposable. This behavior relates to the partial superimposition of the DMF oxidation wave and the oxidation wave of rubrene. At positive potentials, ca. 1.5 V, significant solvent oxidation accompanies oxidation of

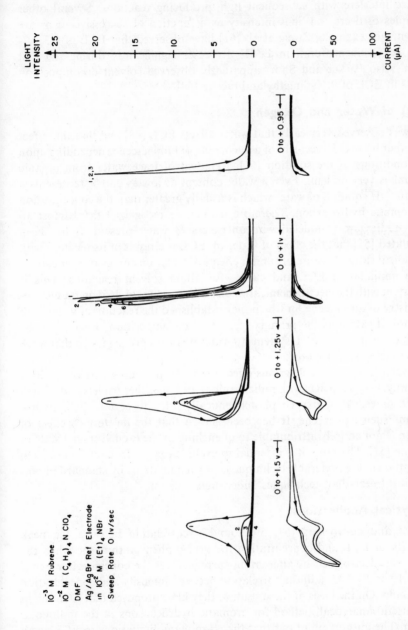

Fig. 13.10 Effect of subsequent scanrates on the intensity-potential curves for rubrene [51].

10^{-3} M Rubrene
10^{-2} M $(C_4H_9)_4$ N ClO_4
DMF
Ag / AgBr Ref Electrode
in 10^{-2} M $(Et)_4$ NBr
Sweep Rate 0 Iv/sec

LIGHT INTENSITY

CURRENT (μA)

0 to + 0.95

0 to + Iv

0 to + 1.25v

0 to + 1.5 v

the hydrocarbon, and products of solvent oxidation produced at the electrode surface interfere with subsequent light-producing reactions. Several other examples of decreased light intensity as a function of successive scans are known. For example, Zweig et al. [61] have observed that ECL of 1,3,4,7-tetraphenylisobenzofuran in DMF decreases significantly during the first 4 min. Also Parker and Short apparently observed solvent decomposition effects in ECL of 9,10-dimethylanthracene [64].

Effect of Water and Oxygen

It was observed very early that water affects ECL [48] and that this effect can either be an enhancement or a quenching of luminescence depending upon the conditions of the solution [51]. Removal of trace water from organic solvents is very difficult. Even a water content as low as 0.01 % represents a 5×10^{-3} M solution of water which is usually greater than the concentration of aromatic hydrocarbon. Therefore it must be recognized that almost all ECL studies are conducted with an excess of water present. It has been postulated [51] that the effect of water on ECL is a result of its reaction with the radical cation because of similar effects of water on curves run for cation-anion annihilation ECL and curves for anion solvent reactions. This is consistent with the electrochemical studies of Majeski et al. [65] on the electro-chemistry of anthracene, in which they established the reaction of water with the radical cation as the primary step in its decomposition. Because of the extreme sensitivity of ECL systems to water it is strongly suggested that work be conducted in a dry box.

Oxygen has a very deleterious effect on ECL, providing sort of a triplet whammy. Oxygen reacts with radical anions and quenches triplets and excited singlet states. Also, oxygen photochemically adds to certain ECL hydro-carbons such as rubrene. It has been shown that the deleterious effect of oxygen is not entirely attributable to quenching of the excited singlet state of rubrene [51]. Therefore it is essential to exclude oxygen from all solutions in ECL studies; the preferable technique is to vacuum degas by standard photo-chemical freeze-thaw techniques under high vacuum.

Analytical Applications

Bard and co-workers [58, 59] found a correlation between the peak intensity of ECL and concentration for 9,10-diphenylanthracene when the latter was electrolyzed by alternating current. Over the concentration range 0.2 to 10 $\times$ 10^{-3} M, a linear correlation between intensity and concentration was found. On the basis of these studies, they have proposed that ECL might be a useful analytical method for aromatic hydrocarbons in the millimolar region. The authors point out that there are many limitations to ECL as an analytical technique, such as the nonlinear effect of mixtures, the variable effect of quenchers and impurities, and the fairly specific nature of the phenomenon.

Fleet et al. [66] also have investigated the use of ECL for the detection and determination of aromatic hydrocarbons. ECL was generated in a cell having an electrode of platinum wire coiled around a straight platinum wire and an ac voltage of 3 V applied. They compared ECL and fluorescence spectra for 9-phenylanthracene, coronene, rubrene, purene, and anthracene, and in all cases except rubrene the spectra did not match. Log-log plots of emission intensity versus concentration gave linear calibration curves for anthracene, 9-phenylanthracene, pyrene, and coronene.

It is possible that ECL could have advantages as an analytical technique over conventional spectrofluorometry in that small amounts of a fluorescent aromatic hydrocarbon might be excited in the presence of large amounts of another, even though by photoexcitation it would not be possible to excite one selectively. Under current conditions of development, ECL appears to be less sensitive than spectrofluorometry by several orders of magnitude, although a new electrode used by Fleet et al. [66] allowed them to record data and spectra for solutions ca. 10^{-7} to 10^{-5} M. ECL as an analytical method lacks the precision of spectrophotometry or gas chromatography or simply cyclic voltammetry. It seems as though ECL combines the disadvantages of both optical and electrochemical methods.

ECL of Organic Compounds

Criteria for ECL

The most probable mechanism for ECL involves electrochemical production of a radical or radicals, reaction of these radicals to give an excited state, and light emission from an excited state which may or may not be the one originally produced. Such a mechanism imposes certain limitations on the types of organic compounds and reactions which give rise to ECL. Five of these limitations are summarized:

1. *Electrochemical.* The organic compound used for ECL must be electroactive and must have radical anions and/or radical cations generated within the anodic and cathodic limits of the solvent-electrolyte system used. For an annihilation reaction, it is necessary to have both the cation and anion radicals generated.

2. *Radical Stability.* For an annihilation reaction both R^+ and R^- should be stable during the time interval required for observation. This is one of the most serious limitations on organic compounds giving ECL, usually because of cation instability. Cation decomposition can result in some compounds not giving ECL, can cause unequal peaks on switching from anodic to cathodic versus cathodic to anodic, and can cause certain solvent effects in

which one solvent may react with the cation and another not. Also, decomposition products can give rise to light emission which does not match the fluorescence spectrum of the parent compound.

3. *Reaction Kinetics.* The chemical reaction giving rise to ECL must occur at a sufficiently rapid rate to give detectable light emission. To date this has not proved to be a serious limitation in ECL studies since most ECL results from electron transfer reactions that are characteristically rapid.

4. *Energetics.* If an excited state is to be produced from an ECL reaction, then the reaction must provide sufficient energy for formation of the excited state. In many annihilation reactions sufficient energy is barely available to produce an excited singlet state. Initial formation of a triplet state with an excited singlet state produced by triplet-triplet annihilation is a possible ECL mechanism.

5. *Emissive Excited State.* Since ECL ultimately results from an excited singlet state, fluorescence from this state is necessary for light emission. All other factors being equal, ECL intensity should be related to the fluorescence efficiency of the emitter. If a hydrocarbon does not show an intrinsically high quantum efficiency of fluorescence, then weak ECL emission would be anticipated.

Fortunately, substituent effects on each of the above requirements can usually be evaluated and thus one can qualitatively predict which factors will affect ECL intensity in any given system. The remainder of this section discusses pertinent electrochemical studies, the structural correlations that have been made for aromatic hydrocarbons, substituted aromatic hydrocarbons, and heterocyclic compounds.

Electrochemical Studies

Generally, electrochemical studies provide three kinds of information pertinent to ECL: They permit identification and study of cation and anion radicals, sometimes in conjunction with ESR studies; they permit determination of the stability of radical cations and anions in solution; and they give evidence about the reactivity of radicals and how this may affect ECL. Several selected electrochemical studies are summarized, mainly for aromatic hydrocarbons since these compounds have been described in greater detail. A general review of the electrochemistry of aromatic hydrocarbons has been given by Peover [56].

Many studies of the electrochemical generation of radical anions have been reported and are not dealt with here in detail. For hydrocarbons of interest in ECL studies, the radical anions are most often stable. Sioda and Koski first reported the electrochemical generation of the radical cation of 9,10-diphenylanthracene [67]. Malachesky et al. [68] have successfully generated radical cations for tetracene, perylene, pentacene, 9,10-diphenylanthracene,

9,10-dimethylanthracene, coronene, rubrene, and 1,3,6,8-tetraphenylpyrene. They used nitrobenzene as a solvent, containing 1 M methonesulfonic acid.

Although the reduction of aromatic hydrocarbons is generally a simple one-electron process, oxidation is usually more complicated, the complications often arising from radical cation reactivity with the solvent or trace impurities such as water. Peover and White have studied the electrochemical oxidation of several aromatic hydrocarbons of interest in acetonitrile [69]. Of those studied they found that only 9,10-diphenylanthracene gave two simple one-electron oxidation waves independent of the scan rate employed. No cathodic peak could be observed for 1,2-benzanthracene on return sweep at a sweep rate of 0.8 V/sec, but a cathodic peak was observed at a sweep rate of 40 V/sec. Anthracene, pyrene, chrysene, and phenanthrene showed poorly developed cathodic currents even at high sweep rates, indicating unstable cations. For the case of triphenylene, no cathodic portion of the oxidation wave could be observed even at the highest sweep rates used. Similar results were obtained by Phelps et al. [70], who studied the electrochemistry of various hydrocarbons in methylene chloride. They observed that the radical cations of 9,10-diphenylanthracene, rubrene, and 1,3,6,8-tetraphenylpyrene were stable, while those of naphthacene and anthracene were not.

Marcaux et al. [71] studied the one-electron oxidation of aromatic hydrocarbons in nitrobenzene and acetonitrile. They divided the compounds studied into two classes: class A compounds, exhibiting clear one-electron reversible oxidations leading to stable cations; class B compounds, exhibiting follow-up reactions so rapid and extensive that the net observable electrochemical process appeared to involve two or more electrons, in general leading to unidentified products. Members of class A were compounds such as 9,10-diphenylanthracene, perylene, rubrene, tetraphenylpyrene, 9,10-dimethylanthracene, and 5,10-dihydrodimethylphenazene. Class B compounds were anthracene, 9-methylanthracene, and naphthacene. They also observed that plots of $i_p V^{-1/2} C^{-1}$ against $V^{1/2}$ were horizontal lines over most of the region for class A compounds but were curved for class B compounds. They found the radical cation for 9,10-diphenylanthracene more stable than for 9,10-dimethylanthracene.

Majeski et al. [65] have carried out a detailed study of the controlled-potential oxidation of anthracene in acetonitrile, in which the radical cation has a lifetime of only a few milliseconds. After exhaustive electrolysis bianthrone was the major product, coulometric runs showing an average of two electrons lost per anthracene molecule. Also, 9-anthrone and anthraquinone were isolated. These authors postulated reaction of the radical cation with water to form 9-anthranol with subsequent oxidation to bianthrone. The reaction sequence shown in Fig. 13.11 is only a postulate since

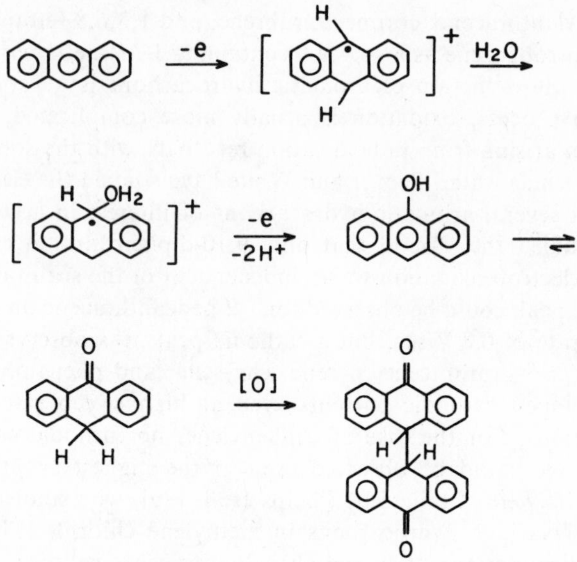

Fig. 13.11 Mechanism for production of compounds identified in the electroexcitation of anthracene [65].

it was found [65] that direct electrochemical oxidation of 9-anthrone to bianthrone in acetonitrile was not possible. It is probable that the sequence of reactions leading to bianthrone is oxidation of the hydrocarbon, hydrolysis, deprotonation, tautomerization, and chemical oxidation of 9-anthrone. If a second hydrolysis were to occur before dimerization of 9-anthrone, 9,10-dihydroxyanthracene would be produced which is easily oxidized to anthra-quinone, possibly accounting for the anthraquinone observed in the electrolyzed solution.

Sioda has carried out an extensive study on the electrochemical oxidation of 9,10-diphenylanthracene and the properties of the 9,10-diphenylanthracene radical cation [72]. He reconfirmed earlier findings that the first step is a reversible one-electron oxidation followed by an irreversible oxidation to the dication. Sioda has also reported the visible solution spectrum for 9,10-diphenylanthracene radical cation. Under anhydrous conditions, he found the radical cation to be stable in acetonitrile, even in air, a half-life of approximately 50 min being reported.

Sioda found that 9,10-diphenylanthracene cation easily underwent addition reactions, water being the most extensively studied reagent. The most probable equation for the reaction with water is:

$$2DPA^+ + 2H_2O \rightarrow +DPA + DPA(OH)_2 + 2H^+\cdot . \qquad (13.17)$$

Attachment of the hydroxyl groups takes place at the 9- and 10-positions. Sioda actually isolated *trans*-9,10-dihydroxy-9,10-dihydro-9,10-diphenyl-anthracene [DPA(OH)$_2$] as a product of the reaction with water. The kinetics of the reaction were first order in respect to both 9,10-DPA$^+$ and water. The small rate of decomposition, even in the presence of no added water, was probably caused by the small amount of water present in most acetonitrile. This correlates well with other findings that the lifetime of radical cations is generally limited by the water content of organic solvents.

A number of other reactions which were investigated have relevance to ECL studies. 9,10-DPA$^+$ was found to react with alcohols and phenols, probably according to the equation:

$$2DPA^+ + 2ROH \rightarrow DPA + DPA(OR)_2 + 2H^+ \qquad (13.18)$$

Although secondary and primary alcohols did react, no diether was found in the presence of *tert*-butyl alcohol. 9,10-DPA$^+$ was found to react with DMF, amines, and ammonia, although the nature of the reaction and the final products was not studied. This also correlates with earlier studies relating to ECL of radical cations by reaction with amine derivatives [51]. Sioda also carried out qualitative chemiluminescence studies with the radical cation in acetonitrile, using reactions with amines, ammonium salts, amides, and sodium salts. Again, these studies confirmed those of earlier workers [5].

ECL of Aromatic Hydrocarbons

The aromatic hydrocarbons for which ECL has been observed are listed in Table 13.3 along with available electrochemical data, fluorescence and ECL maxima, and fluorescence efficiencies. Structures of selected compounds from Table 13.3 are shown in Fig. 13.12. The correlation between the ECL spectrum and the fluorescence spectrum varies from one hydrocarbon to another. For example, a good match is observed in the case of naphthacene, rubrene, 9,10-diphenylanthracene, 1,4,5,8-tetraphenylnaphthylene, 1-phenyl-4(9-anthracenyl)1,3-butadiene; while with other compounds such as anthracene, phenanthrene, *trans*-stilbene, 1,2-benzanthracene and bifluorenyl, spurious bands are observed. Rubrene has probably been the most extensively studied aromatic hydrocarbon and appears to be ideal in many respects, having stable radical anions and cations and showing a high fluorescence efficiency. The rubrene cation is unstable in DMF, exhaustive electrolysis showing the presence of pseudo-rubrene [62]. 1,4,5,8-Tetraphenylnaphthalene has been reported to be a good ECL compound, rivaling rubrene in intensity. Apparently none of the hydrocarbons can match the ECL intensity of 1,3,4,7-tetraphenylisobenzofuran [62].

In many aromatic hydrocarbon systems, ECL results from the anion-cation annihilation reaction:

$$R^{\cdot+} + R^{\cdot-} \rightarrow {}^1R^* + R$$

Table 13.3 ECL of Aromatic Hydrocarbons

Compound	$E_{1/2}$(Ox) A → A⁺	$E_{1/2}$(Red) A → A⁻	Emission Maxima (mμ)		Fluorescence Efficiency	References
			Fluorescence	ECL		
Anthracene	+1.29	−1.95	412	412, 455 569	0.36	[47, 48, 49] [56, 59, 106] [109]
Chrysene	+1.59	−2.32	361	—	0.14	[47, 56, 106] [107]
Pyrene	+1.42	−2.08	374	—	0.32	[47, 49, 56] [74, 106, 109]
Naphthacene (tetracene)	+0.83	−1.55	520	520	0.21	[47, 49, 59] [61, 101] [106, 109]
Perylene (I)	+1.01	−1.80	442	—	0.14	[47, 48, 49] [51, 56] [106, 109]
Coronene	+1.23	−2.05	—	—	—	[47, 107, 108]
Rubrene (II)	+0.88	−1.47	560	560	—	[47, 48, 49] [51, 54, 55] [59, 73]

Compound						References
Decacyclene	+1.00	−1.49	—	—	—	[47, 107]
1,2,5,6 Dibenzanthracene		−2.04	—	—	—	[47, 107]
9,10 Diphenylanthracene (III)	+1.32	−1.72	440	440	1.0	[108, 109] [48, 49, 51] [52, 58, 59]
Quaterphenyl		−2.28	—	—	0.89	[106]
1,1,4,4 Tetraphenyl-butadiene		—	—	—	—	[48, 106, 107] [48]
9,10-Dimethylanthracene	+1.16	−1.82	—	—	—	[49, 64]
Phenanthrene	+1.75	−2.47	412	412, 516	—	[49, 50, 56] [59, 109]
Benzo[a]pyrene	+0.76	−1.84	—	—	—	[49, 107, 108] [109]
3,5,8,10-Tetraphenylpyrene		—	—	—	—	[51]
1,4,5,8 Tetraphenyl naphthalene	+1.39	−1.98	440	440	—	[62, 74]
1-Phenyl-4-(9-anthracenyl)-1,3-butadiene	+0.98	−1.73	538, 398	538, 506	0.23	[62]
trans-Stilbene		−2.22	—	—	—	[56, 59]
1,2 Benzanthracene	+1.39	−2.00	408, 420	420, 538	—	[56, 59]
Bifluorenyl		—	384	526	—	[107]

However, hydrocarbon radicals have been observed to react with other species to produce light. The most widely studied of these latter reactions involve the radical cation, but some have also been observed for the radical anion. For example, the rubrene radical cation was observed to react with DMF, triethylamine, N-butylamine, and water in acetonitrile. The relative intensity of ECL emission was from 10 to 10^3 lower than the intensity from the annihilation reaction. The same spectrum was observed for the annihilation reaction as for the reaction with other donors. ECL has been observed for the reaction of rubrene radicals with other radical ions and the rubrene radical anion with radical cations such as that derived from N,N,N',N'-tetramethyl-p-phenylenediamine. The rubrene radical cation gives ECL with the semiquinone of benzoquinone, p-benzoquinone, naphthoquinone, and anthraquinone [55]. In addition to the normal fluorescence spectrum produced by hydrocarbon ECL reactions, other spectra has been observed. It has been postulated that excimer emission occurs for some compounds, although some of the long wavelength emission originally attributed to excimer formation probably results from radical cation decomposition products [49, 64]. An interesting and unusual type of ECL has been reported and has been termed preannihilation luminescence. This type of luminescence occurs in potential regions where the radical ion annihilation reaction cannot occur [73]. Preannihilation ECL is usually 10 to 100 times less intense than annihilation ECL. A detailed discussion of both excimer and preannihilation luminescence is given later.

The correlation between ECL and structure of the aromatic hydrocarbons relates to the stability of the radical cation. A comparison of ECL for unsubstituted ring systems with those having phenyl or methyl groups blocking the reactive position indicates that ECL for the latter type compound is usually much more intense. For example, the 9,10-disubstituted anthracenes have more intense ECL than 9-substituted anthracenes, which in turn have greater ECL than anthracene itself; rubrene ECL is more intense than that of naphthacene. It is interesting to note that the 1,4-diaryl,1,3-butadienes, although efficient fluorescers, are poor ECL compounds because of radical instability. Generally, there is poor correlation between ECL intensity and quantum efficiency of fluorescence, implying again that the radical cation stability is the dominating factor. Upon repeated electrolysis however, even "stable" systems can give rise to spurious luminescence.

Substituted Aromatic Hydrocarbons

The only systematic study reported to date on the effect of aromatic substitution on ECL is that of Zweig et al [74], who studied donor-substituted polycyclic aromatic hydrocarbons. As might be expected, substituents influence ECL as they influence the properties of moleucles important in the

ECL process such as radical stability, fluorescence efficiency, solubility, photochemical stability, and so on. The donor-substituted aromatic hydrocarbons studied to date are listed in Table 13.4, with two characteristic structures shown in Fig. 13.12. Generally, the wavelengths of fluorescence and ECL matched when both R+ and R− were stable. The factors relating to the effect of substitution on ECL stability that were most extensively studied were radical stability and redox potentials.

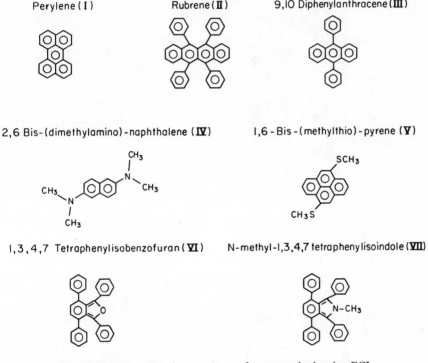

Perylene (I)

Rubrene (II)

9,10 Diphenylanthracene (III)

2,6 Bis-(dimethylamino)-naphthalene (IV)

1,6-Bis-(methylthio)-pyrene (V)

1,3,4,7 Tetraphenylisobenzofuran (VI)

N-methyl-1,3,4,7 tetraphenylisoindole (VII)

Fig. 13.12 Representative structures of compounds showing ECL.

In many of the compounds studied, radical anion stability was not a problem, whereas radical cation stability was a severe problem and therefore those substituents that improve cation stability also improve ECL. Generally, electron donor substituents improve radical cation stability, the specific effect of the substituent depending upon the position and number of groups on the aromatic nucleus [74]. One cannot be certain that radical stability will always be enhanced by electron donor substituents, for these may be compensated by negative effects on fluorescence efficiency, radical anion stability, and so on. The fact that IV is more stable than its isomers stresses

Table 13.4 ECL of Substituted Aromatic Hydrocarbons [74]

Compound	$E_{1/2}$(Ox)	$E_{1/2}$(Red)	Radical Stability (sec)		Emission Maximum (mμ)		Fluorescence Efficiency
			Cation	Anion	ECL	Fluorescence	
1,4 Dimethoxynaphthalene	+1.10	−2.69	0.2	0.01	560	460	0.57
9-Methoxyanthracene	+1.05	−1.92	0.01	15	—	420	—
9,10 Dimethoxyanthracene	+0.98	−1.90	0.01	15	—	435	—
9,10-Bis(2,6-dimethoxyphenyl)anthracene	+1.18	−2.08	15	15	425	425	0.78
1-Dimethylaminonaphthalene	+0.75	−2.58	—	10	465	435	—
2-Dimethylaminonaphthalene	+0.67	−2.63	0.09	15	—	415	—
2,6-Bis(dimethylamino)naphthalene (IV)	+0.26	−2.71	15	5	450–455	450–455	0.48
2,7-Bis(dimethylamino)naphthalene	+0.57	−2.77	0.01	15	—	400–425	—
N,N'tetramethylbenzidine	+0.43	Not Red	15	—	403	—	—
1,6-Bis(dimethylamino)pyrene	+0.49	−2.16	15	3	545	453	0.60
1,6-Bis(methylthio)pyrene (V)	+0.96	−1.83	0.03	15	550	438	0.32

the importance of delocalization and coplanarity. A radical anion cleavage mechanism has been postulated for the relative instability of the radical anion of **IV** as compared to its isomer [74].

The effect of substituents on redox potentials for an aromatic system is also important in ECL. Donor substitution raises the energy of the highest filled molecular orbital, lowering the potential required for oxidation relative to the hydrocarbon. This can be seen by comparing Tables 13.3 and 13.4. As in radical cation stability, steric effects can be more important than resonance on the oxidation potential, for example, in the α-substituted dimethylaminonaphthalenes [74]. Generally, reduction potentials are less influenced by both the number and position of substituents. Because of the change in both oxidation and reduction potentials, the energy available from the annihilation reaction is smaller for substituted hydrocarbons than for the parent compounds. If the nature of the lowest excited state of a molecule changes with the introduction of electron donor groups, the change in the energy of the state may not be commensurate with the change in energy available from the reaction and the mechanism of ECL may be affected.

Heterocyclic Compounds

A number of heterocyclic compounds showing ECL have been studied, and these are listed in Table 13.5 along with several structures shown in Fig. 13.12. Most heterocycles show a good match between the fluorescence and ECL spectra, although some do not [59, 74, 75]. It has been reported that **VI** shows bright green ECL which is orders of magnitude brighter than ECL observed for aromatic hydrocarbons [62]. A number of other compounds listed in Table 13.4 electrochemiluminesce brightly, which establishes the isobenzofurans and N-alkylisoindoles as two general series of compounds showing ECL.

As for other compounds, radical stability is a key factor in ECL. A particularly interesting example involves the two isomers of the tetraaryliso-benzofurans. From the current-voltage curves [61], both 1,3,4,7- and 1,3,5,6-isobenzofurans show stable anion radicals, but the 1,3,4,7 isomer has a stable cation whereas the 1,3,5,6 isomer does not. The quantum yield of fluorescence for the 1,3,4,7 isomer is 0.5, while that for the 1,3,5,6 isomer is 0.84. Intense ECL emission is observed from the 1,3,4,7 isomer but virtually no ECL is observed from 1,3,5,6 isomer. The reason for the difference in stabilities of the radical cations is not readily apparent, although HMO calculations indicate that the 4- and 7-positions on the isobenzofuran nucleus should be reactive. Therefore it is likely that in the 1,3,4,7 isomer these two positions are blocked by the phenyl substituents and reactivity of the ring is significantly reduced.

Although most of the discussions of radical instability to date have involved

Table 13.5 ECL of Heterocyclic Compounds

Compound	$E_{1/2}$(Ox)	$E_{1/2}$(Red)	Emission Maximum Fluorescence and ECL (mμ)	Fluorescence Efficiency	Radical Lifetime (sec)		References
					Cation	Anion	
1,3,4,7-Tetraphenylisobenzofuran (VI)	+0.92	−1.96	530	0.50	1	>20	[61, 62, 75, 101]
1,3-Di-p-anisyl-4,7-diphenylisobenzofuran	+0.70	−2.06	568	0.53	0.6	>20	[61, 62 75]
1,3-Di-p-biphenyl-4,7-diphenyliso-benzofuran	+0.88	−1.84	540	0.47	5	>20	[62, 75]
1,3,4,7-Tetra-p-anisylisobenzofuran	+0.68	−2.15	547	0.49	0.5	>20	[62, 75]
1,3-Diphenyl-4,7-di-p-anisyliso-benzofuran	+0.85	−2.02	515	0.33	4	>20	[62, 75]
N-Methyl-1,3,4,7-tetraphenyl-isoindole (VII)	+0.66	−2.51	490	0.53	>20	2	[61, 62, 75, 101]

N-Methyl-1,3-di-p-anisyl-4,7-diphenylisoindole	+0.54	−2.60	507	0.52	>20	2	[61, 62, 75]
1,3-Di-p-methoxyphenyl-4,7-diphenylisobenzofuran	+0.84	−1.92	—	—	—	—	[101]
N-Methyl-1,3-di-p-methoxyphenyl-4,7-diphenylisoindole	+0.59	−2.42	—	—	—	—	[101]
1,3-Diphenylisobenzofuran	+0.73	−1.98	486	—	<0.1	>20	[62]
1,3,5,6-Tetraphenylisobenzofuran	+0.79	−1.85	492	0.84	<0.01	>20	[61, 62]
1,3,4,5,6,7-hexaphenylisobenzofuran	+0.89	−2.04	503	0.64	<0.01	>20	[62]
1,3,4-Triphenyl-7-(9-anthracenyl)isobenzofuran	+0.87	−1.92	530	0.23	1	>20	[62]
N-Methyl-1,3-diphenylisoindole	+0.63	−2.46	453	0.73	>20	<0.1	[62]
1,2,3-Triphenylisoindole	+0.70	−2.36	448	0.11	>20	<0.03	[62]
1,3,4,7-Tetraphenylisobenzothiophene	+1.0	−1.91	523	0.24	—	5	[62]
2,5-Diphenylfuran	+1.23	−2.51	385	—	0.03	0.5	[62]
2,5-Di-p-anisylfuran	+0.89	−2.60	—	0.38	0.2	0.5	[62]
Carbazole	—	−2.68	406/538	—	—	—	[59, 106]
Dibenzo[c, g]carbazole	—	—	440/530	—	—	—	[59]

unstable cation radicals, in the case of carbazole ECL is complicated by radical anion instabilities [59]. Radical ion stability has been reported to affect the lifetime of ECL [62], that is, how long significant light emission can be caused to occur from an ECL cell. In general, the N-methylisoindoles have more stable radical cations than the isobenzofurans. This is reflected in the fact that the N-methylindoles emitted light for 30 hr as opposed to 6.75 hr for the isobenzofurans.

Theoretical Aspects

Energy Requirements

For a radical ion reaction to produce ECL, sufficient energy must be liberated by the reaction to form an excited state of the emitter. Figure 13.13 shows

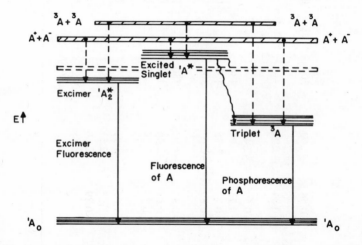

Fig. 13.13 Energy relationships for excimer formation and triplet-triplet annihilation for a typical aromatic hydrocarbon A. $^1A_0$, Ground state; A^+, radical cation; A^-, radical anion; ^3A, lowest triplet state; $^1A^*$, lowest excited singlet state; $^1A_2^*$, excimer.

the energetics of various processes for a typical aromatic hydrocarbon, A. The ground state, $^1A_0$, lowest excited singlet state, $^1A^*$, and lowest triplet state, ^3A, of the hydrocarbon are shown along with their superimposed vibrational levels. Fluorescence and phosphorescence transitions are indicated as solid arrows, while the wiggly arrow represents intersystem crossing. The energy level for the excimer, $^1A_2^*$, is also shown, the level of an excimer usually being about 6000 cm^{-1} below that of the lowest excited singlet state as indicated by Birks et al. [76]. Excimer fluorescence is also indicated by a solid arrow. The energy available from the radical ion reaction is shown by the longest horizontal hatched line labeled A$^+$ + A$^-$, assuming the energy is above the 0,0-band of the lowest excited singlet state. The dashed arrows from this line indicate that either the excited singlet, an excimer, or a triplet may be formed directly. The higher horizontal hatched line is the energy available from triplet-triplet annihilation from which any of the three states may also be formed. For all aromatic hydrocarbons with the possible exception of tetracene, the energy of triplet-triplet annihilation is greater than the excited singlet state.

The possibility exists that insufficient energy would be available from the radical ion annihilation reaction to form an excited singlet state directly. This is indicated by the horizontal dashed line in Fig. 13.13. In such a situation direct excited singlet state formation is not possible unless sufficient thermal energy is supplied to overcome the difference between the excited singlet state and the energy of the reaction. In such cases, however, sufficient energy is still available to form an excited singlet state by triplet-triplet annihilation.

The question of triplet-triplet annihilation versus direct singlet state formation as the major mechanism in ECL relates to the magnitude of the $T \Delta S$ correction applied to electrochemical data Hoytink [77] has indicated the magnitude of the $T \Delta S$ correction to be about 0.2 eV, although Chandross and Visco have indicated it is somewhat smaller for rubrene [54]. In order to make meaningful calculations, the magnitude of the $T \Delta S$ term must be known accurately for each system, but 0.2 eV seems like a reasonable value for most aromatic hydrocarbons. Table 13.6 summarizes the energetics for several of the brighter ECL compounds. Applying the 0.2 eV correction to the electrochemical data, sufficient energy is available for excited singlet state formation in the heterocyclic compounds but insufficient energy for the aromatic hydrocarbons reported; for 9,10-diphenylanthracene the correction is very small, however. In none of the cases is the deficit extreme, 0.27 V being the largest for 9,10-dimethylanthracene. Such an energy deficit does not prohibit ECL by direct formation of an excited singlet state but limits the maximum possible quantum efficiency and rate. For ECL to occur, the energy deficit has to be supplied by activation energy which will be reflected in a lower quantum efficiency and a slower reaction rate. At room temperature (300°K) kT is 0.026 eV, which limits the rate and quantum efficiency as shown in Table 13.6. It is interesting to note that the maximum quantum yield calculated on the basis of direct singlet state formation for rubrene is approximately equal to that measured [57]. The rate for the ruberne reaction predicted is approximately an order of magnitude greater than present experimental techniques can measure.

Kinetic Requirements

The question arises as to competition between excited state and ground state formation in a chemical reaction. In most cases the products are formed

Table 13.6 Energy and Kinetic Relationships in ECL

Compound	$(E_{1/2})_{Ox}$ Ar → Ar+	$(E_{1/2})_{Red}$ Ar → Ar−	ΔE*	ΔE_{corr}†	Energy of Lowest Excited Single State	Energy Deficit‡	ϕ_{max} at 25°C§	$k_{6(max)}$‖
Rubrene	+0.88	−1.47	2.35	2.15	2.30	−0.15	0.004	4×10^7
9,10-Diphenyl anthracene	+1.32	−1.72	3.04	2.84	2.85	−0.01	0.67	7×10^9
9,10-Dimethyl anthracene	+1.16	−1.82	2.98	2.78	3.05	−0.27	3×10^{-5}	3×10^5
Anthracene	+1.29	−1.95	3.24	3.04	3.29	−0.25	6×10^{-5}	6×10^5
1,3,4,7-Tetraphenyl isobenzofuran	+0.92	−1.96	2.88	2.68	2.51	+0.17	1.00	10^{10}
N-Methyl-1,3,4,7-tetraphenyl-isoindole	+0.66	−2.51	3.17	2.97	2.89	+0.08	1.00	10^{10}

* $\Delta E = (E_{1/2})_{Ox} - (E_{1/2})_{Red}$.

† $\Delta E_{corr} = \Delta E - T \Delta S$. In general, the $T \Delta S$ term has been estimated to be ca. 0.2 V.

‡ The energy deficit is the difference between ΔE_{corr} and the energy of the lowest excited singlet state.

§ This is an order-of-magnitude estimation, based on the assumption that activation energy is the only barrier to formation of a radiative singlet state.

‖ This assumes a purely diffusion-controlled reaction and would have a rate constant of 10^{10} M^{-1} sec^{-1}.

in electronic ground states, but if product excited state curves cross the ground state reaction coordinate then excited state formation is possible. Which state will be formed becomes a matter of competition between two different pathways. Several different relationships between reactant and product curves are shown in Fig. 13.14. It is evident from Fig. 13.14 that

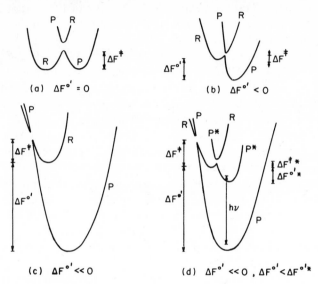

Fig. 13.14 Energetics of electron transfer reactions. Some nomenclature after Marcus [78]. *R*, reactant; *P*, product found in its ground state; *P**, product found in an excited state; *hv*, light emission corresponding to $P^* \to P$; $\Delta F^{0'}$, free energy change for $R \to P$; $\Delta F^{\ddagger}$, free energy activation for $R \to P$; $\Delta F^{0'*}$, free energy change for $R \to P^*$; $\Delta F^{\ddagger*}$, free energy activation for $R \to P^*$.

both the positioning of the potential surfaces describing the electron transfer reaction and free energy of activation are important in determining the course the reaction will follow. Therefore even if the free energy of a reaction is favorable for excited state formation, if the activation energy is too large the rate of excited state formation will be slow and light emission will be weak.

According to electron transfer theory [77]:

$$k = Z\kappa\rho \exp\left(-\Delta F^*/kT\right), \qquad (13.19)$$

where Z is a diffusion-controlled rate constant, κ and ρ are approximately unity and

$$\Delta F^* = \omega^r + (\lambda/4)[1 + \Delta F_{R^{0'}}/\lambda)]^2, \qquad (13.20)$$

where

$$\Delta F_{R^{0'}} = \Delta F^{0'} + \omega^p - \omega^r. \qquad (13.21)$$

Here ω^r is the work required to bring the reactants together to the most probable separation distance in the activated complex and ω^p is the work required to bring the products together to the same distance; $\Delta F^{0'}$ is the standard free energy of the reaction and λ is a reorganization term depending upon differences in bond lengths in the initial and final electronic states. Marcus has used these considerations to discuss the kinetics of ECL produced by an electron transfer reaction in homogeneous solution [78], and the discussion in this section is based largely on his treatment.

From (13.19) and (13.20) it is evident that when $\Delta F^{0'} = 0$, ΔF^* is large, and as $\Delta F^{0'}$ increases, ΔF^* decreases until it reaches a minimum at $\Delta F^{0'} = \lambda$. This situation is shown in Fig. 13.14, curves a and b, for general electron transfer reactions. As $\Delta F^{0'}$ increases further, intersection of reactant and product curves occurs at more extreme configurations and ΔF^* increases until it becomes quite large as is shown by curve c of Fig. 13.14. It is apparent from these three figures that ΔF^* is smallest at moderate values of $\Delta F^{0'}$, whereas for very energetic reactions ΔF^* becomes large.

Since an excited state probably lies nearer in energy to the reactants than to the products, $\Delta F^{0'}$ for the reactants going to an excited state of the product is generally smaller than $\Delta F^{0'}$ for reactants going to a product ground state. This situation is shown by Fig. 13.14, curve d, where P^* represents the potential energy profile for formation of products in an excited state. The vertical arrow labeled $h\nu$ reflects the normal fluorescence emission of the product, while $\Delta F^{\ddagger *}$ represents the free energy of activation for formation of an excited state from the reactants. If the reactants start from their equilibrium configuration, it is evident from Fig. 13.14 that formation of a product in an excited state is more probable than formation in a ground state. Although the considerations here apply only to simple electron transfer reactions, they can readily be extrapolated to other types of reactions. The importance of configurational similarity between the product excited state and the reactants in order that the curves intersect as shown in Fig. 13.14 cannot be overstressed. If there is a large configurational change between the product excited state and the reactants, then the R and P^* curves will be displaced horizontally from each other and the free energy of activation to form an excited state will become large. The importance of the considerations just described can be illustrated by simple calculation [78] The ratio of the rates of electron transfer to form an excited state versus a ground state is 10^9 for the situation in which $\Delta F^{0'} = -70$ kcal/mole for ground state formation and $\Delta F^{0'} = -10$ kcal/mole for excited state formation.

A major difference is noted for heterogeneous electron transfer reactions such as those occurring at an electrode surface. For a given electronic state of a reactant, there are a number of potential energy surfaces vertically shifted from each other, each being a different many-electron quantum state of the surface [77]. This corresponds in effect to a series of curves similar to those shown in Fig. 13.14, each displaced slightly vertically from the other. Each R corresponds to a curve for a given electronic state of the reactant and one of the many-electron states of the electrode. Similarly, each P corresponds to a given curve for the electronic state of the product and one of the many-electron states of the electrode.

Generally, electron transfer at electrodes occurs from one-electron quantum states that are within kT of the Fermi level. Transfer of an electron to a high P-level is difficult because of ΔF^* and also because it is difficult to transfer to a lower level because of the unavailability of an electron hole in such a level. If electron transfer occurs from an ion to an electrode under very exothermic conditions (such as diffusion of a radical anion to an electrode poised at positive potential), the electron will be transferred to a high level of the conduction band on the electrode rather than to the product molecule. This is equivalent to saying that the electrode has become excited rather than the product molecule. Similarly, if a radical cation diffuses to a negatively poised electrode, the electron will be removed from a low-lying electrode level and again excitation will reside on the electrode rather than with the product molecule. These considerations have led Marcus to conclude [78] that for a metal electrode direct generation of an excited electronic state at the electrode surface is very unlikely. He has also suggested the possibility of direct excited state generation for electrodes in which the conduction bandwidth is small, such as semiconductor electrodes.

Recently, Marcus [79] had expanded his ideas on electron transfer at electrodes and in solution, with particular emphasis on comparison between theory and experiment. Experimental verification of predicted correlations has given information about "intrinsic" and "driving force" factors for electron transfer reactions. The intrinsic factors are properties of the species, such as bandlength, solvent orientation, and so on. The driving force term is related to the free energy of reaction for homogeneous reactions and to the activation overpotential for electrode reactions.

Hoytink [80] has briefly reviewed certain aspects of the ECL of aromatic hydrocarbons. He has considered the thermodynamics of cation-anion annihilation and discussed the reduction and oxidation potentials of aromatic hydrocarbons and their temperature dependence. He has also considered reaction coordinate diagrams for the aromatic hydrocarbons: benzene, naphthalene, anthracene, and tetracene, as well as some generalizations relating to the kinetics of cation annihilation from diagram of this sort. Because there is little or no configurational change between the ground and the excited states for large aromatic hydrocarbons, the greatest source of activation energy is probably solvent reorientation. The probability of crossing from the initial to final state in the transition state of an activated complex has been considered to take place with unit probability. The only statistical factor necessary to be considered is that of electron spin, since triplet configurations are three times more probable than singlet configurations.

An interesting conclusion from Hoytink's work is that cation-anion annihilation of aromatic hydrocarbons can lead to either formation of a singlet state or a triplet state, depending upon the relative energy of the states in the molecules and the energy available from a cation-anion annihilation reaction. It is also considered that only a small fraction of encounters could possibly lead to excimer formation. Hoytink has considered the possibility that excited molecules produced by the ECL reaction could be deactivated by quenching reactions with triplets or radical ions present in solution, a result that has been confirmed by other workers [55].

The Boundary Value Problem

Quantitative calculations relating light intensity–time measurements for the double potential step method of generating ECL have been performed by Feldberg [81]. The method consists of a computerized estimation of diffusion equations considering the solution as an array of small homogeneous volume elements parallel to the electrode surface, diffusion occurring by transfer of material from one volume element to the other. This particular method is valuable for solving problems involving nonlinear partial differential equations such as the boundary value problem in ECL. The method utilizes three assumptions, namely, that radiative decay of the excited state is fast relative to other reactions, that mass transport to the electrode surface is diffusion-controlled, and that no quenching processes occur.

The results of the computerized solution are presented in terms of two normalized dimensionless parameters, ω and β, where

$$\omega = \frac{IF}{\pi^{1/2}\phi i_f},$$

$$i_f = \frac{FAC_A D^{1/2}}{(\pi t_f)^{1/2}},$$

and

$$\beta = \frac{i_r}{i_f}.$$

The time duration of the first pulse is t_f, that is the second pulse t_r, with i_f and i_r currents for the two pulses, respectively; C_A is the bulk concentration of aromatic hydrocarbon, A the electrode area, ϕ the probability of radiative emission of an excited state of A, I the rate of light emission in einsteins per second, and F the value of the faraday. As is evident from above, ω is essentially the intensity of light emission recorded in a double potential step experiment.

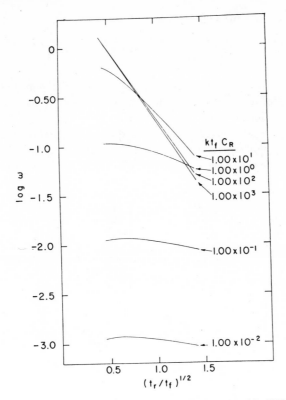

Fig. 13.15   Normalized light intensity–time relationship [81].

A plot of $\log \omega$ as a function of $(t_r/t_f)^{1/2}$ for various combinations of the product $k_5 t_f C_A$ is shown in Fig. 13.15, where k_5 is the homogeneous second-order rate constant for reaction (5) in Table 13.2. As the product $k_5 t_f C_A$ increases, a maximum negative slope of -1.45 is reached when $k_5 t_f C_A > 10^3$, the point at which light-producing reactions change from kinetic control to diffusion control. For diffusion control the relationship between ω and time is given by

$$\log \omega = -1.45(t_r/t_f)^{1/2} + 0.71 \tag{13.22}$$

The validity of (13.22) has been established by two independent laboratories [55, 67], both of which report theoretical slopes for the ECL of rubrene in benzonitrile. Also these experimenters have measured a minimum value of $k_5 > = 5 \times 10^6 \ M^{-1} \ \text{sec}^{-1}$.

Measurement of ω is not difficult since the output of the photomultiplier tube p_x can be related to the rate of light emission,

$$f = I/p_x, \tag{13.23}$$

such that one can rewrite (13.22) as

$$\log \frac{fpF}{\pi^{1/2}\phi i_f} = -1.45(t_r/t_f)^{1/2} + 0.71. \tag{13.24}$$

Equation (13.24) shows the interesting result that if the photomultiplier tube can be calibrated in terms of absolute response (i.e., the value of f determined), the quantum efficiency ϕ can be estimated.

A particularly interesting aspect of Feldberg's calculation is that the concentration and light emission profiles of ECL can be computed as a function of distance from the electrode surface as shown in Fig. 13.16. Both the abscissa and

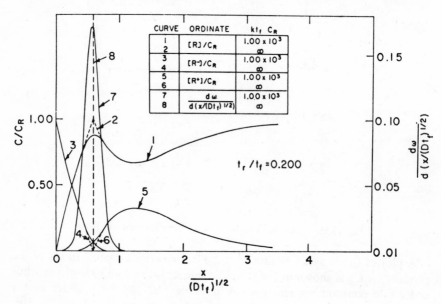

Fig. 13.16 Normalized concentration profile and light-emission profile [81].

the two ordinates are plotted in normalized terms: the left-hand ordinate a normalized concentration parameter, the right-hand ordinate normalized emission intensity, and the abscissa a normalized distance parameter. The odd-numbered solid curves in Fig. 13.16 correspond to $k_5 t_f C_r = 10^3$, while the even-numbered dashed curves correspond to $k_5 t_f C_r = \infty$. Curve 3 represents the concentration-distance profile of the species generated on the reverse part of the cycle, while curve 5 represents the concentration-distance profile of the species generated on the forward part of the cycle. Curve 1 represents the concentration-distance profile of the parent hydrocarbon, while curve 8 is the light intensity–distance profile for ECL emission. As was observed by many of the earlier workers, the maximum light intensity does not occur at the electrode surface but occurs some distance from it, depending upon the diffusion coefficient of the species and the time of electrochemical generation.

Cruser and Bard [85] have studied intensity-time and concentration-intensity relationships for aromatic hydrocarbons in DMF. They have reported an extension of Feldberg's approximation for the solution of the boundary value problem in ECL. Their modification allowed for additional reactions of ions and for multiple electrochemical cycles. They also allowed for pseudo-first-order decomposition of the radical cation. Their treatment involved the assumption that the rate of the annihilation reaction was diffusion controlled, radiation of the excited state was fast, triplets and excimers were not involved, and other oxidizing and reducing species were not present.

By use of the relationships derived, Cruser and Bard were able to estimate the rate constants for decay of several radical cations under double potential step conditions in DMF. These were 9,10-diphenylanthracene, 225 sec^{-1}; rubrene, 0.56 sec^{-1}; and tetraphenylpyrene, 13 sec^{-1}.

Anomalies in the intensity-time relationship generally could be attributed to electrochemical generation of diions or products from the solvent or supporting electrolyte that reacted with unstable cation radicals. They observed a linear concentration-intensity relationship for anthracene at concentration ca. 10^{-3} M, a range where fluorescence emission is nonlinear. This probably arises from the fact that the annihilation reaction occurs in a very thin diffusion layer and effects attributable to attenuation of the fluorescence exciting beam across the cell are unimportant.

Livingston and Leonhardt [82] have studied the oxidation of the perylene radical anion in dimethoxyethane with $HgCl_2$, $SnCl_4$, $SbCl_5$, benzoylperoxide, and tetracyanoethane; the perylene radical amine with benzoylperoxide in DMF; and the 9,10-diphenylanthracene radical amine with $HgCl_2$ and dimethoxyethane. These authors used a straight-flow rapid-mixing reactor having a time resolution of approximately 7×10^{-4} sec. The rate of light production appeared to be limited by diffusional mixing in the reactor and gave lower limits for rate constants of 5×10^7 and 3×10^6 M^{-1} sec^{-1} at room temperature and $-75°C$, respectively, in dimethoxyethane and a limit of 9×10^6 M^{-1} sec^{-1} in DMF at room temperature.

Feldberg has also obtained a computerized solution of the boundary value problem for the situation in which triplet-triplet annihilation is responsible for ECL [83]. In this process two triplets come together in a diffusion-controlled reaction to form an excited singlet state as indicated in reaction (6) of Table 13.2. It is not possible to distinguish between direct excited singlet state formation and triplet-triplet annihilation by the method described earlier [81]. However, when a triplet quencher is added to the solution, distinction between the two mechanisms is possible. In the presence of a triplet quencher, the normalized light emission ω_b is defined as

$$\omega_b = \frac{\beta}{\delta}\left[1 - \left(1 + \frac{8\gamma\omega_a}{\beta}\right)^{1/2}\right] + (1 - \tfrac{1}{2}\gamma)\omega_a,$$

where   (13.26)

$$\beta = \frac{C_Q^2 k_{11}^2 t_f}{k_6 C_A} \qquad \text{and} \qquad \gamma = \frac{k_5}{k_3 + k_5},$$

where k_3, k_5, k_6, and k_{11} refer to the appropriate rate constants from Table 13.2. Other terms have the meanings as defined above, and C_Q is the concentration of triplet quencher. When $\gamma = 0$, (13.26) reduces to (13.22), that is, no triplet-triplet annihilation occurs and only direct singlet excitation is observed. When $\gamma > 0$, (13.25) depends strongly on the magnitude of the triplet quenching term β. When significant triplet quenching occurs and for the situation in which $\gamma = 1$, one obtains the equation:

$$\log \omega_b = -2.90(t_r/t_f)^{1/2} - \log \beta + 1.42 \qquad (13.27)$$

Equation (13.27) requires a plot of $\log \omega$ versus $(t_r/t_f)^{1/2}$ to yield a slope more negative than -1.45 for the case in which triplet quenching occurs, reaching a limit of -2.90. This provides workers with a criterion for establishing the presence of triplet-triplet annihilation in ECL, although it is difficult to evaluate the extent to which this occurs. Chang et al. [55] have measured light intensity versus time relationships for rubrene in benzonitrile and have observed the slope of -2.90 predicted by (13.25).

ECL EFFICIENCY MEASUREMENTS

The relationships just derived point out the difficulty in obtaining meaningful quantum efficiency measurements for ECL. From Fig. 13.16 it is evident that not all radical cations and anions produced at the electrode surface are able to react to emit light under the conditions of the double potential step experiment. Therefore to simply measure the ratio of photons produced to the coulombs passed in such an experiment gives an erroneous value of the quantum efficiency even if one is careful to measure only the faradaic component of the current. However, if one can do an absolute calibration of the photomultiplier so that absolute light intensity measurements can be performed, then (13.25) can be used to calculate ϕ which will be the apparent quantum efficiency of the system. If a competing process occurs either before or after an excited state formation in ECL, which does not occur for the same excited state by photoexcitation, this will be reflected in a lower value of ϕ than the value measured by photoexcitation. Therefore ECL efficiency can be defined as the probability of excited state formation by the ECL process as compared to the probability of excited state formation by direct photoexcitation or, $\Phi = \phi_{\text{ECL}}/\phi_f$.

To date there have been only three attempts to measure the quantum efficiency of ECL processes. Zweig et al [67] have performed ECL efficiency measurements on N-methyl-1,3-di-p-anisyl-4,7-diphenylisoindole. They calculated a coulombic efficiency of 0.6%, that is, *the number of light emitters produced divided by the number of coulombs passed*. The faradaic current efficiency must be somewhat higher since their results are based upon calculations of total current, both charging and faradaic. Watne [57] has measured the ECL efficiency of rubrene in benzonitrile and found the results were highly variable, depending upon conditions of the experiment. His results indicated the efficiency to be 1% or less. Such low values for the ECL efficiency of rubrene serve to emphasize that although a chemiluminescent reaction may be bright to the eye, the quantum efficiency need not necessarily be high since rubrene has been described by several investigators as one of the brightest known ECL reactions. The preliminary ECL measurements reported by Lansbury et al. at the American Chemical Society Meeting at Phoenix, Arizona, and quoted by Kuwana [84] have now been shown in our laboratory to be too high.

Reports of Excimer Emission in ECL

Because all available evidence indicates that radical ions react to generate ECL via a diffusion-controlled reaction, electron transfer occurs only when they are at the appropriate transfer distance. Under normal conditions of photoexcitation, excimer formation is accomplished by the reaction: $^1A^* + A \rightleftharpoons {}^1A_2^*$ which is also diffusion controlled, requiring that the two species approach to within bonding distance. Therefore it is not unreasonable to expect that radical ion reactions could produce excimers by two different mechanisms. One would be diffusion-controlled excimer formation by collision of an excited singlet, produced in the ECL process, with a ground state molecule. This can be regarded as a trivial process for ECL. The other would involve direct excimer formation during the electron transfer reactions by the process: $A^+ + A^- \rightarrow {}^1A_2^*$. It is altogether conceivable that an excimer formed by the second process could be different from a photoexcimer produced by the normal diffusion-controlled reaction. Therefore the key question is, can excimer formation in ECL be observed under conditions in which photoexcimer formation does not occur. A corollary question is, can excimer formation occur for systems in which photoexcimer formation is unknown?

The first report of excimer emission in ECL is attributable to Chandross et al. [49]. These authors observed that ECL spectra obtained for solutions of anthracene, 9,10-dimethylanthracene, phenanthrene, perylene, and 3,4-benzpyrene contained broad structureless bands which were red-shifted relative to the normal fluorescence of the hydrocarbon. Examples of three of

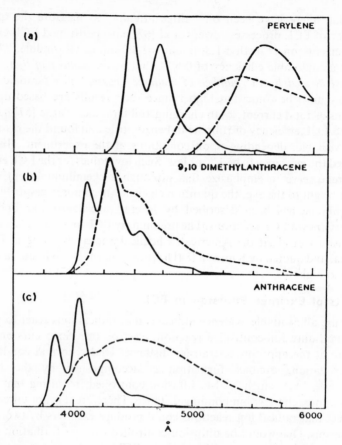

Fig. 13.17 Fluorescence (———) and EL (– – – –) spectra. Perylene crystalline excimer (– · – · – ·) shown in (a) [49].

these spectra are shown in Fig. 13.17. For 9,10-dimethylanthracene and phenanthrene, both monomer emission and excimer emission were observed, while for anthracene, perylene, and 3,4-benzpyrene, no monomer emission could be detected. Unfortunately, most of the hydrocarbons studied by Chandross et al. do not normally form excimers and therefore direct comparison of the reported emission with known excimer spectra is difficult. The crystal excimer for perylene is known, and the emission occurs in the same region of the spectrum as the ECL excimer emission although there is considerable mismatch in the two spectra [49]. No excimer emission could be observed for 9,10-diphenylanthracene, naphthacene, and rubrene, all three of which have been reported not to form photoexcimers. Both 9,10-diphenyl-anthracene and rubrene have bulky phenyl substituents which sterically hinder excimer formation, and naphthacene is an unusual hydrocarbon in most every respect. The solutions used by Chandross et al. [49] were ca. 10^{-3} to 10^{-2} M, requiring excimers to be formed directly from the radical annihilation reaction, since photoexcimers are not observed for these compounds in this concentration range. Anthracene and phenanthrene show self-quenching of their excited singlet states, accounting for the lack of excimer formation in these compounds. Therefore, anthracene and phenanthrene excimers formed in the annihilation reaction must be different from their photoexcimers, an excimer derived from a charge transfer state being suggested as a possibility [49].

Parker and Short have also observed excimer emission in the ECL of 9,10-dimethylanthracene in DMF [64] at concentrations somewhat greater than those used by Chandross et al. [49]. The spectra observed by Parker and Short are shown in Fig. 13.18. It is evident that the large band around 1.8 μm^{-1} in the ECL spectrum (spectrum 1) corresponds closely to the photo-excited excimer (spectrum 3), leaving little doubt that Parker and Short

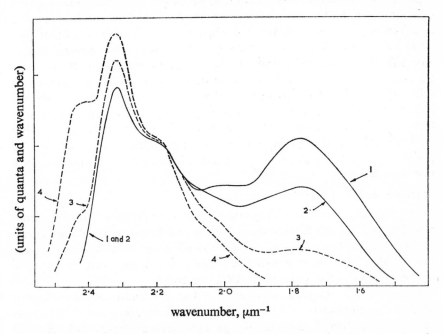

Fig. 13.18 Spectra of ECL and prompt fluorescence of 9,10-dimethylanthracene in DMF. Curves 1 and 2, ECL of 1.63×10^{-2} M solution at 3.6 and 4.6 V peak to peak; curves 3 and 4, prompt fluorescence of 1.63×10^{-2} M and 1.63×10^{-5} M solutions. Bandwidth of quartz prism analyzing monochromator was 0.1 μm^{-1} (18 nm) at 2.3 μm^{-1} [64].

observed excimer emission. Based on the assumption that the monomer and the eximer are the only emitting species in the spectral region investigated, Parker and Short derived the expression:

$$\frac{\phi_D}{\phi_M} = K' + K''C,$$

where ϕ_M and ϕ_D are the quantum efficiencies of the monomer and dimer, respectively, C is the concentration of the aromatic hydrocarbon, and K' and K'' are constants [64]. They observed that a plot of ϕ_D/ϕ_M versus C was linear and that extrapolation to infinite dilution gave values for the ratio greater than those observed from delayed-fluorescence experiments. Also the extrapolated ratio varied with temperature and applied voltage. That the ratio ϕ_D/ϕ_M tends to a finite value at infinite dilution implies direct excimer formation results from the annihilation reaction rather than from a diffusion-controlled reaction between the excited singlet state and a ground state hydrocarbon.

Some question can be raised about the validity of the conclusions reported by both sets of authors, that is, whether or not Chandross et al. [49] actually observed *any* excimer emission and whether or not Parker and Short [64] observed excimer emission in excess of that produced by photoexcitation. The difficulty in unambiguously proving excimer formation by the electron transfer step results from two sources. Instability of radical ions is a common difficulty in ECL studies, particularly those in DMF [51]. Scanning into the region of solvent oxidation is known to produce luminescence other than from the radical ion annihilation reaction [51]. However, there are other studies indicating that excimer formation in the systems studied might be possible. Therefore both the pros and cons of the excimer interpretation are discussed below.

Studies Supporting Excimer Formation

One difficulty with the excimer interpretation for the spectra of Chandross et al. [49] is that most of the systems investigated do not show photoexcimers. However, recent studies on photodecomposition of anthracene dimers indicate that for some compounds excimer emission can occur in the same spectral region as the bands in the ECL spectra.

Ferguson [86] observed emission at 420 nm for anthracene dissolved in crystalline cyclohexane, which he attributed to excimer formation. Chandross [87] photodissociated dianthracene in cyclohexane glasses and observed emission at 480 nm, which he too attributed to an excimer. Annealing the cyclohexane glass caused the 480-nm fluorescence to change to an emission similar to that observed by Ferguson. Chandross commented [87] on the similarity of excimer fluorescence observed from irradiation of dianthracene to the ECL excimer emission. In subsequent studies [88–90], it was shown that the 480-nm emission for anthracene was from a sandwich dimer (the angle between the short axes of two anthracene molecules, $\theta = 0°$), while another dimer with $\theta = 55°$ was responsible for the emission at 420 nm. Similar emission was observed [91] for 9-methyl-, 9-chloro-, 9-bromo-, 9-cyano-, 9,10-dichloroanthracene, and weakly for 9,10-dibromoanthracene. For all compounds, the emission occurred at about the same wavelength as for anthracene. Aggregate emission and mixed excimer formation for various anthracene derivatives was also observed.

These results clearly indicate that anthracene derivatives produce excimer emission even though it is not observed under the conditions of normal photo-excitation. Also, the spectrum of the sandwich-type excimer lies in the same spectral region as the emission attributed to ECL excimers. Under the conditions of photodissociation, sandwich excimer formation is favored, and this excimer is the one that would be formed in the ECL process. These studies also demonstrate that more than one excimer is possible for anthracene derivatives, which correlates with the conclusions of Chandross et al. [49] that it is most likely that the ECL excimer would be different from the normal photoexcimer of anthracene derivatives.

Additional support for excimer formation in ECL comes from the work of Weller and Zachariasse [92], who studied chemiluminescence from the reaction of Wurster's blue cations with aromatic hydrocarbon radical anions. When pyrene was used as the aromatic hydrocarbon, an excimer band was observed which correlated well with the frequency of the known excimer band, and the relative intensities were comparable to those from the delayed-fluorescence spectrum. When naphthalene and biphenyl were used as hydrocarbons, a broad structureless emission occurred at longer wavelengths then normal hydrocarbon fluorescence, which was attributed to a charge transfer emission. Also, Yamamoto et al. [93] have observed charge transfer fluorescence from the reaction of tetramethyl-p-phenylenediamine radical cations with pyrene anions.

Photoexcitation can also produce charge transfer fluorescence in solutions containing donors and acceptors [93–95] under conditions in which charge transfer complex formation in the ground state is absent. This emission is attributed to excited state charge transfer complex formation between a donor D and an acceptor A. In the limit where D = A, the charge transfer emission is the normal excimer fluorescence. This fluorescence is not accompanied by any change in the absorption spectrum; the charge transfer fluorescence increases and the acceptor fluorescence decreases as the donor concentration is raised. The nature of the charge transfer emission is strongly solvent dependent [94], which normal excimer fluorescence is not, indicating the charge transfer nature of the excited state. An interesting result was observed with diethylaniline in biphenyl when toluene was used as a solvent [96]. Here only the donor was excited, whereas in other studies only the acceptor was excited. Observation of a long wavelength emission band in this system requires an electron transfer from D* to A, giving a charge transfer state and then emission, that is, an electron exchange mechanism is operative.

Evidence Suggesting Another Interpretation

One of the problems in attributing long wavelength ECL emission to excimer formation is that in many systems radical cations are unstable. In many cases there is a correlation between the ability of a compound to show long wavelength bands in ECL and the instability of its radical cation. Anthracene is a prime example. Decomposition of the anthracene radical cation yields bianthronyl, bianthrone, 9-anthrone, anthraquinone, and 9,10-dihydroxyanthracene [65]. Because hydrocarbon anions can react with added acceptors to give chemiluminescence [55, 92], decomposition products of radical cations could react with radical anions to give chemiluminescence. This emission might or might not be the fluorescence of the hydrocarbon from which the anion was derived. Recent work tends to support the idea that ECL emission attributed to excimer formation may result from species other than those derived directly from the parent hydrocarbon [59, 97, 98].

A correlation has been observed between the ability of hydrocarbons to show excimer emission and the instability of the radical cation [98]. The current voltage curves of 9,10 diphenylanthracene and anthracene point out the difference in the stability of the respective radical cations as shown in Fig. 13.19 [98]. As a general rule, blocking the 9- and 10-positions stabilizes the cation radical. 9,10-Diphenylanthracene gives no excimer luminescence either in self-quenching or ECL. The stability of the anthracene radical cation results in decomposition of the anthracene solution during the ECL experiment. This has been shown by a comparison of the products formed in ECL experiments with those of the potentiostatic oxidation of anthracene. Product identification has confirmed the presence of anthraquinone, bi-anthronyl, and hydrogen ion, and from the data accumulated, residual water of the solvent and even the electrolyte may take part in the decomposition reactions.

Because of the observation of product fluorescence in the region of reported anthracene emission, an attempt was made to establish the possibility of energy transfer and both trivial and nontrivial from excited anthracene to a product molecule. One product, 9,10-dihydroxyanthracene, was selected as acceptor since its fluorescence lies in the region of suggested excimer emission. Excitation spectra taken while monitoring the 560-nm fluorescence of 9,10-dihydroxyanthracene showed an increase in the 378- and 358-nm

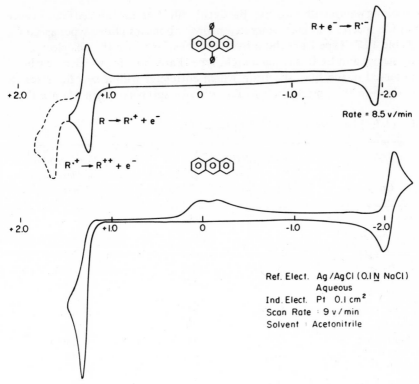

$R + e^- \rightarrow R^{\cdot -}$

Rate = 8.5 v/min

$R \rightarrow R^{\cdot +} + e^-$

$R^{\cdot +} \rightarrow R^{++} + e^-$

Ref. Elect. Ag /AgCl (0.1 N NaCl)
              Aqueous
Ind. Elect. Pt 0.1 cm^2
Scan Rate : 9 v/min
Solvent : Acetonitrile

Fig. 13.19 Current-voltage Curves for anthracene and 9,10-diphenylanthracene in acetonitrile.

regions in the presence of anthracene. These bands correlate with the anthracene absorption bands, and since anthracene does not fluoresce at 360 this establishes energy transfer from anthracene to 9,10-dihydroxyanthracene. Therefore there appears to be a definite relationship between the reported excimer chemiluminescence emission and cation stability. Anthracene, phenanthrene, and perylene are reported to show excimer emission, and all three have unstable radical cations. Rubrene, tetracene, and 9,10-dimethylanthracene have stable cations and show no long wavelength band in their ECL spectra.

Bard et al. [59] have observed long wavelength emission for phenanthrene, *trans*-stilbene, anthracene, and 1,2-dibenzanthracene, all of which have unstable cation radicals. It was also observed that the solution fluorescence after electrolysis matched the long wavelength component of the ECL spectrum, correlating with the idea that a new chemical species is responsible for the long wavelength emission. Bard et al. [59] have summarized fluorescence and ECL spectra and have separated hydrocarbons into three types as shown in Table 13.7. Type I are those hydrocarbons for which the postelectrolysis fluorescence and ECL maxima match; type II are those for which a new band is observed in the ECL spectrum which correlates with a new fluorescence maximum in the postelectrolysis fluorescence spectrum. Type III are those

Table 13.7   Fluorescence and ECL Spectra* [59]

Compound	Preelectrolysis Fluorescence Maximum (mμ)	ECL Maximum (mμ)	Postelectrolysis New Fluorescence Maximum
Type I			
9,10-Diphenyl anthracene	440	440	None†
Rubrene	560	560	None†
Tetracene	520	520	None†
Type II			
Phenanthrene	412	412, 516	486
trans-Stilbene	398	398, 506	506
Anthracene	412	412, 455, 569	480
1,2-Benzanthracene	408, 420	420, 538	452
Type III			
Bifluorenyl	384	526	None†
Carbazole	406	538	None†
Dibenzo[c, g] carbazole	440	530	None†

* The solution contained 0.1 M tetra-*n*-butylammonium perchlorate and was 10^{-3} M in organic compound.

† Only original, preelectrolysis fluorescence band found.

systems in which the ECL spectrum differs from the fluorescence spectrum but no new fluorescence maximum is observed in the postelectrolysis spectrum. Type-I hydrocarbons have stable radical cations, while type-II hydrocarbons do not [98], suggesting that the new emission band in the ECL spectrum is derived from an electrolysis product. It was also observed for type-II compounds that as electrolysis was continued the normal fluorescence band decreased and the long wavelength band increased in intensity until after extended electrolysis only the long wavelength component was observed. The reason for the behavior of type-III compounds is not currently understood.

Faulkner and Bard [97] also have extensively studied excimer emission in anthracene ECL, identifying 9-anthranol as a decomposition product of the radical cation. The spectral distribution of ECL in DMF depends on the applied voltage, the time of electrolysis, and the method of solvent purification. Figure 13.20 shows some emission spectra obtained for ECL of anthracene [97]. The spectral distribution remains approximately constant until the peak-to-peak applied voltage is 5 V, at which a new component of the spectrum appears corresponding to the dashed line in Fig. 13.20. At about

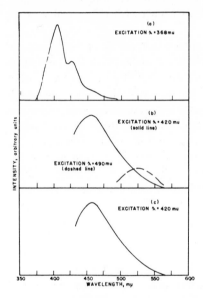 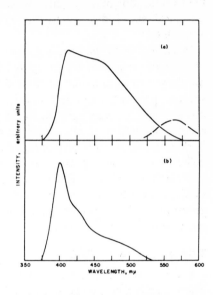

Fig. 13.20   Right: ECL emission spectra from 1 mM anthracene solutions: (*a*) DMF purified by method A; (*b*) DMF purified by method B. TBAP concentration is 0.1 M [97]. Left: Fluorescence emission spectra: (*a*) preelectrolysis fluorescence of anthracene; (*b*) new bands appearing during electrolysis; (*c*) fluorescence spectrum of anthranol in DMF [97].

6 V applied, the emission from the shorter wavelength band drops off while the intensity of the 565-nm band increases. Also, new fluorescence bands appear as a result of electrolysis. At applied voltages less than 6 V, a fluorescence spectrum peaking around 460 nm is observed. If voltages greater than 6 V are used, a second band appears at ca. 565 nm. The ECL emission spectrum also changes with time of electrolysis. Below 5 V the bands at 412 (anthracene) and 470 nm decrease slowly and no major change in the spectrum is observed. Above 5 V, however, the intensity of the 565-nm band increases as the electrolysis proceeds. The fluorescence emission at 470 also varies with

time, rising with a maximum and then slowly decreasing as the electrolysis is continued.

Both of the fluorescent products produced by the decomposition of the anthracene cation, 9-hydroxyanthracene and 9,10-dihydroxyanthracene, are capable of excitation by energy transfer from an excited anthracene molecule [97, 98], by trivial and nontrivial mechanisms. Therefore it is reasonable to assume that the long wavelength component in the anthracene ECL spectrum is caused by products of radical cation decomposition receiving their excitation energy by energy transfer from an excited anthracene singlet, produced either directly by the radical ion reaction or by triplet-triplet annihilation.

In view of both the pros and cons, the question arises as to the likelihood of excimer formation occurring in ECL processes. It appears that in a large number of cases emission attributed to excimer formation arises from other sources, probably from decomposition of the radical cations. Because of the broad band emission spectra, it is not possible to exclude completely some excimer formation in the systems Chandross et al. studied. In the case of Parker and Short, it is certain that excimer formation occurred, the question being whether or not excimers arose from excimer formation during the electron transfer step. Because the applied voltages used by these authors were sufficiently large to cause solvent oxidation simultaneously with ECL generation, direct excimer formation in the case of 9,10-dimethylanthracene must be regarded as tentative.

Triplet States in ECL

Considerable experimental evidence has indicated that ECL can occur when insufficient energy is available from a reaction to form an excited singlet state directly. Triplet-triplet annihilation is a well-known process under the conditions of photoexcitation and thus has often been invoked as an ECL mechanism. Also, direct generation of triplet states at electrode surfaces has been offered as an explanation for weak "preannihilation" ECL. In this section we review energy-deficient systems and consider evidence, pro and con, for the involvement of triplets in ECL.

Recalling from Table 13.6 in the cases of rubrene, 9,10-dimethylanthracene, and anthracene, there is an energy deficiency in the cation-anion annihilation reaction when an entropy correction is applied to the electrochemical oxidation and reduction data. The energy discrepancy in itself *may* be indicative of a process other than direct singlet excitation, but the validity of this conclusion is not certain in the absence of *good* quantum efficiency measurements. If the observed quantum efficiencies were significantly higher than those calculated in Table 13.5, it would constitute evidence for another process, possibly triplet-triplet annihilation.

It was also observed that reaction of the rubrene radical cation with DMF, amines, and water [51] produced rubrene fluorescence even though insufficient energy was available to form the excited singlet state. Also, fluorescence was observed for perylene and 9,10-diphenylanthracene where the energy deficiency was even greater than for rubrene [51]. The energy discrepancy could not be attributed entirely to irreversible electrochemical processes; it is more likely that ECL was caused by reactions between intermediates in the solvent oxidation and radical cations.

Maricle and Mauer [73] first reported preannihilation ECL for rubrene. Preannihilation ECL is a term used to describe the light produced under conditions in which the radical anion–radical cation annihilation reaction cannot occur. For example, if the radical anion of rubrene is first generated at -1.6 V and the potential is stepped to a voltage more positive than 0.2 V, light emission is observed even though rubrene oxidation occurs in the vicinity of $+0.9$ V. One interpretation of these data is the heterogeneous oxidation of the radical anion to a triplet state with subsequent triplet–triplet annihilation to give an excited singlet. Similarly, Zweig et al. [50] observed ECL for oxidation of phenanthrene radical anions, the emission being attributed to phenanthrene phosphorescence.

Convincing evidence that ECL can be produced from electron transfer reactions in which insufficient energy is available comes from the work of Chang et al. [55]. They observed ECL from reaction of rubrene radical anions with tetramethyl-p-phenylenediamine and p-phenylenediamine radical cations, as well as reaction of the rubrene radical cation with the radical anions of benzoquinone, naphthoquinone, and anthraquinone. These data are summarized in Table 13.8. For example, oxidation of rubrene occurs at $+0.88$ V, while the reduction of naphthoquinone occurs at -0.72 V, giving a net energy of 1.60 V available from the reaction of these radical ions. The excited singlet state of rubrene without the applied entropy correction requires 2.39 V. Similarly, Weller and Zachariasse [92] have observed large energy discrepancies for light-emitting reactions of Wurster's blue cation with radical anions of chrysene, perylene, anthracene, pyrene, 1,2-benzanthracene tetracene, and picene.

Red chemiluminescence has been observed during the electrolysis of pyrene in DMF [99], along with the normal blue emission visibly interpreted as pyrene fluorescence. An emissive triplet state of pyrene has been postulated to be the source of the red emission. The chemiluminescence emission spectrum observed falls in the same region as pyrene phosphorescence. The possibility of singlet oxygen emission was ruled out by observations in deoxygenated solution.

Angel and Signore [100] have studied ECL of 9,10-diphenylanthracene, naphthacene, and rubrene in DMF. These authors have presented evidence

Table 13.8   Energies of Electron-Transfer Reactions [55]

A	$E_{1/2}(A \rightarrow A^+)$ (V)	$E_{1/2}(A \rightarrow A^+) - E_{1/2}(R \rightarrow R^-)$ (V)
N,N,N',N'-Tetramethyl-p-phenylenediamine	+0.16	1.63
p-Phenylenediamine	+0.24	1.71
Rubrene*	+0.88	2.35

D	$E_{1/2}(D \rightarrow D^-)$	$E_{1/2}(R \rightarrow R^+) - E_{1/2}(D \rightarrow D^-)$
p-Benzoquinone	−0.60	1.48
Naphthoquinone	−0.72	1.60
Anthraquinone	−0.80	1.68
Rubrene*	−1.47	2.35

* Energy of excited singlet of rubrene = 2.39 eV.

that the simultaneous existence of both Ar$^+$ and Ar$^-$ is not necessary to obtain ECL. Comparing the energy gaps between singlets and triplets of the molecules studied, they have concluded that luminescence may appear for electrical excitation energy lower than the optical threshold and have assumed that a two-step mechanism is operative involving the lowest excited triplet state of the aromatic hydrocarbon.

All of the experimental evidence cited above is convincing that some process (or processes) are operative in ECL other than direct formation of a singlet state or an excimer. On the basis of known photoexcitation processes, the involvement of triplet states is likely, but in no case has this been conclusively proven. Also, the experimental evidence seems to point to some reaction other than simple radical anion and cation annihilation occurring, possibly heterogeneous generation of triplets at the electrode surface. In this section both processes are reviewed and evidence pro and con cited.

Preannihilation ECL

Most work on preannihilation ECL has come from the group at American Cyanamid [50, 73, 67, 101]. They have observed it for widely varying compounds in DMF, including rubrene, phenanthrene, isobenzofurans, and isoindoles. A summary of the experimental observations relating to preannihilation ECL follows.

Maricle and Mauer [73] observed light emission for rubrene solutions in

DMF after generating one radical ion and stepping the potential insufficiently anodic or cathodic to generate the oppositely charged ion. For example, when the radical anion was generated at -1.6 V and the potential stepped to -0.2 V, light emission was observed; likewise, if a radical cation was generated at $+1.0$ V and the potential stepped to -0.95 V, light emission was observed even though the cathodic and anodic half-wave potentials are -1.37 and $+0.95$ V, respectively. The intensity of preannihilation ECL was about 10^2 lower than for the cation-anion annihilation reaction, but the spectrum observed was that of rubrene fluorescence. One possible explanation put forth by these authors [73] was heterogeneous generation of the rubrene triplet at the electrode surface and subsequent triplet-triplet annihilation to produce the excited singlet. Another possible explanation was that the effect was a result of impurities. After titrating the solution with electrochemically generated rubrene radical anions to remove all impurities reactive with this species, preannihilation ECL was still observed. However, the intensity was about 10^3 lower than for the radical cation-anion annihilation reaction.

Zweig et al. [50] claimed direct generation of the phenanthrene triplet at an electrode surface. When phenanthrene radical anion was generated in DMF at -2.4 V and the potential step successively positive, at $+0.145$ V light emission occurred. As the potential was stepped successively more positive, the light emission became brighter. The solution was purged by anion generation as before [73], and the emission was still observed. The ECL spectrum was not phenanthrene fluorescence but was reasonably similar to phenanthrene phosphorescence observed in solution by Parker and Hatchard [102]. In addition to the spectral similarity to phenanthrene phosphorescence, phenanthrene ECL was quenched by 1,3,5-transhexatriene and 2,3-dimethylbutadiene (triplet energies = 47 and 59 kcal/mole, respectively), but not quenched by biphenyl (triplet energy = 65 kcal/mole, phenanthrene triplet energy = 62 kcal/mole).

Zweig et al. [61, 101] have carried out extensive investigations of preannihilation ECL for some heterocyclic compounds using both the double potential step method and other organic compounds to poise the potential of the system. Preannihilation ECL was observed for 1,3,4,7-tetraphenylisobenzofuran, 1,3,5,6-tetraphenylisobenzofuran, 1,3-di-p-anisyl-4,7-diphenylisobenzofuran, N-methyl-1,3,4,7-tetraphenylisoindole, N-methyl-1,3-di-p-anisyl-4,7-di-phenylisoindole, and tetracene. These authors attempted to establish the energy levels of the triplets for these compounds by spectroscopic techniques but were unable to do so. It was observed that the triplet quenchers 1,3-cyclohexadience and trans-1,3,5-hexatriene did not quench preannihilation ECL for these compounds.

Zweig et al. [61] have discussed four possible mechanisms for preannihilation ECL: triplet-triplet annihilation, two impurity mechanisms, and a mechanism involving ion aggregation. They rule out triplet-triplet annihilation on the basis of observing preannihilation ECL for tetracene and the lack of quenching by triplet quenchers. The first impurity mechanism suggested is generation of the impurity along with the radical anion and, on oxidation, exothermic decomposition giving energy sufficient to be transferred to the fluorescer. This mechanism is ruled out because preannihilation ECL is not detected on the oxidative cycle after the reduction of N-methyl-1,3-di-p-anisyl-4,7-diphenylisoindole to an unstable species. The second impurity mechanism requires the impurity to be oxidized and to undergo a rapid reaction at threshold potential to generate a stronger oxidant which can then react with the radical anion to give an excited singlet. This mechanism is ruled out because of a large number of experimental observations to the contrary [67]. The mechanism favored by Zweig et al. is that radical ion aggregates are oxidized or reduced at the electrode with the accumulation of excess energy on one molecule of the aggregate to provide excitation. Recognizing that such aggregates are not favored by low radical ion concentration and polar solvents or the presence of counterions such as quaternary ammonium salts, this mechanism does not seem to be particularly probable.

Maricle et al. [63] recently carried out a more extensive investigation of preannihilation ECL for rubrene and phenanthrene. They have considered as a possible explanation the oxidation or reduction of impurities, followed by a homogeneous chemiluminescent electron transfer reaction. They have found the impurity mechanism to account for a major fraction of preannihilation ECL for the rubrene anion in DMF. Upon titrating a solution by generation of the rubrene anion, it was determined that about 10^{-4} to 10^{-3} equiv per liter of impurity were present. When ECL was observed on a freshly titrated solution, the threshold voltage of the ECL was shifted from -0.2 to $+0.5$ V, and the intensity was several orders of magnitude lower than the intensity produced by the annihilation reaction. On the basis of their studies, they concluded that it was likely that some impurity reacted with the radical anion of rubrene to generate a species that could subsequently react with the rubrene anion to produce light. Although their experiments still require preannihilation ECL to result from a triplet-triplet annihilation mechanism, they avoid the necessity of invoking heterogeneous generation of triplets at an electrode surface.

Maricle et al. [63] also studied preannihilation ECL from the oxidation of phenanthrene radical anion in DMF and acetonitrile and confirmed the earlier observation that the emission was similar to phenanthrene solution phosphorescence. No cation-anion annihilation observed in the phenanthrene system because of cation instability. Based on a series of experiments involving triplet quenchers, along with the spectral similarity observed, these authors concluded that the triplet state of phenanthrene is the emitter. Purging experiments similar to those conducted for rubrene could not prove the involvement of anion decomposition products in the light-emitting reaction.

Chandross and Visco have criticized the idea that preannihilation ECL results from heterogeneous generation of an excited state directly at an electrode surface [54, 103] on the basis of some experimental results and thermodynamic arguments. Zweig and Maricle have replied to their criticism [104]. As indicated earlier [78], heterogeneous generation of triplets at an electrode surface is contrary to the theory of electron transfer reactions. Chandross and Visco were unable to generate preannihilation ECL for 9,10-diphenyl-anthracene and 9,10-dimethylracene in acetonitrile as well as for rubrene in benzonitrile, solvents in which both the radical anions and cations are stable. They point out that heterogeneous generation of triplets is unlikely to be so solvent sensitive and that the preannihilation ECL may arise from radical cation decomposition. Zweig and Maricle feel that this is not pertinent since potentials involved in preannihilation ECL do not require generation of the alternate radical ion. Chandross and Visco also state that a triplet should be oxidized at less positive potentials and reduced at more positive potentials than the cation and anion radicals, respectively, a process that would result in a rapid electron exchange quenching of triplets at the electrode surface. Zweig et al. point out that the thermodynamic arguments are not totally valid in the absence of relative rate data for emission and electrode reactions, that is, little is really known about the rate of triplet quenching at electrode surfaces. Chandross and Visco also argue that even if triplets could be produced at electrode surfaces over a narrow potential range intensity of preannihilation luminescence should decrease with decreasing electrode voltage in opposition to observed behavior.

Parker and Short [105] have studied the weak solution phosphorescence of phenanthrene under high resolution and have observed structure in the spectrum. This has led them to question the observation of phenanthrene phosphorescence from the radical ion reaction observed by Zweig et al. [50], since presumably the spectrograph used by the later authors to observe the triplet-singlet emission should have resolved the spectral structure.

Although one might adopt the attitude that "theory guides but experiment decides," the theoretical arguments put forth against direct generation of triplets at an electrode surface are quite convincing. Also, by implication, the ion aggregate theory of Zweig et al. [61] requires direct excitation at an electrode as well in order to distribute the excitation energy of the aggregate on one member. Therefore no reasonable mechanism exists for heterogeneous generation of triplets that is consistent with current electron transfer theory.

Unfortunately, most of the work of preannihilation ECL had been done in DMF, a solvent known to contain low-level impurities capable of causing light emission. These impurities lie below the 10^{-4} M level but are sufficient to cause low-level light emission. The experience in our laboratory has been that many times spurious luminescence arises in DMF solutions which cannot be produced in other solvents. The observations of Chandross and Visco [54] that some preannihilation ECL could not be produced in acetonitrile and benzonitrile are consistent with this. We observed a low-level preannihilation ECL for rubrene in benzonitrile as quoted by Zweig and Maricle [104]. However, in the potential region that they quote, the intensity of this emission is reduced by greater than 10^3 below the annihilation ECL. We have attempted to repeat the observations of Zweig et al. [50] on the preannihilation ECL of phenanthrene and, although we could observe emission in DMF, when carefully purified, acetonitrile was used as a solvent, no light emission was observed.

We have also observed light emission comparable to preannihilation ECL, which is caused by submillisecond pulses attributable to overshoot on the potentiostat used in the double potential step experiment. The addition of other compounds to poise the potential is not particularly relevant since radical cations other than the rubrene cation react with the rubrene anion to give ECL emission [55]. One must be careful about interpreting the effect of triplet quenchers on ECL. It seems risky to base any mechanistic interpretation on such experiments unless the effect of the quencher on the triplet has been demonstrated by an independent technique such as flash photolysis.

On the basis of all of the arguments and evidence presented heretofore, it seems that preannihilation ECL must be attributable mostly to impurities contained in the solvent. The fact that many reactions can produce low-level chemiluminescence is widely known, and preannihilation ECL probably belongs in this category.

Triplet-Triplet Annihilation in ECL

ECL has been observed for many systems in which the radical ion combination reaction can not supply sufficient energy to produce an excited singlet state directly. This is the case both for ECL and regular chemiluminescent reactions [55, 92]. All evidence, both pro and con, for the occurrence of triplet-triplet annihilation in ECL is circumstantial, although the evidence pro seems to be more convincing. The reports of Zweig et al. [50] showed an effect of triplet quenchers on the ECL of phenanthrene. However, one must be cautious of these results because detailed knowledge of the ECL process and the nature of the emitting species is lacking. Likewise, Bard [59] suggested the ECL observed for carbazole resembled its phosphorescence. However, one must view this interpretation skeptically since the carbazole anion is unstable under the conditions of the experiment; basing indentification of a species on similarity of broad band solution emission spectra is risky.

Weller and Zachariasse [92] studied the reaction between Wurster's blue (WB) cation and hydrocarbon radical anions. Of particular interest is reaction of Wurster's blue cation with the chrysene anion. The energy required for the formation of a chrysene singlet is 3.43 eV, but the WB cation–chrysene anion reaction can provide only 2.66 eV. The chrysene triplet energy is 2.44 eV. Therefore, in chrysene, triplet-triplet annihilation can produce a singlet and the WB cation–chrysene anion reaction can produce a triplet. Structured emission spectra were observed for the chemiluminescence of chrysene as shown in Table 13.9. In addition to the regular fluorescence bands, three peaks were observed that showed a close correlation with the peaks of the phosphorescence spectrum. Because of the structured emission and the correlation between peaks, identification of the chemiluminescent emitter in this reaction as the chrysene triplet is reasonable. Observing phosphorescence in solution can be taken as evidence that triplet-triplet annihilation can occur. Because the ECL process involves radical ion reactions similar to the chemiluminescent reactions of Weller and Zachariasse, their observations support triplet-triplet annihilation in ECL.

Probably the most convincing evidence for the occurrence of triplet-triplet annihilation comes from the work of Chang et al. [55], who studied the ECL of rubrene in benzonitrile. These workers have presented evidence that rubrene triplets are involved in the ECL process, although it was not possible for them to evaluate the relative percentage of rubrene singlets formed directly versus those formed by triplet-triplet annihilation.

Figure 13.21 shows a plot of $\log p_x$ versus $(t_r/t_f)^{1/2}$ over a wide range of t_f values; the terminology is that used in Section 4, pages 316–320. Over the range $t_f = 1$ sec to $t_f = 9.2$ sec, the plots are linear with average slopes of approximately -1.45 as predicted by (13.22). At large values of t_f, a deviation upward occurs as is evident for the curve for $t_f = 9.2$ sec. This is consistent with subsequent computer evaluation of the boundary value problem [55]. As t_f becomes smaller than 1 sec. the slope of the curve changes from ca. -1.45 to values ranging between -2.5 and -3.1, with an average value of -2.8. According to (13.22), a slope of -2.9 is to be expected when triplet-triplet annihilation occurs in the presence of a triplet quencher. Chang et al. [55] interpreted these measurements to mean that quenching of the rubrene triplet is occurring, the probable quenching agent being rubrene radical ions.

Quenching of rubrene triplets by radical ions depends on the relative probabilities of the rubrene triplet encountering a radical ion or another triplet. When t_f is small, it is more probable for a triplet to migrate out of the reaction zone (curve 8 in Fig. 13.16) than to encounter another triplet in the zone. Therefore the triplet will encounter a radical ion outside the zone and be quenched. When t_f is large, it is more probable that the triplet will remain in the reaction region and encounter another triplet, than to diffuse out of the zone and encounter a radical ion. One cannot be certain that the rubrene

Table 13.9 Energies and Spectral Data of Chemiluminescent Reactions between Hydrocarbon Anions and Wurster's Blue Cation (D⁺)[†] [92]

A	$E(A^-/A)$ versus SCE (V)	$-\Delta H(A^- + D^+)$ (eV)	$\Delta E(A^*)$ (eV)	$\Delta E(A^*)$ (eV)	Chemiluminescence Bands (kK) Fluorescence Bands (kK)						
Chrysene	−2.30	2.66	2.44	3.43	27.6	26.3	24.9	23.5	19.8	18.7	17.4
					27.6	26.25	24.8	23.3	19.9‡	18.6‡	17.1‡
Picene	−2.28	2.64	2.58	3.31	26.4	25.1	23.8	22.4	—	—	—
					26.4	25.05	23.7	22.3	—	—	—
Pyrene	−2.10	2.46	2.09	3.34	26.7	26.1	25.5	—	21.0	—	—
					26.8	26.1	25.5	—	20.9§	—	—
1,2-Benzan-thracene	−2.00	2.36	2.05	3.22	25.9	24.5	23.0	—	—	—	—
					25.9	24.5	23.0	—	—	—	—
Anthracene	−1.96	2.32	1.82	3.29	26.3	25.0	23.6	22.3	—	—	—
					26.4	25.0	23.6	22.4	—	—	—
Perylene	−1.65	2.01	1.55	2.83	22.3	21.2	19.8	—	—	—	—
					22.4	21.1	19.9	—	—	—	—
Tetracene	−1.54	1.90	1.28	2.60	21.1	19.8	18.5	—	—	—	—
					21.0	19.7	18.5	—	—	—	—
Pentacene	−1.36	1.72	≤1.0	2.12	No chemiluminescence						

[†] $E(D/D^+) = 0.16$ V. A. Zweig, J. E. Lancaster, M. T. Neglia, W. H. Jura [*J. Am. Chem. Soc.*, **86**, 4130 (1964)] measured −0.10 V versus Ag/Ag⁺ (0.01 N). This value should be increased by 0.26 V, which is the potential of this reference electrode measured against the saturated calomel electrode [R. C. Larson, R. T. Iwamoto, and R. N. Adams, *Anal. Chim. Acta*, **25**, 371 (1961).]
 [‡] Phosphorescence bands.
 [§] Excimer band.

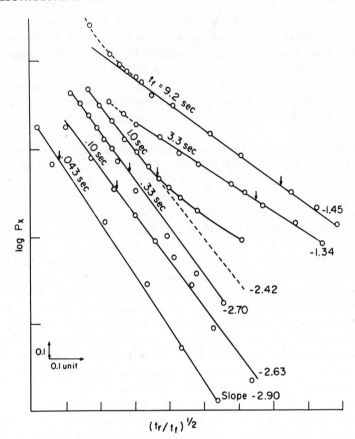

Fig. 13.21 Plots of log Px versus $(t_r/t_f)^{1/2}$ for values of t_f as indicated. Plots have been displaced along abscissa to avoid overlap. Plots are displaced along ordinate because of gain of recorder amplifier. Small vertical arrows are located at $(t_r/t_f)^{1/2} = 0.75$.

triplets are being quenched by the radical ions in absence of evidence for quenching by an independent method. However, these results, coupled with those of Weller and Zachariasse [92], constitute reasonable evidence that triplet-triplet annihilation is involved to some extent in the ECL of rubrene.

Visco and Chandross [54] have considered the occurrence of triplet-triplet annihilation for the case of rubrene to be questionable, based on the energy levels of naphthacene. They consider that if the shift on the π,π-triplet of rubrene were the same as on the π,π-singlet relative to naphthacene there would be insufficient energy for the rubrene triplet to form an excited singlet state by triplet-triplet annihilation. Likewise, Zweig et al. [61, 101] have found no effect of triplet quenchers on the ECL of substituted benzofurans, isoindoles, and tetracene. They have interpreted these results to mean that triplet-triplet annihilation is not significant in the ECL of these compounds. Likewise, Parker and Short have considered the mechanism of triplet-triplet annihilation unlikely in the ECL of 9,10-dimethylanthracene in DMF because extrapolation of ϕ_D/ϕ_M for ECL should be equal to the same ratio for photoexcited delayed fluorescence if triplet-triplet annihilation occurs. However, they observed this behavior only at high temperatures and at high applied voltages.

Attempting to reconcile the data on triplet-triplet annihilation, both pro and con, points out some interesting results. The fact that Zweig et al. [61, 101] did not observe triplet quenching of ECL is not conclusive because they did not study the effect of the quenchers on the triplets by an independent method. Also, according to Table 13.6, there is sufficient energy from the cation-anion annihilation reaction in their compounds to produce excited singlet states directly. Therefore triplet-triplet annihilation may not occur.

The evidence put forth by Parker and Short against triplet-triplet annihilation must be viewed with caution because of the excursion of their electrode potentials into the region of solvent decomposition and the known effects such solvent decomposition products can have on ECL intensities. Because of the large energy discrepancy for 9,10-dimethylanthracene for ECL by the singlet mechanism, it seems likely that if triplet-triplet annihilation occurs for other compounds it would be likely for 9,10-dimethylanthracene as well. The arguments put forth by Visco and Chandross [54] against the occurrence of triplet-triplet annihilation in rubrene are not necessarily valid. Because the ECL efficiency of rubrene is low, it is altogether possible that thermal activation could supply the energy necessary to overcome the discrepancy calculated for the energy-doubling process. In fact, this may be the explanation for the occurrence of ECL in tetracene itself, in which triplet-triplet annihilation is just slightly short of the energy necessary to form an excited singlet state.

In summary, it appears that triplet-triplet annihilation probably does account for some ECL in a number of systems. In those systems in which there is a large energy discrepancy (ca. 0.5 V), it is probably the major ECL mechanism. In systems in which the energy discrepancy is small (<0.1 V) triplet-triplet annihilation and direct singlet formation are probably competitive mechanisms. In systems in which there is clearly sufficient energy to form the excited singlet state directly, triplet-triplet annihilation probably still occurs to some extent, considering the statistical preference for triplet production by electron transfer reactions.

Acknowledgments

I want to thank the United States Atomic Energy Commission for support of our chemiluminescence research under contract AT(30-1)-905, and the

Massachusetts Institute of Technology Laboratory for Nuclear Science for their support.

Many persons have contributed significantly to the work described in this chapter: G. D. Short, R. Lansbury, R. Bardsley, J. Chang, S. Ness, K. D. Legg, T. C. Werner, and B. Watne deserving special thanks. I want to acknowledge very fruitful discussions with J. P. Paris in the early stages of our ECL work and to thank E. A. Chandross, A. J. Bard, and G. J. Hoytink for letters describing early stages of their ECL work; A. Weller for providing corrected data; and Mrs. Linda Margolis for typing the manuscript.

I particularly want to thank Professor David Roe (now of the Oregon Graduate Center) for a very beneficial and enjoyable collaboration while we were both at Massachusetts Institute of Technology.

References

1. H. F. Ivey, *Electroluminescence and Related Effects*, Academic, New York, 1963.
2. G. G. Guibault, Ed., *Fluorescence: Theory, Instrumentation, and Practice*, Marcel Dekker, New York, 1967.
3. D. M. Hercules, Ed., *Fluorescence and Phosphorescence Analysis*, Wiley, New York, 1966.
4. H. P. Kallmann and G. M. Spruch, Eds., *Luminescence of Organic and Inorganic Materials*, Wiley, New York, 1962.
5. C. A. Parker, *Photoluminescence of Solutions*, Elsevier, Amsterdam, 1968.
6. W. W. Piper and F. E. Williams, *Phys. Rev.*, **98**, 1809 (1955).
7. M. A. Lampert, *Rept. Prog. Phys.*, **27**, 329 (1964).
8. H. Kallmann and M. Pope, *J. Chem. Phys.*, **32**, 300 (1960).
9. H. Kallmann and M. Pope, *Rev. Sci. Inst.*, **30**, 44 (1959).
10. P. Mark and W. Helfrich, *J. Appl. Phys.*, **33**, 205 (1962).
11. M. Pope, H. P. Kallmann, and P. Magnante, *J. Chem. Phys.*, **38**, 2042 (1963).
12. M. Sano, M. Pope, and H. Kallmann, *J. Chem. Phys.*, **43**, 2920 (1965).
13. W. Helfrich and W. G. Schneider, *Phys. Rev. Letters*, **14**, 229 (1965).
14. W. Helfrich and W. G. Schneider, *J. Chem. Phys.*, **44**, 2902 (1966).
15. G. E. Johnson, W. M. McClain, and A. C. Albrecht, *J. Chem. Phys.*, **43**, 2911 (1965).
16. A. Bernanose, M. Comte, and P. Vovaux, *J. Chim. Phys.*, **50**, 64 (1953).
17. A. Bernanose and P. Vovaux, *J. Chim. Phys.*, **50**, 261 (1953).
18. A. Bernanose and P. Vovaux, *Bull. Soc., Chim. France*, **20**, 962 (1953).
19. A. Bernanose and F. Michon, *J. Chim. Phys.*, **51**, 622 (1954).
20. A. Bernanose and G. Marquet, *J. Chim. Phys.*, **51**, 255 (1954).
21. A. Bernanose, *J. Chim. Phys.*, **52**, 396 (1955).
22. A. Bernanose and P. Vovaux, *J. Chim. Phys.*, **52**, 508 (1955).
23. A. Bernanose, *Brit. J. Appl. Phys.*, **6**, 554 (1955).
24. A. Bernanose and P. Vovaux, *Bull. Soc. Chim. France*, **20**, 962 (1953).

25. S. Namba, M. Yoshizawa, and H. Tamura, *Oyo Butsuri*, **28**, 439 (1959).
26. L. Tumerman and B. A. Czayanov, *Investigations on Experimental and Theoretical Physics*, Moscow, 1959, p. 231.
27. L. Tumerman, *Izv. Akad. Nauk. SSSR Ser. Fiz.*, **20**, 552 (1956).
28. H. Lozykowski and H. Meczynska, *Bull. Acad. Polon. Sci. Ser. Sci. Chim.*, **9**, 235 (1961).
29. E. F. Gurnee and R. T. Fernandez, U.S. Patent 3,172,862, March 9, 1965.
30. E. F. Gurnee, *Organic Crystal Symposium*, National Research Council, Ottawa, Canada, October 1962, p. 109.
31. W. Lehmann, *J. Electrochem. Soc.*, **109**, 540 (1962).
32. G. D. Short and D. M. Hercules, *J. Am. Chem. Soc.*, **87**, 1439 (1965).
33. N. Harvey, *J. Phys. Chem.*, **33**, 1456 (1929).
34. T. Kuwana, B. Epstein, and E. Seo, *J. Phys. Chem.*, **67**, 2243 (1963).
35. T. Kuwana, *J. Electroanal. Chem.*, **6**, 164 (1963).
36. B. Epstein and T. Kuwana, *Photochem. Photobiol.*, **4**, 1157 (1965).
37. B. Epstein and T. Kuwana, *J. Electroanal. Chem.*, **15**, 389 (1967).
38. B. Epstein and T. Kuwana, *Photochem. Photobiol.*, **6**, 605 (1967).
39. V. Yo. Shlyapintokh, L. M. Postnikov, O. N. Karpukhin, and A. Ya. Veretil'nyi, *Zh. Fiz. Khim.*, **37**, 2374 (1963).
40. T. C. Werner and D. M. Hercules, unpublished studies, Massachusetts Institute of Technology, Cambridge, Massachusetts, 1967.
41. J. M. Bader and T. Kuwana, *J. Electroanal. Chem.*, **10**, 104 (1965).
42. R. T. Dufford, D. Nightingale, and L. W. Gaddum, *J. Am. Chem. Soc.*, **49**, 1858 (1927).
43. R. L. Bardsley and D. M. Hercules, *J. Am. Chem. Soc.*, **90**, 4545 (1968).
44. B. Tamamushi and H. Akiyama, *Trans. Faraday Soc.*, **35**, 491 (1939).
45. K. D. Legg and D. M. Hercules, *J. Am. Chem. Soc.*, **91**, 1902 (1969).
46. G. Ahnstrom, *Acta Chem. Scand.*, **15**, 463 (1961).
47. D. M. Hercules, *Science*, **145**, 3634 (1964).
48. R. E. Visco and E. A. Chandross, *J. Am. Chem. Soc.*, **86**, 5350 (1964).
49. E. A. Chandross, J. W. Longworth, and R. E. Visco, *J. Am. Chem. Soc.*, **87**, 3259 (1965).
50. A. Zweig, D. L. Maricle, J. S. Brinen, and A. H. Maurer, *J. Am. Chem. Soc.*, **89**, 473 (1967).
51. D. M. Hercules, R. C. Lansbury, and D. K. Roe, *J. Am. Chem. Soc.*, **88**, 4578 (1966).
52. K. S. V. Santhanam and A. J. Bard, *J. Am. Chem. Soc.*, **87**, 139 (1965).
53. B. Brocklehurst and R. D. Russell, *Nature*, **213**, 65 (1967).
54. R. E. Visco and E. A. Chandross, *Electrochim. Acta*, **13**, 1187 (1968).
55. J. Chang, D. M. Hercules, and D. K. Roe, *Electrochim. Acta*, **13**, 1197 (1968).
56. M. E. Peover, "Electrochemistry of Aromatic Hydrocarbons and Related Substances," in *Electroanalytical Chemistry*, A. J. Bard, Ed., Marcel Dekker, New York, 1966, Chapter 1.
57. B. M. Watne, Sc.B. Thesis, Massachusetts Institute of Technology, Cambridge, Massachusetts, June 1967.
58. S. A. Cruser and A. J. Bard, *Anal. Letters*, **1**, 11 (1967).

59. A. J. Bard, K. S. V. Santhanam, S. A. Cruser, and L. R. Faulkner, "Electro-generated Chemiluminescence," in *Fluorescence: Theory, Instrumentation and Practice*, G. G. Guilbault, Ed., Marcel Dekker, New York, 1967, Chapter 14, p. 627.

60. J. T. Maloy, K. B. Prater, and A. J. Bard, *J. Phys. Chem.*, **72,** 4348 (1968).

61. A. Zweig, A. K. Hoffmann, D. L. Maricle, and A. H. Maurer, *J. Am. Chem. Soc.*, **90,** 261 (1968).

62. A. Zweig, G. Metzke, A. Maurer, and B. G. Roberts, *J. Am. Chem. Soc.*, **89,** 4091 (1967).

63. D. L. Maricle, A. Zweig, A. H. Maurer, and J. S. Brinen, *Electrochim. Acta*, **13,** 1209 (1968).

64. C. A. Parker and S. D. Short, *Trans. Faraday Soc.*, **63,** 2618 (1967).

65. E. J. Majeski, J. D. Stuart, and W. E. Ohnesorge, *J. Am. Chem. Soc.*, **90,** 633 (1968).

66. B. Fleet, G. F. Kirkbright, and C. J. Pickford, *Talanta*, **15,** 566 (1968).

67. R. E. Soida and W. S. Koski, *J. Am. Chem Soc.*, **87,** 5573 (1965).

68. P. A. Malachesky, L. S. Marcoux, and R. N. Adams, *J. Phys. Chem.*, **70,** 2064 (1966).

69. M. E. Peover and B. S. White, *J. Electroanal. Chem.*, **13,** 93 (1967).

70. J. Phelps, K. S. V. Santhanam, and A. J. Bard, *J. Am. Chem. Soc.*, **89,** 1752 (1967).

71. L. S. Marcoux, J. M. Fritsch, and R. N. Adams, *J. Am. Chem. Soc.*, 5766 (1967).

72. R. E. Sioda, *J. Phys. Chem.*, **72,** 2322 (1968).

73. D. L. Maricle and A. Maurer, *J. Am. Chem. Soc.*, **89,** 188 (1967).

74. A. Zweig, A. H. Maurer, and B. G. Roberts, *J. Org. Chem.*, **32,** 1322 (1967).

75. A. Zweig, G. Metzler, A. Maurer, and B. G. Roberts, *J. Am. Chem. Soc.*, **88,** 2864 (1966).

76. J. B. Birks, M. D. Lumb, and I. H. Munro, *Proc. Roy. Soc. (London)*, **280,** 289 (1964).

77. R. A. Marcus, *Ann. Rev. Phys. Chem.*, **15,** 155 (1964).

78. R. A. Marcus, *J. Chem. Phys.*, **43,** 2654 (1965).

79. R. A. Marcus, *Electrochim. Acta.*, **13,** 995 (1968).

80. G. J. Hoytink, *Discussions Faraday Soc.*, **45,** 14 (1968).

81. S. W. Feldberg, *J. Amer. Chem. Soc.*, **88,** 390 (1966).

82. R. Livingston and H. R. Leonhardt, *J. Phys. Chem.*, **72,** 2254 (1968).

83. S. W. Feldberg, *J. Phys. Chem.*, **70,** 3928 (1966).

84. T. Kuwana, "Photochemistry and Electroluminescence," in *Electroanalytical Chemistry*, A. J. Bard, Ed., Vol. 1, Marcel Dekker, New York, 1966, Chapter 3, p. 197.

85. S. A. Cruser and A. J. Bard, *J. Am. Chem. Soc.*, **91,** 267 (1969).

86. J. Ferguson, *J. Chen. Phys.*, **43,** 306 (1965).

87. E. A. Chandross, *J. Chem. Phys.*, **43,** 4175 (1965).

88. E. A. Chandross and J. Ferguson, *J. Chem. Phys.*, **45,** 397 (1966).

89. E. A. Chandross and J. Ferguson, *J. Chem. Phys.*, **45,** 3564 (1966).

90. E. A. Chandross, J. Ferguson, and E. G. McRae, *J. Chem. Phys.*, **45**, 3546 (1966).
91. E. A. Chandross and J. Ferguson, *J. Chem. Phys.*, **45**, 3554 (1966).
92. A. Weller and K. Zachariasse, *J. Chem. Phys.*, **46**, 4984 (1967).
93. N. Yamamoto, Y. Nakato, and H. Tsubomura, *Bull. Chem. Soc. Japan*, **40**, 451 (1967).
94. H. Beens, H. Knibbe, and A. Weller, *J. Chem. Phys.*, **47**, 1183 (1967).
95. H. Knibbe, D. Rehm, and A. Weller, *Z. Phys. Chem. N. F.*, **56**, 95 (1967).
96. H. Knibbe and A. Weller, *Z. Phys. Chem. N. F.*, **56**, 99 (1967).
97. L. R. Faulkner and A. J. Bard, *J. Am. Chem. Soc.*, **90**, 6284 (1968).
98. J. Chang, T. C. Werner, and D. M. Hercules, 155th National Meeting, American Chemical Society, March 31–April 5, 1968, San Francisco, California, Paper No. R042., *J. Amer. Chem. Soc.*, **92**, 763 (1970).
99. M. Sano and F. Egusa, *Bull. Chem. Soc. Japan*, **41**, 1490 (1968).
100. Y. Angel and R. Signore, *Compt. Rend.*, **266**, 870 (1968).
101. A. Zweig, A. K. Hoffmann, D. L. Maricle, and A. H. Maurer, *Chem. Commun.*, **1967**, 106.
102. C. A. Parker and C. G. Hatchard, *J. Phys. Chem.*, **66**, 2506 (1962).
103. E. A. Chandross and R. E. Visco, *J. Phys. Chem.*, **72**, 378 (1968).
104. A. Zweig and D. L. Maricle, *J. Phys. Chem.*, **72**, 377 (1968).
105. C. A. Parker and G. D. Short, *J. Phys. Chem.*, **72**, 3071 (1968).
106. I. Berlman, *Handbook of Fluorescence Spectra of Organic Molecules*, Academic, New York, 1965.
107. G. J. Hoytink, *Rec. Trav. Chim.*, **74**, 1525 (1955).
108. N. L. Weinberg and H. R. Weinberg, *Chem. Rev.*, **68**, 449 (1968).
109. G. J. Hoytink, *Rec. Trav. Chim.*, **77**, 555 (1968).

Chapter **XIV**

ZONE ELECTROPHORESIS

Seymour L. Kirschner

I INTRODUCTION

Electrophoresis is the electrokinetic method that physically separates charged particles in an aqueous medium under the influence of an electric field. Many systems, procedures, and apparatus have been developed since

Picton and Linder [1] introduced moving boundary electrophoresis. However, this technique was not accepted until Tiselius [2] described a substantially improved apparatus. The theory, methodology, applications, and interpretation of separation pattern, as well as the advantages and disadvantages, of the Tiselius method were reviewed by Bull [3], Moore [4], Tiselius [5], and Longworth [6]. Disadvantages of the moving boundary technique include problems in stabilizing the boundaries of the migrating particles, boundary anomalies, incomplete separation of the molecules, the need for large samples, and costly complicated equipment.

All electrophoresis systems contain an electrical field and charged particles in an electrically conducting liquid medium. In moving boundary electrophoresis the particles move freely in solution and form a boundary. The boundaries are detected by optically measuring the changes in the refractive index throughout the solution. In zone electrophoresis the particles migrate in liquid contained in a relatively inert stabilizing medium. When separated, the particles remain as discrete areas or zones which are detected by physical, chemical, or biological methods.

The many disadvantages associated with moving boundary electrophoresis prevented its widespread use as an analytical separation technique. Researchers required and actively sought simpler, less costly methods. At the same time much research was undertaken on separation techniques, especially those involving chromatography, and rapid advances using paper chromatography for separating lower-molecular-weight polar compounds occurred. However, the limitations of paper chromatography, for example, the inability to separate large molecules, particularly proteins, were soon evident and prompted reconsideration of electrophoresis on support media. Tiselius [5] recently stated that the real breakthrough in the field of electrophoretic analysis and its clinical application in certain pathological conditions came with the introduction of the much simpler method of filter paper electrophoresis compared to moving boundary electrophoresis.

Popularization and development of zone electrophoresis occurred after 1950 even though it was introduced by Lodge in 1886. Strickland [7–9] has biennially reviewed the electrophoresis literature listing 946, 2484, and 2703 references in each succeeding review. In 1962 the electrophoresis review by Strickland [10] was titled electrochromatography and contained only 184 references.

Zone electrophoresis is an excellent method for isolating, separating, characterizing, and identifying macromolecules, for example, proteins. Consequently, it is extensively used for the analysis of biological tissues and fluids, for genetic differentiation, and for the characterization of different molecular forms of enzymes as well as other biologically important macromolecules and their subunits. Analytical electrophoresis techniques are now routinely used in biological, biochemical, toxicological, and control laboratories. Electrophoresis is considered a necessary diagnostic technique in clinical laboratories. It should, however, be understood that identical electrophoretic mobility does not necessarily indicate molecular identity.

Preparative electrophoresis techniques allowing separation on a much larger scale are being improved. This technique should become useful to the organic chemist.

The purpose of this chapter is to describe the fundamentals of zone electrophoresis, to describe some factors affecting the quality of electrophoretic separations, and to discuss some representative applications and separations.

2 THE INFLUENCE OF VARIOUS FACTORS UPON THE MIGRATION OF CHARGED PARTICLES

General

The rate and direction of particle movement in zone electrophoresis depends upon many interrelated factors which involve the strength of the electrical field, character of the particle, and type of electrically conducting medium. Under working conditions these factors may enhance or retard the migration, thereby making it difficult to predict the results of a given separation. The following discussion of influencing factors provides generalities and guidelines to help the investigator empirically evaluate electrophoretic operating conditions.

When a direct electric current is passed through a liquid medium containing charged particles, the positively charged cations move toward the cathode and the negatively charged anions move toward the anode. A dry cell battery is a usable but impractical dc power source compared to a rectified ac source that is filtered to remove ripple. The filtered dc electrical energy is conducted to the cathode which supplies free electrons to the electrolyte (buffer) solution. The electrons then flow through the buffer-containing, stabilizing medium, through the anode, and back into the power supply thereby completing the circuit. Ions in the electrolyte solution carry the current and the passage of current (I) through an electrically conducting medium is expressed by Ohm's law:

$$V_{volts} = R_{ohms} \times I_{amps} \qquad (14.1)$$

Potential and/or Current

Two different physical factors, namely, electrical field and heat, originate from the electrical energy during electrophoresis. The electrical field or motive force F causes migration of the charged particles in the buffer and sample. When all other factors are maintained constant, the motive force exerted on the charged particle is the product of the net charge q and the field strength on the particle. This is shown in (14.2):

$$F = qE = q\frac{V}{x}.\qquad(14.2)$$

The field strength, in volts per centimeter, is the electrical potential V divided by the distance x between the electrodes as measured where the stabilizing bed contacts the buffer. From the above expression it is seen that the migration of a charged particle can be increased by increasing the voltage or by decreasing the distance between the electrodes, for example, at a potential of 200 V the field strength is 100 V/cm when the electrodes are 2 cm apart and 10 V/cm at 20-cm separation. The field strength is only 20 V/cm at 400 V with a 20-cm separation. In practice, the rate of migration is increased by increasing the voltage (Fig. 14.1).

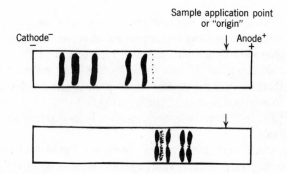

Fig. 14.1   Electrophoregrams of a mixture of six amino acids at 3000 V for 25 min (top) and 500 V for 110 min.

Smith [11] considered a potential gradient greater than 20 V/cm as the distinguishing condition between high- and low-voltage paper electrophoresis. When other stabilizing media are used, approximately 30–40 V/cm is the distinguishing condition.

If the voltage is increased while maintaining constant resistance, the current will increase as governed by Ohm's law. These conditions generate heat according to Joule's law of electric heating:

$$P = VI = I^2R,\qquad(14.3)$$

where power P is measured in watts. The resulting temperature rise causes the particle mobility and evaporation of liquid from the stabilizing medium to increase. If a constant-voltage power supply is used, these events lead to a

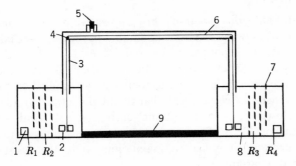

Fig. 14.2a Diagrammatic cross-section representation of a typical zone electrophoresis chamber. 1, Electrode preferably running the full length of the electrode compartment; R_1, R_4, resistances between electrode and buffer; R_2, R_3, resistances of the buffer; 2, plastic-coated magnets to hold strip of wick, paper or membrane taut; 3, inner support wall of chamber; 4, stabilizing medium support; 5, device in tight fitting lid allowing sample application with little loss of vapor-saturated atmosphere; 6, stabilizing medium; R_6, resistance of the stabilizing medium; 7, baffles separating electrode and buffer compartments; 8, buffer; 9, chamber base.

steadily decreasing resistance in the stabilizing medium and a further rise in current. The initial buffer pH, conductivity, and ionic strength are then modified. In extreme situations sufficient heat is generated to burn or char the stabilizing medium.

With a constant-current power supply, any increase in current flow is automatically compensated by voltage drop, resulting in decreased field strength and migration velocity. It is therefore preferable to operate at constant current rather than constant voltage.

To show how voltage gradient irregularities affect the quality of electrophoresis, Strickland [12] considered an electrophoretic system as a voltage divider. This is shown diagrammatically for a typical zone electrophoresis chamber (Fig. 14.2a) and its electrical schematic (Fig. 14.2b) showing

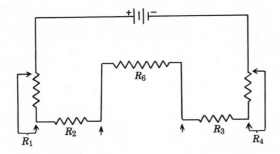

Fig. 14.2b Electrical schematic showing resistances in analogous positions of the electrophoresis chamber.

resistances in analogous positions. For illustrative purposes only the resistances R_1 and R_4 between electrode and liquid in the electrode compartment, the resistance R_2 and R_3 of the buffer, and the resistance R_6 in the stabilizing medium are shown. Strickland stated that voltage gradients can differ across every resistance interval even if the total voltage applied to the system is maintained constant. These local changes in potential variably affect ion migration. However, with a constant-current supply and varying total resistance, the problem of maintaining a constant-voltage gradient in the stabilizing medium simplifies to maintaining only the resistance in the stabilizing bed invariant.

Character of the Particle

Those substances possessing no net charge do not migrate when subjected to a potential difference. Particles with a net negative charge migrate toward the anode and those with a net positive charge migrate toward the cathode. The net particle charge results from the ionization of intrinsic groups or from buffer-induced charges. The buffer is considered as any electrically conductive solution. The pH of the buffer and pK value(s) of the dissociable groups are of prime importance in particle mobility because they determine the net charge exhibited by most particles. An example of this principle is given in Fig. 14.1 and described in Section 4.

Amphoteric substances such as amino acids or proteins behave as anions or cations, depending upon the pH of the buffer, and do not migrate at the isoelectric point (pH at which the particle has a zero net charge). At a pH below the isoelectric point the amphoteric particle exists as a cation, and at a pH above the isoelectric point it exists as an anion. Thus at pH 2.0 all amino acids migrate toward the cathode (Fig. 14.1) because the carboxyl group is protonated. However, at the very alkaline pH 12.0, all amino acids are completely dissociated (having relinquished the amino group proton) and act as anions. As a case in point, the isoelectric point of glycine is at pH 6.1 and the two dissociation constants are: $pK_1 = 2.4$ and $pK_2 = 9.5$. At a buffer pH less than 2.4, glycine rapidly migrates toward the cathode; around pH 6.1 glycine does not migrate; and at a pH above 9.5 it rapidly migrates toward the anode. The rate of migration depends on the amount of dissociation of each of the ionizable groups at the particular pH considered. As expected, completely dissociated molecules migrate more rapidly than partially dissociated molecules.

Neutral particles may be caused to migrate in an electrophoretic system if a component of the buffer associates with the particle. Carbohydrates, for example, complex in borate buffer with the borate anions and thereby electrophoretically migrate to the anode. The rate of migration is a function of the number of borate anions that complex with the neutral particles, the pH, the concentration of electrolyte, and the molecular structure of the particle.

In the electrophoretic system every charged particle migrates according to individual properties. This phenomenon may be visualized as zones of individual ionic species moving in both directions throughout the fluid in the buffer compartments and stabilizing medium. The ions in free solution in the buffer compartments rapidly migrate into the stabilized bed. They then move slowly through the bed at the opposite electrode compartment at a slower rate than they entered the bed. This sets up a sharply defined, highly concentrated leading edge for each particular ionic species. The leading edge progressively diminishes as the supply of ions from the buffer compartment becomes exhausted. These so-called concentration waves progress at different rates for each ionic species present. The conductivity and pH of the buffer as well as the rate of electroosmotic (defined in the discussion on stabilizing media) flow in each section of the stabilizing medium is thereby modified according to the laws of equilibrium. Thus the electrophoresis system is only homogeneous or stabilized prior to subjecting it to the electrical field.

When the electrical current is applied, the electrolyte ions move much faster than the charged macromolecules of the sample and sweep over the macromolecules as tides. Thus the migration rates of the sample constituents are influenced. To minimize the distortions in an electrophoregram (electrophoretic pattern) caused by concentration tides and electroosmotic flow, it is necessary to bring the stabilizing medium into a steady state. This may be accomplished by running the apparatus for a period of time with buffer recycling that maintains the supply of ions in the buffer compartments. The sample is introduced after the steady state is attained. If the electrolyte in the stabilizing medium is maintained in the steady state throughout the electrophoretic run (as in the ideal case), each charged particle will migrate linearly with time.

When all parameters are held constant, relatively small molecules, such as amino acids, migrate at a faster rate than larger molecules, such as proteins. The migration rate of a particle is also governed by its shape. As a case in point, a thin, oval-shaped molecule migrates faster than a spherical molecule.

Electrophoretic behavior of particles may be considered (in the simplest case) as similar in behavior to an isolated, charged sphere. At the steady state the migration-producing force given in (14.4) is equated to the migration resistance factor for spheres in solution given by the Stokes factor $6\pi r\eta u$, where η is the viscosity of the medium, r the radius, and u the particle velocity through the medium.

Thus

$$qE = 6\pi r\eta u, \qquad (14.4)$$

and, rearranging:

$$u = \frac{qE}{6\pi r \eta}.$$ (14.5)

From these simple considerations it can be seen that the velocity of a particle is directly proportional to net charge and field strength and inversely proportional to the size of the particle and the viscosity of the medium.

Electrically Conducting Medium

The inert support material and the electrolytic solution comprise the electrically conducting medium. The support material stabilizes the sample ions against dispersion caused by convective disturbances. Stabilizing media are discussed in detail later in this section and in Section 3.

Electrolyte

The electrolyte solution provides background electrolytes (ions) and liquid to the inert support material. The electrolytes carry the majority of the current; liquid is necessary for current to flow through the support bed.

BUFFERING CAPACITY

In order for the particles to exhibit constant migration rates, the electrolytic solution must have sufficient buffering capacity to maintain the pH during the electrophoretic run. This requires the buffer pH to be near the pK of the acid or base. Additionally, the dissociated ions should have the same migration velocity in order to avoid irregular distribution of buffer ions resulting from ionophoresis. Other desirable characteristics of the buffer include low conductivity (to avoid high current and undesirable effects of heat production) and monovalent ions (to avoid heavy double layers that decrease mobility exclusively). The latter characteristic is an aspect of ionic strength.

IONIC STRENGTH

The ionic strength of the buffer has another very important influence on particle mobility. High ionic strength buffer solutions generally yield lower mobilities because sample ions surrounded by the oppositely charged, excessive buffer ions are slowed down by their attraction. Thus decreasing the concentration of electrolyte ions increases the migration rate. However, this has a practical limit that is governed by the loss of the sharp discrete zones obtainable with high ionic strength buffers.

It is easy to calculate the ionic strength for a given buffer but not the actual strength inside the stabilizing medium. This is because of variations of water content in the bed, variations introduced by the sample itself, and local variations in field strength. These variations together with other considerations, make it impossible to measure absolute mobilities in stabilizing media. There are additional factors to consider in selecting a particular buffer, such as the isoelectric point of the particles to be separated, the solubilities of the particles in the buffer (sample ions if completely insoluble in the buffer do not migrate from the origin or form a comet), and the type of buffer (tris, acetate, Veronal, borate, citrate, phosphate, EDTA, barbitone, and so on).

PH

As previously discussed, the pH of the buffer is of prime importance because it determines the net charge of the migrating particle. However, use of an extreme pH may alter other properties of the particle(s) in the sample, for example, immunochemical reaction. This may negate an otherwise good separation that possibly could be accomplished under less harsh conditions.

TEMPERATURE

The temperature of the electrically conducting medium is also of prime importance. It directly and indirectly affects the electrolyte ions and charged particles. Increased temperature such as that generated during electrophoresis directly causes the particle and electrolyte ions to move faster. It also increases the current flow and the conductivity of the system. Indirect effects, primarily in the center section of the bed occur because of the increased evaporation of aqueous solvent. The resulting more concentrated ionic strength in the center of the bed decreases particle migration and causes a flow of water from the electrode chambers into the stabilizing medium toward the center of the bed. The charged particles of the sample then must travel against the flow of electrolyte which may cause separated zones to be altered or even recombined.

If the stabilizing medium is suspended in air, the edges present more evaporative surface than the midline. When evaporation occurs, a concentration gradient of buffer salts increasing from the midline to the edges is established. Under these conditions the sample particles migrate more rapidly at the less concentrated midline than at the edges because particle mobility increases with decreased ionic strength. Another indirect effect of a temperature rise is that the pH of the electrolyte solution may be sufficiently changed. This may affect the mobilities of incompletely dissociated sample molecules.

Stabilizing Medium

Zone electrophoresis has been done on many types of support materials. The most useful, successful, and popular materials have been filter paper [11, 13–16], gels prepared from agar [17–21], agarose [22, 23], starch [24–26], and acrylamide [27–32], and cellulose acetate membranes [33–38]. These media, considered as a polymeric matrix, contain many capillaries and exhibit differences in inertness relative to the electrical processes in electrophoresis.

Stabilizing media contain various types and amounts of ionizable groups. At a particular pH this factor may be pertinent, for example, filter paper and starch have a considerable number of carboxyl groups which become negatively charged at neutral and alkaline pH. Consequently, in these media the migration of positively charged particles is retarded by adsorption. This property is undesirable when it causes streaking (tailing, comets) or unduly prolongs the time required for separation. The amount of adsorption attributable to a given stabilizing medium may be determined by chromatography and/or electrophoresis in different directions followed by measurement of the extent of comet formation. Another method [39] uses the yellow dye Apolon, which has zero charge in the pH range of 3.3 to 9.3, as a visible nonmigrating marker.

Electroendosmosis is also caused by the ionized groups attached to the stabilizing medium. In alkaline buffers these negatively charged groups tend to move toward the anode. However, movement is not possible because of attachment to the stationary medium. To counter this restraint, positively charged water molecules (H_3O^+) migrate toward the cathode. The resulting electroosmotic water flow may augment or supplement the electromigration velocity of the sample particles. The extent of electroendosmotic effect upon migration velocity depends upon the buffer and stabilizing medium. Hard, thin filter paper exhibits much less electroosmotic effect than thick, soft paper at the same pH, and cellulose acetate membranes exhibit much less than paper.

Kunkel and Tiselius [16] and other investigators found that particles exhibit lower mobilities in zone electrophoresis media than in the free solution of moving boundary electrophoresis. The differences have been attributed to the tortuous path theory [16] and the barrier theory [40]. Simply, the barrier theory considers the particle as being slowed by collision with stabilizing medium structural molecules or by mechanical restriction of free pathways in the media. The tortuous path theory considers that the support medium structure presents extra distance or path length for the particle to travel. Giddings and Boyack [41–43] improved this theory by considering the additional factor of constriction, of tortuous path, and particle retardation attributable to absorption or adsorption in or on the ionized groups of the stabilizing medium. However, these considerations are only of importance if it is necessary to determine the true, absolute mobility of a molecule in a particular stabilizing medium. This need is rare and primarily of academic interest.

Another consideration of particle migration in stabilizing media is molecular sieving. The capillary spaces of starch, polyacrylamide gels, and Sephadex gels approach the molecular dimensions of the sample molecules and thereby influence migration. Preferential retardation of larger molecules occurs with starch and polyacrylamide gels because the gel structure acts as a barrier. However, in Sephadex gels the smallest molecules are retarded most because they penetrate into more of the gel structure and thereby increase their effective migration distance.

3 PRACTICAL CONCEPTS IN ZONE ELECTROPHORESIS

General

Researchers and manufacturers have been modifying and developing electrophoretic apparatus and techniques in order to qualitatitively and quantitatively expand the usefulness and overcome shortcomings of certain electrophoretic systems and procedures. These developments concern the strength of the electric field, the substances to be separated, the stabilizing medium, the electrophoretic chamber containing the electrodes, the electrically conducting liquid, and identification methods. Usually simplification ensues allowing the novice to obtain separations. However, simplification often cloaks the analytical difficulties. Thus some investigators and technicians use (and sometimes extend) the technique without considering the individual effects and interactions of the various factors involved in electrophoresis and understanding of the observed phenomena.

The apparatus for zone electrophoresis may be purchased or fabricated. Most commercially available apparatus is good and usually preferable to fabricated equipment. Martinek [44] recently tabulated the technicial characteristics of commercial electrophoresis equipment. Scherago [45] and Hull [46] compiled guides to commercially available laboratory equipment including electrophoresis. Most manufacturers provide excellent technical information on the capabilities and operation of their equipment. Techniques for separating, isolating, and identifying substances, as well as pertinent journal references, are usually obtainable from manufacturers' literature.

The relative merits of different electrophoresis apparatus depend primarily upon the stabilizing media used, the kinds of molecules to be detected, the number of samples to be examined in a given time, versatility, ease of operation, safety, and cost.

Power Supply

The dc power supply should be capable of providing either constant current or constant voltage (preferably both) after stabilization of the electrophoretic system. The relative low cost of more-than-adequate commercially available power supplies negates the need to assemble them from kits.

Practically all low-voltage electrophoretic separations can be accomplished with a power pack delivering up to 50 mA at 500 V. The less popular high-voltage technique requires a power supply capable of delivering upward of 100 mA at 3000 V.

Electrophoresis Chamber

The electrophoresis chamber contains the buffer reservoirs, electrodes, and the means of support for the stabilizing medium. The elaborateness and cost of the chamber is predicated on the applied potential gradient, the stabilizing medium, and the method to dissipate heat. Considerations in chamber design (not necessarily in order of importance) include:

1. Simplicity of operation
2. Ease of positioning and/or tensioning the stabilizing medium
3. Cost
4. Safety
5. Maintenance and ease of cleanliness
6. Sufficient height of stabilizing medium above the buffer level (to minimize the undesirable hydrodynamic flow of buffer from reservoirs to support medium)
7. Method for preventing loss of vapor-saturated air
8. Break and leak resistance
9. Electrodes running the full chamber length (preferably made of platinum because of its long life, unreactivity, and ease of cleaning)
10. Provision for heat dissipation by circulating cooling liquids
11. Possibility of electrode deposition of contaminating electrolytic decomposition products on the stabilizing medium
12. Minimization of the time required to saturate the chamber atmosphere
13. Versatility allowing use with more than one type of stabilizing medium
14. Means of equalizing buffer level in the electrode compartments
15. Chemical unreactivity of structural components

The stabilizing medium may be arranged in the chamber by suspending, supporting, enclosing, or immersing. Suspension and support techniques require the buffer solvent to be in equilibrium with the surrounding atmosphere and can only be used with low-voltage techniques. Enclosing the stabilizing medium between plates (either or both of which may be equipped for heat dissipation) or immersing in a coolant fluid eliminates the air space surrounding the stabilizing medium and saturation equilibration problems. High-voltage electrophoresis requires enclosure or immersion of the stabilizing medium and provision for cooling. Enclosed chamber arrangements equipped for circulating cooling liquid are best because they have the most cooling capacity and can completely eliminate evaporation.

The most common chambers are horizontal. Vertical chambers are used for certain electrophoretic systems, for example, disk electrophoresis. Further design details of electrophoresis chambers can be found in manufacturers' literature, patents, and publications by Block et al. [47], Peeters [48], Bier [49, 50], Durrum [51, 52], Williams et al. [53], Whitaker [54], Raymond [55], Gross [56], Yaron and Sober [57], Sargent [58], Clotten and Clotten [59] and Steere and Davis [60]. Additional references may be found in the literature review articles by Strickland [7–10].

Stabilizing (Support) Media

The various materials used for stabilizing media provide advantages and disadvantages. Selection of the "best" material for a particular separation is complex because empiricism and judgment by the investigator is necessary. Filter paper was the support material selected by Kunkel and Tiselius [16] to obtain serum protein separations similar to moving boundary results. Subsequently, a vast literature of applications and methodologies using paper electrophoresis was published (especially on proteins). This is understandable considering that paper is simple to use, economical, and readily available in many different grades.

The widespread use of paper exposed notable disadvantages. These include strong adsorption of proteins, comparatively high stain-absorbing capacity, and an inability to distinguish proteins on the basis of size. Thus paper poorly resolves proteins.

Paper is the best material for separating compounds of relatively low molecular weight especially by high- rather than low-voltage electrophoresis. Substances such as amino acids, simple peptides, and simple nucleotides are examples of low-molecular-weight compounds. The two-dimensional technique using electrophoresis in the first direction and chromatography in the second increases the effectiveness of separating and identifying amino acids and peptides.

Grabar and Williams [17] used agar gel to develop the immunoelectrophoretic technique because of its low adsorption to most proteins. The sharp zones resulting with agar gel are requisite for analysis of the complex immunochemical patterns. Other features of this support medium are ready availability, ease of preparation, and protein mobilities approaching those in free solution because agar forms a gel at very low concentrations. Agar can also handle large quantities of sample innocuously so that it is good for preparative electrophoresis.

Unfortunately, agars from various sources contain different amounts and types of contaminating substances bearing sulfate and carboxyl groups. The acidic nature of agar as a result of the presence of these contaminants cause marked electroendosmotic flow toward the cathode in most alkaline buffers. Consequently, it is necessary to purify the agar or purchase special agar. Hjertén [23] and others [61, 62] removed the acidic agaropectin fraction from the agar, leaving the purified neutral agarose fraction. Agarose causes very little endoosmosis and absorption of basic proteins compared to agar.

The most useful medium presently available for the routine examination of proteins is cellulose acetate membrane. Kohn [33, 34] first reported the use of this material for electrophoresis. Since then, applicability and procedures for use have been reported with increasing frequency. Advantages of cellulose acetate membranes include rapidity of electrophoretic protein separation and better resolution with little trailing compared to filter paper because cellulose acetate membranes are relatively pure and uniform. Additionally, stains and proteins are not strongly absorbed. Thus proteins migrate faster and excess stain is easily rinsed off. Quantitation of membranes is better because they are easily made transparent for direct optical scanning or can be easily eluted or dissolved for indirect quantitation.

Electroendoosmotic flow is a slight problem, as is fragility and the need to soak the membrane in buffer to produce the porous matrix. However, membranes have excellent wet strength and manufacturers have eliminated fragility by supporting the membranes. Decreased cost actually accrues because of the use of economical, simple electrophoretic chambers and short electrophoresis running time. Consequently, cellulose acetate membranes have supplanted the various support materials for protein electrophoresis in clinical and other routine laboratory applications.

Starch gel was first described by Smithies [24]. This material provides remarkably high resolving power because it combines differences in electrophoretic mobility with molecular sieving. Consequently, starch gel separations based on both molecular charge and dimension allowed Smithies and subsequent investigators to resolve between 20 and 30 human serum proteins in contrast to the five to eight zones on nonsieving media, for example, paper, cellulose acetate membranes, and agar. However, starch is not an ideal electrophoretic medium because it is difficult to prepare and obtain reproducibly, has little mechanical strength, and is opaque. Additionally, the resolving power varies between starches because of inherent differences in residual electric charge and consequent endoosmotic effects.

Polyacrylamide gel was suggested by Raymond [27, 28] as an improvement over starch gel. It is used either as horizontal or vertical slabs [27, 63] or as vertical cylinders in the disk electrophoresis technique [30, 32]. Gel electrophoresis media are distinguished by the ability to sieve or effect *molecular filtration*. Starch, acrylamide, and Sephadex are examples of gel media. Although porous, paper, cellulose acetate membrane, and agar are not gels.

Acrylamide gel is transparent, flexible, and stable. It is easily and reproducibly prepared from a highly soluble monomer mixture which is compatible with all types of buffers. Once formed, the gel is completely insoluble in water. The neutral gel does not exhibit electroendosmosis but can be modified to incorporate charged groups into the gel structure for an ion-exchange effect [64]. It provides rapid separations and requires a small quantity of even a dilute sample. Most importantly, it can readily be prepared in a wide range of pore sizes allowing a high degree of resolution. However, too fine resolutions make it difficult to interpret the electrophoregram from a complex multicomponent biological sample and thereby have little practical application [29]. Indeed, the capability of currently available densitometers may be exceeded. Hansl [65] discussed various aspects of this problem.

Special Requirements of Electrophoretic Equipment

A number of requirements for electrophoretic systems have been discussed, but some rate special mention.

Safety

The amount of current flowing (amperage) is the determining factor in electrical shock. The "let-go" threshold for most persons is 15 mA. Cellulose acetate membrane separations are run between 10 and 25 mA, polyacrylamide gel equipment requires between 50 and 100 mA, and high-voltage paper electrophoresis equipment regularly operates at amperages greater than 100 mA. These are dangerous, possibly lethal conditions and great care in the design and manufacture of equipment must be exercised. Spencer and co-workers [66] reported on a lethal accident and suggested precautions such as fail-safe methods designed into the equipment.

Heat Dissipation

Excessive heat must be kept under control and may require a regulated system in order to prevent evaporation of buffer from the support medium, for example, paper [67], acrylamide gel [29]. Heat dissipation must be efficient and uniform in all parts of the stabilizing medium. It must, however, not be overlooked that support materials are poor heat conductors. A further constraint is that the heat-dissipating material between the cooling liquid and stabilizing medium must be electrically highly insulating. Unfortunately, such insulating materials generally are rather poor heat conductors. Another requirement is that the temperature gradient between the stabilizing medium and cooling liquid be as low as possible, thereby allowing stable equilibria.

Handling

Apparatus operation should be relatively simple, versatile to permit use with different stabilizing media, capable of routinization, and easily cleaned and maintained.

Nomenclature

The word electrophoresis has been combined with many other words to indicate a particular characteristic, modification, or specialized application of the basic electrophoretic technique. Confusion in terminology has fortunately decreased because certain terms are no longer used. Some of the terminologies presently in use include: immunoelectrophoresis; gel electrophoresis; electrochromatography; low- and high-voltage electrophoresis; analytical, column, preparative, and microelectrophoresis; paper, sucrose density gradient, cellulose acetate membrane, thin-layer, starch block, starch, and polyacrylamide gel electrophoresis; continuous flow; liquid, continuous particle, and crossing electrophoresis; zone and free or moving boundary electrophoresis. Strickland [8] discussed the problem of terminology and suggested the word *electrophoregram* for the sample pattern produced by electrophoresis rather than such words as electrophoretogram, zymogram, electropherogram, electrochromatogram, proteinogram, and electrophoretic pattern.

Standardization, Detection, and Quantitation

Even carefully controlled conditions between electrophoretic runs are unlikely to yield the same migration rates for duplicate samples. Differences are to be expected because there are a number of sources and causes of variation. To minimize variation it is necessary to standardize apparatus, supplies, and technique. Ranges of acceptable values for the various samples electrophoresed should be established.

It is recommended that stable reference compounds be periodically run to ensure that unaccountable variation has not occurred. Appropriate reference compounds can serve to adjust slight differences that occur from run to run. Appropriate reference dyes have been suggested [39] and are easily obtained commercially.

Detection of the separated components is usually accomplished on the electrophoregram. Detection techniques appropriate to one stabilizing medium may not necessarily be utilizable with another unless modified. This is obvious when considering the differences in physical and chemical properties of the different media.

There is no single reagent that can detect all substances. Detection may be accomplished by direct colorimetric straining, ultraviolet fluorescence or absorbance, or by chemical reaction(s) of specific fractions with special reagents.

Zone electrophoresis readily lends itself to quantitation by various methods. These methods include direct densitometric scanning of the colored electrophoregram zones or indirectly by eluting the stain from each zone and measuring in a spectrophotometer. Commercial scanning densitometers now provide many advantages over the elution method including ease, rapidity, cost, and accuracy. It must be realized that these quantitation methods only give the relative density in each zone. Measurement of the total substance present is required if the proportions are to be converted to absolute values.

4 APPLICATIONS

It is neither the purpose of this chapter nor is it possible to give a review of the literature on electrophoresis applications, methodologies, and examples of separations. The comprehensive biennial reviews [7–9], manufacturers' literature, and a recent practical laboratory manual by Nerenberg [68] cover these topics. However, a few typical applications and separations are presented in this section with comments on the exhibited electrophoretic principles. The examples given are on paper and cellulose acetate membranes primarily because most of the author's experience has been with these stabilizing media.

Separation of Amino Acids on Paper

For screening samples, especially mixtures containing known and relatively few substances as in quality control, Kirschner [69] found that it is usually sufficient to use the one-dimensional technique (Fig. 14.1). A mixture of six amino acids was applied to 2.5-cm wide Schleicher and Schuell 2043 B paper at the anode end. The pH 2.0 buffer contained 15% acetic acid, 5% formic acid, and 80% distilled water. The amino acids present are lysine, glycine, alanine, serine, glutamic acid, and tyrosine in the order of fastest to slowest migration. Electrophoresis was performed at 3000 V for 25 min and 500 V for 110 min. A 0.2% ninhydrin spray was used to detect the amino acids.

Identification of each amino acid was made by comparison with the migration of known amino acids and their color reaction with ninhydrin (varies from light gray through deep purple). It is apparent that higher voltage caused a further migration and better resolution between zones. This is even more dramatic considering the much shorter separation time.

Lysine migrated faster because at pH 2.0 it has two positive charges whereas the others only have one. The amino acids with one positive charge migrated in the order of increasing molecular weight. Blackburn's chapter [67] is suggested for detailed treatment of amino acid analysis by high-voltage paper electrophoresis. However, the most complete tabulation and summary of high-voltage electrophoresis operating conditions is found in Table 11 of the book by Clotten and Clotten [59].

Separation of Proteins on Cellulose Acetate Membranes

Diagrammed examples of clinically normal and abnormal human serum protein electrophoregrams are given in Fig. 14.3. Electrophoretic conditions

Point of sample application

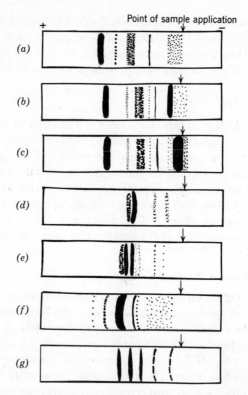

Fig. 14.3 Protein electrophoregrams on cellulose acetate membranes.

were: pH 8.8, 0.05 M tris–barbital buffer; 360 V/13 cm (2 mA/2.5-cm-wide strip) for 60 min; Ponceau S stain (red). The actual width of the cellulose acetate membrane is 2.5 cm. The arrow at the cathode end indicates the sample application site using a double wire band applicator.

The normal human serum protein electrophoregram in Fig. 14.3a clearly shows the fastest migrating, concentrated (dense) albumin band. The four zones following albumin are α_1-, α_2-, β- and γ-globulin, respectively. The diagrams also show relative concentrations of the various fractions. A representative densitometric optical scan of a normal human serum protein electrophoregram (Fig. 14.3a) is shown in Fig. 14.4. The area under each peak is related to the concentration of the appropriate serum protein fraction. Electrophoregrams of serum from patients with multiple myeloma and macro-globulinemia are shown in Figs. 14.3b and 14.3c, respectively. Note the differences in the γ-globulin zone and the appearance of some endoosmosis because of the large quantity of γ-globulin.

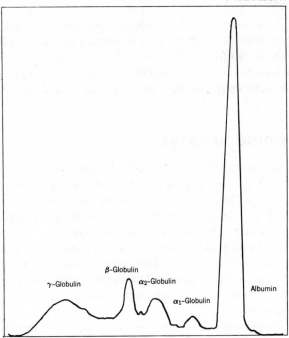

Fig. 14.4 Densitometric optical scan of a normal serum protein electrophoregram (Fig. 3a).

Hemolyzates of nonclotted blood contain various hemoglobins. Briere and co-workers [70] reported a procedure for rapid qualitative and quantitative hemoglobin fractionation using cellulose acetate electrophoresis. The electrophoregrams shown in Figs. 14.3d and 14.3e were obtained under conditions similar to those given for serum proteins except that a pH 9.1, 0.13 M tris–EDTA–borate buffer was used. Note the differences between the normal serum protein electrophoregram and the normal hemoglobin electrophoregram in Fig. 14.3d. Figure 14.3e represents the electrophoregram from a patient manifesting sickle-cell trait. Sickle cell disease is an example of a genetic abnormality identifiable by electrophoresis.

The normal human serum protein electrophoregram shown in Fig. 14.3f was made under the same conditions as given for Fig. 14.3a except that a periodic acid Schiff stain was used. This stain method shows the amount and location of glycoproteins in the various serum protein fractions.

The electrophoregram shown in Fig. 14.3g was made of the same serum sample under the same conditions as given for Fig. 14.3a except that a complex mixture of nitro blue tetrazolium dye, phenazine methosulfate, nicotinamide adenine dinucleotide, and lithium lactate was used instead of Ponceau S. The five sites containing lactic dehydrogenase isoenzymes appear blue to blue-black. The amount of each isoenzyme present is related to the stain intensity. Isoenzyme electrophoresis is important because it allows a diagnostic clinician to distinguish pathological organ and tissue damage based upon the relative differences in the isoenzyme electrophoregram zones, whereas total lactic acid dehydrogenase activity reflects a multitude of origins [67, 71–74].

5 CONCLUDING REMARKS

Electrophoresis as commonly connoted is based on the principle that a charged molecule or particle migrates toward one of the electrodes when placed in an electric field. In order to extend the usefulness and overcome shortcomings of certain electrophoresis systems or separation procedures, many researchers and manufacturers have modified and developed electrophoretic apparatus and techniques. These developments encompass areas such as the strength of the electrical field, the substances to be separated, and the electrically conducting medium. The various relationships of these and other factors and their effect upon electrophoretic separations have been presented in this chapter.

Presently, insufficient knowledge of electrophoretic theory, stabilizing media, and material interactions is available. Therefore *a priori* selection of the optimum separation conditions or the sequences in which the components will migrate is not possible. However, qualitative and quantitative electrophoregrams for a multitude of organic and biochemical compounds have been reported, which is indicative of the value of zone electrophoresis. The separation is the important aspect.

References

1. H. Picton and S. E. Linder, *J. Chem. Soc.*, **61**, 148 (1892).
2. A. Tiselius, *Trans. Faraday Soc.*, **33**, 524 (1937).
3. H. B. Bull, *Physical Biochemistry*, 2nd ed., Wiley, New York, Chapman & Hall, London, 1959, pp. 161–190.
4. D. H. Moore, "Electrophoresis," in *Physical Methods of Organic Chemistry (Technique of Organic Chemistry, Vol. I)*, A. Weissberger, Ed., 3rd ed., Part IV, Interscience, New York, 1960, pp. 3113–3153.
5. A. Tiselius, *Ann. Rev. Biochem.*, **37**, 1 (1968).
6. L. G. Longworth, "Moving Boundary Electrophoresis—Theory," in *Electrophoresis: Theory Methods and Applications*, M. Bier, Ed., Academic, New York, 1959, pp. 91–136.
7. R. D. Strickland, *Anal. Chem.*, **36**, 80R (1964).

8. R. D. Strickland, *Anal. Chem.*, **38**, 99R (1966).

9. R. D. Strickland, *Anal. Chem.*, **40**, 74R (1968).

10. R. D. Strickland, *Anal. Chem.*, **34**, 31R (1962).

11. I. Smith, *Chromatographic and Electrophoretic Techniques* (*Zone Electro-phoresis, Vol. II*), W. Heinemann, London, and Interscience, New York, 1960, pp. 1–35.

12. R. D. Strickland, "Electrokinetic Phenomena as Purification Tools," *Ann. N.Y. Acad. Sci.*, **137**, Art. 1, 139 (1966).

13. T. Wieland and E. Fischer, *Naturwissenschaften*, **35**, 29 (1948).

14. E. L. Durrum, *J. Am. Chem. Soc.*, **72**, 2943 (1950).

15. E. L. Durrum, *J. Colloid Sci.*, **6**, 274 (1950).

16. H. G. Kunkel and A. Tiselius, *J. Gen. Physiol.*, **35**, 89 (1951).

17. P. Grabar and C. A. Williams, *Biochim. Biophys. Acta*, **10**, 193 (1953).

18. C. A. Williams and P. Grabar, *J. Immunol.*, **74**, 158, 397, 404 (1955).

19. J. Hirschfield, "Immunoelectrophoresis-Procedure and Application to the Study of Group Specific Variations in Sera," in *Handbook of Immunodiffusion and Immunoelectrophoresis*, O. Ouchterlony, Ed., Ann Arbor Science, Ann Arbor, Michigan, 1968, pp. 137–159.

20. J. Claussen, "Immunoelectrophoresis—A Survey of its Application in Clinical Chemistry," in *Handbook of Immunodiffusion and Immunoelectrophoresis*, O. Ouchterlony, Ed., Ann Arbor Science, Ann Arbor, Michigan, 1956, pp. 163–208.

21. R. J. Wieme, *Agar Gel Electrophoresis*, Elsevier, Amsterdam, 1965.

22. S. Hjertén, *Biochim. Biophys. Acta*, **53**, 514 (1961).

23. S. Hjertén, *Biochim. Biophys. Acta*, **62**, 445 (1962).

24. O. Smithies, *Biochem. J.*, **61**, 629 (1955).

25. O. Smithies, *Advan. Protein Chem.*, **14**, 65 (1959).

26. M. D. Poulik, *Ann. N. Y. Acad. Sci.*, **121**, Art. 2, 470 (1964).

27. S. Raymond and L. S. Weintraub, *Science*, **130**, 711 (1959).

28. S. Raymond and Y. J. Wang, *Anal. Biochem.*, **1**, 39 (1960).

29. S. Raymond, *Ann. N. Y. Acad. Sci.*, **121**, Art. 2, 350 (1964).

30. L. Ornstein, *Ann. N. Y. Acad. Sci.*, **121**, Art. 2, 321 (1964).

31. J. T. Clarke, *Ann. N. Y. Acad. Sci.*, **121**, Art. 2, 428 (1964).

32. B. J. Davis, *Ann. N. Y. Acad. Sci.*, **121**, Art. 2, 404 (1964).

33. J. Kohn, *Clin. Chim. Acta*, **2**, 297 (1957).

34. J. Kohn, *Biochem. J.*, **65**, 9 (1957).

35. H. O. Hultin and J. H. Southard, *J. Food Sci.*, **32**, 503 (1967).

36. M. Mager, W. F. Blatt, and W. H. Abelman, *Clin. Chim. Acta*, **14**, 689 (1966).

37. R. O. Briere and J. D. Mull, *Am. J. Clin. Pathol.*, **42**, 547 (1964).

38. W. C. Romel, S. J. LaMancusa, and J. K. Dufrene, *Clin. Chem.*, **14**, 47 (1968).

39. L. N. Werum, H. T. Gordon, and W. Thornburg, *J. Chromatog.*, **3**, 125 (1960).

40. H. J. McDonald, R. J. Lappe, E. P. Marbach, R. H. Spitzer, and M. C. Urbin, *Ionography: Electrophoresis in Stabilized Media*, Year Book, Chicago, 1955.

41. J. C. Giddings and J. R. Boyack, *J. Theoret. Biol.*, **2**, 1 (1962).

42. J. R. Boyack and J. C. Giddings, *Arch. Biochem. Biophys.*, **100**, 16 (1963).

43. J. C. Giddings and J. R. Boyack, *Anal. Chem.*, **36**, 1229 (1964).

44. R. G. Martinek, *Lab. Management*, **6**(9), 26 (1968).

45. E. J. Scherago, "Guide to Scientific Instruments," *Science*, **162A**, 49 (1968).

46. W. Q. Hull, Ed. Mgr., "ACS Laboratory Guide to Instruments, Equipment and Chemicals," *Anal. Chem.*, **41**(9), 170LG (1969).

47. R. J. Block, E. D. Durrum, and G. Zweig, *A Manual of Paper Chromatography and Paper Electrophoresis*, Academic, New York, 1955.

48. H. Peeters, "Paper Electrophoresis: Principles and Techniques," *Advances in Clinical Chemistry*, Vol. II, Academic, New York, 1959, pp. 7–16.

49. M. Bier, *Electrophoresis: Theory, Methods and Applications*, Academic, New York, 1959.

50. M. Bier, *Electrophoresis: Theory, Methods and Applications*, Vol. 2, Academic Press, New York, 1967.

51. E. L. Durrum, *J. Am. Chem. Soc.*, **72**, 2943 (1950).

52. E. L. Durrum, *J. Colloid Sci.*, **6**, 274 (1951).

53. F. G. Williams, Jr., E. G. Pickels, and E. L. Durrum, *Science*, **121**, 829 (1955).

54. J. R. Whitaker, "General Considerations," in *Paper Chromatography and Electrophoresis* (*Electrophoresis in Stabilizing Media*), G. Zweig and J. R. Whitaker, Eds., Vol. II, 1967, pp. 19–40, Academic Press, Inc., New York and London.

55. S. Raymond, *Clin. Chem.*, **8**, 455 (1962).

56. D. Gross, *J. Chromatog.*, **5**, 194 (1961).

57. A. Yaron and H. A. Sober, *Anal. Biochem.*, **12**, 173 (1965).

58. J. R. Sargent, *Methods in Zone Electrophoresis*, British Drug Houses, Dorset, England, and Gallard-Schlesinger, New York, 1966, pp. 4–10, 30–34, 55–59, 80–102.

59. R. Clotten and A. Clotten, *High Voltage Electrophoresis* (in German), Thieme, Stuttgart, 1962, pp. 18–37.

60. R. L. Stere and R. E. Davis, *Anal. Biochem.*, **22**, 511 (1968).

61. B. Russell, T. H. Mead, and A. Polson, *Biochem. Biophys. Acta*, **86**, 169 (1964).

62. J. C. Hegenaur and G. W. Mace, *Biochem. Biophys. Acta*, **111**, 334 (1965).

63. S. Raymond, *Clin. Chem.*, **8**, 455 (1962).

64. S. Raymond and M. Nakamichi, *Anal. Biochem.*, **3**, 23 (1962).

65. R. Hansl, Jr., *Ann. N. Y. Acad. Sci.*, **121**, Art. 2, 391 (1964).

66. E. W. Spencer, V. M. Ingram, and C. Levinthal, *Science*, **152**, 1722 (1966).

67. S. Blackburn, " The Determination of Amino Acids by High-Voltage Paper Electrophoresis," in *Methods of Biochemical Analysis*, D. Glick, Ed., Vol. XIII, Interscience, New York, 1965, pp. 1–45.

68. S. T. Nerenberg, *Electrophoresis—A Practical Laboratory Manual*, F. A. Davis, Philadelphia, 1966.

69. S. L. Kirschner, *Solutions*, **VI**(2), 18 (1967).

70. R. O. Briere, T. Golias, and J. G. Batsakis, *Am. J. Clin. Pathol.*, **44**, 695 (1965).

71. B. M. Lance, *Am. J. Clin. Pathol.*, **46**, 401 (1966).

72. J. A. Preston, R. O. Briere, and J. G. Batsakis, *Am. J. Clin. Pathol.*, **43**, 256 (1965).

73. J. Bergerman, *Clin. Chem.*, **12**, 797 (1966).

74. L. Cohen, J. Djordjevick, and S. Jacobson, *Med. Clin. N. Am.*, **50**, 193 (1966).

Chapter **XV**

ELECTRODIALYSIS

John L. Eisenmann and Frank B. Leitz

1 INTRODUCTION

Electrodialysis is a process by which electrolytes are transferred through membranes, preferably ion-selective membranes, under the influence of an electric potential applied across the membrane. Such transport can be effected against a concentration gradient and the transport rate varied by adjustment of the current passed. This process resembles normal dialysis in its use of membranes and the necessity for providing supports for them compatible with the required solution compartments and flow paths. The two processes differ in equipment design, in objectives, especially in large-scale plants, and in the properties of suitable membranes. The simplest electrodialysis apparatus consists of a vessel containing an anode and cathode and divided into three cells by two parallel, usually vertical, membranes. The solution to be electrodialyzed is placed in the center compartment and negatively or positively charged electrolytes move toward the appropriate electrode through the membranes and into the electrode compartments under the force of the applied potential; the efficiency and extent of the deionization depends on the time of operation but primarily on the ion selectivity of the membranes. Processes involving a solution divided into two electrode compartments by a single membrane functioning to prevent mixing of the electrolysis products are usually considered to be extensions of electrolysis rather than electrodialysis, although pertinent experiments may be cited in this article.

The earliest work in electrodialysis dates from ca. 1900 when the German inventor-lawyer, Count Botho Schwerin, was granted the first of many patents [1, 2]. Patents to Winkler on the purification of albumin and protein degradation products with the aid of an electric current, and to Maigrot and Sabates on an apparatus to purify sugar syrup, are apparently the only precedents [3]. Schwerin, because of his relatively nontechnical background, used the incorrect term electroosmosis in much of his work and exemplifies the usual caveat that care should be exercised in interpreting the terminology used in the early literature.

In spite of, or probably because of this, credit for the invention of electrodialysis is usually given to Morse and Pierce [4, 5, 6], although Dhere [7, 8] has claimed priority based on the failure of Morse and Pierce to recognize the general applicability and value of the technique. Pauli has also been mentioned, apparently incorrectly, as discoverer [2, 7–9], although he himself made no claims to priority. Electrodialyzers of his design [10] have been used by many investigators.

The earliest experiments with electrodialysis used membranes that were virtually nonselective, but the process nevertheless proved a valuable technique for freeing solutions from ionic impurities and/or controlling pH. It was widely used in the laboratory for the purification and separation of biocolloids and deionizing a variety of other colloidal suspensions. The products were generally pure and uniform and useful for further research. It was, however, in 1931, still considered a "neglected method" [6] relative to its possible applications and was to remain so for some 20 years. Reviews of much of this early work have been presented by Dhere [7], Reitstotter [2], Pauli [11], and Prausnitz and Reitstotter [12]. Manegold and Kalauch [13] emphasized the need for vastly improved ion-selective membranes in 1939, and Meyer and Straus [14] indicated the usefulness of a multicell configuration in 1940, usefulness that also depended on the availability of better membranes.

The formulation of the Meyer-Sievers-Teorell fixed-charge theory to account for the properties of selective membranes [15, 16], the development of synthetic ion-exchange technology during World War II, and the impetus given by the interest in desalination of the Organization for European Economic Cooperation and the United States Department of the Interior through the Office of Saline Water combined to create a modern electrodialysis technology starting in the early 1950s. Membranes with suitable electrochemical and mechanical properties were devised [17, 18] and design data provided [19]. This technology has been used primarily to design and build large-scale brackish water desalination plants [20, 21] but electrodialysis is also used in various fields of chemistry, for example, to deash whey and sugar solutions, treat industrial wastes, sweeten citrus juices, and to concentrate seawater for salt production [22–25]. These applications of electrodialysis are the subject of this article. An exhaustive treatise is not claimed but we have tried to include sufficient references, with *Chemical Abstracts* citations where deemed useful, to indicate the scope and value of the method and hope to encourage others to explore further applications.

2 DIALYSIS

A brief description of dialysis, as the precursor of electrodialysis, is presented here. More extensive discussions, including many original literature citations, are found in the references. Dialysis is the separation or fractionation of solutes by means of their differential rates of diffusion through membranes. Such membranes are termed "semipermeable" and are used to separate the solution to be dialyzed (eventually the dialyzate) from the receiving solvent, usually water. The process proceeds in response to differences in chemical potential between the solutions and requires that the membrane permit diffusional exchange of at least some of the molecular species present while preventing any convective exchange between the solutions. The semipermeable characteristics of the membranes are considered to derive both from a mechanical sieve action and from a chemical or physiochemical interaction between solute(s), solvents, and membrane.

A simple case is shown in Fig. 15.1. Two solutions, X and Y, are separated by a dialysis membrane M. After a sufficient time the initial situation shown in a is changed to that of b. The transfer of solvent from compartment Y to X by osmosis almost invariably accompanies the dialysis and serves to dilute

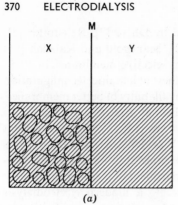
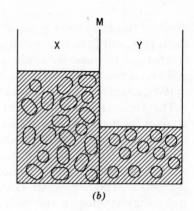

Fig. 15.1 Diagram of dialysis process. (*a*) Initially. (*b*) After several hours.

the dialyzate and decrease the rate. Other concurrent phenomena, generally minor, are ultrafiltration, electrodialysis, electroosmosis, and thermal osmosis.

Dialysis was described by Thomas Graham in 1861 [26] and he is usually given credit as discoverer of the process. It was used by Graham to separate molecules with large differences in size; for example, colloids from crystalloids. For about 100 years after Graham's work, dialysis was regarded principally as a laboratory tool. Cellophane or parchment membranes were used in a variety of small dialyzers. Only one large-scale application had appeared—the recovery of sodium hydroxide from viscose steep liquor or mercerizing baths. Recent years, however, have seen a revival of interest in dialysis [5, 27–29], primarily because of the development of vinyl-based membranes which permit treatment of acid wastes. Commercial units are currently available from Brosites Machine Company and Graver Water Conditioning Company. Further industrial application depends on development of processes in the waste treatment and food and biological materials areas, together with improved membranes and designs to decrease the ratio of transfer area to volumetric throughput. Potential usefulness is greatest for the separation of dissolved materials present in high concentration and/or operations on sensitive systems.

Excellent summaries of early laboratory applications and descriptions of many early dialyzers have been presented by Stauffer [30], Daniel [31], and Tuwiner [5]. Some recent developments are covered by Leonard [27].

In the dialysis process, the transfer rate of materials through a membrane is given by a relationship similar to Fick's diffusion equation:

$$W = U_o A(\Delta C),$$

where W = material transport rate in grams per minute; U_o = overall dialysis coefficient in centimeters per minute; A = effective membrane area in square centimeters, and ΔC = concentration difference across the membrane in grams per cubic centimeter. The overall dialysis coefficient U_o is considered to be a combination of two transfer coefficients, a membrane dialysis coefficient (U_m) and a combined liquid film coefficient (U_f):

$$1/U_o = 1/U_m + 1/U_f.$$

Overall dialysis coefficients can be determined in the laboratory for a given membrane and set of operating conditions. In addition, when two solutes are present, a separation factor may be defined:

$$S_b{}^a = \frac{U_{oa}}{U_{ob}}.$$

Some values for both of these parameters are available in the literature [5, 28, 29, 32].

A growing and important specialty application is hemodialysis, wherein a dialyzer supplements or replaces human kidney function by periodic dialysis of the bloodstream [27, 29, 33]. The process is favored by its simplicity and safety, by its ability to remove a range of low-molecular-weight substances, and by the lack of bacterial exchange. A semicircular shunt of plastic tubing inserted in the patient's arm permits frequent use of the technique. Besides usefulness in chronic kidney disorders, dialysis is valuable in treating certain types of poisoning and mental diseases. Estimates of the market for artificial kidneys have been presented [27, 29].

3 PRINCIPLES OF ELECTRODIALYSIS

Operation

For the purpose of discussion, any process in which the principal operation is the transport of material through a diaphragm or membrane under the influence of an electrical potential gradient is considered as electrodialysis.

Operation with Nonselective Membranes

In electrolysis and electrodialysis, movement of ions is caused by an electrical potential applied across an electrolytically conductive solution. For convenience we discuss the case in which two electrodes occupy the entire ends of a container so that only the one-dimensional flow of current need be considered.

Normally, the electrodes are constructed of a material that does not participate in the cell reaction. If a sufficient potential is applied to cause a flow of current, the cathodic reaction is liberation of hydrogen and formation of base:

$$H_2O + e^- = \tfrac{1}{2}H_2 + OH^-$$

The anode reaction is liberation of oxygen and formation of hydrogen ions.

$$\tfrac{1}{2}H_2O = \tfrac{1}{4}O_2 + H^+ + e^-$$

In the solution these reactions are accompanied by the net migration of anions to the anode and of cations to the cathode.

Electrodialysis is differentiated from electrolysis through interposition of one or more porous membranes (diaphragms) between the electrodes. In a common case two membranes are used. This arrangement of apparatus, usually referred to as a three-chamber or Pauli cell, is shown in Fig. 15.2 in its

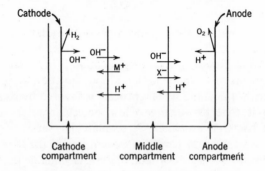

Fig. 15.2   Diagram of three-chamber electrodialysis cell.

simplest form. The membrane is a porous water-permeable body which prevents convective mixing between the compartments. In addition, in most cases the pores of the membranes are sufficiently small in diameter to impede the passage of the larger colloidal or polymeric particles.

Since the various species are transported roughly in proportion to their concentrations, even with totally nonselective membranes passage of current eventually results in accumulation of most of the anions except hydroxyl ions in the anode compartment and of most of the cations except hydrogen ions in the cathode compartment. This causes demineralization of the middle compartment. Uncharged membranes are demineralized simultaneously with the middle compartment. Consequently, the resistance of such a cell can become very high if the demineralization is carried near completion.

Depending upon the initial concentration of nondischargeable ions, the anode and cathode compartments can become, respectively, quite acidic and basic. Because the net transport of hydrogen ions and hydroxyl ions into the middle compartment is not generally equal, a pH change in this compartment is frequently observed.

In the following discussion selectivity refers to separation of ions of different charge, not to separation of ions of the same charge. Ion selectivity is produced by charged groups bonded to the pore surface of the membrane or by adsorption of charged particles to this surface, provided that all or a majority of the charged groups are of the same charge. The majority of mobile ions in the membrane is oppositely charged to these fixed charges. Current passing through the membrane is carried preponderantly by the mobile ions in the majority (the counterions) and only to a small extent by ions of the same charge as the fixed groups (co-ions).

Adsorption can be electrically induced in the case in which there is a charged species which, because of size, cannot pass freely through the diaphragm and instead collects in the pores and on the diaphragm face. This causes a localized selectivity. Adsorption of this type is very common with uncharged porous media. It is not easily predictable and depends upon the prior treatment of the sample. Consequently, it is sometimes difficult to evaluate early work.

Operation with Selective Membranes

The character of electrodialysis changed substantially with the advent of synthetic highly selective ion-exchange membranes. This made it possible to direct the flow of ions and create a large number of diluting chambers between a single pair of electrodes. A diagram of conventional apparatus showing the direction of flow of ionic species is given in Fig. 15.3. The aggregate of one diluting and one concentrating cell and one anion and one cation membrane is a repeating unit termed a "cell pair."

Because of frictional interaction, uncharged molecules are transported through the membranes generally in the direction of net ion flow. This

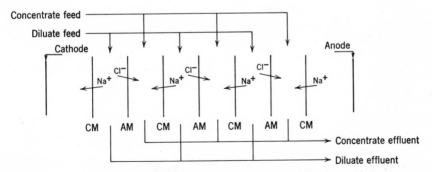

Fig. 15.3 Apparatus for conventional electrodialysis.

becomes particularly significant with selective membranes because almost all of the ion flow is in one direction. The quantity of water transport depends upon the membrane, the ion or ions transported, current density, and solution concentration. No general theory for the rate of water transported has been developed, however, a comprehensive review has been compiled by Lakshminarayanaiah [34].

Uncharged solutes are also transported by frictional interaction. In many cases this represents a loss of product and is to be avoided if possible. As a general rule, membranes having a low water transport have a low solute carry-over.

In practice, a multichamber apparatus is usually run with solutions continuously flowing through the compartments. The membranes are separated by spacer/gaskets which both contain the fluid and direct its flow.

The performance of an electrodialysis unit depends strongly upon the type of membranes used. The requirement for proper physical support of membranes has dictated the internal structure of the spacer. Consequently, different types of membranes are frequently not interchangeable in a particular apparatus. Properties of a variety of commercial membranes are presented later in this section.

In the following derivation the nomenclature used is:

A, Effective transfer area, cm²/cell pair

a, Costs proportional to current density, \$/mA cm⁻²

b, Costs inversely proportional to current density, \$ mA/cm²

C, Concentration, equiv/liter

C_m, Average concentration $= 2(1/C_c + 1/C_d)$, equiv/liter

c, Costs not proportional to current density, \$

D, Diffusion constant, cm²/sec

d, Total costs, \$

e, Current efficiency

F_t, Total flow rate, liters/sec

f, Degree of demineralization, $= (C_{di} - C_{do})/C_{di}$

$\mathscr{F}$, 96,500 C/equiv

I, Current, mA

i, Current density, mA/cm²

n, Number of cell pairs

P, Permselectivity

P, Without subscript, Power, W

R_p, Resistance, ohm-cm²/cell pair

r, Component resistance, ohm-cm²/cell pair

r_p, Effective polarization "resistance," ohm-cm²/cell pair

t, Transport number in solution

t, Without subscript, Time, sec
$\hat{t}$, Transport number in membrane
V, Volume of diluting compartment, cm³
V_p, Applied electrical potential, V/cell pair
δ, Diffusion layer thickness, cm

Subscripts or superscripts are: a, anion; b, concentrating stream; c, cation; d, diluting stream; i, inlet; m, membrane; o, outlet; $+$, cation; $-$, anion.

Operating equations are given below for the salt removal process. Similar equations can be developed for other applications. The permselectivity of the membrane is defined [35] as:

$$P_{cm} = \frac{\hat{t}_+{}^c - t_+}{1 - t_+} \qquad P_{am} = \frac{\hat{t}_-{}^a - t_-}{1 - t_-}.$$

The current efficiency e for the process in the absence of concentration polarization is then:

$$e = P_{cm}t_- + P_{am}t_+.$$

For a solution in which $t_+ = t_-$, the efficiency reduces to the mean of the permselectivities.

In a batch demineralization the extent of the demineralization or "cut" f increases with time according to:

$$f = \frac{Ae}{V_d C_{di} \mathscr{F}} \int_{t=0}^{t=t} i(t)\, dt.$$

For steady-state operation of a stack run with continuous flow the salt removal capacity is:

$$F_t C_{di} f = \frac{iAen}{1000 \mathscr{F}}.$$

The resistance per cell pair can be calculated as the sum of separate resistive elements:

$$R_p = r_{am} + r_{cm} + r_b + r_d + r_p.$$

This has been empirically expressed [19] as

$$R_p = \frac{2.4}{C_m} + 45$$

for sodium chloride solutions between 0.01 N and 0.5 N with Nepton CR61 and AR111 membranes with 0.04-inch-thick spacers.

In commercial practice the number of cell pairs between one pair of electrodes is so large that the electrode cell voltage, normally 5 to 10 V, is negligible in power consumption calculations. The voltage per cell pair is:

$$V_p = \frac{iR_p}{1000}.$$

The power required per unit capacity for a given demineralization is:

$$\frac{P}{F_t} = \frac{C_{di}^2 \mathscr{F}(1-f)f(i/C_d)_o R_p}{1000e}.$$

The total effective area per unit capacity for a given demineralization is:

$$\frac{nA_p}{F_t} = \frac{1000\mathscr{F}}{(1-f)R_{po}(i/C_d)_o e} \int_o^f R_p \, df \cong \frac{1000\mathscr{F}R_p f}{(1-f)(i/C_d)_o e R_{po}}.$$

The approximation is very close at 50% cut and progressively poorer at higher cuts.

The most important parameter not set by external requirements is the operating current density. Demineralization costs can be considered in three classes: proportional to power, proportional to area, and fixed. The first two are, respectively, directly proportional to current density and inversely proportional to current density. This leads to a total cost equation of the form:

$$d = ai + b/i + c.$$

From this, the most economical current density is:

$$i = (b/a)^{1/2}.$$

Because of polarization it is usually necessary to operate at lower than optimum current density. Polarization is discussed below.

Further economic evaluation of the electrodialysis process is not within the scope of this article. However, more precise calculations can be made using the equations of Mason and Kirkham [19]. Economics of operating water desalination plants are given by Wilson [36] for the Free State Geduld plant, by Hamner and Katz [37] for the Buckeye, Arizona plant and by Katz [38] for the Dell City, Texas plant. A summary of operating plant cost is given by Gilliland [39].

Polarization

In demineralization of natural waters, it is normally the anion membrane that polarizes first. In the following discussion this is assumed and equations are written for polarization of an anion membrane.

Since only the fraction t_-/t_-^a of the ions transported through the membrane is carried from the bulk solution to the solution-membrane interface by electrical forces, the balance must be carried by diffusion resulting from the concentration gradient near the interface. This reaches a maximum value when the concentration of transportable species approaches zero at the membrane surface.

As the concentration of other anions at the membrane surface becomes very low, water is decomposed and hydroxyl ion is transported through the (anion) membrane. This causes a decrease in pH of the diluting stream and an increase in pH of the concentrating stream. The latter effect can lead to scaling and precipitation if the feed solution contains bicarbonates or heavy metal ions. The energy required for water splitting must be supplied by an increase in voltage per cell pair. In a badly polarized stack, current efficiency drops. Finally, the anion membranes may show an irreversible resistance increase if operated too close to polarization.

The polarizing or limiting current density may be determined from the apparent increase in resistance of the stack. Cowan and Brown [40] suggested a plot of V_p/I versus $1/I$. Below polarization this gives a straight line with a positive slope and a y-intercept equal to the stack resistance. Above polarization an apparently straight line with a negative slope is observed. The limiting current density occurs at the intersection of the two straight lines. The onset of polarization can also be determined by the change in pH of the effluent streams [41].

The limiting current can be calculated from:

$$i_{\lim} = \frac{n\mathscr{F}DC}{t_- - t_-}\frac{1}{\delta}.$$

Mason and Kirkham have empirically related flow rate per cell pair to the ratio of current density to normality:

$$\left(\frac{i}{C_d}\right)_{\lim} = 16{,}500\,F_d^{0.6}.$$

This expression was developed using long, narrow channels and a 40-mil channel height. The proportionality constant is thought to be a mild function of channel height. Both of these expressions show the possibility of increasing the limiting current density by increasing the hydrodynamic agitation, that is, by decreasing δ or increasing F_d.

To avoid these difficulties operation with an anion membrane of lower permselectivity has been proposed [42]. It is claimed that this lowers the current efficiency but increases the limiting current density, a process referred to as "transport depletion."

Other Electrodialytical Operations

In addition to salt dilution or concentration, other operations can be carried out which can be loosely classified as electrodialysis and which may require a rearrangement of components and feed streams.

ION REPLACEMENT

The replacement of an electrodialyzable anion or cation in an ionic compound can be carried out in the apparatus shown in Fig. 15.4. This equipment is used in milk modification for replacement of calcium by sodium to make cow's milk more digestable by infants and for removal of radioactive strontium and calcium with or without changing the ionic balance. In general this cannot be carried to completion, but some residual of the original ion remains.

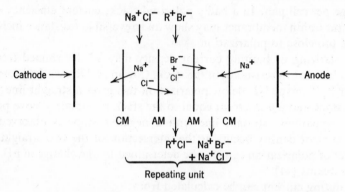

Fig. 15.4 Apparatus for ion replacement.

ION FRACTIONATION

An extension of ion replacement can be used to separate two ions of similar charge based on the differential electrodialytical permeability, as shown in Fig. 15.5. This attractive method of separation has received little of the careful investigation required to provide a proper evaluation of its potential.

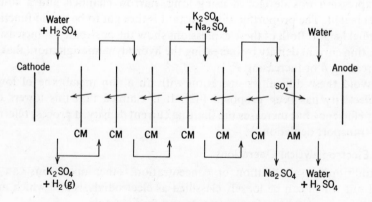

Fig. 15.5 Ion fractionation still.

METATHESIS OR DOUBLE DECOMPOSITION

This operation requires that both species be electrodialyzable. The apparatus is shown in Fig. 15.6. The separation in this case is very good with reasonably selective membranes but there may be significant loss of starting materials.

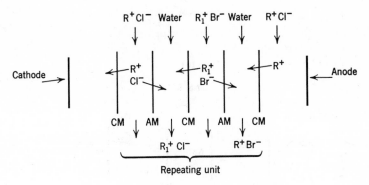

Fig. 15.6 Apparatus for electrometathesis.

PRODUCTION OF FREE BASE OR ACID

The simplest apparatus for this operation consists of a single membrane between two electrodes as shown in Fig. 15.7a. For materials that are easily oxidizable (or reducible), an extra membrane (Fig. 15.7b) is used to separate the reactant from the anode (cathode). The figure shows production of acid. For production of base an anion membrane is used and the reactant is fed to the cathode chamber.

ELECTROOXIDATION OR ELECTROREDUCTION

A membrane is frequently used when it is desired that an electrooxidation (or -reduction) be carried out without contaminating the solution with products from the opposite electrode or without the reactant loss that might result. This allows the electrodes to be placed close to each other with consequent power savings. The reaction taking place determines which type of membrane should be used. If the ion being transferred takes part in the reaction, then the process is related to electrodialysis and the considerations mentioned herein may apply.

High-Temperature Electrodialysis

Under certain conditions operation at high temperature is more favorable than ambient operation. This is because of the increases in electrical conductivity and in mass transport with increased temperatures. High-temperature

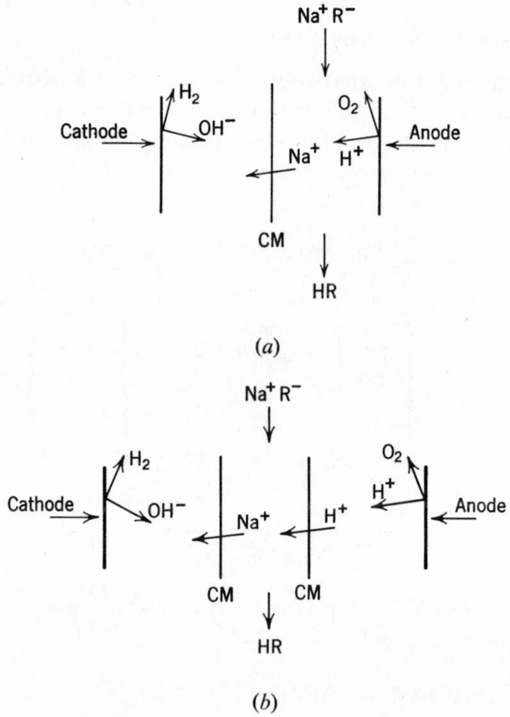

Fig. 15.7 Apparatus for free acid production. (a) Without anode isolation. (b) With anode isolation.

operation has been studied by Bejerano et al. [43] and by Casolo and Leitz [44]. An evaluation of the effects of increased temperature on the economics of water demineralization is given by Leitz and McRae [45].

Equipment

Laboratory electrodialysis equipment is basically very simple, consisting usually of an electrodialysis cell with a few accessories such as gravity-flow reservoirs and/or pumps and a source of direct current. Any commercial or laboratory-built rectifier may be used as power supply and in some cases an ordinary storage battery is adequate. Many of the standard membrane characterization procedures are performed in test cells powered by an automobile battery.

Early investigators of electrodialysis constructed their own cells and there are literally dozens of cell designs described. They include units made from rubber battery jars [46], glass tubing [47], and standard Pyrex pipe [48]. Capacities are from a few milliliters to several liters. Two of the most useful early cells were described by Pauli [10] and Brintzinger [49].

More recently, Samec [50] has reviewed and discussed several laboratory electrodialyzers. Wood [51] described in detail a small cell easily constructed from Perspex (Lucite), which can be used for the desalting or fractionation of complex organic mixtures. A water-jacketed apparatus consisting of two identical glass electrode vessels and a Lucite center or sample cell was designed by Katz and Ellinger [52]. The center cell has a capacity of 35 ml and can be stirred mechanically or magnetically. Its use was demonstrated by the preparation of isoionic protein.

Today, three-compartment laboratory cells are available from several manufacturers. The Schleicher and Schuell Company distributes transparent plastic cells in 12-, 100-, and 500-ml sizes with graphite or platinum electrodes. The 100-ml cell is shown in Fig. 15.8. Brinkman Instruments, Inc. has almost identical cells available. The Chemical Rubber Company lists a series of very small capacity (5- to 10-ml) electrodialysis cells which they recommend for purification work. Gelman Instruments markets a 15-ml-capacity cell.

In a somewhat larger, but still laboratory size, at least two companies

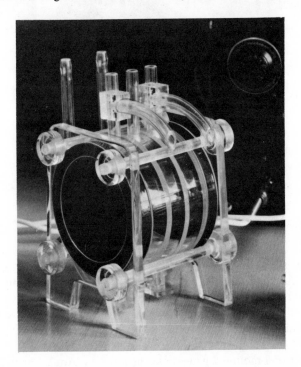

Fig. 15.8 Laboratory electrodialysis cell, 100-ml capacity. (Courtesy Schleicher and Schuell.)

Fig. 15.9 "Stackpack," bench-scale electrodialysis unit. (Courtesy Ionics, Inc.)

offer bench-scale units. Ionics, Inc. sells the "Stackpack," a 9 × 10 in. membrane stack consisting of 20 cell pairs assembled from Nepton membranes and tortuous path spacers. It has a hydraulic capacity up to 50 gal/hr. Normally, this stack is supplied as part of a complete small-scale electrodialysis plant to be used for process design and cost projections. Figure 15.9 is a view of the complete unit. The stack itself is on the left of the picture behind the panel-mounted gauges and flowmeters. Aqua-Chem, Inc. manufactures two comparable units of 4 and 14 gal/min flow capacity based on a 50 cell pair stack. Any commercial membranes may be used. Both Aqua-Chem and Ionics provide technical service and perform test runs and feasibility studies in their own laboratories.

Ionics also manufactures a home electrodialysis unit for use in those areas where local water is saline. It is virtually maintenance-free and has a 300 to 500 gal/day capacity. Similarly, the American Machine and Foundry Company has produced a home electrodialysis unit [53] that desalts approximately 20 gal/day of brackish water. Either of these, with suitable modifications could probably be adapted for laboratory evaluation work.

Lists of manufacturers of commercial electrodialysis equipment have been given by Farrell and Smith [54] and Rickles [29].

The bulk of commercial electrodialysis installations operating today are designed for brackish water desalination. In the United States, there are municipal plants at Buckeye, Arizona [37], Port Mansfield [55] and Dell City [38], Texas, and Coalinga, California [56]. The Office of Saline Water has a demonstration plant at Webster, South Dakota [57] and test facilities at Denver, Colorado and Wrightsville Beach, North Carolina. The annual report of the Office of Saline Water summarizes their work in this area and generally contains a worldwide listing of currently operating desalting plants. McRae [58] and Rickles [29] also provide compilations of saline water electrodialysis plants and Gilliland [39] has reviewed current economics. Solt [59] has discussed some of the problems involved in scaling up to larger plants and, in a later article [60], describes some recent advances and presents some typical case histories.

In 1962 installations of full-scale plants for the demineralization of whey by electrodialysis were completed [61]. These plants are indicative of growing interest in electrodialysis for uses other than demineralizing saline water.

Figure 15.10 shows one of Ionics' Mark III electrodialysis stacks from the Dell City, Texas plant. It is typical of the production stacks used in large-scale commercial desalting installations. Membranes are 18 × 40 in. and a stack can contain up to 300 cell pairs and process to 250,000 gal per day. Combinations of these units in series or parallel have been used in plants designed to produce 50,000 to over 1 million gal per day of potable water.

Membranes for Electrodialysis

The early experimenters in electrodialysis worked, *inter alia*, with membranes prepared from animal skins, insolubilized gelatins, proteins, fabrics, parchment, cellophane, and regenerated cellulose. Summaries of this work can be found in Wilson [36], Tuwiner [5], Helfferich [62], Sollner [63] and, recently Lakshminarayanaiah [34]. Such membranes, prior to Sollner's activated collodion films, were generally physically weak and nonselective relative to the transport of anions and cations.

In the 1950s, however, the development of the high-capacity, mechanically

Fig. 15.10 Commercial electrodialysis stacks; 50,000 gal/day plant capacity. (Courtesy Ionics, Inc.)

strong, highly ion-selective membranes called for by Manegold and Kalauch [13] and Meyer and Straus [14] began. The necessary research was carried out in many countries and a wide variety of techniques explored. Eventually there evolved a family of ion-exchange (or ion-transfer or permselective or electric) membranes, generally based on a styrene-divinylbenzene copolymer matrix carrying either sulfonic acid cation-exchange groups or quaternary ammonium anion-exchange groups. Either type can be fabric-backed for mechanical strength and can be heterogeneous or homogeneous. In this context a heterogeneous membrane is one consisting of particles of ion-exchange material held together in a sheet form by an inert binder. A homogeneous membrane is a continuous coherent gel of cross-linked polymer having covalently bonded ionogenic groups; it is normally the preferred form.

Commercial membranes are manufactured by a variety of methods. Amfion membranes are made by graft-polymerizing polyethylene or polychlorotrifluoroethylene films with styrene, followed by sulfonation for cation exchangers or chloromethylation/amination for anion exchangers. Asahi Chemical Industries produces Aciplex membranes by bulk-polymerizing styrene-divinylbenzene and planing or skiving the block into thin sheets. Functional groups are added later via the usual reactions. The Asahi Glass Company's Selemion membranes are based on a styrene-butadiene copolymer backed by a woven continuous-filament fabric. To form the membrane the backing cloth is dipped into the latex, stripped of excess solution, dried, and reacted. The Ionac membranes are a heterogeneous fabric-reinforced series. Nepton membranes are also cloth-reinforced but are homogeneous cast sheets of styrene-divinylbenzene with sulfonic or ammonium functions. Tokuyama Soda also uses stryrene-divinylbenzene copolymer applied as a paste to a woven backing with subsequent heating under pressure to form a film. Toyo Soda uses a procedure similar to Asahi Glass, employing a styrene-butadiene latex applied to a backing cloth by repeated dipping, calendering, curing, and reacting.

Typical properties of the principle commercially available membranes currently produced are listed in Tables 15.1–15.7. Properties listed in the tables are taken from the individual manufacturer's literature and care should be used in comparing the data for various membranes to allow for variations in procedure. External solution concentrations are especially important. Bergsma [64] has discussed the relative importance and interdependence of the various membrane properties. Summaries of preparative methods, with leading references, are available [62, 65–67]. Attempts have been made to compare selected commercial membranes on a common basis [67, 68]. A test manual published by the Office of Saline Water [69] gives standard analytical methods, and Wilson [36] has included a chapter that discusses test and experimental methods.

Many other groups are actively working on the development of new membranes and participants in the field are constantly changing. The Negev Institute in Israel [70] is interested in membranes based on activating polyvinylchloride or polyethylene sheets. In the United States, RAI Research Corporation produces Permion membranes by radiation and chemical grafting techniques on polyolefins. The Polymer Research Corporation of America uses similar methods with cellophane. The Russians employ a variety of techniques, producing both homogeneous and heterogeneous membranes. Some of these types and their application to desalination have been described [71, 72]. Inorganic membranes have also been investigated [73, 74].

Most of the industrial organizations have continuing development programs aimed at producing improved membranes and are generally more than willing to supply developmental samples of these if their standard product is not adequate. In addition, they may be amenable to specifically synthesizing a membrane to suit a particular application. This latter ability becomes more and more important as new uses for electrodialysis appear.

Table 15.1 Amfion Membranes*

Membrane	Features	Capacity (meq/gm Dry Membrane)	Resistance (Ω cm²)†	Thickness (mm)	Water Content (% of Dry Membrane)	Burst Strength (psi)	Perm-selectivity (%)‡
C-60	Cation selective sulfonic acid type; polyethylene support	1.5	5	0.31	35	45	80
C-100	Similar to C-60	1.3	7	0.20	22	60	93
A-60	Anion selective quaternary ammonium type; polyethylene support	1.6	6	0.31	28	45	82
A-100	Similar to A-60	1.5	9	0.15	20	50	92
C-310	Cation selective sulfonic acid type; polyfluorocarbon support; more oxidation resistant	0.6	4.5	0.28	17	110	86
C-313	Similar to C-310	0.6	4.5	0.15	17	55	85

* American Machine and Foundry Company, 689 Hope Street, Stamford, Connecticut.
† In 0.6 N potassium chloride.
‡ Electrometric technique (0.5 N/1.0 N potassium chloride).

Table 15.2 Aciplex Membranes*

Membrane	Features	Capacity (meq/gm Dry Resin)	Resistance (Ω cm²)†	Thickness (mm)	Water Content (% of Wet Membrane)	Burst Strength (psi)‡	Transport Number‡§
CK-1	Cation selective acid type; unbacked; for salt concentration	2.8	3.3	0.23	38	25	0.90#
DK-1	Similar to CK-1; for desalination	—	14.3	1.0	—	70	—
CA-1	Anion selective quaternary ammonium type; unbacked; for salt concentration	2.6	4.2	0.23	36	25	—
CA-2	Anion selective "strong base type"; unbacked; for salt concentration	2.0	2.1	0.21	31	28	0.97
DA-1	Similar to CA-1; for desalination	1.5	4.5	0.40	21‡	47	0.98
		1.6	3.5	0.23	26	27	—

* Asahi Chemical Industries Company, Ltd., 12, 1-chome, Yurakucho, Chiyoda-ku, Tokyo, Japan.
† In 0.5 N seawater.
‡ From Ref. 67 or unpublished data.
§ Hittorf technique (0.6 N sodium chloride).
# This membrane is available in two thicknesses.

Table 15.3 Selemion Membranes*

Membrane	Features	Capacity (meq/gm Dry Membrane)†	Resistance (Ω cm²)‡	Thickness (mm)	Water Content (% of Wet Membrane)†	Burst Strength (psi)	Transport Number§
CMV	Cation selective; PVC reinforced; homogeneous, strong acid type	1.30	7.0	0.24	23	90	0.91
CSG	Cation selective; fiberglass backing; homogeneous, strong acid type	0.84	12.0	0.22	23	70	0.92
AMT	Anion selective; polyester backing; strong base type	2.08	3.0	0.19	30	135	0.92
AST	Anion selective; polyester backing; strong base type	1.75	8.0	0.22	24	120	0.95
DMT	Anion selective; polyester backing; weak base type; use in acidic solution	0.88 (strong) 1.72 (weak)	1.5	0.11	32	85	0.93

* Asahi Glass Company, Ltd., 14, 2-chome, Marunouchi, Chiyoda-ku, Tokyo, Japan.
† From Ref. 67 or unpublished data.
‡ In 0.5 N sodium chloride.
§ Electrometric technique (0.5 N/1.0 N sodium chloride).

Table 15.4 Ionac Membranes*

Membrane	Features	Capacity (meq/gm)	Resistance (Ω cm²)†	Thickness (mm)	Water Content (% of Wet Membrane)‡	Burst Strength (psi)	Perm-selectivity (%)§
MC-3142	Cation selective; hetero-geneous, fabric-backed; strong acid type	1.06	9.1	0.155	19	185	94
MC-3235	Similar to MC-3142	1.26	18	0.31	25	185	95
MC-3470XL	Similar to MC-3142; useful to higher temperatures	1.05	9.6	0.31	23	190	96
MA-3148	Anion selective; hetero-geneous; fabric-reinforced; strong base type	0.96	10	0.17	13	190	90
MA-3236	Similar to MA-3148	0.77	35	0.31	18	185	93
MA-3475XL	Similar to MA-3148; useful to higher temperatures	0.74	18	0.31	24	205	94

* Ionac Chemical Company, Birmingham, New Jersey.
† In 0.1 N sodium chloride.
‡ From Ref. 67.
§ Electrometric technique (0.5 N/1.0 N sodium chloride).

Table 15.5 Nepton Membranes*

Membrane	Features	Capacity (meq/gm Dry Resin)†	Resistance (Ω cm²)†	Thickness (mm)	Water Content (% of Wet Resin)	Burst Strength (psi)	Transport Number‡
61AZL-183	Cation selective sulfonic acid type; Dynel fabric backing	2.7	12	0.58	46	115	0.95
61CZL-183	Similar to 61AZL; denser resin matrix	2.5	13	0.60	40	115	0.96
111BZL-183	Anion selective quaternary ammonium type; Dynel fabric backing	1.8	15	0.60	43	125	0.93
111EZL-219	Similar to 111BZL; denser resin matrix	1.6	17	0.58	36	120	0.94

* Ionics, Inc., 65 Grove Street, Watertown, Massachusetts.
† In 0.01 N sodium chloride.
‡ Hittorf technique (0.6 N sodium chloride).

Table 15.6   Neosepta Membranes*

Membrane	Features	Capacity (meq/gm Dry Membrane)	Resistance (Ω cm²)†	Thickness (mm)	Water Content (% of Dry Membrane)	Burst Strength (psi)	Transport Number‡
CL-2.5T	Strong acid; cation-selective; PVC fabric backing	1.9	3.0	0.16	35	50	0.98
AV-4T	Strong base; anion-selective; PVC fabric backing	1.8	3.5	0.15	25	90	0.98
AVS-4T	Similar to AV-4T	1.8	4.2	0.16	30	70	0.98

* Tokuyama Soda Company, Ltd. No. 5-4, 1-chome, Nishi-Shimbashi, Minato-ku, Tokyo, Japan.
† In 0.5 N sodium chloride.
‡ Hittorf technique (0.5 N sodium chloride).

Table 15.7 Toso Membranes*

Membrane	Features	Capacity (meq/gm Dry Membrane)	Resistance⁵ (Ω cm²)†	Thickness (mm)	Water Content (% of Dry Membrane)	Transport Number‡
C	Cation selective; Saran- or polyethylene-backed; strong acid type	1.0	7	0.44	22	0.93
A	Anion selective; Saran-backed; strong base type	1.2	5	0.38	29	0.93

* Toyo Soda Manufacturing Company, Ltd., 4560 Tonda Nanyo-Cho Yamaguchi-ken, Japan.
† In 0.5 N sodium chloride.
‡ Electrometric technique (0.5 N/2.5 N sodium chloride).

4 SURVEY OF ORGANIC APPLICATIONS

The principles and techniques of electrodialysis described above have been applied by numerous investigators to almost all fields of chemistry. The following sections attempt to outline some of this work and to give an idea of the scope and usefulness of the process. Care should be taken in evaluating the earlier work because of changes in terminology and the unpredictable effects caused by use of higher voltages, nonselective and difficultly reproducible membranes, and extended periods of electrodialysis. Specific details should be obtained from the original references. Applications in wide and representative areas are included but some omissions have necessarily been made.

The largest area left undiscussed is that concerned with the demineralization of saline water, primarily for human consumption. As previously mentioned, this has been the major application of electrodialysis in the last two decades. The publications by Wilson, Mintz, Helfferich, and Spiegler listed in the general references are comprehensive and valuable expositions of this work. Design, economics, theory, and capabilities are all covered.

Reports of current investigations and novel applications of electrodialysis appear in the literature with increasing frequency. There is undoubtedly a promising future for the technique, founded on the successful research and development effort devoted to desalination.

Biochemistry

Some of the most extensive early work utilizing electrodialysis was in the biochemical area and is summarized in the two reviews by Reitstotter and by Dhere already mentioned [2, 7]. Following the preliminary work of Dhere [75], Pauli [10, 76] and Freundlich and Loeb [9], Ettisch [77] published a series of about a dozen papers on the purification and fractionation of serum proteins by electrodialysis. Ettisch, as did Freundlich and Loeb, attributed the observed pH changes chiefly to the character of the membranes used [78]. He described optimal conditions for fractionation [79, 80] and prepared improved membranes based on collodion impregnated with blood protein [79, 81] or glycine [82]. The latter membranes were also used to obtain an electrolyte-free hemoglobin solution from red blood cell pulp [83]. Later authors [84, 85] used Bakelite or phenol-resin membranes to aid in control of pH and precipitation.

Others have studied the effect of electrodialysis on the plasma protein fibrinogen [86] and investigated the electrodialytic behavior and complexing of inorganic electrolytes, particularly calcium, in blood serum [87, 88]. Total base determination in human serum and heparinized plasma via electrodialysis using an aluminum oxide filter disk has been reported [89, 90]. Adair and Keys [91, 92] have developed a method for the determination of total base in blood and other biological fluids using more conventional electrodialysis membranes. Modifications of Adair's procedure allow it to be used for simultaneous chloride analysis [93] or for the determination of equivalent weights of organic acids [94]. Horse and dog serums have also been subjected to electrodialysis [76, 95, 96].

Various antitoxic serums have been fractionated by electrodialysis and a study with a view to possible large-scale application has been reported [97]. Antidiphtheric and antitetanic serums have been obtained in high yields [98] and the effect of pH and protein concentration on their fractionation studied [96]. Antipneumococcus [99] and antitoxic scarlet fever serums [100] have been electrodialyzed and a comparison of electrodialytic purification versus the salting-out method was made [100].

Relatively limited work has been done on the electrodialysis of hormones and enzymes. Zondek and Ucko [101] claim that the action of insulin on blood sugar is destroyed or reversed when an insulin solution is subjected to electrodialysis. Taylor and co-workers [102] also obtained a nearly inactive solution after electrodialysis of insulin but recovered a sediment with nearly doubled activity. The oxytocic hormone of the posterior lobe of the pituitary gland [103] migrated to the cathode compartment during electrodialysis at pH 6 but was apparently uncharged and immobile at pH > 8. Electrodialysis of ACTH [104] transferred almost all of the activity to the cathode cell. The method has been used to assign a molecular weight to thyrotropic hormone [105]. The enzymes trypsin, invertase [106], and cholam malt diastase [107] increased in activity after electrodialysis, but enolase in muscle extract apparently was inactivated by electrodialysis [108].

Electrodialysis has been shown to be useful in the removal of inorganic compounds from suspended biological material. Oldfeldt [109] has published a procedure for the determination of the alkali content of organs, and Oster and co-workers [110, 111] have described a method for removing chloride from animal tissues which is based on the work of Adair and Keys [92, 93]. They suggest that the rate of electrodialysis is an indication of the type of binding of the chloride in the various tissues. Isolation of mercury from the internal organs of poisoned animals with the aid of electrodialysis has been demonstrated [112].

A technique has been developed for the identification of nucleic acid components by combining electrodialysis and circular paper chromatography [113]. Electrodialysis has also been used in conjunction with starch gel electrophoresis to characterize proteins [114, 115].

Food Products, Plants, and Colloids

The principal use of electrodialysis in the fields of food products, plants, and colloids has been for demineralization. Among the materials so treated are: agar [116], gelatin [117], polysaccharides [118], glutin [119], protein [120], cellulose [121, 122] and nitrocellulose [121], plant extracts [122], keratin [123], alginic acid [124], protein solutions [52], and albumin [125]. However, a wide variety of other uses have been found by various investigators.

Many workers have considered the use of electrodialysis for salt removal in the refining of cane and beet sugar. Among these are Riley [118], Elder [126], Hardy [127], Taketomi [128], Reininghaus [129], Coleman [130], Mizuguchi [131], Burianek [132–135], Rosenberg [136], van Dorsser [137], Leszko [138], Bobrovnik [139–143], Mishchuk [144, 145], Zelikman [146], and co-workers. It was frequently discovered that the pH of the sugar solution decreased, which was counteracted by addition of base to the central compartment. Pretreatment of sugar solutions before electrodialysis has also been considered [147, 148]. Burianek and Slechtova [149] have performed a mathematical analysis of the demineralization of sugar solutions. Ciz and Cejkova [150] reported on the effect on membrane properties of electrodialysis of sugar solutions. In the synthesis of sugars by hydrolysis of starches, recovery of sulfuric acid in addition to demineralization is conveniently effected by electrodialysis. This has been studied by Ulitin et al. [151–153], Idaszak [154], and Gulyuk and Zelikman [155].

Paronetto [156] and Kagami [157] used electrodialysis to raise the pH of acidic wines. The latter claims no detrimental effect on flavor. Börger [158] discussed electrodialytic clarification of fruit juices. Zang [25] reported on the deacidification of citrus juices.

Substitution or removal of ions has led to electrodialytic preparation of free agar acid [159] and β-amylose [160], precipitation of soybean protein [161], removal of bitter tastes, caused by metal ions, from forage crop extracts [162, 163], black rotted sweet potato and fructose syrup from *Helianthus tuberosus* [164], and acidification of tanning liquor [165].

A four-compartment cell was used for preparation of inosinic acid from meat extracts containing this material [166]. The acid passes through the central diaphragm. Kanai [167] used a two-compartment cell to separate odorless fish liver oil, which was collected in the anode compartment, from odorous components.

A recent patent [168] describes a method of separating pyroglutamic acid from other organic acids based on the difference in permeability at different concentrations. This is a two-step process in which nonamino organic acids are electrodialyzed out of a concentrated solution; the solution is diluted, whereupon the pyroglutamic acid is electrodialyzed more rapidly than the other amino acids.

Electrodialysis has been used for investigation of many natural materials such as lecithin [169], amylose [170], gum jeol and gum arabic [171], yeast

[172–174], vegetative litter [175], solutions of gelatin, gum arabic, polyvinyl alcohol, egg albumin, sodium protalbin, and pectin [176], and algae [177].

Organic acids and bases, because of their different ionic charges, can frequently be separated from plant products. Shmuk [178] reported isolation of citric acid and nicotine. Collins and Rigler [179] separated various nitrogenous materials from cotton plants. Becker et al. [180] used electrodialysis of trichloroacetic acid extracts for determination of nonprotein nitrogen in soybean meal. Kato [181] studied electrodialysis of soybean protein with various agents and noted recovery of the extracting agents in the electrode solutions. Gorbacheva [182] determined the amino acids in various animal and vegetable products.

Samec [183–185], Dahl [186], Caldwell [187], and Richter [188] investigated the separation of starch into linear chains (amylose) and branched chains (amylopectin). The former passed through the diaphragm and the latter collected on the anode wall of the central compartment. Samec [50] reviewed the electrodialysis of starch in 1941.

Several investigators [189, 190] have used electrodialysis to determine the ionizable fraction of metal atoms in plants and seeds. Prolonged electrodialysis severely reduces germination. This subject has been reviewed by Maksimow [191].

Pertinent reviews are given by Zang [192] in the field of food processing and by Pauli [11] in the purification of colloids.

Amino Acids

The behavior of amphoteric amino acids under electrodialysis has drawn the attention of numerous investigators interested both in desalting and in the group separation and isolation of these materials. Blainey and Yardley [193] have reported briefly on the deionization of arginine, lysine, and aspartic acid using a three-compartment cell with heterogeneous ion-exchange membranes and acidic catholyte and basic anolyte. Peers [194], employing the same amino acids plus alanine, improved on their technique and obtained higher percentage retention of the amino acids by reversing the composition of the electrode compartments to exploit a pH barrier effect. Bulk solution pH and current density (probably because of membrane polarization) were found to be important. Electrodialytic removal of ammonium chloride from solutions of ω-aminoenanthic acid has also been studied [195], and Kawamura and Akabane [196] have published data on the efficiency of desalting various common amino acids and degraded soybean protein. Their results demonstrate the advantage of ion-exchange membranes over cellophane. Cell configurations specifically designed for the desalting of amino acids have been patented [197, 198].

Alternatively, DiBenedetto and Lightfoot [199] have studied glycine–sodium chloride solutions to determine the transport of glycine relative to chloride through an anion-exchange membrane. Tests were run at pH $>$ isoelectric point. The relative ionic transport was found to be primarily a function of current density, relative concentrations, and mobility ratios. Permeability of glutamic and aspartic acids has also been reported and the effects of some half-dozen experimental variables noted [200]. Other groups have recorded the permeabilities of glutamic acid, glycine, and lysine [201], and of glycine and methionine [202]. Optimum desalting conditions were selected.

The possibility of separating amino acids into acidic, basic, or neutral groups by electrodialysis was discovered early [203–206] and has recently attracted renewed interest. Hara has presented cell configurations and results for the formation of free amino acids, for the separation or concentration of amino acids, and for the group separation of 15 amino acids [207–209]. He used modern stryrene-butadiene ion-exchange membranes and believes that industrial electrodialysis of amino acids is now feasible because of the availability of large-sized membranes with superior properties and life. By using similar membranes the group separation of glutamic acid, glycine, and lysine has also been studied by Takai [210]. Ryazanov and co-workers [211, 212] have used electrodialysis for the separation of pure amino acid fractions from gelatin hydrolyzate.

Pharmaceuticals

Substantial work has been done on applications of electrodialysis to toxicological analysis and research and in the isolation and analysis of pharmaceuticals and medicinal compounds. Fabre [213, 214] showed that barbituric acid derivatives could be localized in and separated from complex biological media by electrodialysis using a simple apparatus of concentric cylinders and cellophane membranes. He also obtained high recovery of the alkaloids strychnine, brucine, and quinine by electrodialyzing aqueous solutions of their salts or suspensions of suitable organs from test animals [215, 216]. Morphine, cocaine, atropine, and ergot alkaloids did not give satisfactory results, probably because of hydrolysis or reaction at the electrode. Maricq and Rochat [217] overcame this difficulty by inserting an extra compartment between the material dialyzed and the cathode. An organic solvent, for example, chloroform, was placed in the compartment to extract the liberated alkaloid and prevent secondary reactions. They obtained high yields from the salts of cocaine and barbituric acids and their mixtures with biological materials.

Later workers [218–222] investigated and extended the possibilities of isolation and analysis by electrodialysis to some dozen alkaloids and other medicinals. Pure solutions and suspensions of finely ground plant matter were used for the experiments. A qualitive estimation of the migration rate of various alkaloids into the cathode compartment has been given [218] and a more extensive study [223] of the transport behavior of quinine has been made by Kamii, who has also examined the permeability of a variety of common alkaloids [224]. A pH of 3 was reported as optimum for quinine and permeability was greater through a weak-acid than through a strong-acid cation transfer membrane. Specialized apparatus was described [219, 225] and both parchment [218, 220] and cellophane [219] membranes were employed. A review on the application of electrodialysis to extraction of pharmaceuticals is available [226].

A technique for shortening the time of electrodialysis of medicinal substances such as barbituric acid has been described [227, 228], and the electrodialytic method has been suggested as suitable for analysis of barbiturates in legal cases in Russia [229]. Electrodialysis can also be used to concentrate solutions of streptomycin sulfate and chloride [230].

Carboxylic Acids

Lightfoot and Friedman [231] were interested in the potential usefulness of electrodialysis for the purification of carboxylic acids. They determined the transport numbers, permselectivities, and relative transference of several aliphatic monobasic acid anions and of the polybasic fumaric, maleic, itaconic, and citric acids, through heterogeneous membranes. Transport numbers decreased with increasing molecular weight for monocarboxylic acids but dibasic acids had higher transport numbers than monobasic acids of the same molecular weight. Lower pH, producing more free acid, also decreased the transport of carboxylates but not to zero even at pH 1.0.

Kelman [232] has also found that the transfer of organic anions decreased with molecular weight in the series formic, acetic, propionic, butyric, and valeric acids. Steric effects began to be important with butyrate, and the valerate anion appeared to foul the membrane. Lowering the pH to reduce dissociation again decreased transfer.

Kamii [224, 233] has electrodialyzed oxalic and citric acids. A $0.1 N$ solution of acid was decarboxylated in 10 hr, while a similar concentration of the sodium salt was free of the anion after 3 hr. Purification of acetic acid has been studied [234], and sebacic acid has been recovered from the alkaline hydrolyzate of castor oil via electrodialysis [235].

Polymers

The investigation of polymeric materials is another area in which electrodialysis has been found to be useful. The glycolic acid ethers of cellulose [236] and polyvinyl alcohol [237] have been obtained in the free acid form and purified for further study by means of electrodialysis of the sodium salts. Polyvinyl alcohol itself was readily deashed [238] from 1.27 to 0.04% in 90 min using the previously described Schleicher and Schuell electrodialyzer equipped with a rhodium anode and a graphite cathode. Use of dilute hydrochloric acid in the anode and dilute sodium hydroxide in the cathode chambers increased utilization of the field. A natural polymer, silk, was purified by electrodialysis during an investigation of the surface electrochemical properties of fiber proteins [239]. The carboxylic acid groups present in natural cellulose have been completely liberated with the aid of electrodialysis [240] and the method made the basis of an improved technique for their determination.

Electrodialysis is claimed to be the most effective method for deashing various wood pulps intended for conversion to insulation paper for condensers and electrical cables [241, 242]. Using a Pauli electrodialyzer a 0.06 to 0.04% minimum ash content could be obtained, while the main characteristics of the pulps did not change. A small decrease in viscosity was attributed to the removal of cations responsible for weak cross-linkages.

Residual monomeric vinyl organic sulfonates have been removed from solutions of poly(vinylsulfonates) [243] by passing an aqueous dispersion of the impure polymer through an electrodialysis cell. The anion-permselective membranes used were shielded on the purification chamber side with a nonselective cellophane membrane. Kargin [244] employed cellophane membranes with a cutoff at molecular weight 10,000 in a study of the transfer rates and structure of polyacrylic acid and gelatin.

D'Yachkovskii [245] has investigated the formation of positive ions as the catalytically active moiety in Ziegler-Natta initiators. Using a two-chamber cell with cellophane membranes, with ethylene in one compartment and the catalyst in the other, he showed that polymerization occurred only when the ethylene compartment electrode was negative. He concluded that positive titanium complexes are the active constituents. Later work [246] on the electrodialysis of labeled dicyclopentadienyltitanium has further elucidated the catalyst structure.

Kazaryan [247] used a three-chamber electrodialysis cell to demonstrate the importance of cations in the ionic polymerization of styrene in nitromethane. Polystyrene was formed in the center compartment only when the cell was arranged so that carbonium ions could move toward the cathode, into the center compartment.

Sethu has shown [248] that ammonia can be recovered from skim latex by electrodialysis of the serum. Three- and five-compartment cells were used and current efficiencies of 83% (NH_4^+) were obtained with heterogeneous membranes. Current reversal was recommended to avoid deposits of negatively charged latex on the cathode face of the anion-exchange membrane.

Simultaneous electrodialysis and electrodecantation was suggested as a means of concentrating the latex while recovering ammonia from it.

Dairy Processes

Electrodialysis of milk and milk products, particularly whey, has been studied widely.

Woljagin and Scheimpflug [249] investigated the deacidification of milk by using it as the cathode fluid in a two-compartment cell. However, Pien and Baisse [250] did not consider electrically neutralized milk a saleable product.

Kato [251] prepared casein by electrodialysis of skim milk in a three-compartment cell. He found that at a pH of 5.7 to 5.0 the casein deposited on the membrane near the anode, while below pH 5.0 it accumulated on the cathode membrane.

The desalting or deashing of whey has been extensively studied [251–257] because the product, largely lactose, has considerable nutritional value. Solutions of various salinities, 5% to <1%, were investigated and reduction in salinity of 50 to 80% was generally accomplished in a single operation. Removal of monovalent ions, for example, Na^+, K^+, and Cl^-, is more complete than that of higher-valence ions. Removal of OH^- is generally more rapid than H^+ removal so sodium hydroxide is occasionally added to prevent a drop in pH. At high solids content ($> 50\%$) the process may be retarded, but little loss of nonionic species occurs. The demineralized solution is dried and generally used as a component in infant foods.

Bakhvalov and Klimovskii [258] suggested the neutralization of whey with calcium hydroxide for removal of protein prior to electrodialysis. Others [257] precipitated the residual protein with ferric iron, while a patent [259] describes a method for increasing the demineralization rate by adjusting the whey pH to 4.5, heating to 140°F for 1 hr. and filtering the resulting precipitate.

Various authors [260–263] have investigated the removal of radioactive contaminants, notably ^{90}Sr and ^{137}Cs, from milk. The removal, which required lowering of the pH to 5.1 to 5.3 with citric acid, ran Cs > Sr > Ba ≫ La ≲ Ce. The salt composition of the milk was maintained by controlling the composition of the solution from which replacement cations were obtained. Only small losses of organic materials occurred and appearance, taste, and nutritional value were essentially unaffected.

A thorough review of electrodialysis of milk and whey, covering both ion removal and ion substitution, has been presented by McRae and Sanders [264]. Commercial apparatus for such electrodialysis has been patented by Francis and Treleven [265] and is described by Stribley [266].

Organic Wastes

The possibility of using electrodialysis for the treatment of sewage was apparently first considered in 1936. Murray [267] electrodialyzed centrifuged raw sewage in a three-compartment cell based on Pauli's design, using electrode compartments filled with distilled water and platinum and copper electrodes. Cellophane membranes were preferred and several temperatures were employed. After several hours at a current density ≤ 1.2 mA-cm^{-2}, the pH had decreased from 8 to about 3.1 to 5.2, most of the electrolyte was removed, and the sewage was solubilized and deodorized. Electrodialysis of sewage [268] and distillery slops from molasses fermentation [269] using electrolysis cells with membranes to separate anolyte and catholyte has been found to reduce the biochemical oxygen demand (BOD) of the cathode solutions. Advantageous changes in pH and suspended solids were also obtained in the treated sewage. Electrodialysis has been used [270] for the electrochemical purification of alkaline hydrolyzates in the production of glutamic acid from wastes of food production.

More recently, on the basis of laboratory work [271], it has been claimed that electrodialysis can reduce the amount of orthophosphate and ammonia-nitrogen in filtered raw sewage. A more extensive study [272] of electrodialysis as a possible tertiary treatment for sewage indicated that it was practical for partial demineralization of secondary effluent. Pretreatment considered necessary was clarification for removal of colloidal matter and carbon adsorption treatment for removal of soluble organics. Membrane fouling occurred with unpretreated wastewater. Operation of a pilot-scale system [273] has confirmed the applicability of electrodialysis for advanced waste treatment and indicated alternate solutions to the fouling problem. A second pilot plant study [274] on a 5 gal/min unit has further defined the required pretreatment and presented additional cost estimates. Electrodialysis also has been reported to show promise in coagulating solids for flotation operations both in the sanitary and industrial waste treatment fields [275].

The treatment of pulping spent liquors by electrodialysis has been shown [276–279] to be valuable in recovering pulping chemicals, sugars, and low-molecular-weight organic acids and lignosulfonic acids from sulfite mill wastes. The major work in this area has been sponsored by the Sulfite Pulp Manufacturers Research League and resulted in the development of the so-called BALC process based on a modified electrodialysis configuration [276, 280]. This arrangement employs a barrier cell and neutral membranes for producing the three main process streams. The technique can treat almost all types of spent liquors and is also valuable in the control of water pollution [276, 279]. Additional development in membranes and equipment is deemed desirable [277]. Economics of the process are further improved by the trend of sulfite pulp mills toward the use of more costly bases and the continuing research effort to find applications for recovered liquor solids. As a recent example, electrodialyzed lignosulfonates from the BALC process have been proposed and successfully demonstrated as a component in thermosetting adhesives [281].

Mintz et al. [279] have suggested several alternate electrodialysis systems for treatment of pulping liquors. The processes involve modified stack configurations, use of neutral membranes, and various combinations of electrodialysis and electrogravitation. These authors also propose processes for treatment of kraft liquor, which offer the possibility for recovery of tall oil, hemicelluloses, and pulping chemicals.

Miscellaneous

Electrodialysis has been used to control the electrical conductivity of a recirculating aqueous glycerol coolant [282]. An experimental program and cost estimate for the industrial deashing of 33% glycerol using modern electrodialysis equipment and homogeneous membranes has been described [283]. A batch system was used to obtain 97% removal from a feed solution containing 1% ash. Typical capital and operating costs are shown and extrapolations made to higher ash content feed.

It has been recommended [284] that before determining vitamin B_{12} in seawater the salt be removed by electrodialysis. An apparatus for this purpose has been described. Electrodialysis has also been screened as a technique for separating the organic and inorganic constituents of seawater [285]. Poor retention of organics was obtained using cellulose acetate membranes, but it was believed that the use of ion-exchange membranes might be capable of substantial improvements in the separation of certain organic compounds. In one such attempt 97% of the organic matter was retained with almost complete demineralization.

An electrodialysis apparatus has been described [286] for the removal of weakly ionized bases, such as amines, from aqueous solutions, and the composition of an electrocoating bath containing such organics can be maintained by electrodialysis [287].

Deiodination of aromatics, including thyroxine, triiodothyronine, and, diiodotryosine has been observed [288] during electrodialysis for salt removal. Electrodialysis of antipyrine solutions was used to demonstrate formation of molecular addition compounds [289].

Electrodialysis of sodium dodecyl sulfate in a two-compartment cell has been used to study [290, 291] micelle formation and critical micelle concentration in surface-active agents. Millipore filters and cellophane were employed as membranes. Advantages claimed over simple dialysis were rapid measurements and elimination of inorganic salt additives to inhibit micelle permeation.

Briere and co-workers have published a series of papers [292–299] in which they describe the electrodialysis of various polar solvents with the aim of obtaining liquids of high resistivity and purity.

Working initially with methanol, ethanol, and isopropanol they first demonstrated that, in general, the properties of high conductivity and permselectivity possessed by (commercial) ion-exchange membranes in aqueous solutions are conserved when they are placed in alcoholic media [292]. They found that the procedure developed for obtaining high-purity water [293] could be applied also to methanol and ethanol [294], in particular, producing methanol in a degree of purity within 10 % of the natural ionization state. Limiting resistivity of the alcohols is obtained by proper selection of the anolyte and catholyte solutions; current density affects only the rate of deionization [295, 296]. Purification of a solution of acetic acid in methanol could also be achieved [297].

Deionization of aprotic polar liquids could be accomplished by use of a novel electrodialysis cell in which the membranes are placed in direct contact with the electrodes [298, 299]. Purification of nitrobenzene, sulfolane, and dimethyl sulfoxide were shown [299] as examples. Use of electrodialysis and ion-exchange membranes was preferred over conventional ion exchange since the catalytic activity of the particulate resin caused degradation of the solvent, increasing the nonionic contamination during deionization [299].

A large electrochemical plant employing a hybrid electrolysis-electro-dialysis process has recently been constructed by Monsanto Chemical Company. An ion-exchange membrane is used to separate the electrodes in a cell in which acrylonitrile is electrohydrodimerized to adiponitrile, one of the intermediates in nylon 66 production [300].

References

1. German Patent, 167, 853 (1900).
2. J. Reitstotter, *Kolloid-Z.*, **41**, 243, 315 (1927).
3. British Patent, 5,749 (1896); German Patent, 59, 443 (1889).
4. H. W. Morse and G. W. Pierce, *Z. Physik. Chem.*, **45**, 606 (1903).
5. S. B. Tuwiner, *Diffusion and Membrane Technology*, Van Nostrand Reinhold, New York, 1962.
6. A. I. Kendall and E. Gebauer-Fuelnegg, *J. Chem. Educ.*, **8**, 1634 (1931).
7. C. Dhere, *Kolloid-Z.*, **41**, 243, 315 (1927).
8. C. Dhere, *Biochem. Z.*, **153**, 504 (1924).
9. H. Freundlich and L. F. Loeb, *Biochem. Z.*, **150**, 522 (1924).

10. W. Pauli, *Kolloid-Z.*, **31**, 252 (1922).
11. W. Pauli, *Helv. Chim. Acta*, **25**, 137 (1942).
12. P. H. Prausnitz and J. Reitstotter, *Elektrophorese, Elektroosmose, Elektrodialyse in Flussigkeiten*, Steinkopff, Dresden, 1931.
13. E. Manegold and K. Kalauch, *Kolloid-Z.*, **86**, 313 (1939).
14. K. H. Meyer and W. Straus, *Helv. Chim. Acta*, **23**, 795 (1940).
15. K. H. Meyer and J. F. Sievers, *Helv. Chim. Acta*, **19**, 649, 665, 987 (1936).
16. T. Teorell, *Proc. Soc. Exptl. Biol. Med.*, **33**, 282 (1935).
17. W. Juda and W. A. McRae, *J. Am. Chem. Soc.*, **72**, 1044 (1950).
18. T. R. E. Kressman, *Nature*, **165**, 568 (1950).
19. E. A. Mason and T. A. Kirkham, *Chem. Eng. Progr. Symp. Ser.*, **55**, 24 (1959).
20. W. E. Katz, paper presented at the International Conference on Water for Peace, Washington, D.C., May 23–31, 1967.
21. T. A. Kirkham, *Mech. Eng.*, **90**(3), 47 (1968).
22. H. Z. Friedlander and R. N. Rickles, *Chem. Eng.*, **73**(5), 111 (1966).
23. Anon., *Chem. Eng. News*, July 18, p. 46 (1966).
24. W. K. W. Chen, "Electrodialysis," in *Kirk-Othmer Encyclopedia of Chemical Technology*, 2nd ed., Interscience, New York, 1965.
25. J. A. Zang, *Proc. Symp. Membrane Processes Ind., Birmingham, Alabama, 1966*, p. 35.
26. T. Graham, *Trans. Roy. Soc. London*, **151**, 183 (1961).
27. E. F. Leonard, "Dialysis," in *Kirk-Othmer Encyclopedia of Chemical Technology*, 2nd ed., Interscience, New York, 1965.
28. B. H. Vromen, *Ind. Eng. Chem.*, **54**(6), 20 (1962).
29. R. N. Rickles, *Membranes—Technology and Economics*, Noyes Development Corp., Park Ridge, New Jersey, 1967.
30. R. E. Stauffer, "Dialysis and Electrodialysis," in *Technique of Organic Chemistry*, A. Weissberger, Ed., Vol. III, Interscience, New York, 1950.
31. F. K. Daniel, "Dialysis," in *Kirk-Othmer Encyclopedia of Chemical Technology*, Interscience, New York, 1950.
32. Y. Oda et al., *Ind. Eng. Chem. Prod. Res. Develop.*, **3**(3), 244 (1964).
33. J. P. Merrill, *Sci. Am.*, **205**, 56, July (1961).
34. N. Lakshminarayanaiah, *Chem. Rev.*, **65**, 491 (1965).
35. A. G. Winger, G. W. Bodamer, and R. Kunin, *J. Electrochem. Soc.*, **100**, 178 (1953).
36. J. R. Wilson, *Demineralization by Electrodialysis*, Butterworths, London, 1960.
37. W. G. Hamner and W. E. Katz, *J. Am. Water Works Assoc.*, **56**, 1537 (1964).
38. W. E. Katz, *Proc. Symp. Western Water Power, Los Angeles, California, April 1968*, p. C113.
39. E. R. Gilliland, *Intern. Symp. Water Desalination, 1st, Washington, D.C.*, Vol. III, p. 389 (1965).
40. D. A. Cowan and J. H. Brown, *Ind. Eng. Chem.*, **51**, 1445 (1959).
41. N. W. Rosenberg and C. E. Tirrell, *Ind. Eng. Chem.*, **49**, 780 (1957).
42. *Demineralization by Transport Depletion*, Report No. 80, U. S. Dept. of Interior, Office of Saline Water, Washington, D. C.

43. T. Bejerano, C. Forgacs, and J. Rabinowitz, *Desalination*, **3**, 129 (1967).
44. A. J. Casolo and F. B. Leitz, paper presented at the Symposium on Electrodialysis, Electrochemical Society Meeting, Boston, Massachusetts, May 1968.
45. F. B. Leitz and W. A. McRae, paper presented at 158th National Meeting, American Chemical Society, New York, 1969.
46. R. Bradfield, *Ind. Eng. Chem.*, **20**, 79 (1928).
47. D. B. Roxburgh and M. H. Power, *Ind. Eng. Chem., Anal. Ed.*, **9**, 578 (1937).
48. P. E. Lovering and M. L. Smith, *Chem. Ind. (London)*, **1946**, 298.
49. H. Brintzinger, A. Rothhaar, and H. G. Beier, *Kolloid-Z.*, **66**, 183 (1934).
50. M. Samec, *Kolloid-Z.*, **94**, 350 (1941).
51. T. Wood, *Biochem. J.*, **62**, 611 (1956).
52. S. Katz and F. Ellinger, *Biochemistry*, **2**, 406 (1963).
53. W. K. W. Chen, M. S. Mintz, and D. G. Conning, *Dechema Monograph.*, **47**, II, 619 (1962).
54. J. B. Farrell and R. N. Smith, *Ind. Eng. Chem.*, **54**(6), 29 (1962).
55. J. C. Oliver, *Public Works*, **96**, 137 (1965).
56. E. S. Cary and H. S. Ongerth, *J. Am. Water Works Assoc.*, **52**, 585 (1960).
57. B. W. Calvit and J. J. Sloan, *Intern. Symp. Water Desalination, 1st, Washington, D. C.*, Vol. III, p. 11 (1965).
58. W. A. McRae, "Demineralization by Electrodialysis" in *Encyclopedia of Electrochemistry*, C. A. Hampel, Ed., Von Nostrand Reinhold, New York, 1964.
59. G. S. Solt, *Intern. Symp. Water Desalination, 1st, Washington, D. C.*, Vol. II, p. 13 (1965).
60. G. S. Solt, *Desalination*, **2**, 21 (1967).
61. Anon., *Chem. Eng. News*, **40**(41), 44 (1962).
62. F. Helfferich, *Ion-Exchange*, McGraw-Hill, New York, 1962.
63. K. Sollner, *Svensk Kem. Tidskr.*, **6–7**, 267 (1958).
64. F. Bergsma, *Dechema Monograph.*, **47**, II, 449 (1962).
65. J. F. A. Hazenberg, *Dechema Monograph.*, **47**, II, 487 (1962).
66. T. D. Morgan in *Demineralization by Electrodialysis*, J. R. Wilson, Ed., Butterworths, London, 1960, Chapter 3.
67. J. L. Eisenmann and E. T. Roach, paper presented at the Symposium on Electrodialysis, Electrochemical Society Meeting, Boston, Massachusetts, 1968.
68. M. Block, *Chem. Ind. (London)*, **1967**, 2099.
69. *Test Manual for Permselective Membranes*, Report No. 77 U. S. Dept. of Interior, Office of Saline Water, Washington, D. C., 1964.
70. F. de Korosy and J. Shorr, *Dechema Monograph.*, **47**, II, 477 (1962).
71. V. A. Klyachko, *Intern. Symp. Water Desalination, 1st, Washington, D. C.*, Vol. I, p. 331 (1965).
72. A. B. Pashkov et al., *Intern. Symp. Water Desalination, 1st, Washington, D. C.*, Vol. II, p. 561 (1965).
73. K. S. Rajan, D. B. Boies, A. J. Casolo, and J. I. Bregman, *Desalination*, **1**, 231 (1966).
74. U. S. Patent, 3,346,422 (1967).

75. C. Dhere and M. Gorgolewski, *Compt. Rend*, **150**, 993 (1910); *Chem. Abstr.*, **4**, 2007 (1910).
76. W. Pauli, *Kolloid-Z.*, **31**, 252 (1922); *Biochem. Z.*, **152**, 355, 360 (1924).
77. G. Ettisch and W. Beck, *Biochem. Z.*, **171**, 443 (1926).
78. G. Ettisch, R. Bradfield, and W. Ewig, *Kolloid-Z.*, **45**, 141 (1928).
79. G. Ettisch and W. Ewig, *Biochem. Z.*, **195**, 175 (1928).
80. G. Ettisch, *Biochem. Z.*, **266**, 436 (1933).
81. G. Ettisch and W. Ewig, *Biochem. Z.*, **216**, 401 (1929).
82. G. Ettisch and J. A. de Loureiro, *Biochem. Z.*, **266**, 422 (1933).
83. G. Ettisch and G. Groscurth, *Biochem. Z.*, **266**, 441 (1933).
84. A. V. Markovich, *J. Appl. Chem.* (*USSR*) (*English Transl.*), **8**, 1444 (1935); *Chem. Abstr.*, **30**, 5245 (1936).
85. N. R. Chowdhury, *Sci. Cult.* (*Calcutta*), **3**, 678 (1938); *Chem. Abstr.*, **32**, 7946 (1938).
86. R. Rabinovich, *Anales Asoc. Quim. Arg.*, **14**, 139 (1926); *Chem. Abstr.*, **21**, 2002 (1927).
87. A. Bernhard and J. J. Beaver, *J. Biol. Chem.*, **69**, 113 (1926).
88. G. Peretti, *Boll. Soc. Ital. Biol. Sper.*, **9**, 1333 (1934); *Chem. Abstr.*, **29**, 4035 (1935).
89. M. U. Tsao, *Scand. J. Clin. Lab. Invest.*, **2**, 102 (1950); *Chem. Abstr.*, **45**, 5219b (1951).
90. O. J. Malm, *Scand. J. Clin. Lab. Invest.*, **2**, 92 (1950); *Chem. Abstr.*, **45**, 5219a (1951).
91. G. S. Adair and A. B. Keys, *J. Physiol.*, **81**, 162 (1934); *Chem. Abstr.*, **28**, 6168 (1934).
92. A. B. Keys, *J. Biol. Chem.*, **114**, 449 (1936).
93. N. R. Joseph and W. C. Stadie, *J. Biol. Chem.*, **125**, 795 (1938).
94. K. H. Dittmer and R. G. Gustavson, *Ind. Eng. Chem. Anal. Ed.*, **12**, 297 (1940).
95. E. DiBenedetto, *Rev. Soc. Arg. Biol.*, **8**, 497 (1932); *Chem. Abstr.*, **27**, 3232 (1933).
96. A. V. Markovich and I. M. Khaustova, *J. Appl. Chem.* (*USSR*) (*English Transl.*), **11**, 1648, 1657 (1938); *Chem. Abstr.*, **33**, 6893 (1939).
97. F. Modern, *Rev. Inst. Bacteriol.*, **5**, 695 (1930); *Chem. Abstr.*, **25**, 1895 (1931).
98. P. Wernicke and F. Modern, *Anales Asoc. Quim. Arg.*, **14**, 158 (1926); *Chem. Abstr.*, **21**, 452 (1927).
99. A. V. Markovich et al., *J. Appl. Chem.* (*USSR*), **12**, 1755 (1939); *Chem. Abstr.*, **34**, 7950 (1940).
100. A. V. Markovich et al., *Z. Microbiol. Epidemiol. Immunitatsforsch.* (*USSR*) **1939**, No. 11–12, 88; *Chem. Abstr.*, **36**, 1381 (1942).
101. H. Zondek and H. Ucko, *Klin. Wochschr.*, **5**, 1861 (1926); *Chem. Abstr.*, **21**, 261 (1927).
102. T. C. Taylor et al., *Am. J. Physiol.*, **74**, 539 (1925); *Chem. Abstr.*, **20**, 966 (1926).
103. M. Freeman et al., *Biochem. J.*, **29**, 2211 (1935).
104. G. P. Hess et al., *J. Am. Chem. Soc.*, **73**, 5918 (1951).

105. J. G. Pierce and M. E. Carsten, *J. Am. Chem. Soc.*, **80**, 3482 (1958).

106. R. Fricke et al., *Kolloid-Z.*, **39**, 152 (1926).

107. D. Narayanamurti and R. V. Norris, *Proc. Indian Sci. Congr.*, *15th, 1928*, p. 166; *Chem. Abstr.*, **25**, 2741 (1931).

108. P. Ohlmeyer and R. Dufait, *Naturwissenschaften*, **29**, 672 (1941); *Chem. Abstr.*, **37**, 2761 (1943).

109. C. O. Oldfeldt, *Biochem. Z.*, **251**, 235 (1932).

110. R. H. Oster and E. J. Kemp, *J. Biol. Chem.*, **131**, 13 (1939).

111. R. H. Oster and W. R. Amberson, *J. Biol. Chem.*, **131**, 19 (1939).

112. I. A. Marenich and A. A. Shcherbina, *Farmatsevt. Zh. (Kiev)*, **21**(2), 37 (1966); *Chem. Abstr.*, **66**, 16983 (1967).

113. E. K. Alimova et al., *Biokhimiya*, **26**, 221 (1961); *Chem. Abstr.*, **55**, 18860h (1961).

114. J. G. Pierce and C. A. Free, *Biochem. Biophys. Acta*, **48**, 436 (1961).

115. A. L. Koen and C. R. Shaw, *Anal. Biochem.*, **9**(4), 495 (1964)

116. E. H. Harvey, *Am. J. Pharm.*, **97**, 66 (1925); *Chem. Abstr.*, **19**, 1363 (1925).

117. S. Oka, *J. Soc. Chem. Ind. (Japan)*, **30**, 396 (1927); *Chem. Abstr.*, **22**, 509 (1928).

118. J. Reilly and D. T. McSweeney, *Sci. Proc. Roy. Dublin Soc.*, **19**, 451 (1930); *Chem. Abstr.*, **24**, 3763 (1930).

119. G. S. Vozdvizhenskii, *Trans. Butlerov Inst. Chem. Tech.*, *Kazan* No. **1**, 99 (1934); *Chem. Abstr.*, **29**, 3897 (1935).

120. F. W. Bernhart, L. E. Arnow, and A. C. Bratton, *Ind. Eng. Chem.*, *Anal. Ed.* **9**, 387 (1937); *Chem. Abstr.*, **31**, 7916 (1937).

121. V. A. Kargin and E. Ya. Vinetskaya, *J. Phys. Chem. (USSR)*, **10**, 788 (1937); *Chem. Abstr.*, **32**, 8131 (1938).

122. F. D. Collins and R. E. R. Grimmett, *New Zealand J. Sci. Tech.*, **27A**, 198 (1945); *Chem. Abstr.*, **35**, 7270 (1941).

123. C. G. Fink and H. A. Golle, *J. Electrochem. Soc.*, **97**(2), 59 (1950); *Chem. Abstr.*, **44**, 2389b (1950).

124. Y. Kojima, *Nippon Suisangaku Kaishi*, **22**, 180, 184, 191 (1956–1957); *Chem. Abstr.*, **52**, 5165h (1958).

125. L. A. Lapaeva, *Lab. Delo*, **1964**(1), 58; *Chem. Abstr.*, **60**, 11029e (1964).

126. A. L. Elder et al., *Ind. Eng. Chem. Anal. Ed.*, **6**, 65 (1934); *Chem. Abstr.*, **28**, 1279 (1934).

127. V. R. Hardy, *Trans. Illinois State Acad. Sci.*, **26**(3), 80 (1934); *Chem. Abstr.*, **28**, 5277 (1934).

128. N. Taketomi, *J. Soc. Chem. Ind.*, *Japan*, **41**, Suppl. Binding 220 (1938); *Chem. Abstr.*, **32**, 9116 (1938).

129. French Patent, 848,624 (1939); *Chem. Abstr.*, **35**, 6017 (1941).

130. G. H. Coleman and A. Miller, *Proc. Iowa Acad. Sci.*, **49**, 257 (1942); *Chem. Abstr.*, **37**, 5636 (1943).

131. J. Mizuguchi et al., *J. Pharm. Soc. Japan*, **71**, 1284 (1951); *Chem. Abstr.*, **46**, 2931i (1952).

132. J. Burianek and D. Slechtova, *Listy Cukrovar.*, **75**, 62 (1959); *Chem. Abstr.*, **53**, 14553e (1959).

133. J. Burianek and D. Slechtova, *Listy Cukrovar.*, **75**, 82 (1959); *Chem. Abstr.*, **53**, 17544e (1959).

134. J. Burianek, D. Slechtova, and O. Lisy, *Listy Cukrovar.*, **76**, 193 (1960); *Chem. Abstr.*, **55**, 7873e (1961).

135. Czechoslovakian Patent, 94,142 (1958); *Chem. Abstr.*, **56**, 1657h (1962).

136. U. S. Patent, 2,860,091 (1958); *Chem. Abstr.*, **53**, 16769g (1959).

137. U. S. Patent, 2,897,130 (1959); *Chem. Abstr.*, **53**, 16770b (1959).

138. M. Leszko, *Gaz. Cukrownicza*, **64**(2), 38 (1962), *Chem. Abstr.*, **58**, 8126d (1963).

139. L. D. Bobrovnik and I. M. Litvak, *Sakharn. Prom.*, **36**(11), 18 (1962); *Chem. Abstr.*, **58**, 9317b (1963).

140. L. D. Bobrovnik and I. M. Litvak, *Tr. Kievsk. Tekhnol. Inst. Pishchevoi Prom.*, **27**, 31 (1963); *Chem. Abstr.*, **61**, 2517d (1964).

141. L. D. Bobrovnik and I. M. Litvak, *Ionoobmen. Tekhnol.*, *Akad. Nauk SSSR, Inst. Fiz. Khim.*, **1965**, 96; *Chem. Abstr.*, **63**, 8596c (1965).

142. A. P. Kozyavkin, L. D. Bobrovnik, and K. D. Zhura, *Izvest. Vysshikh. Uchebn. Zavedenii Pishchevaya Tekhnol.*, **1967**(5), 126; *Chem. Abstr.*, **68**, 28596 (1968).

143. L. D. Bobrovnik, G. P. Voloshanenko, and A. P. Kozyavkin, *Sakharn. Prom.*, **42**(2), 13 (1968); *Chem. Abstr.*, **68**, 88365 (1968).

144. R. T. Mishchuk and I. M. Litvak, *Sakharn. Prom.*, **40**(4), 26 (1966); *Chem. Abstr.*, **65**, 4086d (1966).

145. R. T. Mishchuk, L. D. Bobrovnik, and K. D. Zhura, *Sakharn. Prom.*, **41**(2), 8 (1967); *Chem. Abstr.*, **66**, 106109 (1967).

146. I. F. Zelikman and D. M. Leibovich, *Izvest. Vysshikh. Uchebn. Zavedenii Pischevaya Tekhnol.*, **1968**(1), 80; *Chem. Abstr.*, **68**, 106237 (1968).

147. Swiss Patent, 252,130 (1948); *Chem. Abstr.*, **43**, 8290b (1949).

148. French Patent, 1,468,519 (1966); *Chem. Abstr.*, **67**, 65702 (1967).

149. J. Burianek and D. Slechtova, *Listy Cukrovar*, **75**, 62 (1959); *Chem. Abstr.*, **53**, 14553e (1959).

150. K. Ciz and V. Cejkova, *Listy Cukrovar*, **84**(1), 17 (1968); *Chem. Abstr.*, **68**, 88374 (1968).

151. O. A. Ulitin, *Izvest. Vysshikh. Uchebn. Zavedenii Pishchevaya Tekhnol.*, **1963**(6), 73; *Chem. Abstr.*, **60**, 11028h (1964).

152. O. A. Ulitin, *Izvest. Vysshikh. Uchebn. Zavedenii Pishchevaya Tekhnol.*, **1965**(3), 82; *Chem. Abstr.*, **63**, 10159d (1965).

153. U.S.S.R. Patent, 196,767 (1967); *Chem. Abstr.*, **68**, 41254 (1968).

154. Belgian Patent, 645,544 (1964), *Chem. Abstr.*, **63**, 11845c (1965).

155. N. G. Gulyuk and I. F. Zelikman, *Sakharn. Prom.*, **42**(1), 53, 60 (1968); *Chem. Abstr.*, **68**, 106229, 106238 (1968).

156. L. Paronetto, *Annuar. Staz. Sper. Viticolt. Enol. Conegliano*, **10**, 123 (1941); *Chem. Abstr.*, **40**, 3222 (1946).

157. M. Kagami, *Yamanashi Daigaku Hakko Kenkyusho Kenkyu Hokoku*, **6**, 1 (1959); *Chem. Abstr.*, **55**, 12758h (1961).

158. H. E. Börger, *Zucker*, **7**(4), 78 (1954); *Chem. Abstr.*, **48**, 6149d (1954).

159. W. F. Hoffman and R. A. Gortner, *J. Biol. Chem.*, **65**, 371 (1925); *Chem. Abstr.*, **20**, 534 (1926).

160. S. Redfern, *Cereal Chem.*, **15**, 712 (1938); *Chem. Abstr.*, **32**, 9541 (1938).

161. A. K. Smith and S. J. Circle, *Ind. Eng. Chem.*, **31**, 1284 (1939); *Chem. Abstr.*, **33**, 9480 (1939).

162. U.S. Patent, 2,465,967 (1949); *Chem. Abstr.*, **43**, 6334g (1949).

163. U.S. Patent, 2,483,634 (1949); *Chem. Abstr.*, **44**, 1623f (1950).

164. K. Matsumoto, Y. Ogata, and H. Mochkizui, *Shokuryo No Kagaku*, **2**, 210 (1948); *Chem. Abstr.*, **47**, 2395c (1953).

165. E. Sugano and I. Nishiyama, *Nippon Hikaku Gijutsu Kyokaishi*, **5**, 71 (1959); *Chem. Abstr.*, **54**, 15977c (1960).

166. Japanese Patent, 732 (1956); *Chem. Abstr.*, **51**, 3870b (1957).

167. Japanese Patent, 3632 (1958); *Chem. Abstr.*, **53**, 8668e (1959).

168. British Patent, 883,922 (1961); *Chem. Abstr.*, **56**, 11870f (1962).

169. I. Kose, *Bull. Kagami Res. Inst.*, **2**, 1 (1929); *Chem. Abstr.*, **24**, 1118 (1930).

170. H. Luers and R. Lechner, *Wochschr. Brau.*, **50**, 49 (1933); *Chem. Abstr.*, **27**, 5347 (1933).

171. S. N. Mukherjee, *J. Indian Chem. Soc.*, **25**, 333 (1948); *Chem. Abstr.*, **43**, 2797e (1949).

172. G. Batta and H. Lecoq, *Rev. Ferment. Ind. Aliment.*, **3**, 127 (1948); *Bull. Soc. Chim. Biol.*, **31**, 785 (1949); *Chem. Abstr.*, **44**, 2072e (1950).

173. G. Batta and H. Lecoq, *Ind. Chim. Belge* **17**, 150 (1952); *Chem. Abstr.*, **46**, 7619a (1952).

174. G. Batta and H. Lecoq, *Bull. Soc. Chim. Biol.*, **34**, 108 (1952); *Chem. Abstr.*, **47**, 168f (1953).

175. S. Mattson and E. Koutler-Andersson, *Kgl. Lantbruks-Hogskol. Ann.*, **21**, 389 (1954); *Chem. Abstr.*, **49**, 9854a (1955).

176. W. Wojciak, *Poznan. Towarz. Pryjaciol Nauk, Wydzial Mat. Przyrod. Prace Komisji Mat. Przyrod.*, **12**(1), 27 (1965); *Chem. Abstr.*, **65**, 1430e (1966).

177. R. G. Tischer et al., *Biophys. Acta*, **156**(2), 403 (1968); *Chem. Abstr.*, **68**, 85237 (1968).

178. A. A. Shmuk, *Sb. Rabot Khim. Tabak, Bull.*, **125**, 47 (1935); *Chem. Abstr.*, **30**, 4992 (1936).

179. E. R. Collins and N. E. Rigler, *Soil Sci.*, **44**, 217 (1937); *Chem. Abstr.*, **31**, 8793 (1937).

180. H. C. Becker, R. T. Milner, and R. H. Nagel, *Cereal Chem.*, **17**, 447 (1940); *Chem. Abstr.*, **34**, 6716 (1940).

181. J. Kato, *J. Soc. Chem. Ind. Japan*, **45**, 771 (1942); *Chem. Abstr.*, **43**, 5257c (1949).

182. A. P. Gorbacheva, *Dokl. Vses. Akad. Sel'skokhoz. Nauk.*, **14**(9), 31 (1949); *Chem. Abstr.*, **44**, 243b (1950).

183. M. Samec and A. Mayer, *Compt. Rend.*, **173**, 321 (1921); *Chem. Abstr.*, **15**, 3983 (1921).

184. M. Samec and M. Blinc, *Kolloidchem. Beihefte*, **30**, 163 (1930); *Chem. Abstr.*, **24**, 2495 (1930).

185. M. Samec, *Oesterr. Chemiker-Ztg.*, **63**(1), 12 (1962); *Chem. Abstr.*, **56,** 15715d (1962).

186. O. Dahl, *Kolloid-Z.*, **92,** 70 (1940); *Chem. Abstr.*, **35,** 2077 (1941).

187. C. G. Caldwell and R. M. Hixon, *J. Am. Chem. Soc.*, **63,** 2876 (1941); *Chem. Abstr.*, **36,** 677 (1942).

188. M. Richter and M. Ulmann, *Kolloid-Z.*, **176,** 98 (1961); *Chem. Abstr.*, **55,** 26487d (1961).

189. W. R. Mullison, *Plant Physiol.*, **14,** 583 (1939); *Chem. Abstr.*, **39,** 1897 (1945).

190. J. D. Nelly, *Plant Physiol.*, **19,** 19 (1944); *Chem. Abstr.*, **39,** 3810 (1945).

191. A. Maksimow, *Acta Soc. Botan. Polon.*, **13,** 231 (1938); *Chem. Abstr.*, **33,** 6385 (1939).

192. J. A. Zang et al., *Chem. Eng. Progr. Symp. Ser.*, **62**(69), 105 (1966); *Chem. Abstr.*, **67,** 42592 (1967).

193. J. D. Blainey and H. J. Yardley, *Nature*, **177,** 83 (1956); *Chem. Abstr.*, **50,** 9492i (1956).

194. A. M. Peers, *J. Appl. Chem. (London)*, **8,** Pt. I, 59 (1958).

195. K. Saotome and H. Komoto, *Kogyo Kagaku Zasshi*, **67**(10), 1536 (1964); *Chem. Abstr.*, **62,** 8423f (1965).

196. A. Kawamura and K. Akabane, *Nippon Nogei Kagaku Kaishi*, **33,** 922 (1959); *Chem. Abstr.*, **57,** 17000a (1962).

197. Japanese Patent, 6433 (1951); *Chem. Abstr.*, **47,** 3154h (1953).

198. Israeli Patent, 16,270 (1961); *Chem. Abstr.*, **59,** 6036b (1963).

199. A. T. DiBenedetto and E. N. Lightfoot, *Ind. Eng. Chem.*, **50,** 691 (1958).

200. Y. Hara, *Bull. Chem. Soc. Japan*, **36,** 187 (1963); *Chem. Abstr.*, **58,** 8431h (1963).

201. N. Takai, M. Seno, and T. Yamabe, *Kogyo Kagaku Zasshi*, **67**(6), 893 (1964); *Chem. Abstr.*, **61,** 10888d (1964).

202. S. Itoi and T. Utsunomiya, *Asahi Garasu Kenkyu Hokoku*, **15,** 171 (1965); *Chem. Abstr.*, **64,** 13432b (1966).

203. U. S. Patent, 1,015,891 (1912); *Chem. Abstr.*, **6,** 717 (1912).

204. G. L. Foster and C. L. A. Schmidt, *J. Am. Chem. Soc.*, **48,** 1709 (1926).

205. E. Gebauer-Fuelnegg and A. I. Kendall, *Chem. Ber.*, **64B,** 1067 (1931).

206. S. E. Severin, *Z. Physiol. Chem.*, **230,** 109 (1934); *Chem. Abstr.*, **29,** 1115 (1935).

207. Y. Hara, *Kogyo Kagaku Zasshi*, **65,** 885 (1962); *Chem. Abstr.*, **57,** 14459c (1962).

208. Y. Hara, *Bull. Chem. Soc. Japan*, **36,** 1373 (1963); *Chem. Abstr.*, **60,** 7125a (1964).

209. U. S. Patent, 3,330,749 (1967); *Chem. Abstr.*, **68,** 30051 (1968).

210. N. Takai, M. Seno, and T. Yamabe, *Kogyo Kagaku Zasshi*, **68**(2), 415 (1965); *Chem. Abstr.*, **63,** 2421f (1965).

211. A. I. Ryazanov et al., *Tr., Vses. Nauch.-Issled. Inst. Khim. Reaktivov Osobo Chist. Khim. Veshchestv* No. 30, 69 (1967); *Chem. Abstr.*, **68,** 27428 (1968).

212. A. I. Ryazanov et al., *Tr., Vses. Nauch.-Issled. Inst. Khim. Reaktivov Osobo Chist. Khim. Veshchestv* No. 30, 77 (1967); *Chem. Abstr.*, **68,** 57286 (1968).

213. R. Fabre, *J. Pharm. Chim.*, **27,** 467 (1938); *Chem. Abstr.*, **32,** 5927 (1938).

214. R. Fabre, *Bull. Acad. Med. Roumanie*, **3,** 55 (1938); *Chem. Abstr.*, **33,** 8816 (1939).

215. R. Fabre and P. Oficjalski, *J. Pharm. Chim.*, **28,** 335, 369 (1938); *Chem. Abstr.*, **33,** 7961 (1939).

216. P. Oficjalski, *Wiudomosci Farm.*, **66,** 145, 161 (1939); *Chem. Abstr.*, **34,** 6761 (1940).

217. L. Maricq and F. Rochat, *Bull. Soc. Chim. Belges.*, **49,** 245 (1940); *Chem. Abstr.*, **36,** 215 (1942).

218. S. Kh. Babich. *Zh. Prikl. Khim.*, **20,** 652 (1947), *Chem. Abstr.*, **43,** 3975c (1949).

219. L. Molle, *Ann. Soc. Roy. Sci. Med. Nat. Bruxelles*, **5,** 9 (1952); *Chem. Abstr.*, **46,** 9345i (1952).

220. I. V. Sokolova, *Veterinariya*, **29**(4), 56 (1952); *Chem. Abstr.*, **46,** 7612c (1952).

221. Japanese Patent, 1593 (1951); *Chem. Abstr.*, **47,** 426b (1953).

222. Z. Drabent and Z. Podeszewski, *Acta Polon. Pharm.*, **16,** 299 (1959); *Chem. Abstr.*, **54,** 5014g (1960).

223. I. Kamii, T. Tanaka, and T. Yamabe, *Yakugaku Zasshi*, **81,** 931 (1961); *Chem. Abstr.*, **55,** 24799g (1961).

224. I. Kamii and T. Yamabe, *Yakugaku Zasshi*, **80,** 1642 (1960); *Chem. Abstr.*, **55,** 8766c (1961).

225. H. P. Kraft and H. Auterhoff, *Pharm. Ztg.*, **90,** 916 (1954); *Chem. Abstr.*, **50,** 3714b (1956).

226. L. Molle, *Ann. Soc. Roy. Sci. Med. Nat. Bruxelles*, **9,** 5, 109 (1956).

227. R. L. Elicabe, *Ciencia Invest.*, **12,** 134 (1956); *Chem. Abstr.*, **50,** 12699d (1956).

228. R. L. Elicabe, *Rev. Fac. Cienc. Quim. Univ. Nac. La Plata*, **32,** 25 (1959); *Chem. Abstr.*, **55,** 22466a (1961).

229. S. Kh. Babich, *Zdravookhr. Kazakhstana*, **1958** (9), 72; *Chem. Abstr.*, **55,** 908a (1961).

230. H. Fischbach, *J. Am. Pharm. Assoc. Sci. Ed.*, **37,** 470 (1948); *Chem. Abstr.*, **43,** 7195i (1949).

231. E. N. Lightfoot and I. A. J. Friedman, *Ind. Eng. Chem.*, **46,** 1579 (1954).

232. S. Kelman, *Dissertation Abstr. B*, **28**(5), 1963–1964 (1967); see also S. Kelman and R. B. Grieves, *J. Appl. Chem. (London)*, **18**(1), 20 (1968).

233. I. Kamii, *Showa Yakka Daigaku Kiyo*, **1,** 1 (1963); *Chem. Abstr.*, **62,** 1112d (1965).

234. A. G. Koblyanskii et al., *Izvest. Vysshikh Uchebn. Zavedenii Pishchevaya Tekhnol.*, **1964**(4), 72; *Chem. Abstr.*, **61,** 15395c (1964).

235. M. Nishimura et al., *Kagaku To Kogyo (Osaka)*, **37**(4), 176 (1963); *Chem. Abstr.*, **60,** 3996h (1964).

236. I. Kagawa and K. Tsumura, *J. Soc. Chem. Ind. Japan*, **47,** 437 (1944); *Chem. Abstr.*, **42,** 6205g (1948).

237. M. Hida, *J. Chem. Soc. Japan, Ind. Chem. Sect.*, **55,** 221 (1952); *Chem. Abstr.* **48,** 8175d (1954).

238. H. Thiele and J. Lange, *Kolloid-Z.*, **169,** 86 (1960).

239. K. Kanamaru and T. Hata, *J. Soc. Chem. Ind. Japan*, **47,** 544 (1944); *Chem. Abstr.*, **42,** 6120f (1948).

240. O. Ant-Wuorinen, *Valtion Tek. Tutkimuslaitos, Tiedoitus*, No. **131**, 23 (1954); *Paperi Puu* No. **4a** (1954); *Chem. Abstr.*, **49**, 5829a (1955).

241. S. Kh. Kitaeva and V. V. Korolev, *Bumazh. Prom.*, **32**(6), 4 (1957); *Chem. Abstr.*, **52**, 3336f (1958).

242. S. Kh. Kitaeva, *Sbornik*, **1959**, 100; *Chem. Abstr.*, **56**, 8973e (1962).

243. U. S. Patent, 3,310,481 (1967); *Chem. Abstr.*, **68**, 40585 (1968).

244. V. A. Kargin et al., *Vysokomolekul. Soedin.*, **4**(12), 1881 (1962); *Chem. Abstr.*, **59**, 4107g (1963).

245. F. S. D'Yachkovskii, *Vysokomolekul. Soedin.*, **7**(1), 114 (1965); *Chem. Abstr.*, **63**, 4394h (1965).

246. E. A. Grigoryan et al., *Vysokomolekul. Soedin. Ser. A*, **9**(6), 1233 (1967); *Chem. Abstr.*, **67**, 82443 (1967).

247. G. A. Kazaryan et al., *Vysokomolekul. Soedin.*, **8**(7), 1314 (1966); *Chem. Abstr.*, **65**, 15511a (1966).

248. S. Sethu, *J. Appl. Polymer Sci.*, **8**(5), 2249 (1964).

249. A. Woljagin and W. Scheimpflug, *Osterr. Milchwirtsch. Ztg.*, **43**, 200 (1936); *Chem. Abstr.*, **31**, 166 (1937).

250. J. Pien and J. Baisse, *Lait*, **16**, 20 (1936); *Chem. Abstr.*, **30**, 1881 (1936).

251. Z. Kato, *J. Soc. Chem. Ind. Japan*, **42**, Suppl. binding 376 (1939); *Chem. Abstr.*, **34**, 2476 (1940).

252. P. D. Watson, *Ind. Eng. Chem.*, **26**, 640 (1934).

253. A. H. W. Aten, E. Wegelin, and S. G. Wiechers, *Proc. Intern. Dairy Congr. 12th*, Stockholm, **3**, 381 (1949); *Chem. Abstr.*, **44**, 9078d (1950).

254. S. G. Wiechers and C. L. de Vries, *Voeding*, **10**, 60 (1949); *Chem. Abstr.*, **43**, 4393e (1949).

255. U. S. Patent, 2,631,100 (1953); *Chem. Abstr.*, **47**, 5041e (1953).

256. W. H. Wingerd and R. J. Block, *J. Dairy Sci.*, **37**, 932 (1954); *Chem. Abstr.*, **48**, 13113f (1954).

257. U. S. Patent, 2,758,965 (1956); *Chem. Abstr.*, **51**, 636e (1957).

258. V. T. Bakhvalov and I. I. Klimovskii, *Molochn. Prom.*, **4**, 22 (1937); *Chem. Abstr.*, **33**, 8939 (1939).

259. U. S. Patent, 3,325,389 (1967); *Chem. Abstr.*, **67**, 115958 (1967).

260. E. J. Parsi and W. B. Iaconelli, U. S. Dept. Commerce, Office Tech. Serv., AD 429,917 (1964); *Chem. Abstr.*, **61**, 4875g (1964).

261. E. Lanzola, *Nuovi Ann. Igiene Microbiol.*, **14**(6), 422 (1963); *Chem. Abstr.*, **61**, 8819g (1964).

262. British Patent, 1,005,125 (1965); *Chem. Abstr.*, **63**, 18943h (1965).

263. J. L. Greatorex and W. Glass, AEC Accession No. 12997, Rept. No. AD 626210; *Chem. Abstr.*, **65**, 4065a (1966).

264. W. A. McRae and B. H. Sanders, *Fette, Seifen, Anstrichem.*, **68**(10), 888 (1966); *Chem. Abstr.*, **66**, 36626 (1967).

265. Belgian Patent, 670,614 (1966); *Chem. Abstr.*, **65**, 9628a (1966).

266. R. C. Stribley, *Proc. Ann. Natl. Dairy Eng. Conf.*, **13**, 34 (1965); *Chem. Abstr.*, **66**, 74983 (1967).

267. K. A. Murray, *J. Soc. Chem. Ind.*, **55**, 302T (1936).

268. E. A. Slagle and L. M. Roberts, *Sewage Works J.*, **14**, 1021 (1942).

269. L. N. Bonacci and W. Rudolfs, *Sewage Works J.*, **14**, 1281 (1942).

270. U.S.S.R. Patent, 156,159; *Chem. Abstr.*, **60**, 7374a (1964).

271. Tsuan Hua Feng, Am. Chem. Soc. Div. Water Waste Chem., Preprints, **1963** (January), 22; *Chem Abstr.*, **61**, 13031g (1964).

272. J. D. Smith and J. L. Eisenmann, *Electrodialysis in Advanced Waste Treatment*, Water Pollution Control Res. Ser. Publ. No. WP-20-AWTR-18, 1967.

273. C. A. Brunner, Paper presented at the 39th Annual Conference of the Water Pollution Control Federation, Kansas City, Missouri, September 1966; *J. Water Pollution Control Federation*, **39**(10), Pt. 2, R1 (1967).

274. J. W. Arnold, Paper presented at the Symposium on Electrodialysis, Electrochemical Society Meeting, Boston, Massachusetts, May 1968.

275. W. E. Mayo, *Ont. Ind. Waste Conf.*, Proc. No. 13, 169 (1966).

276. G. A. Dubey, T. R. McElhinney, and A. J. Wiley, *Tappi*, **48**(2), 95 (1965).

277. G. A. Dubey, T. R. McElhinney, and A. J. Wiley, *Proc. Symp. Membrane Processes Ind. Birmingham, Alabama, 1966*, p. 61.

278. French Patent, 1,387,935 (1965); *Chem. Abstr.*, **63**, 7680d (1965).

279. M. S. Mintz, R. E. Lacey, and E. W. Lang, *Tappi*, **50**(3), 137 (1967).

280. U. S. Patent, 3,136,710 (1964); *Chem. Abstr.*, **61**, 4994d (1964).

281. J. M. Holderby, H. S. Olson, and W. H. Wegener, *Tappi*, **50**(9), 92A (1967).

282. G. Untermann, *Chem. Ing.-Tech.* **23**, 522 (1951); *Chem. Abstr.*, **46**, 1849d (1952).

283. B. H. Sanders and E. J. Parsi, *Proc. Symp. Less Common Means Separation, 1st, Birmingham, England, 1963*, p. 16 (1964).

284. K. Kashiwada, *Bull. Japan. Soc. Sci. Fisheries*, **24**, 591 (1958); *Chem. Abstr.*, **53**, 13700c (1959).

285. L. M. Jeffrey and D. W. Hood, *J. Marine Res.*, **17**, 247 (1958); *Chem. Abstr.*, **55**, 8709g (1961).

286. U. S. Patent, 3,291,713 (1966); *Chem. Abstr.*, **66**, 40662 (1967).

287. U. S. Patent, 3,304,250 (1967); *Chem. Abstr.*, **66**, 86720 (1967).

288. N. Etling and S. B. Barker, *Proc. Soc. Exptl. Biol. Med.*, **98**, 780 (1958); *Chem. Abstr.*, **53**, 3320h (1959).

289. F. J. Taboury and C. Mangin, *Bull. Soc. Chim. France*, **1948**, 47.

290. K. Yamamoto et al., *Kolloid-Z.*, **178**, 97 (1961).

291. H. Ashizawa and T. Sasaki, *Kolloid-Z.*, **199**(2), 155 (1964).

292. G. Briere and G. Pierre, *J. Chim. Phys.*, **62**(9), 959 (1965).

293. S. Barret and G. Briere, *J. Chim. Phys.*, **62**(9), 970 (1965).

294. S. Barret, G. Briere, and G. Pierre, *J. Chim. Phys.*, **63**(5), 725 (1966).

295. G. Briere and G. Pierre, *J. Chim. Phys.*, **62**(9), 964 (1965).

296. French Patent, 1,381,307 (1964); *Chem. Abstr.*, **62**, 11291b (1965).

297. S. Barret, G. Briere, and F. Gaspard, *J. Chim. Phys.*, **64**(11–12), 1714 (1967).

298. G. Briere, N. Felici, and J.-C. Filippini, *Compt. Rend.*, **261**(23) (Group 7), 5097 (1965).

299. G. Briere and B. Rose, *J. Chim. Phys.*, **64**(11–12), 1720 (1967).

300. C. L. Wilson, *Intern. Sci. Technol.*, March 1966, p. 82.

General

Chen, W. K. W., "Electrodialysis," in *Kirk-Othmer Encyclopedia of Chemical Technology*, 2nd ed., Interscience, New York, 1965.

Farrell, J. B., and R. N. Smith, *Ind. Chem.*, **54**(6), 29 (1962).

Friedlander, H. Z., and R. N. Rickles, *Anal. Chem.*, **37**(8), 27A (1965).

Helfferich, F., *Ion-Exchange*, McGraw-Hill, New York, 1962.

Lakshminarayanaiah, N., *Chem. Rev.*, **65**, 491 (1965).

Mason, E. A., and T. A. Kirkham, *Chem. Eng. Prog. Symp. Ser.*, **55**, 173 (1959).

Mintz, M. S., *Ind. Eng. Chem.*, **55**(6), 18 (1963).

Parsi, E. J., "Electrodialysis" and "Electrodialysis Applications," in the *Encyclopedia of Electrochemistry*, C. A. Hampel, Ed., Van Nostrand Reinhold, New York, 1964.

Prausnitz, P. H., and J. Reitstotter, *Elektrophorese, Elektroosmose, Elektrodialyse in Flussigkeiten*, Steinkopff, Dresden, 1931.

Rickles, R. N., *Membranes-Technology and Economics*, Noyes Development Corp., Park Ridge, New Jersey, 1967.

Shaffer, H., and M. S. Mintz, in *Principles of Desalination*, K. S. Spiegler, Ed., Academic, New York, 1966, Chapter 6.

Sonin, A. A., and R. F. Probstein, Paper presented at the Symposium on Electrodialysis, Electrochemical Society Meeting, Boston, Massachusetts, May 1968.

Spiegler, K. S., in *Ion-Exchange Technology*, F. C. Nachod and J. Schubert, Eds., Academic, New York, 1956, Chapter 6.

Stamberger, P., "Electrodialysis," in *Kirk-Othmer Encyclopedia of Chemical Technology*, 1st ed., Interscience, New York, 1950.

Stauffer, R. E., "Dialysis and Electrodialysis," in *Technique of Organic Chemistry*, Vol. III, A. Weissberger, Ed., Interscience, New York, 1950.

Tuwiner, S. B., *Diffusion and Membrane Technology*, Van Nostrand Reinhold, New York, 1962.

Wilson, J. R., *Demineralization by Electrodialysis*, Butterworths, London, 1960.

INDEX

415